IRONMAKING AND STEELMAKING

Theory and Practice

AHINDRA GHOSH
Formerly Professor
Materials and Metallurgical Engineering
Indian Institute of Technology Kanpur

AMIT CHATTERJEE
Formerly Chief Technology Officer
Currently Adviser to the Managing Director
Tata Steel Limited, Jamshedpur

PHI Learning Private Limited
New Delhi-110001
2012

Rs. 375.00

IRONMAKING AND STEELMAKING: Theory and Practice
Ahindra Ghosh and Amit Chatterjee

ISBN-978-81-203-3289-8

Fifth Printing ... ... **January, 2012**

Published by Asoke K. Ghosh, PHI Learning Private Limited, M-97, Connaught Circus, New Delhi-110001 and Printed by Rajkamal Electric Press, Plot No. 2, Phase IV, HSIDC, Kundli-131028, Sonepat, Haryana.

IRONMAKING AND STEELMAKING

To

Jamsetji Nusserwanji Tata

(3rd March 1839–19th May 1904)

Doyen of the Indian Iron and Steel Industry

Contents

Part B BLAST FURNACE IRONMAKING

Part E CASTING OF LIQUID STEEL

Preface

Traditionally, Metallurgical Engineering has been subdivided into two broad categories, namely, *Ferrous Metallurgy* and *Non-Ferrous Metallurgy*. Ferrous metallurgy includes the metallurgy of iron and steel, while non-ferrous metallurgy deals with all other metals like aluminium, copper, zinc, etc. Since steel is by far the most important engineering material known to mankind, ferrous metallurgy has been the dominant branch of metallurgical engineering, in terms of scale of production, size of the industry, manpower employed, and so on.

Since the 1940s, advances in sophisticated high-technology areas such as nuclear engineering, aerospace science, aviation and solid-state electronics, have necessitated the development of a variety of special materials—both metallic and non-metallic. A fundamental understanding of metals as well as that of atomic and solid-state physics has provided the scientific foundation for the growth of these materials. As a result, the scope of metallurgical engineering has, over the years, become more broad-based in order to encompass Materials Science and Engineering.

A plethora of literature is now available in the 'exciting' field of materials science. This is not always the case with ferrous metallurgy, perhaps because it is traditional and perceived to be out-of-sync with 'modern' developments. Yet, steel continues to be the most widely used engineering material. All Metallurgical Engineering Departments in engineering colleges, particularly in countries like India, where iron and steel production is expected to increase substantially in the next decade or two, have and will continue to have, substantial teaching programmes in the area of iron and steel. The paucity of up-to-date textbooks for undergraduate and postgraduate students in this field is a real problem area. It is also worth noting that ironmaking and steelmaking technologies have made tremendous advances in the last forty years or so, making the need for the up-to-date textbooks even greater.

It is worth pointing out that contrary to popular perception associated with the attribute of being traditional, the last five decades have witnessed revolutionary advances in the fundamental understanding of the theories of ironmaking and steelmaking. This has resulted in major changes in the associated metallurgical processes. The insight gained is primarily based on the sciences of thermodynamics and physical chemistry, as well as on a more comprehensive understanding of the role of both fluid flow and heat and mass transfer in the 'dynamics' of these processes. As a result, the design, development, control and operation of modern ironmaking and steelmaking processes are today based on scientific fundamentals, to a much greater degree than what it was earlier. Consequently, even well-established processes (for example, blast furnace ironmaking) have undergone revolutionary changes with the passage of time to such an extent that the 'old' processes have become 'new'.

This book aims at providing current information in the broad field of ironmaking and steelmaking. The historical facts and general aspects of iron and steel are presented in Chapter 1 of this book. The following twenty-three chapters deal with both the science and technology of ironmaking and steelmaking in a balanced manner, covering both theory and practice. The book has been designed as a textbook for the basic undergraduate course(s) on the subject. It can also partly serve as a textbook in elective and postgraduate courses.

The two authors, with totally different backgrounds covering the entire spectrum of the theory and practice of iron and steel, hope that the book they have written will fulfil a long-felt need of this type of treatment of the subject of ironmaking and steelmaking.

Ahindra Ghosh taught iron and steel metallurgy and allied subjects, besides being engaged in other academic and professional activities, while he was at the Indian Institute of Technology Kanpur for thirty-eight years. His visits, interactions and association with professionals in several steel plants, especially at Tata Steel, have considerably enhanced his knowledge of the subject. He wishes to gratefully acknowledge all of them.

Amit Chatterjee expresses his gratitude to his late father, Dr. A.B. Chatterjee, for introducing him to the 'romance' of iron and steel, which has inspired him throughout his career spanning four decades. He gratefully acknowledges the assistance of his Secretary, Mr. K.H. Kartha, in typing the manuscript. He also wishes to thank profusely, Mr. Bikash Nandy, Executive Assistant in his office, since without his painstaking efforts, this book would not have seen the light of day. He is also grateful to Tata Steel for providing him with all the opportunities to 'learn the nitty-gritty of iron and steel production' during his thirty-five years association with the Steel Company.

Both the authors wish to sincerely thank their wives and other members of their family for their continuous help and encouragement, without which work of this nature could not have been undertaken.

Ahindra Ghosh
Amit Chatterjee

Part A

General

- Introduction
- Overview of Blast Furnace Ironmaking
- Overview of Modern Steelmaking
- General Physicochemical Fundamentals

1 Introduction

The earth's crust contains about 5% iron. However, it is present as a compound, mostly as iron oxide. Iron is *extracted* as metallic Fe from the oxide by reduction with a reducing agent. The principal agent that is used is naturally occurring carbon in the form of coke, coal or charcoal.

For economic extraction of iron, relatively rich deposits of *iron ore*, with Fe contents above 55–60%, are generally used. The most abundant iron oxide mineral is *haematite* (i.e. Fe_2O_3) followed by *magnetite* (i.e. Fe_3O_4). Iron ores also contain oxide minerals of some other elements such as aluminium, silicon, manganese and phosphorus. These minerals are physically mixed with earthy materials such as sand, rock and clay. Some of these substances are harmful for the properties of the finished products. These are treated as impurities that ought to be removed during extraction. Iron has the ability to form *alloys* with many elements. Such alloying is done intentionally to produce various grades of iron alloys having the properties required for various applications.

Broadly speaking, iron products can be classified into three categories, viz. *wrought iron*, *cast iron* and *steel*. Today, steel is the most important product of iron, followed by cast iron, while wrought iron is used in very small quantities for ornamental purposes.

1.1 EARLY HISTORY OF IRON (STEEL)

This type of classification of iron into wrought iron, cast iron, steel, etc. was not prevalent in the early days, i.e. these terminologies were not known. All the products were known as iron. This should be kept in mind while going through the topics that follow.

1.1.1 Meteoric Iron and Wrought Iron

Since iron objects rust and get destroyed over the years when in contact with soil, air and water, the antiquity of use of iron is uncertain. The earliest sample preserved in the British Museum dates back to about 3500–4000 BC. Reduction of iron oxide by charcoal is possible at appreciable rates only above a temperature of 900–1000°C. This phenomenon was probably discovered accidentally while making fire. There is evidence that the first iron objects containing small percentages of nickel were made from metallic iron present in the elemental state in meteorites. The first definite evidence of ironmaking by the reduction of oxide dates back to about 1500 BC.

The melting point of pure iron is 1536°C, but when iron absorbs carbon, the melting point is lowered significantly. The lowest melting composition (i.e. the *eutectic*) containing 4.26% carbon melts at 1153°C. The primitive furnaces that were used to extract iron were small in size and were shaped like a deep bowl, about 1–1.5 m high with diameters ranging from 0.4 to 0.8 m. The lining consisted mainly of dried clay, and charcoal was used as the reducing agent. Oxygen was supplied by blowing air through pipes kept in the mouth, and later on, by bellows. The air supplied resulted in the partial combustion of carbon along with the generation of carbon monoxide and heat, which raised the furnace temperature. The actual reduction was carried out by CO:

$$\text{Fe-oxide(s)} + \text{CO(g)} = \text{Fe(s)} + \text{CO}_2\text{ (g)} \tag{1.1}$$

(This equation is not balanced. It only shows the reaction qualitatively.)

In the small furnaces that were used, it was difficult to attain temperatures higher than 1100°C or so, in the zone of maximum temperature. Under these conditions, metallic iron could not absorb much carbon. Therefore, melting did not take place and hot iron that was obtained remained in the solid state mixed with a low-melting slag containing very high percentages of FeO. Upon repeated heating followed by forging into various shapes using a hammer, most of the slag got 'squeezed out' to leave solid iron (sponge) that was almost pure (with low concentrations of carbon, etc.). This type of product became known as *wrought iron* (wrought meaning worked, i.e. forged).

1.1.2 Cast Iron

Casting of iron into different shapes necessitated the production of iron in the liquid state. This became possible only at a later stage; therefore, historically liquid iron came after wrought iron. Liquid iron was first produced in China, even before the Christian era according to some historians. Some massive cast iron objects dating back to about 1000 AD still exist in China. The success of iron casting in ancient China can be attributed to the following:

- More efficient furnaces with better lining and more powerful blowing equipment
- Introduction of a technique that allowed absorption of carbon by iron, thus lowering the melting point
- High phosphorus content of some Chinese raw materials, and the fact that the ternary Fe–C–P system shows much lower melting points than the corresponding Fe–C binary system.

1.1.3 Evolution of Ironmaking in Europe

The ancient ironmaking process developed around the Mediterranean Sea, then spread northwards to Europe through the Phoenicians, Celts and Romans. The next significant development took place in the Spanish province of Catalonia, known as *Catalan Forge*. Here, water wheels were employed to blow air, resulting in higher production rates and better charcoal utilisation. It was possible to produce about 100 kg of metal in batches, every 12 hours.

The demand for more iron led to the development of the *Stukofen* in Germany. The Stukofen had a height of 3–4.5 m and its shape was similar to that of a modern blast furnace. It had water-driven bellows and a superior furnace lining made of stone and clay. It is rightly considered the forerunner of the modern blast furnace. The hot iron bloom (in the form of a solid) used to be withdrawn from the bottom, and only small amounts of liquid iron was produced, as a by-product. Individual Stukofens could produce 100–150 tonnes of iron per annum. The next important step in ironmaking furnace design was the *Flussofen* (flow oven), which was developed in the Rhine Valley in Germany in the 14th century, essentially to cast cannons for warfare.

The charcoal blast furnaces developed in the European continent then spread to Great Britain, where the next evolution of ironmaking technology occurred. Several improvements led to larger and more efficient furnaces. The major developments that took place till about 1880 are summarised below.

Replacement of charcoal by coke

Use of charcoal led to a large-scale destruction of forests in Great Britain before the Parliament passed legislation to limit iron production. Coke, obtained by carbonisation of coal, was first used in a blast furnace by Dudley in 1709. The use of coke picked-up significantly only by around the year 1800. Since coke is stronger than charcoal, the height of the blast furnace could be increased.

Use of steam engines for air blowing

Steam engine-driven blowers were invented in 1760. These blowers were more powerful than the blowers used earlier and as a result, they were soon employed in all blast furnaces. Bigger furnace sizes and higher production rates began to be obtained following this development.

Pre-heating of the air blast

Neilson in 1829 introduced the concept of pre-heating the air blast. Earlier, about 8 tonnes of coal was required to manufacture coke sufficient to make one tonne iron, but once pre-heating of air to about 150°C became possible, the consumption came down to 5 tonnes. Further modifications allowed the pre-heating temperature to reach about 600°C. In 1857, Cowper patented fire-brick lined stoves, which allowed the pre-heating temperature to be increased even further. These stoves worked on the regenerative principle—two stoves being heated by combustion of blast furnace gas, with one stove actually heating the air that was blown. This was done in a cyclic manner, much in the same way as is in vogue today.

Utilisation of blast furnace gas as fuel

The hot gas that exits from the furnace top is referred to as blast furnace gas. It contains a high percentage of carbon monoxide, which can be burnt with air as a fuel to provide heat. Earlier, the entire gas exiting from the furnace top used to be burnt for pre-heating the air blast. In 1845, Bunsen and Playfair pointed out that the bulk of the calorific value of the gas was being wasted in this approach and suggested that the gas be transported through a pipeline for utilisation, not only for pre-heating of air, but also for using elsewhere in the iron works.

This immediately called for an arrangement to charge iron ore, coke, etc. from the top of the furnace without any leakage of gas into the atmosphere. The cup-and-bell system was invented around 1850, which later led to the development of the double-bell charging device. This became a standard feature of all blast furnaces till about 1970–1980.

Another problem faced during the early days was that the gas contained a lot of dust particles, which used to choke the pipelines, stoves, etc. In order to reduce the dust content, the gas began to be passed through a large chamber where some dust settled owing to the decrease in velocity. However, this arrangement was not very satisfactory—modern blast furnaces are provided with far more elaborate gas cleaning arrangements.

1.1.4 Early History of Steelmaking before the Advent of Modern Processes

There are thousands of grades of steel. Broadly they may be classified as *plain carbon steels* and *alloy steels*. The manufacture of alloy steels began about 100 years ago, and even now, it constitutes only about 10% of the total steel produced.

Plain carbon steels contain 0.1–1.0% carbon and minor concentrations of some other elements such as Mn, Si, etc. Carbon imparts strength to iron, but lowers its ductility. Carbon also allows the development of a range of properties by suitable heat treatment such as annealing, normalising, quenching, etc., all of which change the microstructure. The existence of carbon in steels was first discovered by scientists in the late 18th century. During the next 100 years, the subject of *metallography* developed to such an extent that it became possible to correlate heat treatment, mechanical properties and microstructure of steels. As a result, it became possible to obtain a range of mechanical properties at the same carbon content.

Early steelmakers developed techniques to produce carbon steels in small quantities and then heat treatment was carried out by trial and error, without knowing the underlying science. As per archeological and literary evidence, ironmakers in India were pioneers in this field. They were aware of these phenomena from the 2nd/3rd century BC. In fact, India was exporting steel to the entire civilised world, such as Western Asia, Europe, etc. However, the 'know-how' was kept closely guarded. Countries like Iraq, Syria and Japan began to acquire some knowledge about 1000 years ago, while Europe started making steel only in the Middle Ages.

The earliest process of steelmaking consisted of heating wrought iron with a carbonaceous material in a covered furnace. This allowed carburisation of iron for its conversion into steel. Once the European ironmakers learnt to produce molten iron, they made wrought iron by purifying the melt. Then, it was carburised by heating with a carbonaceous material in a closed furnace, like in the earlier practice. This was known as the *cementation process*. Following sufficient recarburisation, the melting point of steel decreased to such an extent that it could be easily melted using the earlier furnaces. This is known as the *crucible process*, pioneered by

Huntsman in the UK in 1740. The crucible process dominated steelmaking in Europe and North America till Henry Bessemer of the UK developed the famous *Bessemer Process*, which heralded the advent of steel production on a mass scale.

1.1.5 Iron and Steel Heritage of India

Several books and monographs as well as many research/review papers have been published on this topic by scholars, both within and outside India. For general information, the readers may wish to refer to the following books:

1. *Iron and Steel Heritage of India*, S. Ranganathan (Ed.), The Indian Institute of Metals and Tata Steel, Jamshedpur (1997).
2. *Minerals and Metals in Ancient India*, Vols. 1 and 2, Arun Kumar Biswas and Sulekha Biswas, D.K. Printworld, New Delhi (1996).
3. *India's Legendarv Wootz Steel: An Advanced Material of the Ancient World,* Sharada Srinivasan and S. Ranganathan, Tata Steel (2006).

As per evidence available at present, iron objects were in use in India as early as 1500 BC. India's glorious heritage in iron and steel is thus unquestionable. One example of the extent of perfection achieved by Indian artisans in yesteryears is the famous *Delhi Iron Pillar*. The pillar weighing nearly 7 tonnes is about 8 m in height with bottom and top diameters of 0.42 m and 0.31 m respectively. It was made about 1500–1550 years ago by forge-welding individual pieces of wrought iron. What is amazing is that it has resisted rusting for all these years.

The corrosion resistance of the Delhi Iron Pillar has been the subject of investigations by many scientists taking the help of samples collected from the base of the Pillar. What is now accepted is that the 'material' used is astonishingly pure, i.e. low in carbon in particular, vis-à-vis the commercial iron of today. It is made of wrought iron that was never in the molten state. Several pieces of hot lumps of iron 'sponge' were forge-welded together, like separate pan cakes. This resulted in extraordinary inhomogeneity in chemical composition as well as in microstructure, with carbon contents varying from less than 0.1% to as high as 0.3%. This type of 'composite' structure comprising alternate bands of metal and slag as well as the presence of an oxide layer on the surface, is postulated as being the main reasons why the Pillar has not rusted.

Another example of excellence in steel in ancient India is the chronicle of the legendary *wootz steel.* This has long been a subject of much fascination around the globe, with many legends and accounts surrounding it. It is clear that more than two millennia ago, India led the world in developing an impressive tradition of making high-grade steel called wootz (an aberration of the Tamil word *ukku*). It was an important export item to various parts of the world. The famous Damascus swords were fabricated from wootz steel. Figure 1.1 is a conceptual scheme of the process, based on the accounts of Arab and European travellers (Biswas 1996). For about a thousand years or more, wootz was the only advanced material in the world. It had high carbon (1.5–2%) and even exhibited super-plasticity. It evoked interest of scientists in Europe in the nineteenth century. Faraday devised a procedure for its chemical analysis, and many early metallographers studied its watermark-like microstructure.

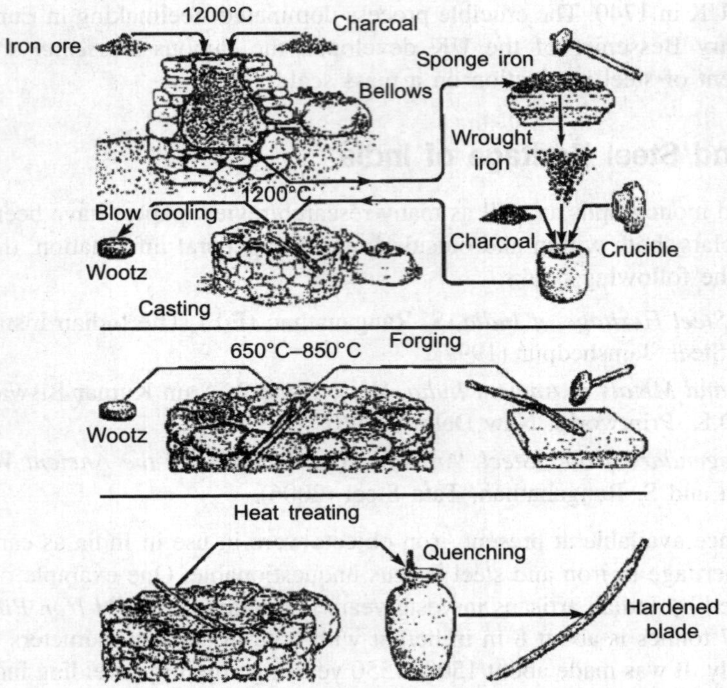

Figure 1.1 Typical manufacturing procedure for a Damascus sword from Indian wootz.

1.2 EVOLUTION OF IRONMAKING TECHNOLOGY SINCE 1880

1.2.1 The Developing Blast Furnace

The period from 1880 to 1950

From the late 19th century, the iron and steel industry started to grow in the USA. The establishment of the Carnegie Steel Co. by Andrew Carnegie was an important landmark following which the US ironmakers as well as those in Europe made several pioneering efforts. From 1880 to about 1950, most of the developments were in the field of furnace design and engineering. There were no significant changes in process technology, the reasons for which were as follows:

- Knowledge of physicochemical and metallurgical aspects of blast furnace reactions was limited. Application of thermodynamics and the consequent development of metallurgical thermodynamics began only around 1930. Knowledge of the kinetics of the reactions involved as well as the related transport phenomena was at a very elementary stage, even in the beginning of the 1950s. However, rapid strides were made between the 1950s and the 1960s.
- The blast furnace was like a blackbox and its internal state was not known, except for some information on the input and output. The first major breakthrough occurred in the

1950s, when a running blast furnace in Japan was rapidly chilled by blowing cold nitrogen through its tuyeres. Then the furnace was sectioned and samples were collected from various zones for chemical and physical examination.

The developments up to 1950 led to the following changes:

- More powerful blowing engines
- Higher blast temperatures
- Bigger furnaces
- Better charging equipment
- Improved raw material storage
- Screening of raw materials to eliminate fines
- More efficient cleaning of blast furnace gas
- Use of better refractories and improved design of the furnace lining
- More versatile facilities for handling iron
- Accurate and quick measurement of the composition and temperature of inputs and outputs.

Some of these features have become standard in blast furnaces today. Considerable improvements have, of course, been made in the interim period; some specific examples are cited below.

1. The double-bell raw material charging system used at the furnace top came into existence around 1880. Earlier, raw materials were hauled to the top using vertical hoists, which were replaced by skip hoists in 1883. The advent of automatic skip charging, however, introduced a serious problem of charge distribution. This was solved in 1890 by the installation of Mckee rotating tops. Figure 1.2 shows a blast furnace of the early 1900s in which these features were incorporated. Most of these features exist even today, except that most modern furnaces now have bell-less top charging.

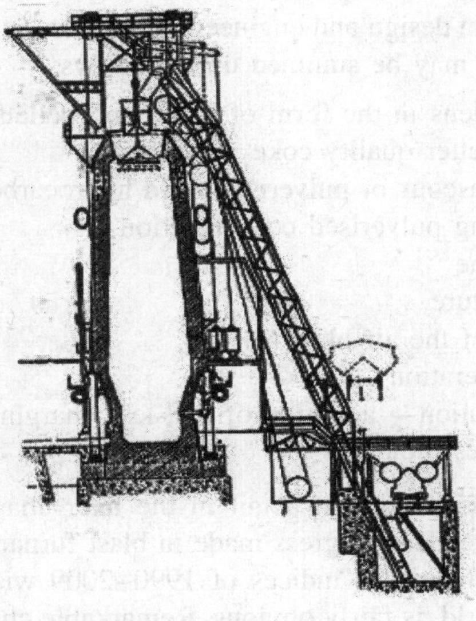

Figure 1.2 Two-bell top with rotating distributor for a blast furnace around the year 1900.

2. The blast furnace gas cleaning system as it exists today consists of a dust catcher, a wet scrubber and an electrostatic precipitator. The last facility was incorporated following the invention of electrostatic precipitators by Lodge and Cottrell in 1919.
3. The life of the lining has been improved significantly by the introduction of water cooling of the lining, including the carbon hearth.
4. Earlier molten iron tapped from blast furnaces used to be cast on sand beds. The pig casting machine was invented by Uehling in 1896. Around the same time, the introduction of hot metal mixers allowed the transfer of liquid iron by ladles over longer distances as well as storage in the steel melting shops.

The impact of all these developments on blast furnace ironmaking may be gauged from Table 1.1, based on the best operating practices over the years.

Table 1.1 Historical developments of blast furnace ironmaking

Year	Furnace size, m		Average production of iron, t**pd	Coke rate, kg coke per tonne hot metal (kg/thm)
	Working height*	Hearth diameter		
1880	20	3.4	110	3400
1901	22	4.5	415	2500
1950	25	8	1500	1000

* Working height is from tuyere to stock level; ** 't' means tonne, i.e. a metric ton = 1000 kg.

Developments after 1950

Since 1950, advances in the field of blast furnace ironmaking have been remarkable. Much of this is because of better understanding of the underlying science and inner working of the furnace following research and development studies. Consequently, major improvements have been brought about not only in design and engineering, but also in the metallurgy of the process. The important developments may be summed up as follows:

- Use of prepared burdens in the form of sinter and pellets
- Properly sized and better quality coke
- Injection of liquid, gaseous or pulverised solid hydrocarbons through the tuyeres — the most widespread being pulverised coal injection
- Larger furnace volume
- Higher blast temperature
- Oxygen enrichment of the air blast
- High top pressure operation
- Better burden distribution — adoption of bell-less charging device
- Computer-aided process control.

These features will be dealt with in detail in the later chapters; and hence, will not be elaborated further at this stage. The progress made in blast furnace ironmaking, summarised in Table 1.2 comparing the performance indices of 1990–2009 with those of 1960 for the *best operating practices* in the world, is fairly obvious. Remarkable changes have taken place in key performance indices like productivity, fuel rate, campaign life (i.e. years of continuous operation before shutdown for repair) and hot metal silicon level, in these 30–40 years. It is generally agreed that the furnaces have reached their near-peak performance, and further significant improvements are not expected.

Table 1.2 Comparison of performance indices of blast furnaces of 1960 with those of 1990–2009 for the best operating practices

Parameters	Year	
	1960	1990–2009
Working height, m	25	25
Inner hearth diameter, m	9	15
Working volume, m^3	2000	5000
Production of iron, tpd	2000	13000
Productivity, thm/day/m^3	1	2.9
Fuel rate, kg/thm	800	380–410
Campaign life, years	4–6	above 10
Silicon in hot metal, weight %	1	0.2

'hm' denotes hot metal, which is the terminology used popularly for liquid iron produced in ironmaking.

1.2.2 Alternative Ironmaking Processes

The blast furnace is the dominant reactor for ironmaking. Alternative ironmaking processes that do not use the blast furnace and are not dependent on coke as the primary reductant, currently account for about 8% of the total global iron production. These alternative processes may be broadly classified into two categories:

- Processes in which iron is produced as a solid, by solid-state reduction
- Processes producing liquid iron by a combination of solid and liquid-state reduction.

Table 1.3 presents the basic features and the year of development of some of the important processes belonging to both these categories.

Table 1.3 Basic features of some alternative ironmaking processes

Process	Basic features				Year	Country
	Reductant	Ore form	Reactor	Product		
Hoganas	Coke breeze	Fines	Retort	Powder	1910	Sweden
Wiberg	Coke	Pellet	Shaft	Sponge	1952	Sweden
HyL I	Natural gas	Pellet	Retort	Sponge	1953	Mexico
Nu-Iron	Natural gas	Fines	Fluidised bed	Powder	1962	USA
SL/RN	Coal lump and fines	Lump	Rotary kiln	Sponge	1964	Canada
Midrex	Natural gas	Pellet	Shaft	Sponge	1967	USA
Fastmet	Coal fines	Fines	Rotary hearth	Sponge	1974	USA, Japan
Corex	Coal lump	Lump and pellets	Smelter	Liquid	1989	Germany and Austria
ITmk3	Coal fines	Fines	Rotary hearth	Solid (liquid)	1996	Japan

Sponge iron

Iron produced as a solid by the reduction of iron oxide is popularly known as *sponge iron*. The ancient ironmakers were in effect making sponge iron, since molten metal temperatures could not be attained. Sponge iron made was used to manufacture wrought iron products directly; even today, sponge iron is a feed for electric furnaces. Therefore, in technical literature, sponge iron is also referred to as *Direct Reduced Iron* (DRI). DRI is often compacted to reduce its porosity — this product is called *Hot Briquetted Iron* (HBI). Chapter 13 contains a detailed presentation; the following is a very brief overview.

It may be noted from Table 1.3 that although the first attempt made to produce DRI was in the form of the Hoganas process as early as 1910, direct reduction did not become widespread until the 1950s. The renewed interest after 1950 stemmed from the following reasons.

- Once electric arc furnace steelmaking started growing, metallic feed in the form of steel scrap became scarce. DRI was used to supplement scrap as auxiliary feed material in EAFs.
- Blast furnace-based steel plants require relatively large capital investment and depend on metallurgical coking coal, which is not available everywhere. On the other hand, the DRI manufacturing units are small in size, the total capital investment is limited, and the reductant can be non-coking coal or gaseous reductants like natural gas. Consequently, the alternative processes are especially attractive for the developing countries.

Tonnage-wise, the gas-based Midrex and HYL processes have always had the largest share of production. The total world production of sponge iron in 1995 and 2009 was 30.8 and 64.5 Mt respectively; the process-wise break-up for both these years is given below.

Process	**Production, Mt**	
	1995	**2009**
Midrex	19.9	38.62
HYL	8.2	7.99
Rotary kiln processes	2.2	17.33
Fluidised bed processes	0.5	0.5
Rotary hearth processes	0	0.0

A novel process which has considerable potential, especially for small and medium scale production units, is ironmaking through the *composite pellet* route. A composite pellet is a mixture of iron ore/oxide fines and carbonaceous reductant (coal/coke/char) fines. These materials are mixed together and made into pellets at room temperature using a binder. The Inmetco process and the Fastmet process (see Table 1.3) are both based on composite pellets reduced in rotary hearth furnaces. Midrex Corp., USA and Kobe Steel, Japan have jointly built a plant in Japan (ITmk3 process) recently, for the production of iron nuggets starting with composite pellets, and other efforts are also underway.

Alternative processes of making liquid iron

Table 1.3 shows that Sweden and Norway developed the Tysland Hole process in 1937, where electrical energy was employed for heating and melting. Electric pig iron furnaces were used even in India at Bhadravati, but all such furnaces were later abandoned. Chapter 14 contains detailed discussions on the status of the smelting reduction processes. The following is a very brief overview.

Liquid hot metal used in BOF steelmaking is normally supplied by blast furnaces. However, there is demand for hot metal in smaller tonnages; for example, in electric arc furnaces that now have the capability of using hot metal (or solid pig) as a part of the charge. Cast iron foundries also require pig iron, particularly high silicon (foundry grade) pig iron in small quantities made in cupolas. Blast furnaces are not capable of meeting such demands. Moreover, coal for blast furnace grade coke is in short supply, and is not available in many countries. Coke is often an expensive commodity, and serious problems of environmental pollution are often encountered during cokemaking. In fact, some countries have adopted legislation either requiring cokemaking installations to be closed, or retrofitted to make them environment friendly.

These factors have led to a worldwide thrust from the 1980s on the so-called *bath smelting processes*, which use non-coking coal to produce liquid hot metal by a combination of solid-state and liquid-state reduction of iron oxide. Because of their smaller unit size, lower total capital investment is involved in installation. The Corex process developed by Korf Stahl, Germany and, Voest Alpine, Austria, is the first commercially successful smelting reduction process. It is producing 2–3 Mt/year of iron in South Africa, India and South Korea. Chapter 14 also contains a list of other promising smelting reduction processes that have been developed over the years in different countries. At this stage, it needs to be pointed out that many of the processes initially suggested/tried have since been abandoned. Only a few, such as Hismelt, Combismelt, Fastmelt, Finex, Redsmelt, ITmk3, Technored and Cleansmelt have had some degree of commercial success. The combined capacity of all these smelting reduction units does not exceed 2 Mt of hot metal/year at present.

China has specialised in the design and construction of a multitude of small blast furnaces (known as *Mini Blast Furnaces*—MBFs). Many other countries are now setting up MBFs for the production of liquid iron in small tonnages. India is one such country having more than 70 MBFs, with a present total capacity of over 3.0 Mt/year. More such units are being planned.

1.3 STEELMAKING SINCE HENRY BESSEMER

1.3.1 Bessemer Process

The history of steelmaking prior to the advent of the Bessemer process has been briefly outlined in Section 1.1.4. Steelmaking went through a paradigm shift when Henry Bessemer patented his process in 1856. Bulk steel production using the Bessemer process started soon thereafter, first in the UK and later in America. There is no doubt that the Bessemer process made steel available in large quantities and made it affordable for a variety of uses. Thus, the introduction of the Bessemer process is looked upon as a second industrial revolution.

The Bessemer process uses a cylindrical vessel (converter) as shown in Figure 1.3. The converter was originally lined with siliceous refractories that could withstand attack from acidic oxides. The entire vessel could be turned from the vertical to a horizontal position, as it was mounted on trunions. Liquid iron (i.e. hot metal) from blast furnaces would first be poured into the converter keeping it in the horizontal position. Blowing of air through the bottom tuyeres would then be started keeping the converter vertical. Oxygen in the air blown would react with Si, C and Mn present in hot metal to form oxides like SiO_2, MnO, etc. These oxides along with some FeO would form an acidic slag. Carbon would be oxidised into CO and CO_2, which would escape into the atmosphere directly from the mouth of the converter.

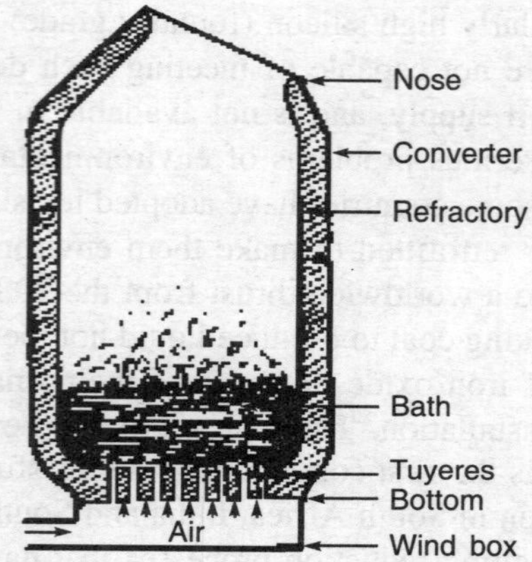

Figure 1.3 Schematic of Bessemer converter steelmaking process.

Since the oxidation reactions are exothermic, the liquid bath temperature would rise automatically, without the need for using any extraneous fuel. This gave economic advantages, and since the process was very fast (refining took hardly 20 minutes), it became ideally suitable for the mass production of steel at a relatively low cost. Once refining was completed, the liquid metal and slag were tapped out separately and the liquid steel cast as ingots. The ingots would be subsequently hot forged/rolled into various shapes.

A major limitation of the process, however, was that it could not remove sulphur and phosphorus present in hot metal. These harmful impurities often caused fractures during hot working of the products (known as *hot shortness*). The oxygen content of Bessemer steel was also inordinately high. In 1864, Mushet found that deoxidation of liquid steel using ferromanganese after tapping into a ladle, lowered the oxygen level. This also increased the Mn content of steel, which contributed towards preventing hot shortness arising from high levels of sulphur. As far as phosphorus was concerned, in the original Bessemer process, hot metal made only from low phosphorus Swedish iron ores was refined. In spite of these shortcomings, the acid Bessemer process was predominant up to around 1910.

The phosphorus issue was tackled following the invention of the *Thomas process* by Sidney G. Thomas in England in 1879. The basic *Bessemer process* or the Thomas process involved the use of a basic oxide (burnt dolomite or magnesite) lining in the vessel. Basic oxides (e.g. CaO) as flux were added during the blow to form a basic slag of high CaO content. This type of basic slag was capable of removing phosphorus in the form of calcium phosphate. This allowed production of steel with acceptable levels of phosphorus even from hot metal containing medium-to-high phosphorus.

However, both acid Bessemer and basic Bessemer (Thomas) steel suffered from the presence of high levels of nitrogen, which got dissolved in the bath following the injection of air from the converter bottom. With the invention of the *Open Hearth* process of steelmaking, where low nitrogen steel could be produced, the Bessemer process started losing importance. Virtually all the Bessemer converters were closed by 1950, and even those that remained were later abandoned. The process is now non-existent; however, it is of historical interest since it heralded the bulk production of liquid steel.

1.3.2 Open Hearth Process

The Bessemer process was incapable of producing low nitrogen steel, and precise control of the final composition and temperature were also difficult. Therefore, the quality of steel made was often not satisfactory. Furthermore, the process was neither capable of accommodating different types of charges, nor could it produce various grades of steel as per specifications.

These problems were resolved with the advent of the open hearth process. Open hearth steelmaking was introduced in 1868, and dominated the world steel production thereafter for almost a century. However, the process was slow and required external heat input, as a result of which it had to give way to oxygen steelmaking, beginning in the late 1950s. Though the open hearth process is also almost non-existent in the world today, there is little doubt that it made an enormous contribution to the progress of science and technology of steelmaking. Therefore, the salient features of open hearth steelmaking will be presented in Chapter 19.

At this stage, it is worth noting that the open hearth process was invented by Karl Wilhelm Siemens and the Martin brothers in the decade of 1860s. The open hearth furnace itself was like a shallow refractory-lined rectangular tray with a roof above it (hence the name open hearth). The charge consisting of steel scrap and hot metal, and lime and iron ore were introduced into the furnace through a number of doors that were provided in the front wall of the furnace. These doors were also used for additions, inspection and sampling of the liquid metal bath during the course of heat making.

Heat was provided to the open hearth furnace by the combustion of gaseous and liquid fuels with air, through burners positioned in the side walls of the furnace. The air used for combustion was pre-heated by the regenerative principle that allowed flame temperatures above 1600°C to be attained. Oxygen for the oxidation of Si, C, Mn and P was supplied by iron ore as well as by atmospheric oxygen. Almost all grades of steel could be made in open hearth furnaces, but the process kinetics was slow and 6–8 hours minimum were required for each heat.

1.3.3 Electric Furnace Steelmaking

The first successful commercial application of electric furnace steelmaking was carried out by Heroult in 1899. In many ways, an electric arc furnace is similar to an open hearth furnace, viz. it has a shallow bath, a roof, a front door, a rear tap hole, etc. The essential difference is that heat is provided by electric arcing and not by any fuel. Electric arc furnaces are capable of making even better quality of steel than that made by open hearth furnaces, owing to precise process control and the ability to make 'tailor-made' slags during the extended refining period. As a result, special and alloy steels are almost exclusively produced by this process. The basic electric arc furnace (EAF) is a major producer of steel at present, and will be discussed further in detail in Chapter 19.

Another type of electric melting furnace is the *coreless induction furnace,* which was first patented by Ferranti in Italy in 1877. The first large installation of an induction furnace was in the USA in 1914. The process is capable of making high-quality special and alloy steels. High frequency induction furnaces are also widely employed in laboratories for making small, trial heats for experimental purposes. The capacity of individual furnaces ranges from a few kilograms to 20–25 tonnes. Induction furnaces have recently become extremely popular in India for the production of pencil (small) ingots for subsequent processing into small shapes in re-rolling mills.

1.3.4 Basic Oxygen Steelmaking

Although the deleterious effect of using air containing about 80% nitrogen by volume was recognised in the Bessemer process, use of pure oxygen was precluded at that stage owing to the following difficulties:

- High cost of pure oxygen
- Rapid wear of the bottom tuyeres of the converter owing to localised high temperatures
- Lack of effective blow control in a very rapid system.

Around the year 1950, the Linde Division of Union Carbide Corporation devised a more efficient air separation process, which made bulk oxygen available at affordable price. This became a watershed event for modern steelmaking, since it triggered the use of pure oxygen for large-scale production of steel. Today, oxygen plants are an integral part of all integrated steel plants as well as many large capacity mini-steel plants. The problem of intense heat generation around the bottom tuyeres following the use of oxygen was resolved by resorting to oxygen blowing from the top, using a lance inserted vertically through the converter mouth. The first commercial plant using such a configuration began operations at **L**inz and **D**onawitz in Austria in 1952–53, giving the process the popular name of LD steelmaking.

Following this humble beginning, the top-blown LD process became extremely popular all over the world. Rourkela Steel Plant in India was amongst the first to adopt the LD process, which later became widely known as BOF (basic oxygen furnace) steelmaking. However, it had limitations in handling high phosphorus hot metal. Bath homogeneity in terms of temperature and composition was also an issue. To get around these problems, at first pure bottom-blown oxygen furnaces (using shrouded tuyeres) and later, combined top- and bottom-blown converter processes were developed.

Since several chapters (Chapters 16, 17 and 18) will be devoted to this subject, these topics will not be discussed here any further. It needs to be pointed out at this stage that different terminologies have been used to denote different steelmaking processes in different parts of the world. As far as this book is concerned, the term basic oxygen steelmaking (BOS) will include all BOFs—top-blown, bottom-blown and combined-blown processes.

BOS along with the EAF accounts for over 98% of world steel production today, as shown in Figure 1.4.

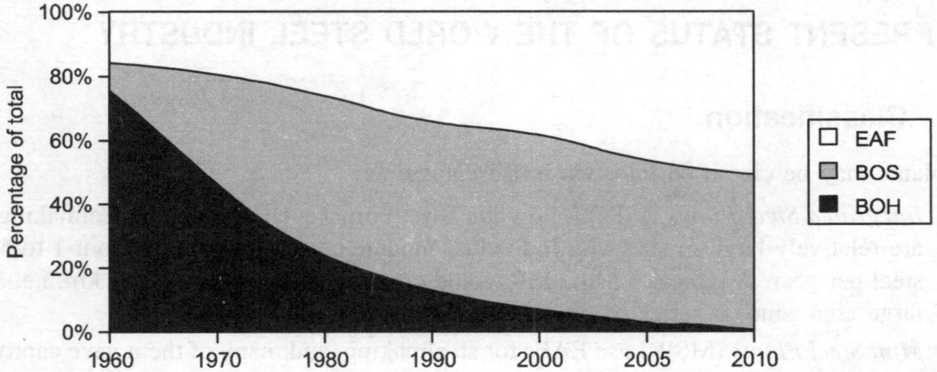

Figure 1.4 Percentage share of world crude steel production by various processes from 1960 to 2010.

1.3.5 Secondary Steelmaking and Continuous Casting of Steel

Once refining of the molten metal bath in the furnace is completed, liquid steel is tapped into a ladle. Earlier, the only operations carried out in the ladle were deoxidation by ferromanganese, ferrosilicon, etc. followed by minor alloying additions. In the last fifty years, the situation has changed dramatically. At present, the ladle is used as a reactor (rather than as a containing vessel) where a variety of secondary processing of liquid steel is carried out. This includes: degassing, desulphurisation, reheating, etc. as well as deoxidation. All these unit processes can be grouped into the broad category of *secondary steelmaking*. Without resorting to secondary steelmaking, it is not possible to produce all the sophisticated qualities of steel in use today. With secondary steelmaking having become a standard feature of modern steel plants, BOS and EAF steelmaking are now classified as *primary steelmaking* processes.

For more than 150 years till the 1960s, liquid steel was batch cast into ingots of various sizes/weights for further shaping by rolling/forging, after reheating the solidified ingots. In the 1960s, continuous casting in which liquid steel is directly cast into slabs/blooms/billets of appreciable lengths, appeared on the scene. This saved energy and reduced the complexities involved in ingot stripping/reheating, etc. It was not surprising, therefore, that very soon continuous casting was widely adopted, and today more than 96% of the world's steel is continuously cast.

Another major development that has occurred over the last 40 years or so is what is known as hot metal *pre-treatment*. Liquid metal tapped from blast furnaces is treated with different reagents in a ladle for lowering the sulphur, silicon, and sometimes even the phosphorus contents, before it is charged into the steelmaking furnace. This helps in the production of purer steel at the primary steelmaking stage itself.

Secondary steelmaking, ingot and continuous casting as well as hot metal pre-treatment are presented in detail in later chapters.

1.4 PRESENT STATUS OF THE WORLD STEEL INDUSTRY

1.4.1 Classification

Steel plants may be classified into two broad categories.

- *Integrated Steel Plants* (ISPs) follow the Blast Furnace–BOF route of steelmaking. They are relatively large in size with individual module capacities ranging from 1 to 5 Mt of steel per year. A typical 3 Mtpa ISP would cover an area of 4–8 square km, i.e. a fairly large area, since a series of processes is involved.
- *Mini Steel Plants* (MSPs) use EAFs for steelmaking, and many of them have captive DRI producing units. MSPs are smaller in size with module capacities generally between 0.5 Mt and 1 Mt per year, and in some cases up to 2 Mt per year. A typical 1 Mtpa MSP would cover an area up to 2 square km to house EAFs and DRI producing facilities.

Downstream process stages, such as secondary steelmaking, continuous casting and rolling are common facilities in both ISPs and MSPs.

As mentioned earlier (Section 1.1.4), steels may be broadly classified into:

1. *Plain carbon steels* account for about 90% of the world's steel production, and are produced in integrated steel plants and some in mini steel plants. Besides carbon, these steels contain some amount of manganese and, in some cases, some other alloying elements in relatively low concentrations. Plain carbon steels may be further classified into low carbon (0–0.2% C), medium carbon (0.2–0.6% C) and high carbon (0.6–1.5% C) steel.
2. *Alloy steels* are those steels where alloying elements like Ni, Cr, Mo, Co, etc. are deliberately added in larger amounts. Alloy steels account for about 10% of global steel production, and are almost always made in MSPs. Alloy steels may be classified into:
   - Low alloy steels — up to 5% alloying elements
   - Medium alloy steels — 5–10% alloying elements
   - High alloy steels — above 10% alloying elements.

Steel products made from plain carbon or alloy steel may be classified according to the shape of the final product as:

- Long products — bars, rounds, rails, channels, angles, etc.
- Flat products — plates, sheets, galvanised/coated sheets, etc.

These products are manufactured by rolling and account for virtually the entire amount of bulk steel products. In addition, small quantities of special steel products (wheels, axles, gun barrels, etc.) are manufactured by forging, and some others by direct casting (engine blocks, small components, etc.).

1.4.2 World Production of Steel

The International Iron and Steel Institute (IISI) regularly publishes data on global steel production, which are reproduced in various other publications. Figure 1.5 presents data on world's *crude steel* (i.e. at the ingot/continuously cast product stage, before finishing) production in Mt/year, from 1900 to 2000 AD (Sarma et al. 2001). It also indicates the major events that have had significant influence on global steel production. Figure 1.5 indicates that the world's crude steel production stagnated in the 1980s, essentially because of lack of growth in demand followed by steel production growing rapidly to reach 730 Mt in 1992. In consonance with the cyclic demand for steel, there was again some slowdown — only 820 Mt of steel was produced in the year 2001. However, in the last few years the growth has again increased. The production was 903 Mt in 2002, 964 Mt in 2003, over the billion tonne mark for the first time in 2004, 1129 Mt in 2005, 1245 Mt in 2006, 1351 Mt in 2007, 1329 Mt in 2008 and 1212 Mt in 2009. China has contributed significantly towards this tremendous growth of rate — China's crude steel production was 90 Mt, 182 Mt and 490 Mt in the years 1992, 2002 and 2007 respectively. China's production went beyond the 500 Mt mark in 2008. In 2009, the Chinese production was 567 Mt.

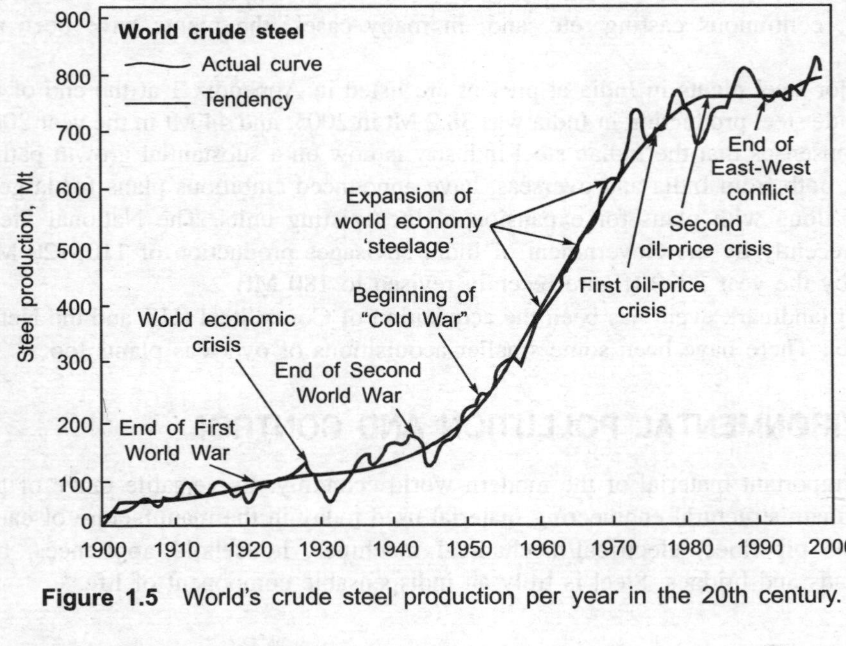

Figure 1.5 World's crude steel production per year in the 20th century.

1.5 STEELMAKING IN INDIA

While recounting the history of the establishment of iron and steel plants in India, the following plants are worth noting.

- The Bengal Iron and Steel Co. at Barakar in 1875.
- The Tata Iron and Steel Co. (now known as Tata Steel Limited) at Jamshedpur in 1907.
- The Indian Iron and Steel Co. at Burnpur in 1918 (Bengal Iron became a part).

- Mysore Iron and Steel Works at Bhadravati in 1918 (later renamed as Visvesvaraya Iron and Steel Ltd.).

Along with these ISPs, some electric furnace-based small-scale steelmakers, notably Guest Keen and Williams, Mukand Iron and Steel Co., J. K. Iron and Steel Co., etc. were also installed. The total crude steel production in India (in 1950) soon after independence was about 1 Mt/year. After 1950, in the second Five-Year Plan, the Government of India decided to go in for large-scale industrialisation for which steel was required. Hindustan Steel Ltd. was established in the public sector and under its overall control, three integrated steel plants, each of around 1 Mt/year capacity, were set up at Durgapur, Rourkela and Bhilai with British, German and Russian collaboration respectively. Later the name of HSL was changed to the Steel Authority of India Ltd. (SAIL). SAIL now has four more steel plants under its control, viz. Bokaro Steel Ltd., Visvesvaraya Iron and Steel, Alloy Steel Plant (Durgapur), and very recently, Indian Iron and Steel, besides a few other auxiliary units. Another major public sector steel plant, Rashtriya Ispat Nigam Ltd. (RINL) was installed at Visakhapatnam.

Many more steel plants with capacities higher than 1 Mt/year as well as a multitude of smaller plants have been commissioned in the private sector throughout India. The existing plants have been modernised to incorporate the latest developments like: BOFs, secondary steelmaking, continuous casting, etc. and, in many cases, the plants have been expanded substantially.

The major steel plants in India at present are listed in Appendix 1 at the end of the book. The total crude steel production in India was 38.2 Mt in 2005, and 44 Mt in the year 2006. There is general consensus that the Indian steel industry is now on a substantial growth path. Several steelmakers, both from India and overseas, have announced ambitious plans for large capacity new plants, along with plans for expansion of the existing units. The National Steel Policy announced recently by the Government of India envisages production of 110–120 Mt/year of crude steel by the year 2020 (figure recently revised to 180 Mt).

A recent landmark event has been the acquisition of Corus Steel (UK and the Netherlands) by Tata Steel. There have been some smaller acquisitions of overseas plants too.

1.6 ENVIRONMENTAL POLLUTION AND CONTROL

Steel is an important material of the modern world economy. Its versatile range of properties make it the main structural engineering material used today in the manufacture of cars, trucks, ships, oil/gas pipelines, electrical/mechanical machines, household appliances, buildings, factories, roads and bridges. Steel is truly an indispensable component of life.

1.6.1 Steps Taken by the Steel Industry

The steel industry recognises that it has a role to play in sustainable development by raising the living standards of people in all parts of the world while not damaging the environment. Steel has a positive environmental profile, particularly with regard to its recyclability (approximately 350 Mt of used steel is re-melted each year). However, the production process can sometimes be polluting. Environmental issues facing both the iron and steel industry locally as well as on a global scale include: air emissions, effluent discharge, and soil/groundwater contamination.

Though the industry has responded to these issues, particularly in recent times, much more will need to be accomplished to meet the ever-increasing pressures of sustainability issues of tomorrow.

The production of steel in an ISP involves a series of processes, each with different input materials and emissions of various residual materials and wastes. Figure 1.6 shows the overall energy/material balance of the major components in a modern, efficient ISP (UNEP and IISI, 1997). In contrast, the energy and material balance of a typical EAF-based MSP showing the major inputs and outputs is presented in Figure 1.7 (UNEP and IISI, 1997).

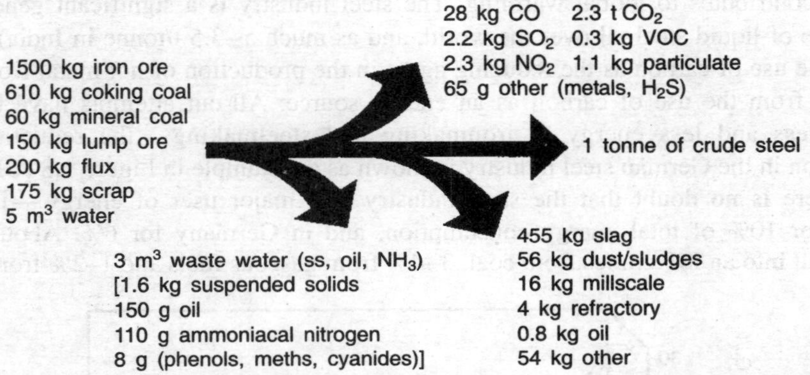

Input energy breakdown: 19.2 GJ coal; 5.2 GJ steam; 3.5 GJ electrical (364 kWh); 0.3 GJ oxygen; 0.04 GJ natural gas

Output energy breakdown: 5.2 GJ steam; 3.4 GJ electrical (359 kWh); 0.9 GJ coal tar; 0.3 GJ benzene

Figure 1.6 Energy/materials balance per tonne of steel for an efficient, modern integrated steel plant.

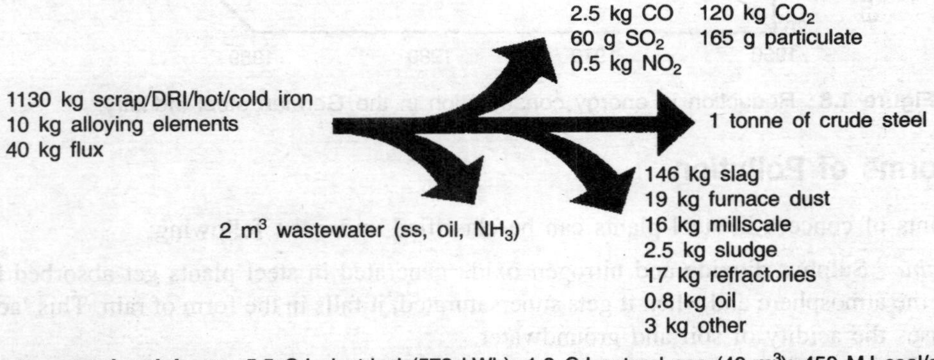

Input energy breakdown: 5.5 GJ electrical (572 kWh); 1.3 GJ natural gas (40 m^3); 450 MJ coal/coke (15 kg); 205 MJ oxygen (30 m^3); 120 MJ electrode consumption (3.5 kg)

Figure 1.7 Energy/materials balance per tonne of steel for an EAF plant.

It can be seen that large quantities of CO, CO_2, SO_2, NO_x as well as suspended solids, waste water, and other liquid effluents are generated during steel production. The quantities involved are relatively lower in the case of EAF-based plants, but potential pollutants are nevertheless present. Governments all over the world under pressure from society at large are actively monitoring the extent of gaseous, solid and liquid discharges, and stricter regulations are being formulated. As a consequence, steel plants are having to invent and adopt many measures to control pollution of air, water and soil. The day is not very far when no new process will be given licence, unless it is environment-friendly.

A beginning has already been made as far as carbon dioxide is concerned, and steel plants all over the world are being given 'CO_2 credits' based on the extent of CO_2 generated vis-à-vis an agreed benchmark. Although CO_2 has no direct adverse impact on the ecosystem, it is increasingly being viewed as an air pollutant because of its importance as a 'greenhouse gas', i.e. a gas contributes to global warming. The steel industry is a significant generator of CO_2 (2.5 t/tonne of liquid steel all over the world, and as much as 3.5 t/tonne in India) owing to the unavoidable use of carbon as the reducing agent in the production of hot metal from iron oxide, and partly from the use of carbon as an energy source. All-out attempts have been made to consume less and less energy in ironmaking and steelmaking — the reduction in energy consumption in the German steel industry is shown as an example in Figure 1.8 (UNEP and IISI, 1997). There is no doubt that the steel industry is a major user of energy — in Japan steel accounts for 10% of total energy consumption, and in Germany for 6%. About 95% of the energy input into an ISP comes from coal, 3–4% from gaseous fuels and 1–2% from liquid fuels.

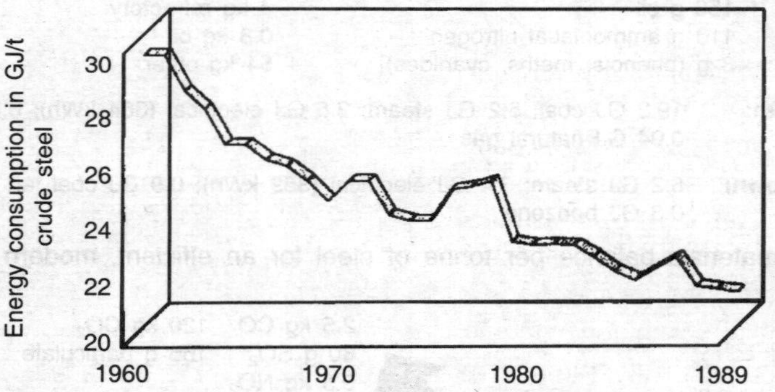

Figure 1.8 Reduction in energy consumption in the German steel industry.

1.6.2 Forms of Pollution

The pollutants of concern in steel plants can be classified under the following:

Acid rain: Sulphur dioxide and nitrogen oxide generated in steel plants get absorbed by moisture in the atmosphere and when it gets supersaturated, it falls in the form of rain. This 'acid rain' increases the acidity of soil and groundwater.

Toxic elements: Heavy elements such as Hg, Th and Pb are most toxic. Several other elements, such as Cd, Bi, As, Cr, etc. also have toxic effects. Many of these elements like lead (which condenses in the upper areas of blast furnaces) and chromium (used in coating steel strips in the form of chromates) are generated in steel plants.

Particulates: Virtually all the iron and steel processing steps (raw materials storage, sinter plants, blast furnaces, steel melting shops, etc.) generate particulates. Unless controlled, they can enter the lungs as dust to cause respiratory difficulties.

Gaseous and volatile compounds: Carbon monoxide, which is a major constituent of blast furnace, and BOF gas are highly toxic. They can prove fatal if their concentration in air exceeds 1000 ppm. Coke oven and by-products effluents, such as ammonia, phenol, benzol, hydrocarbons, etc. can also be potential health hazards.

Noise pollution: Excessive noise can cause hearing impairment, stress, etc. and noise levels above 75 dB are considered harmful. Blast furnaces, oxygen plants, powerhouses, etc. are areas where noise levels can be high in a steel plant.

Solid wastes: Huge quantities of wastes are generated during ironmaking and steelmaking. Sinter fines, coal dust, coke breeze, bag house dust, gas cleaning plant sludge, millscale, blast furnace and BOF slag, etc. are the common solid wastes generated in a steel plant amounting to almost 1.5 t per tonne of crude steel made. Therefore, waste management is an important activity in any steel plant. This not only includes safe disposal so as not to affect soil and groundwater in the long run, but also includes converting the wastes into some useful commodity. Use of blast furnace slag for cement making, recirculation of BOF slag in sinter plants, use of sludge in making tiles, etc. are good examples.

1.7 CONCLUDING REMARKS

It is obvious that the technology and practice of ironmaking and steelmaking have made remarkable strides in terms of productivity, cost, quality and process efficiency in the last few decades. Development and growth of metallurgical and engineering sciences, such as metallurgical thermodynamics and kinetics, heat mass and momentum transfer, numerical and computer techniques, etc. have contributed significantly towards this achievement. Various innovations in the application of modern science and engineering, electronics and instrumentation, information technology, etc. have also played a role. Computer-aided process automation and control is a major outcome of all these efforts.

Steel plants today are truly interdisciplinary in character. However, in the chapters that follow, the emphasis will primarily be on the metallurgical aspects along with the associated theoretical background, wherever necessary.

REFERENCES

Biswas A.K., *Minerals and Materials in Ancient India,* Vol. 1, D.K. Printworld, New Delhi (1996), p. 392.

Fruehan R.J., *Making, Shaping and Treating of Steel,* AISE, 11th ed., Vol. 2 (1999), p. 11.

Sarma S.K., S.N. Rao and B.N. Singh, *Perspectives and Planning for Steel Industry*, RINL, Visakhapatnam (2001).

Steel Industry and the Environment, Technical Report no. 38, UNEP and IISI (1997).

2

Overview of Blast Furnace Ironmaking

2.1 INTRODUCTION

Lump iron ore (at least above 10 mm in size) in the form of haematite (Fe_2O_3) or magnetite (Fe_3O_4) or iron oxide in the form of pellets or sinter prepared from iron ore fines (below 8 mm) are the source of iron units in blast furnaces. To meet the thermal as well as the chemical energy requirements and to support the burden during melting of the iron bearing burden, coke along with coal (as an injectant) and oxygen, primarily as air, are fed to blast furnaces. Within the furnace the solid inputs melt after reduction of the oxide. In order to separate the gangue in the feed materials from liquid iron, flux in the form of limestone/lime/dolomite is added, either independently or through sinter.

Chapter 1, Section 1.1 briefly presented the evolution of blast furnace ironmaking in Europe in the Middle Ages till the end of the nineteenth century. Section 1.2 briefly presented the evolution of blast furnace ironmaking since 1880. This evolution has been divided into the following periods.

(i) The period from 1880 to 1950, when most of the developments were in the nature of engineering, including improved furnace design.

(ii) From 1950s, advances in blast furnace (BF) ironmaking have been remarkable. It is largely because of much better understanding of the underlying sciences and inner working of the furnace. These developments brought about major improvements not only in design and engineering, but also in the metallurgy of the process.

Chapter 1 also itemised the important developments. Chapters 5–12 contain detailed presentations of various aspects of the science and technology of BF ironmaking. However, in order to understand them properly, a general knowledge of the BF ironmaking process is the essential prerequisite. This is the objective of the present chapter. The purpose is to provide a broad exposure to readers so that they have a working knowledge. Here, the descriptions will be brief. Traditional features and modern developments will be put together without distinction for the sake of conciseness and clarity. Some data will also be included to give an overall idea. However, such data should be viewed as approximate only.

2.1.1 Improvements Made in Blast Furnace Technology

The blast furnace process has remained up-to-date and competitive owing to several innovative developments that have taken place over the years. These innovations have led not only to more efficient process technology, but also to improved design and engineering of the equipment involved. Hot metal (i.e. liquid iron) production rates of 8000–10,000 tpd, i.e. tonnes per day fuel rates of around 450–470 kg/thm (i.e. per tonne of hot metal) (270/275 kg coke plus 175/225 kg coal), productivity levels of 2.5–3.0 t/m^3/d (based on inner volume), and furnace availability ranging between 95% and 98% are the results of improved process control, better understanding of the process, stability of operations, and so on. Low silicon (< 0.20%) hot metal is nowadays being produced consistently and a campaign life of 15 years (and more) between two major relinings has become the norm in efficiently-run blast furnaces. Improvements in the raw materials used in terms of better quality coke with lower coke ash, increased use of agglomerates (both sinter and pellets), use of high-grade limestone/dolomite with low alkali content, etc. have lowered the slag rate, which has had a direct bearing on blast furnace productivity and fuel rate.

As a result, amongst all the ironmaking processes, the blast furnace, which has been in existence for the longest, still remains dominant. Many of the alternative ironmaking technologies that have emerged (dealt with later in Chapters 13 and 14) can only complement the blast furnace in the years ahead. It is evident that even after these technologies are fully established in the years to come, the blast furnace will continue to be the principal method of ironmaking.

2.2 BLAST FURNACE REACTIONS AND PROCESS IN A NUTSHELL

Figure 2.1 schematically shows the vertical section of a blast furnace. The inputs and outputs are approximately representative of modern furnace practice. The furnace is refractory lined, and is filled with material from the stockline down to the bottom. The process goes on continuously for several years till it is shutdown for repairs and modifications. The inputs and outputs are per metric ton (i.e. tonne) of *hot metal*.

Solid raw materials at room temperature are charged from the top. Manufacture of metallurgical coke from coal in coke ovens has been presented in Chapter 8. Sinter and pellets are manufactured by agglomeration of iron ore fines. These have been dealt with in Chapter 9.

Pre-heated air above 1000–1100°C is blown through tuyere pipes inserted into the furnace through its wall. Nowadays it is enriched with some pure oxygen and moisture. Most of the modern furnaces are practising injection of pulverised coal as well. Exothermic combustion of coke and coal by oxygen from air gasifies carbon into CO and also provides heat. The highest temperature zone of the furnace (1900–2000°C) is at the level of tuyeres. As the hot reducing gas travels upwards, it heats up the solid charges as well as participates in various reactions at different zones of the furnace. The approximate temperature levels at different heights of the furnace are indicated in Figure 2.1.

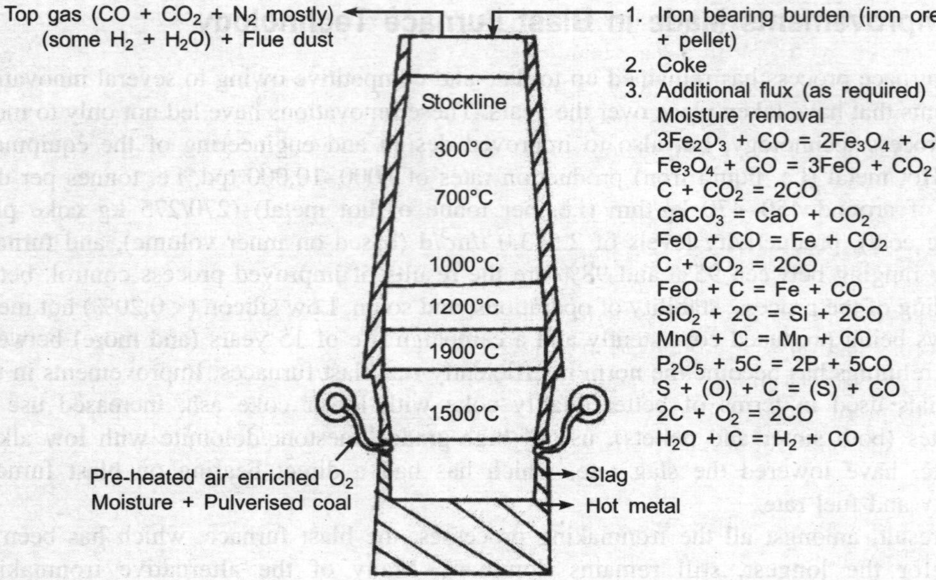

Figure 2.1 Blast furnace reactions and material balance.

The major reactions are also given in Figure 2.1. These may be classified into the following categories:

- Removal of moisture from the raw materials
- Reduction of iron oxides by CO
- Gasification of carbon by CO_2
- Dissociation of $CaCO_3$ (where raw limestone is also added)
- Reduction of FeO by carbon
- Reduction of some other oxides of ore by carbon
- Combustion of coke and coal in front of tuyeres.

The outputs from the furnace are:

- Molten iron (i.e. hot metal)
- Molten slag
- Gas at a temperature of around 200°C, containing CO, CO_2, N_2, moisture and some dust particles.

The hot metal is tapped through the *tap hole* several times a day into either *open ladles* or *torpedo ladles* and transferred to the steelmaking shop for further refining. The ladles are lined with refractory. Excess molten iron is cast into pigs in a pig casting machine for further use as feedstock in foundries or in steelmaking shops. The molten slag is tapped from time to time through the *slag notch* (i.e. separate tap hole) into the slag ladle, and is used as feedstock for the manufacture of slag cement, etc. The top gas is known as *blast furnace gas*. It has a considerable fuel value, since it contains carbon monoxide. However, as stated in Chapter 1, the dust has to be removed first in a gas cleaning unit. The gas is stored and then mostly utilised in the blast furnace shop itself for pre-heating of air and running turbines to drive air blowers.

Chapter 5 will present details of reactions and their physicochemical aspects. Chapter 6 has coverage of thermal-chemical features of the process, Chapter 7 presents various internal zones, gas flow, etc.

2.3 GENERAL CONSTRUCTIONAL FEATURES OF THE FURNACE

Figure 2.2 shows the general constructional features of a blast furnace schematically. It is circular in cross section, and around 30 m in height. The outer shell is made of steel. Inside the shell, there is refractory lining. Nowadays the steel shell is of welded construction rather than the earlier form of rivetted construction. The tall structure has recently been made 'free standing', i.e. the only support is provided by the foundation. The furnace interior is broadly divided into:

- Stack, whose wall slopes outwards going downwards
- Belly, the cylindrical portion below the stack
- Bosh, below the belly and sloping inwards going downwards
- Hearth, below the bosh and tuyere region and the cylindrical portion.

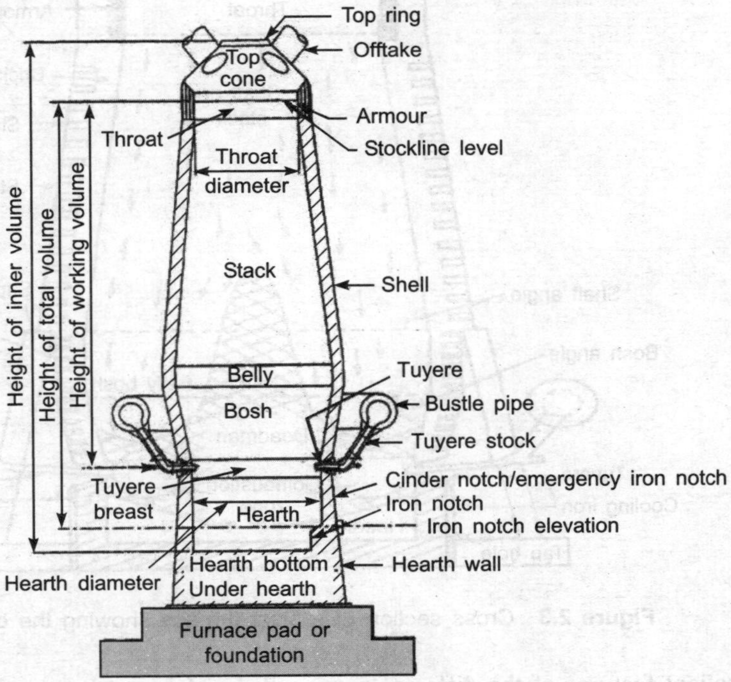

Figure 2.2 Schematic sketch of a blast furnace indicating different parts.

The details of the top arrangement will be presented later. Pre-heated air enters the tuyeres through the refractory lined *bustle pipe*, which is like a horizontal circular ring around the furnace. *Iron notch* is the tap hole for molten iron. It is kept sealed by refractory clay. For tapping, the clay seal is opened by a remote-controlled mechanical device. After tapping, the iron notch is again sealed by clay using the same device. *Cinder notch* is the hole for tapping molten slag. It is above the iron notch, since the slag has a lower density compared to iron and floats above the molten iron in the hearth. The furnace is built on a massive reinforced-concrete foundation.

2.3.1 Different Regions within a Blast Furnace

The different regions within a blast furnace are illustrated in Figure 2.3.

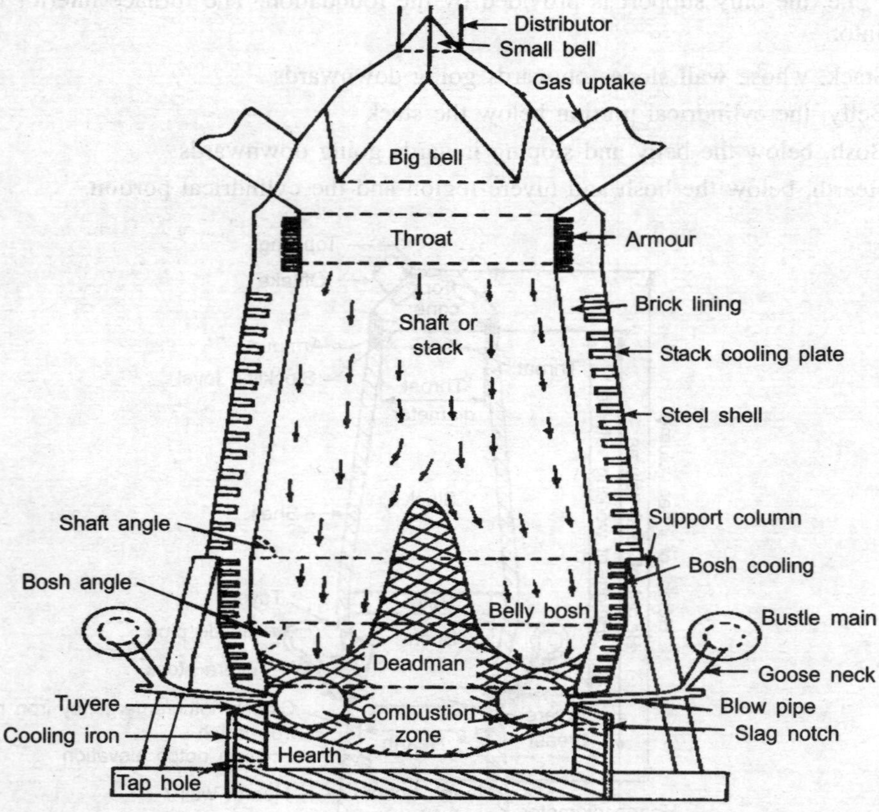

Figure 2.3 Cross section of a blast furnace showing the different zones.

The salient features of the different zones will be elaborated now.

Shaft or stack

This zone extends from the stockline down to the mantle level. It is the zone in which the burden is completely solid. The charge gets heated from 200°C at the stockline level to nearly 1100–1200°C by the time it descends to the bottom of the stack. In order to ensure free fall of the charge material, as it expands progressively with the progressive rise in temperature, the cross section of the furnace is uniformly increased to almost double the size from the stockline to the mantle level. Since much of the iron oxide reduction occurs in the stack, the success of the blast furnace process depends on the efficiency with which the countercurrent gas–solid interaction is brought about in the stack. It is this requirement that has led to the use of agglomerates like sinter and pellets as well as closer sizing (10–20 mm) of lump ore, including screening of fines immediately prior to charging.

Bosh

The charge materials begin to soften and fuse as they come down into the bottom of the stack. The next lower zone is called the bosh in which melting of the burden, except that of coke, takes place. The gangue and flux combine to form the slag. The furnace walls in this region are either parallel to some extent and then taper down, or entirely tapered down in order to reduce the sectional area by about 20–25% in harmony with the resultant decrease in the apparent volume of the charge. The burden permeability in this region is mainly maintained by the presence of solid coke. This, therefore, dictates that only coke of adequate strength and size should be used for efficient operation. Any untoward degradation of coke leads to decreased permeability in the bosh region and adversely affects the operation of the blast furnace.

Tuyere or combustion zone

By the time the charge descends into the area near the tuyeres, except the central column of coke, the entire charge is molten. The oxygen of the blast burns coke to CO and several combustion zones, one in front of each tuyere, exist in the tuyere zone. Thus, there is a 'runway' or 'raceway' in front of each tuyere, which is first horizontal and then smoothly changes its direction to vertical while expanding over the entire cross section of the furnace. Figure 2.4 shows the plan and elevation views of the tuyeres and combustion zone schematically.

Hearth

Although most of the coke burns at the tuyere level, a small fraction descends even into the hearth (to form the 'deadman', which either sits on the hearth or floats just above it), where it dissolves in the metal to its near saturation. The entire charge is molten and tends to stratify into slag and metal layers in the hearth from where these are tapped separately. The cross section of the furnace below the tuyeres decreases since the liquids are dense without pores and voids, thus leading to decrease in volume. The walls of the hearth are parallel and the hearth is the smallest cross section of the furnace.

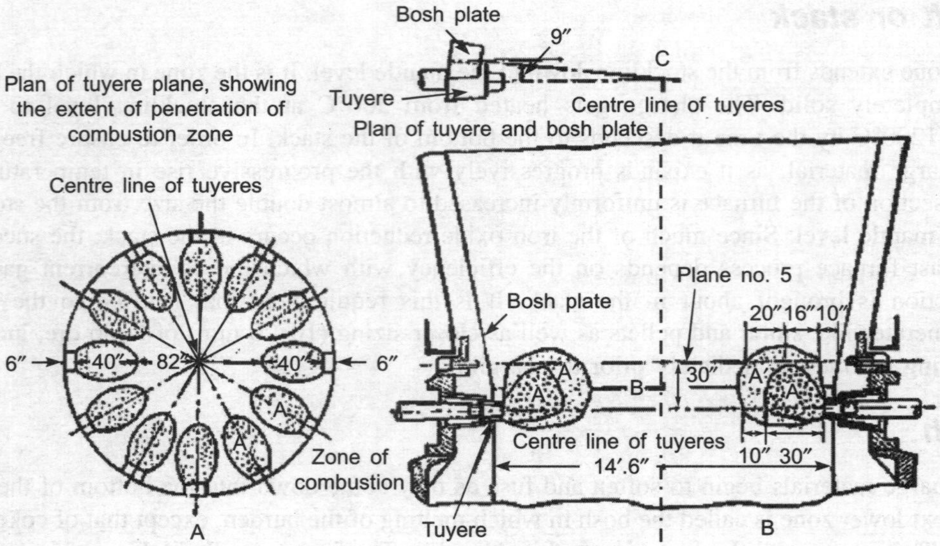

Figure 2.4 Combustion zones in a blast furnace.

2.3.2 Size of Blast Furnace

The design of a blast furnace has evolved primarily through experience and, therefore, the calculation of the furnace dimensions is more or less empirical in nature. However, some general scientific basis exists.

In Chapter 1, it has already been noted that the inner volume of the furnace has increased considerably over a period of last 100 years. Some data also have been presented there. Increasing demand for steel, accompanied by challenges for hot metal production at relatively low fuel rate and cost, has led to the development of large-size blast furnaces around the world. For example, Posco in South Korea has continuously increased the size of their blast furnaces—the hearth area has increased from 1660 m^2 in 1973 to 3800 m^2 in the year 2000, corresponding to hearth diameter increase from 9.2 m to 13.2 m.

It is interesting to note that in 1992, there were 555 blast furnaces existing in the Western World, 390 of which were in operation, and the output amounted to 314 Mt or about 800,000 tonnes per furnace per year, i.e. production of 2250 tonnes per day per furnace. On the other hand, in the socialist countries, in 1992, there were 585 furnaces, the hot metal production was 187 Mt. or 535,000 tonnes/furnace or 1500 tpd per furnace. At present, there are about 700 blast furnaces in operation globally (including 300 in the Western World). The trend to go in for larger furnaces, fewer in number, is clearly visible.

Large blast furnaces with working volumes over 2000 m^3, which have recently been built in Asia, include Baoshan No. 3 (4000 m^3) in China, POSCO's Gwangyang No. 5 (3950 m^3) in South Korea, China Steel's Kaoshung No. 4 (3000 m^3) in Taiwan and Tata Steel's refurbished G furnace (2300 m^3). The height of the stockline from the tuyere is known as the *working height*. It has not changed much over the period of years or with furnace size (see Chapter 1,

Section 1.2.1). It is only the coke which remains solid down to the tuyere level and bears the weight of the overlying burden in the furnace. More working height requires stronger coke. Therefore, the coke strength sets the limit to the working height (and, therefore, working volume).

2.4 PERFORMANCE OF BLAST FURNACE

Over the years, several developments have ensured that the 'old' blast furnace remains 'young' and will continue to be the most widely used method of iron production even in the years ahead. The performance of some of the best blast furnaces in the world is summarised in Table 2.1 (Chatterjee 2006).

Table 2.1 Operational features of some of the blast furnaces in the world

Parameter	Posco (Korea) BF 6	Hoogovens (Netherlands) BF 7	Kimitsu 3 (Japan)	Nippon Steel (Japan)	G blast furnace (Tata Steel)
Production, t/day	8600	7586	10,233	10,051	5150
Inner volume, m^3	3800	2678	4450	4063	2648
Working volume, m^3	3225	2328	3790	NA	2308
Productivity, t/m^3/day*	2.66	3.37	2.7	2.47	2.2
Top pressure, kg/cm^2	2.5	1.64	2.25	2.2	1.3
Oxygen enrichment, %	106/2.0	13.2	4.0	2.4	4.6
Burden, % Sinter (S),	85(S)	48.2(S)	50(S)	93(S)	70(S)
Ore (O), Pellets (P)	15(O)	48.8(P)	50(P)	7(P)	30(O)
Al_2O_3 in sinter, %	1.85	1.24	1.54	1.84	2.4
Coke ash, %	11	11.3	9.5	10.2	15.4
Coke rate, kg/thm	390	268	365	392	410
PCI rate, kg/thm	100	233	125	71(oil)	120
Slag rate, kg/thm	320	203	236	286	300
Al_2O_3 in slag, %	14	15.1	16.7	15.3	19.2
Blast temperature, °C	1200	1162	1180	1278	1080

* Productivity is based on working volume

From the earlier coke rates of around 1000 kg/thm in 1950 without any coal injection, it is possible to operate blast furnaces today with as little as 350 kg/thm of coke with coal injection of 125–175 kg/thm. Efforts towards enhancing the blast furnace performance have been primarily directed at (a) raw materials to improve the furnace permeability and increase wind acceptance for efficient coke burning, (b) changing the operating practices and work culture, and (c) increasing the hot blast temperature to reduce the fuel rate and economise the production.

The decade of 1970 introduced the concept of auxiliary fuel and steam injection. With the use of improved sensors and probes, the understanding of the process has improved and the day is not far away when the 'ideal' situation of 250 kg coke and 250 kg coal per tonne of hot metal will emerge (Table 2.2; Chatterjee et al. 2001). This would be close to the theoretical minimum amount of coke required for blast furnace ironmaking.

Table 2.2 Progressive reduction in blast furnace coke consumption over the years

Year	Coke rate (kg/thm)	Injectant (kg/thm)	Total reductant (kg/thm)	Comments on BF operation including major changes made
1950	1000	0	1000	Lean local ores were used
1965	600	0	600	Rich seaborne ores began to be used
1970	525	50	575	Oil injection, high blast temperature operation, oxygen enrichment were practised
1980	500	50	550	High top pressure operation along with improved burden distribution facilities and permeability control
1990	400	125	525	Increased coal injection as well as improved sinter, coke quality
2000	325	175	500	Increased coal/gas/oil/tar injection
2010	250	250	500	Continued use of metallics like DRI in the burden

2.5 BLAST FURNACE REFRACTORY LINING

Between the outer steel shell and the inner working volume of the furnace, there is a thick refractory lining, which protects the steel shell. The lining life determines the duration of one non-stop campaign. It has been noted in Chapter 1 that the campaign life was 4–6 years in 1960, and is now about 15–20 years, and even more. Such a long life has been possible owing to improved quality of the lining as well as better furnace operation.

The major causes of failure of the lining are the following:

- Carbon monoxide attack
- Action of alkali and other vapours
- High temperature
- Abrasion by moving solid charges
- Attack by molten slag and metal
- Furnace design and operation.

All the above causes are not equally important in all the zones of the furnace. In the stack, the lining has to be primarily withstand abrasion by moving solids as well as attack by CO gas. In the bosh region, dominant causes are high temperature, attack by alkali and other vapours, attack by alkaline and limy slag, as well as erosion by ascending hot gas. In the hearth, action of molten slag and metal is the principal source of corrosion-cum-erosion of the lining. Chapter 5 has presented discussion on physical chemistry of blast furnace reactions, where some of these have been included.

Alumino-silicates and carbon form the two classes of refractory materials most commonly employed for BF lining. The former occur in nature as fire-clay. Ordinary fire-clay bricks containing about 40–45% Al_2O_3 are used in the upper stack, whereas those containing above

60% Al_2O_3 (known as high duty fire-clay) are employed for the lower stack, belly and bosh. There have been attempts to use silicon carbide bricks in the bosh region as inner refractory lining. Carbon is the popular refractory in the hearth. It has a much higher thermal conductivity compared to that of fire-clay (3 W/m/K for amorphous carbon and 40 W/m/K for graphite). This helps to keep the lining cooler owing to the higher rate of heat transfer.

However, for a longer lining life, it is necessary to carry out extensive water cooling of the refractory. This not only keeps the refractory temperature lower, but also allows the formation of a protective layer of frozen metal and slag on the inner wall of the refractory lining. The design of the cooler depends on the size of the furnace and its location in the furnace. *Box coolers* are either cast iron boxes with steel pipes inside for the stack region, or copper boxes with copper tubes for the belly and bosh regions. These coolers are inserted into the refractory brick work at various locations. Modern trend is to go for copper, even for the stack region (shown schematically in Figure 2.3).

Stave coolers are now popular for the bosh and hearth. Staves are large cast iron water jackets that cover almost the entire outer surface of these regions of the furnace. External water sprays are also employed as an alternative to stave coolers. The bottom carbon lining of the hearth is cooled either by forced air circulation or by passage of water through the pipes, which are embedded in the lining.

A major problem concerning cooling by water flow in pipes inserted into the lining, is the deposition of insoluble salts such as calcium carbonate on inner linings of the pipes. This offers resistance to heat transfer. Rise in local temperature leads to the formation of steam in extreme cases and consequent choking of channels. In order to avoid this, only demineralised and cooled water should be circulated in a closed loop.

2.6 CHARGING OF SOLID MATERIALS FROM THE TOP

In Chapter 1, Section 1.1.3, the evolution of ironmaking in Europe was briefly discussed. In order to clean the top gas for its utilisation as fuel, it was necessary to have a top charging device by which solids could be charged into the furnace without significant leakage of gas. This led to the invention of the *two-bell charging system* (one small bell and one large bell), which was a standard feature of all blast furnaces till about 1970. Even now, many smaller furnaces have this arrangement. Figure 2.5 shows the arrangement, and the procedure for its operation is also described therein.

It may be noted that gas flows through uptakes continuously while the charging cycle goes on. The solid burdens are not uniform. Coke is lighter than iron ore (about 3.5–4 times lighter). Again the prepared iron burdens—sinter and pellets—have a range of densities. The sizes of burdens are also not uniform and have a range.

Chapter 7 will deal with internal zones and gas flow in blast furnaces. Figure 2.1 shows the approximate temperature levels at various heights of the furnace. It is an ideal situation and is very much desirable. However, in reality there is considerable variation in temperature, gas composition and gas velocity at any horizontal section of a blast furnace. These are the consequences of non-uniform size of burden, since a finer particle offers more resistance to gas flow.

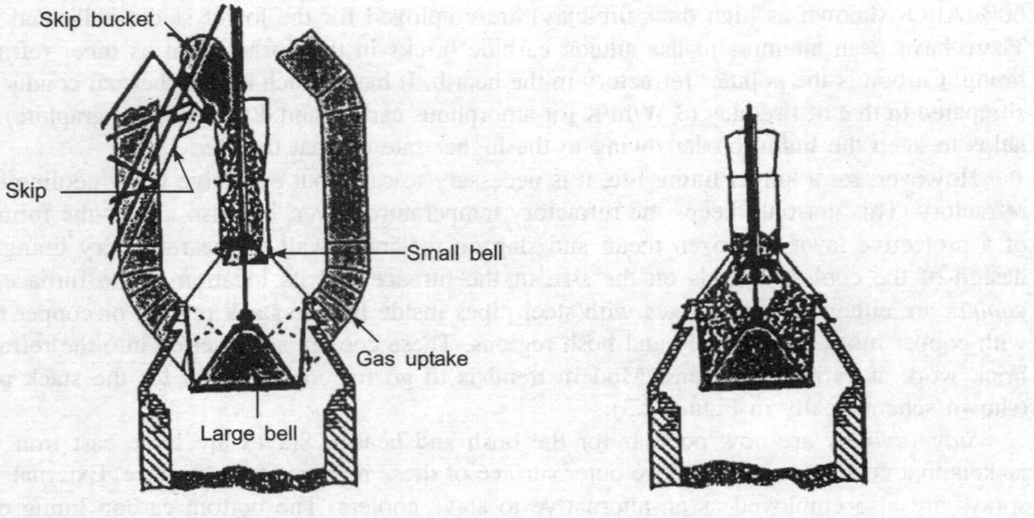

(a) Small bell and large bell both closed; skip bucket tipped to dump charge in hopper above small bell. Gas flowing from top of furnace through uptakes located in dome (top cone).

(b) Large bell remains closed while small bell opens to admit charge to large bell hopper.

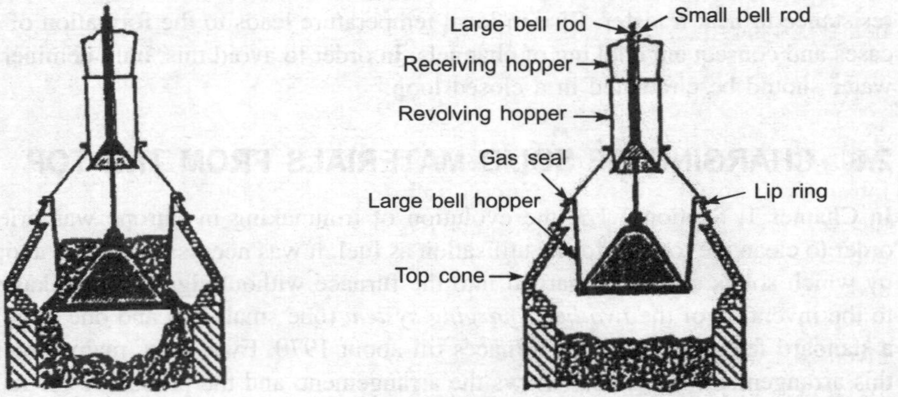

(c) Small bell closed to prevent escape of gas to atmosphere and large bell open to admit charge to the furnace.

(d) Both bells closed, ready to repeat charging cycle. Note that the rod supporting the large bell passes through a hollow rod supporting the small bell, permitting independent operation of bells.

Figure 2.5 Stages in two-bell charging cycle.

Chapter 10 has discussed the importance of uniform gas flow for smooth operation, as well as efficient productivity of a blast furnace. Efforts towards this goal are three-fold, viz.

- Screening of solid charges before charging into the furnace to eliminate fines below a certain size
- Agglomeration of fines by sintering, pelletising
- Proper top charging device to make burden size distribution as uniform as possible on horizontal section.

In order to improve the uniformity of charge distribution in horizontal section of the furnace, a revolving chute is an added feature. Material is introduced onto the small bell through two openings, each equipped with a seal valve, making sealing more effective. The revolving chute distributes the materials evenly on the small bell, and this assists in realising a more uniform distribution. Figure 2.6 shows two types of stockline profiles obtained by this device. It may be noted that there is some segregation of small and large particles. This is due to their different trajectories when they fall into the furnace upon opening of the big bell.

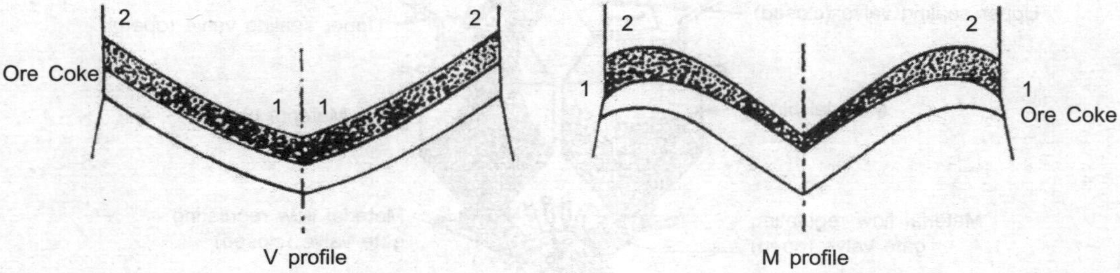

Figure 2.6 Typical burden profiles showing ore and coke layers, qualitative size segregation in ore layer (1 large and 2 small particles); iron ore includes sinter and pellets.

There have been subsequent modifications for improvement of charge distribution of the bell-type charging, as follows.

- Bell-type with movable throat armour
- Four-bell charging device.

With the advent of the movable throat armour systems in which a movable deflector is introduced into the stream of material falling from the big bell, a much wider cross section of the stockline can be controlled. Separate charging of iron-bearing materials and coke at different deflector settings as well as the proper distribution of fines has improved furnace performance and reduced the coke rate.

However, the most modern device is the so-called 'Bell-less Top' charging equipment, invented by Paul Wurth in Luxembourg in 1972. All modern furnaces are now having this system. Figure 2.7 shows this system. This new system comprises a combination of a hopper and gate. The material is fed on to a rotating chute at variable angles, through a system of seal valves and flow control gates. Mathematical models and instrumentation systems are available to predict the stockline profile and to measure the effect of change in the distribution pattern. All modern furnaces incorporate a high top pressure operation, where the exit gas pressure is above 1.5–2 atm gauge. This leads to more leakage as well as rapid erosion of bells. Bell-less top performs much better. In addition to this, the control of charge distribution is much superior. The distribution monitoring system includes the following:

- Heat flux monitoring equipment to measure the heat flow in different zones (both above and under the burden)
- Profile meters for the measurement of surface profiles
- Thermocouples in the throat, stack and bosh regions to measure temperature

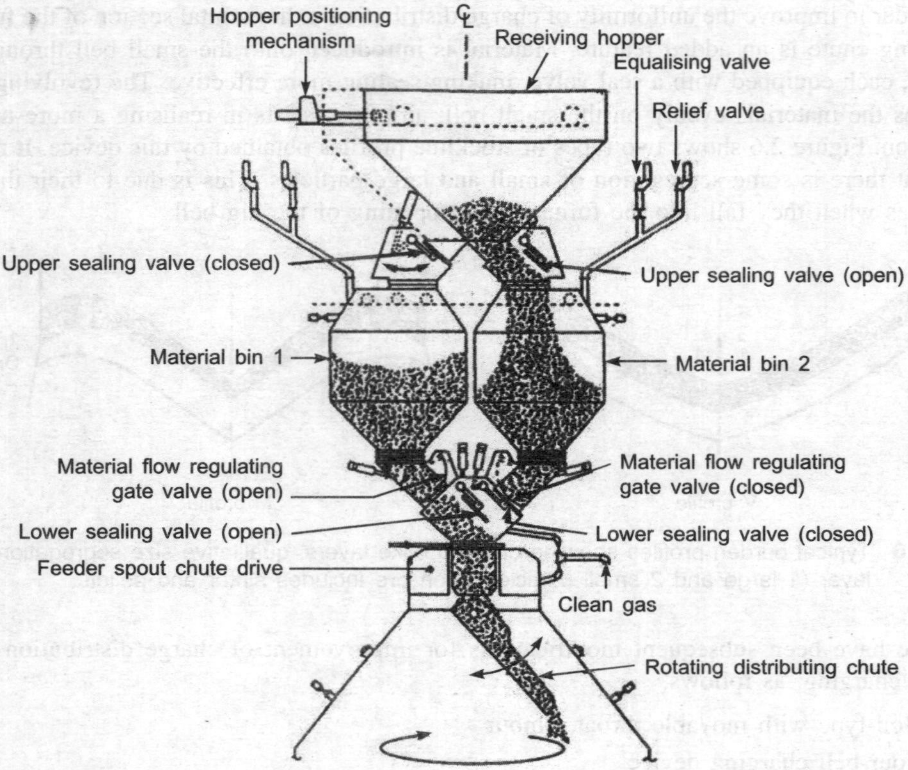

Figure 2.7 Bell-less top with pressurised hoppers and a rotating distributing chute.

- Stack pressure monitoring and pressure drop measurement along the furnace height
- Special instruments such as infrared probes to monitor the burden surface temperature, devices in the stack region to measure individual layer thicknesses and local descent rate, and tuyere probes to sample materials at the tuyeres level
- Mathematical models for charge distribution control, overall heat and mass balance and interpretation of probe data.

The advantages accruing from improved distribution control can be summarised as follows:

- Increased productivity, decreased coke rate, improved furnace life
- Reduced refractory erosion
- Improved wind acceptance and reduced hanging as well as slips
- Improved efficiency of gas utilisation and its indirect reduction
- Lower silicon content in hot metal and consistency in the hot metal quality
- Reduced tuyere losses and minimisation of scaffold formation
- Lower dust emission owing to uniform distribution of fines.

All these advantages have improved the overall efficiency, thereby making the process more competitive.

2.7 BLAST FURNACE PLANT AND ACCESSORIES

In a blast furnace plant, there are several other accessories besides the furnace proper. These accessories may be classified into the following categories:

- Hot blast supply equipment, consisting of turbo-blowers and Cowper stoves for preheating air
- Gas cleaning system and gas storage
- Raw material storage and handling
- Liquid products disposal
- Pulverised coal injection system (not in all plants)
- Process control equipment.

Figure 2.8 shows a schematic two-dimensional vertical section as illustration. Solid raw materials are stored in bins. Weighed quantities are loaded into the skip car, which goes up through an inclined rail to the furnace top to off-load the charges.

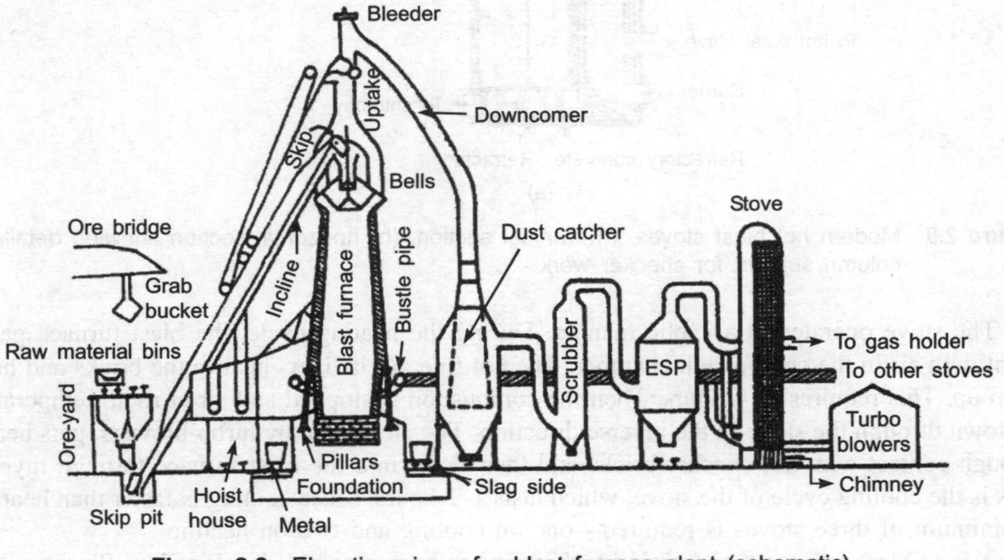

Figure 2.8 Elevation view of a blast furnace plant (schematic).

2.7.1 Hot Blast Stoves

Nearly 25–40% of the total gas generated is consumed in pre-heating the blast. The clean gas is stored in a huge gas holder, and is supplied for use in plant from there. The air blast required for running a blast furnace is first heated in hot blast stoves.

The stove is a tall cylindrical (height 20–36 m, diameter 6–8 m) steel shell, lined with insultating bricks inside. It has dome-shaped top. Figure 2.9(a) shows the vertical section, and Figure 2.9(b) the horizontal section. The interior of a stove has a combustion chamber and a heat regenerator unit, which consists of refractory bricks arranged as a checker work. Gases flow through the checker work and exchange heat with checker bricks.

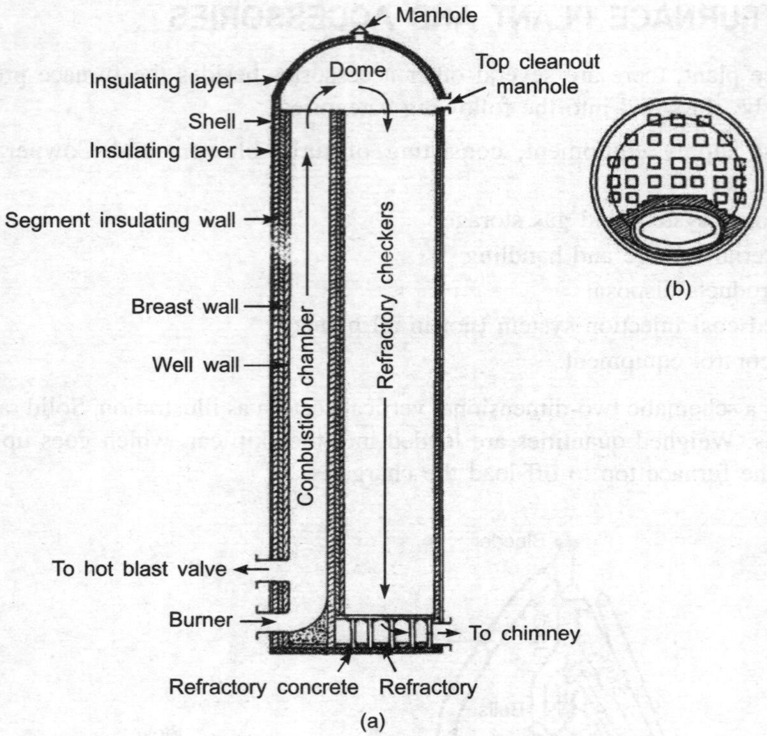

Figure 2.9 Modern hot blast stoves: (a) vertical section, (b) horizontal section showing details of column support for checker work.

The stove operates in a cyclic manner. During the heating cycle, the blast furnace gas is burnt with air in the combustion chamber. The hot flue gas delivers heat to the bricks and heats them up. This requires 2–4 hours. Then the combustion is stopped and air at room temperature is blown through the stove in the reverse direction. The air, blown by turbo-blowers, gets heated through contact with hot checker bricks and then flows into the blast furnace through tuyeres. This is the cooling cycle of the stove, which lasts 1–2 hours. Since cooling is faster than heating, a minimum of three stoves is required—one on cooling and two on heating.

A new blast furnace top charging technique has been recently developed by Siemens VAI and is known as SIMETAL Gimble top. Its design consists of special mechatronic packages that help to generate any burden profile that is desired by directing the charge material on the stock line. The world's first Gimble top has been installed in the 'C' blast furnace of Tata Steel.

REFERENCES

Chatterjee, Amit, in Steel Times International, Nov./Dec., 2006.

Chatterjee, Amit, Ramesh Singh, and Banshidar Pandey, *Metallics for Steelmaking—Production and Use*, Allied Publishers, 2001.

3

Overview of Modern Steelmaking

3.1 INTRODUCTION

In Chapter 1, Section 1.1.4, the early history of steelmaking was presented in brief. It was mentioned there that *plain carbon steels* constitute about 90% of the world's steel, and these steels have a long history. *Alloy steels* are of more recent origin. In Chapter 1, Section 1.3, the evolution of modern steelmaking starting from Henry Bessemer's invention of converter/pneumatic steelmaking, which heralded the advent of the use of steel in large quantities as an important engineering material, was also discussed in brief.

The original Bessemer process, i.e. *acid Bessemer* was invented in 1856, while the *basic Bessemer*, i.e. the *Thomas process* was patented in 1879. The *open hearth* process of steelmaking began in 1868, and soon replaced the Bessemer process. The open hearth process dominated the global production of plain carbon steels for about one hundred years. Electric arc furnaces (EAF) and electric induction furnaces are also about a hundred years old. The LD process was invented in Linz and Donawitz (two towns in Austria) in 1952–1953 and now dominates the world's steel production.

The present chapter contains an outline of the modern steelmaking and casting practices. A detailed description will follow in Chapters 15 to 23.

3.2 METHODS PRESENTLY USED FOR STEEL PRODUCTION

Today, the production of plain carbon steels follows two major routes—the integrated BF (blast furnace)–BOF (basic oxygen furnace, which is the new name for the LD process) and the scrap/DRI (direct reduced iron or sponge iron)—EAF route. Alloy steels are generally made in EAFs and electric induction furnaces.

In the BOF process, pure oxygen at supersonic speed is blown vertically through a lance (with several openings at the tip) onto the surface of molten hot metal contained in a cylindrically-shaped converter. Owing to the simplicity and flexibility of the process in producing high-quality steels, BOF steelmaking rapidly began to replace the then existing open hearth furnaces. The new process was quicker, i.e. steel of the required carbon content could be made in less than 60 minutes instead of 6–8 hours required in open hearth furnaces. Also no external heat was necessary, because the heat generated by the oxidation of carbon and the other impurities in hot metal (mainly silicon and phosphorus) made the BOF process autothermal, i.e. self-sufficient in thermal energy. BOF steelmaking (the terminology to be used to denote LD steelmaking from now on in this book) continued to have a greater share in the years that followed, but a real breakthrough in the maturity of this process came in the late 1970s and early 1980s with the introduction of mixed blowing—a combination of all the advantages of top-blowing along with thermodynamic equilibrium at the slag-metal interface brought about by limited gas injection from the converter bottom.

An important feature of BOF steelmaking is its high productivity, which necessitates a continuous supply of molten iron from blast furnaces since the BOF process cycle cannot be interrupted and the converter kept idle for long intervals. This imposes some restrictions on the overall flexibility of the process. In contrast, the EAF route where electrical energy is used for meeting the thermal requirements and gaseous/solid oxygen sources (like iron ore) fulfil the requirements of oxidising the impurities in hot metal, can be started/stopped as required to match variants like steel demand, availability of input materials, etc. EAFs can be economical in heat sizes ranging from 30 t to 200 t while BOFs are normally between 100 t and 300 t.

The EAFs originally depended on the availability of scrap and were restricted to the production of long products owing to the heat cycle time and the heat size. However, when increased accent on production efficiencies resulted in lower generation of scrap, EAFs were confronted with the problem of scrap availability—both in terms of quantity and quality. At this stage, EAFs resorted to the use of hot metal, DRI and other substitutes for scrap. This not only made EAF steelmaking less dependent on the vagaries of scrap supply, but also made EAFs capable of meeting the stringent demands of final steel composition with respect to the concentration of harmful elements like copper, chromium, nickel, tin, etc. As a result, EAFs can now be used for the production of even flat products, thereby leading to further growth in EAF-based steel production.

It is estimated that by 2010, the EAF route and the BOF route will have virtually equal shares in global production of steel. Figure 1.4 in Chapter 1 has shown the world's share of BOF, EAF and BOH (basic open hearth) steelmaking processes from 1970 to 1995, clearly highlighting the steady growth of BOF and EAF steelmaking and decline of the BOH process in that period. It is estimated that by 2010, the contribution of open hearth furnaces—the dominant method of making steel till the early seventies—will come down to zero.

3.3 OXYGEN STEELMAKING

3.3.1 Top-blown Converter Process

This process is referred to as LD, BOF, BOP (basic oxygen process) or BOS (basic oxygen steelmaking) in various places, but they all denote top-blown converter steelmaking. In this process, a water-cooled lance is introduced at the top of the converter to blow oxygen at *supersonic speed* on the melt surface. Its unique feature is that the blowing itself takes 15 to 20 minutes, regardless of the size of the heat, because the oxygen flow rate through the lance is adjusted to match the melt weight. Inclusive of the charging and discharging of steel and slag, sampling for temperature and bath analysis, the typical tap-to-tap times range between 40 and 60 minutes. Top-blown oxygen steelmaking is thus characterised by high productivity. Therefore, it is not surprising that this system was adopted for bulk steelmaking almost as soon as it was developed.

The impingement of the oxygen jets at supersonic speed on the molten iron bath, results in metal droplets being ejected from the bath by impact, thereby increasing the metal surface area and the rate of oxidation of the impurities in molten iron. Right at the beginning of each heat, scrap is charged into the converter along with hot metal to act as a coolant for the heat generated by the oxidation reactions. More often than not, iron ore is also added during the blow so that the oxidation of silicon, phosphorus, manganese and carbon, which are all exothermic reactions, do not result in inordinate increase in bath temperature. Low carbon steels (around 0.03–0.04% carbon) are normally tapped from such converters at 1620–1660°C. Lime and sometimes other slag forming agents, are added during the blow to form a slag capable of 'holding' the impurities in the form of complex oxides.

A schematic diagram of a top-blown oxygen vessel is presented in Figure 3.1.

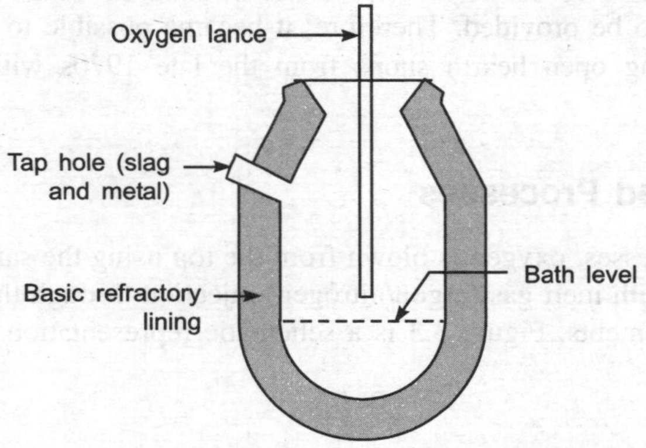

Figure 3.1 Top-blown oxygen converter.

3.3.2 Bottom-blown Converters (Q-BOP/OBM)

The essential feature of bottom-blown steelmaking is that the entire requirement of oxygen (50–55 Nm^3 per tonne liquid steel) is introduced through the bottom of the steelmaking vessel using tuyeres, canned porous elements, or refractories with controlled porosity. Sometimes, lime is also introduced along with oxygen, in which case only tuyeres can be employed.

The oxygen bottom-blowing process (Figure 3.2) is also known by the name OBM (*Oxygen Bottom Maxhuette*—Maxhuette was the steel works in Germany where bottom-blowing trials were first undertaken) or Q-BOP (Q standing for *Quiescent/Quiet*—the state of the bath vis-à-vis LD steelmaking) or LWS (Loire, Wendel and Sprunck—the names of three companies in France who developed this process). In the OBM/Q-BOP process, the oxygen tuyeres are cooled by injecting hydrocarbon gas through an outer pipe surrounding the oxygen pipe. Most bottom-blown processes use methane or propane as the hydrocarbon coolant, but fuel oil was employed in LWS converters. A principal advantage of bottom-blowing processes is that they operate

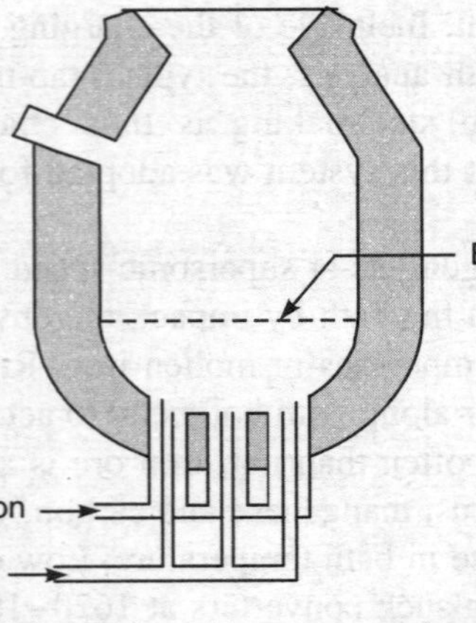

Figure 3.2 Bottom-blown oxygen converter.

closer to equilibrium, encourage early formation of a fluid slag, reduce the oxygen content of the steel tapped, and decrease the height requirements of the converter building since no top lance equipment needs to be provided. Therefore, it became possible to retrofit bottom-blown converters in the existing open hearth shops from the late 1970s with less capital cost in comparison to BOFs.

3.3.3 Bath Agitated Processes

In combined-blown processes, oxygen is blown from the top using the same vertical lance as in the case of BOF along with inert gas (argon/nitrogen) injection through the bottom by means of tuyeres or permeable elements. Figure 3.3 is a schematic representation of a combined-blown converter.

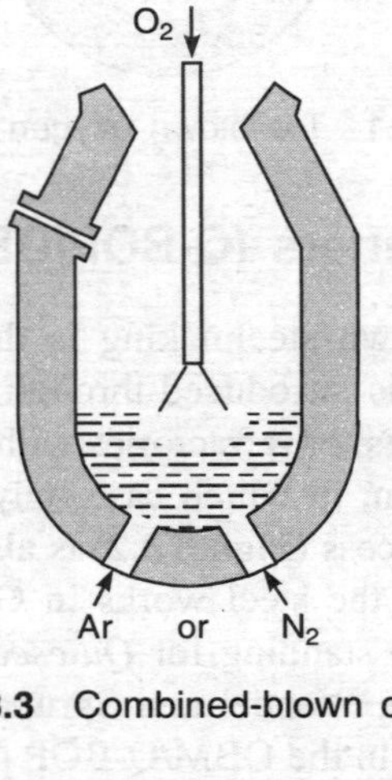

Figure 3.3 Combined-blown converter.

This modification enables the production of ultra-low carbon steels like in bottom-blown processes, along with flexibility in gas-slag-metal interaction like in top-blown converters, where the lance height—distance between the lance tip and the top of the bath—can be altered to match the blowing conditions required for carbon or phosphorus removal (the former is a gas-metal reaction while the latter is a slag-metal reaction).

3.4 ELECTRIC STEELMAKING

When, with increasing sophistication in the electric power industry towards the end of the 19th century, it became possible to generate power at a relatively low cost, use of electricity in steelmaking began to be considered.

3.4.1 Electric Arc Furnace (EAF)

Graphite electrodes are employed to supply the power and arcing takes place between the metal bath and the electrodes in the case of a modern direct current EAF. However, all traditional furnaces operate on alternating current, where arcing is between the electrodes. By 1900, small EAFs capable of melting about one tonne of steel became available and were operated either with a direct or with an indirect electric arc. A modern EAF (Figure 3.4) can be classified as high power or ultra high power (UHP) using AC or DC technology.

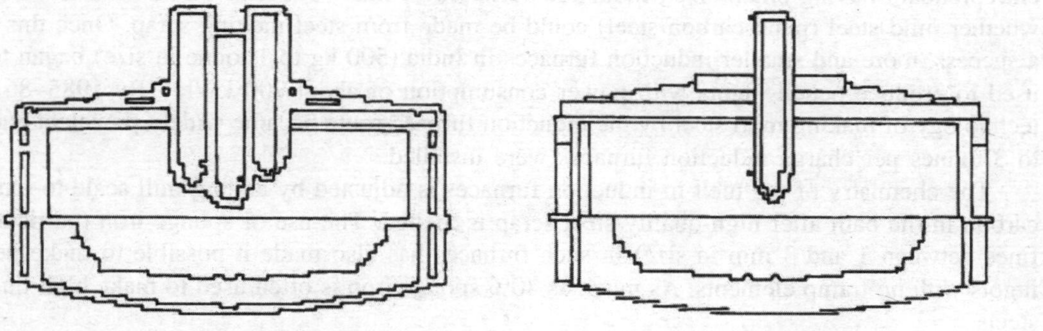

(a) Alternating current (AC) furnance (b) Direct current (DC) furnance

Figure 3.4 Electric arc furnaces.

The main advantage of EAFs lies in their ability to accept scrap, DRI, and molten hot metal in various proportions since whatever external energy is required, can always be provided by controlling the electrical power supplied. Furnace efficiency can be improved by the combined injection of carbon and oxygen through water-cooled supersonic lances at rates as high as 45 Nm^3/t. While earlier, 600–700 kWh of electrical power was used per tonne of liquid steel, modern-day furnaces with injection facilities, ultra-high power transformers, hot metal in the charge, etc. consume 300–400 kWh per tonne.

In fact, EAF designs today are being challenged by the ever increasing thermal loads, created by electric power inputs as high as 1 MW/t, and increasing rates of oxygen injection into the furnace. The aim is to reach heat cycle times of around 40 minutes, thereby producing more than 40 heats per day (like BOFs) in furnaces ranging in size of up to 300 t, though furnaces ranging from 30 t to 150–200 t are more commonly used. The AC electric arc furnace is the ideal melting unit for the production of all steel grades, from standard carbon grades up to high-alloyed special and stainless steel grades. In areas where the power grid is either weak or unstable, DC EAFs are preferred. The unique design of the anode in such furnaces promotes smooth and uniform transfer of the current through the melt.

EAFs can be of normal power or UHP (ultra high power) with one or two electrodes, single or twin-shell, as well as with and without a top shaft furnace (used for pre-heating the scrap before charging). However, a feature of all electric furnaces is that a considerable amount of noise is emitted; typical noise levels are between 125 and 139 dB(A). Moreover, their operation (particularly initial arcing) causes flickering in the grid.

3.4.2 Electric Induction Furnaces

Instead of electricity being used for arcing, it can also be used for melting a solid charge through induction as is done in induction furnaces. The electric induction furnace normally plays an important role in steel plants producing high-quality steels, particularly stainless steels from stainless steel scrap.

Like the rest of the world, the use of induction melting furnaces in India began when such furnaces were installed to produce stainless steel. But in 1981–82, some innovative entrepreneurs having small-sized induction furnaces to make stainless steel, tried to find out whether mild steel (plain carbon steel) could be made from steel melting scrap. Once this was a success, more and smaller induction furnaces in India (500 kg to 1 tonne in size) began to be used to produce pencil ingots with power consumption of about 700 kWh/t. By 1985–86, the technology of making mild steel by the induction furnace route became widely prevalent and up to 3 tonnes per charge induction furnaces were installed.

The chemistry of the melt in induction furnaces is adjusted by adding mill scale to oxidise carbon in the bath after high-quality steel scrap is melted. The use of sponge iron (particularly fines between 1 and 3 mm in size) in such furnaces has also made it possible to make pencil ingots with no tramp elements. As much as 40% sponge iron is often used to make high-quality steels.

3.5 SECONDARY STEELMAKING

Steelmaking can be completed in BOFs and EAFs in less than 45 minutes if the furnaces are pushed to the limit. However, in such a situation the steelmaking furnace itself is not always capable of guaranteeing that the steel made is always of the desired quality. For exact control of chemistry and/or temperature, molten steel tapped from such furnaces producing a large number of heats can be further processed in the ladle. This is known as secondary steelmaking (second stage of refining) in contrast to *primary steelmaking* carried out in BOFs, EAFs, etc. in which steel is actually made.

The demand for steel with stringent quality has made it necessary to adopt this type of downstream processing of liquid steel to guarantee the performance of the final products. Secondary processing of steel (Figure 3.5) decreases the concentration of gases dissolved in liquid steel (oxygen, nitrogen, and hydrogen) as well as sulphur, all of which are harmful for the product properties. In addition, it reduces harmful non-metallic inclusions, allows adjustments of composition and temperature, and can aid the production of ultra-low-carbon steels.

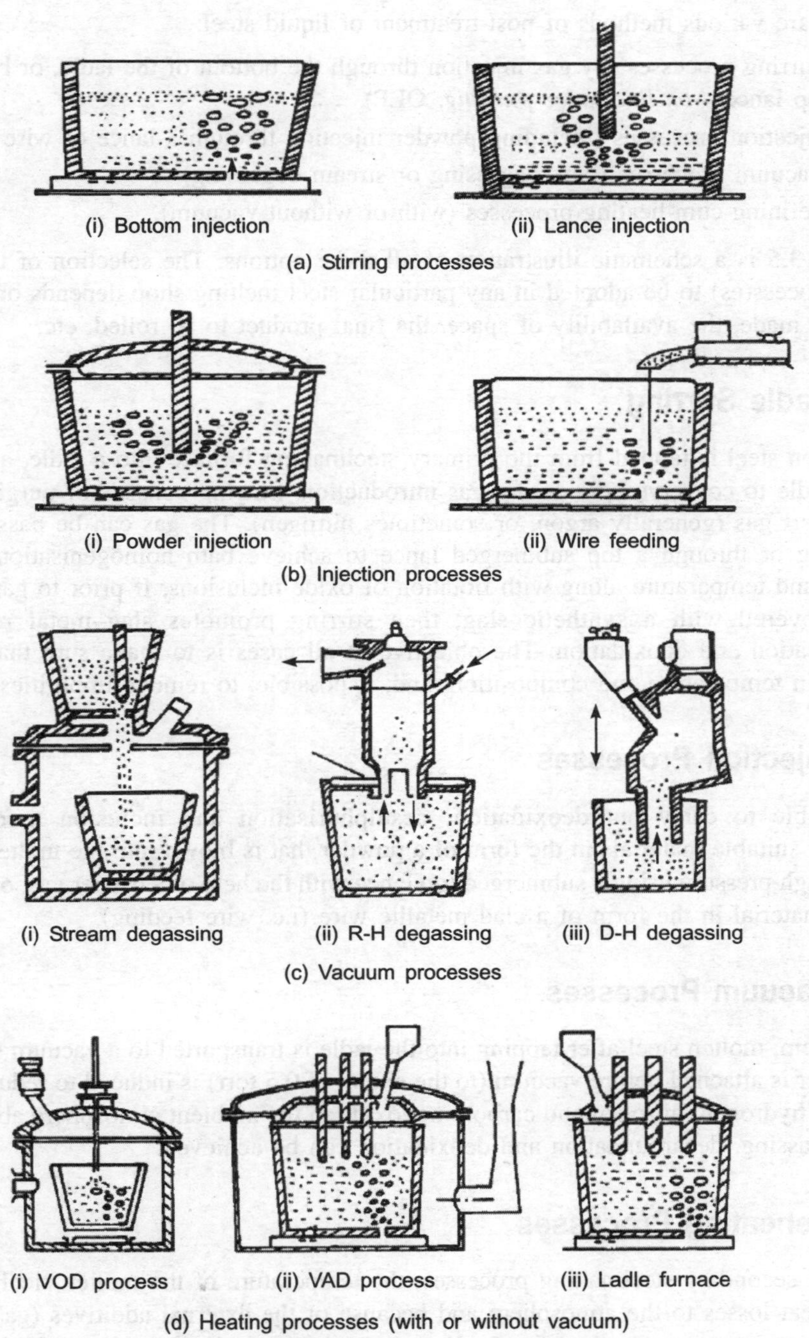

Figure 3.5 Schematic illustration of different secondary steelmaking options.

There are various methods of post-treatment of liquid steel:

(a) Stirring processes (by gas injection through the bottom of the ladle, or by means of a top lance—*on-line lance purging,* OLP)
(b) Injection processes (including powder injection through a lance or wire feeding)
(c) Vacuum processes (tank degassing or stream degassing)
(d) Refining-cum-heating processes (with or without vacuum).

Figure 3.5 is a schematic illustration of all these options. The selection of the secondary refining process(es) to be adopted in any particular steel melting shop depends on the types of steel being made, the availability of space, the final product to be rolled, etc.

3.5.1 Ladle Stirring

After molten steel is tapped from the primary steelmaking furnace into a ladle, a lid is placed over the ladle to conserve heat during gas introduction. Stirring consists of purging the liquid steel by inert gas (generally argon, or sometimes nitrogen). The gas can be passed through a porous plug or through a top submerged lance to achieve bath homogenisation in terms of chemistry and temperature along with flotation of oxide inclusions. If prior to gas stirring, the ladle is covered with a synthetic slag, then stirring promotes slag–metal reactions like desulphurisation and deoxidation. The objective in all cases is to make sure that the steel is consistent in temperature and composition, and, if possible, to remove impurities.

3.5.2 Injection Processes

It is possible to carry out deoxidation, desulphurisation and inclusion modification by introducing suitable materials in the form of a powder that is blown into the molten steel in the ladle at a high pressure using a submerged top lance with the help of a carrier gas, or by encasing the same material in the form of a clad metallic wire (i.e. wire feeding).

3.5.3 Vacuum Processes

In this system, molten steel after tapping into the ladle is transported to a vacuum station where a tight cover is attached before vacuum (to the extent of 0.5 torr) is induced to reduce the partial pressure of hydrogen, nitrogen and carbon monoxide in the ambient atmosphere above the ladle so that degassing, decarburisation and deoxidation can be achieved.

3.5.4 Reheating Processes

Since in all secondary steelmaking processes, the temperature of the molten steel tends to fall owing to heat losses to the atmosphere and because of the external additives (gas or solid), it is often necessary to compensate for the drop in temperature by providing additional heating. This can be done either as an isolated operation in order to even reduce the tapping temperature in primary steelmaking (as done in a ladle furnace), or during the vacuum treatment itself. While electrical energy is normally used to provide the heat, in some cases, particularly in systems operating under vacuum, chemical heating is also resorted to by blowing oxygen along with the addition of aluminium. Blowing of oxygen in vacuum is the technique used to produce ultra low carbon (ULC) steels (less than 0.03% and even as low as 0.001% carbon).

3.6 CONTINUOUS CASTING

As mentioned in Chapter 1, for more than 150 years till the 1960s, batch casting of liquid steel into ingots for further shaping by stepwise rolling or forging, was the only method available for casting liquid steel into a solid shape. In 1846, Sir Henry Bessemer in the UK first conceived and demonstrated the physical possibility of continuously casting thin sheets of steel between two water-cooled rolls positioned below a stream of liquid steel. However, it took about hundred years to establish the technology of continuous casting on a commercial scale.

Since then, continuous casting has come a long way, and today, a staggering 75% of the total crude steel production in the world is continuously cast into one shape or another (slabs, blooms, billets, other shapes) as against 30% in 1980. The main advantage of continuous casting is that the product is ready for direct rolling, sometimes even without further reheating.

Amongst the major producers of steel today, South Korea heads the list with about 94% of the steel being continuously cast. In Japan, the ratio is around 93%, while in the EEC countries as a whole, it is about 88%. Surprisingly, the US is lagging behind with a ratio of only 65%, while the erstwhile USSR and Eastern Europe are even further behind with only 17% and 18%, respectively. In this regard, India has fared not all that badly. At present in India, around 50% of liquid steel is continuously cast and the figure is steadily increasing. Interestingly enough, the number of continuous casting strands available in India is one of the highest in the world, primarily because a multitude of small-scale steel producers that operate in India have billet casting machines.

The basic equipment and operations involved in continuous casting are illustrated in Figure 3.6. These include:

- A source of liquid steel, generally after secondary treatment to ensure temperature homogeneity in the entire ladle
- A ladle for transferring and holding the liquid metal
- A tundish for distributing the metal into the continuous casting moulds made of copper
- The mould(s) to freeze an outer skin
- Water sprays to complete the solidification
- A drive system to control the rate of withdrawal of the cast products from the mould
- A cut-off and discharge system.

Continuous casting has been one of the major innovations made in the area of iron and steel in the last few decades. It has totally transformed the working of most steel plants. Earlier facilities like ingot bogies, ingot moulds, stripping yards, ingot soaking pits, etc. have become a part of history as a result of the advent of continuous casting.

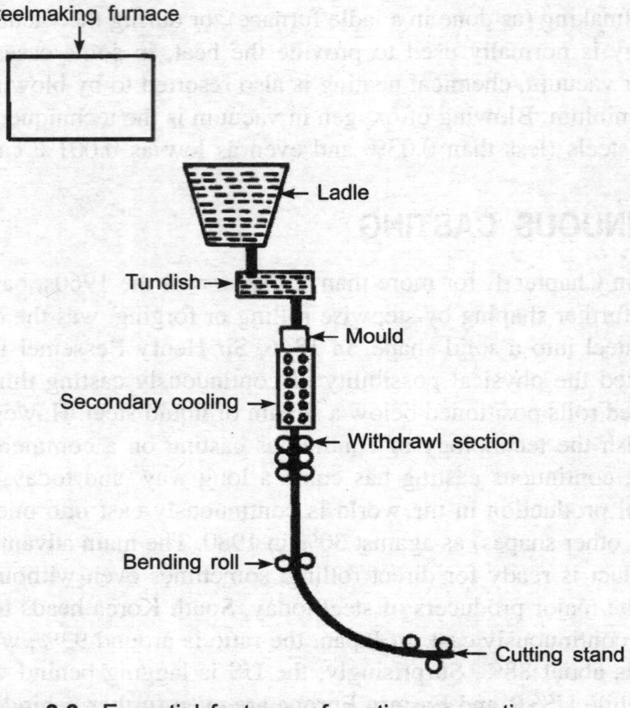

Figure 3.6 Essential features of continuous casting.

The original continuous casting machines were of the vertical type and required very tall buildings for housing the equipment. They were later replaced by vertical mould machines with bending rolls, or by curved mould machines.

4

General Physicochemical Fundamentals

4.1 INTRODUCTION

Ironmaking and steelmaking involve a variety of chemical reactions as well as other physicochemical processes such as viscous flow, interfacial phenomena, mass transfer, etc. at high temperatures. Therefore, physical chemistry constitutes the most important scientific fundamental for understanding the metallurgical aspects of ironmaking and steelmaking. Again, amongst the physicochemical fundamentals, *chemical thermodynamics,* consisting of reaction free energies and enthalpies, chemical equilibria, has found the most widespread application.

Such applications have been possible following research efforts by metallurgists, physical chemists and others over a period of several decades. Studies have been undertaken on thermodynamics, kinetics and other physicochemical phenomena for ironmaking and steelmaking reactions and systems at high temperatures. The laws of thermodynamics were well-established by the beginning of the 20th century. However, they could be applied to ironmaking and steelmaking only after the required data, such as reaction free energies and enthalpies, activity-versus-composition relations, etc. were determined through experimental measurements. Special correlations were also proposed.

Chapters 5, 15, and 20 shall deal with details of physical chemistry for blast furnace ironmaking, primary steelmaking, and secondary steelmaking respectively. Some other chapters will also contain these topics partly, and hence would not be covered here. The purpose of this chapter is to present the basic physicochemical fundamentals, which would constitute the basis for subsequent chapters. The basic objective of this chapter is to make the text self-contained for the convenience of readers. This background needs to be kept in mind before proceeding further.

4.2 CHEMICAL EQUILIBRIUM

Thermodynamic equilibrium is the ultimate stable state of a *system* in co-existence with its *surroundings*. It consists of the following:

(a) *Mechanical equilibrium,* i.e. uniformity of pressure throughout the system in the absence of other force fields.

(b) *Thermal equilibrium,* i.e. uniformity of temperature throughout the system.

(c) *Chemical equilibrium,* i.e. uniformity of *chemical potentials* of all *components* (e.g. elements and compounds) throughout the system.

Chemical potential will be discussed again; at this stage, the relation between chemical equilibrium and Gibbs free energy (G) will be taken up.

4.2.1 Activity, Free Energy, Chemical Potential and Equilibrium

It is to be noted that these are employed for thermodynamic calculations on *isothermal* reactions and processes (i.e. assuming the initial and the final temperatures to be the same).

Activity

By definition,

$$a_i = \frac{f_i}{f_i^0} \tag{4.1}$$

where

a_i = activity of component i (element or compound) in a solution at temperature T

f_i = fugacity of component i in the solution at temperature T

f_i^0 = fugacity of component i in its standard state (i.e. pure element or compound i at T and under 1 standard atmosphere, i.e. 760 mm mercury pressure).

Hence, by definition at standard state, $a_i = \dfrac{f_i^0}{f_i^0} = 1$

In an ideal gas, $f_i = p_i$ and $f_i^0 = p_i^0$. Since $p_i^0 = 1$ atmosphere by definition of standard state, in an ideal gas,

$$a_i = p_i \tag{4.2}$$

where p_i is the partial pressure component i (in atm.) in an ideal gas mixture.

It may be noted here that a_i, by definition of Eq. (4.1), is dimensionless, although in Eq. (4.2) it is numerically equal to p_i in atm. unit.

Activity and free energy

A fundamental relation at constant temperature is

$$\overline{G}_i^m = \overline{G}_i - G_i^0 = RT \ln a_i \tag{4.3}$$

where

$\overline{G}_i$ = *partial molar free energy* of component i in the solution (i.e. per mole of i)

G_i^0 = molar free energy of component i in its standard state

$\overline{G}_i^m$ = partial molar free energy of *mixing* of component i in the above solution.

T is temperature in kelvin, and R is the universal gas constant ($8.314\ \text{J} \cdot \text{mol} \cdot \text{K}^{-1}$).

$\bar{G}_i$ is for component i. The average of any property (including free energy) per mole of the solution is known as *integral molar property*.

Hence, G = integral molar free energy of the solution at temperature T

$$= \sum_{i=1}^{k} X_i \bar{G}_i \tag{4.4}$$

where, for a solution containing k components, X_i = mole fraction of component i

$$= \frac{n_i}{n_1 + n_2 + \cdots + n_i + \cdots + n_k}$$

$$= \frac{n_i}{\sum_{i=1}^{k} n_i} = \frac{n_i}{n_T} \tag{4.5}$$

where n is the number of moles (i.e. gmol). Here n_T means the total number of gmol of all components in the solution. Therefore, at temperature T,

$$\Delta G^m = \sum_{i=1}^{k} X_i \bar{G}_i^m = RT \sum_{i=1}^{k} X_i \ln a_i \tag{4.6}$$

where, ΔG^m is the integral molar free energy of mixing of the solution.

Chemical potential and equilibrium

Chemical potential can be defined in more than one way. However, the most useful definition in chemical thermodynamics is:

Chemical potential of component i in a solution

$$= \mu_i = \bar{G}_i, \qquad \text{at constant } T \text{ and } P \tag{4.7}$$

It can be shown (derivation not included here) that if some *phases* (I, II, ...) in a *heterogeneous system* (for example, a system containing slag, metal and gas phases) co-exist at thermodynamic equilibrium, then

$$\begin{aligned} \mu_1^{(\mathrm{I})} &= \mu_1^{(\mathrm{II})} = \cdots \\ \mu_2^{(\mathrm{I})} &= \mu_2^{(\mathrm{II})} = \cdots \\ &\vdots \\ \mu_i^{(\mathrm{I})} &= \mu_i^{(\mathrm{II})} = \cdots \\ &\vdots \\ \mu_k^{(\mathrm{I})} &= \mu_k^{(\mathrm{II})} = \cdots \end{aligned} \tag{4.8}$$

Again, from Eqs. (4.3) and (4.7),

$$\mu_i - \mu_i^0 = RT \ln a_i \tag{4.9}$$

However, for application purposes, μ_i^0 is taken as zero, by convention. Hence, Eq. (4.9) may be written as

$$\mu_i = RT \ln a_i \tag{4.10}$$

4.2.2 Free Energy and Equilibrium

For chemical reactions, the chemical potential approach to equilibrium is not convenient. The general approach here is to employ integral molar free energy (G). At equilibrium under constant temperature and pressure,

$$(dG)_{T,P} = 0 \qquad \text{for an infinitesimal process} \tag{4.11}$$

and

$$(\Delta G)_{T,P} = 0 \qquad \text{for a finite process} \tag{4.12}$$

At constant temperature and pressure, a process occurs spontaneously, if

$$(dG)_{T,P} < 0, \qquad \text{i.e. } (\Delta G)_{T,P} < 0 \tag{4.13}$$

Let us now consider a chemical reaction,

$$a\text{A} + b\text{B} = l\text{L} + m\text{M} \tag{4.14}$$

occurring isothermally at temperature T. Isothermal here means that the reactants A, B are at T, and the products L, M are also at T. Here a, b, l, m are the number of moles of A, B, L, M respectively. It does not matter at all if the temperature varies during the course of the reaction. It can then be derived (derivation skipped) that

$$\Delta G = \Delta G^0 + RT \ln J \tag{4.15}$$

where,

$$J = \frac{a_{\text{L}}^{l} \cdot a_{\text{M}}^{m}}{a_{\text{A}}^{a} \cdot a_{\text{B}}^{b}} = \text{Activity quotient} \tag{4.16}$$

Here, ΔG = change in Gibbs free energy as a result of reaction (4.14) at any arbitrary condition. ΔG^0 is the value of ΔG, when the reactants and products are at their respective standard states, as defined earlier. Here a_{L}, a_{M}, a_{A}, a_{B} are the activities of L, M, A, B respectively.

If reaction (4.14) further occurs at constant pressure as well, then at equilibrium, $(\Delta G)_{T,P} = 0$ from Eq. (4.12). Therefore, at equilibrium of reaction (4.14), from Eq. (4.15),

$$\Delta G^0 = -RT \ln [J]_{\text{eq}} = -RT \ln K \tag{4.17}$$

where, $K = J$ at equilibrium and is known as the *equilibrium constant.*

4.2.3 Oxidation–Reduction Reactions

Ironmaking is principally a process of reduction of iron oxides in ores. Similarly, steelmaking principally involves oxidation of elements, such as C, Si, Mn, present in liquid iron as impurities. For considering such reactions in a thermodynamically consistent manner, their generalised representation is

$$\frac{2\text{X}}{\text{Y}}\text{M} + \text{O}_2(\text{g}) = \frac{2}{\text{Y}}\text{M}_\text{X}\text{O}_\text{Y} \tag{4.18}$$

Reaction (4.18) has 1 mole O_2. M is the element concerned. M_XO_Y is the oxide of M. Whereas O_2 is a gas, M and M_XO_Y may be solid, liquid or even gas. Examples are:

$$\text{Si} + \text{O}_2(\text{g}) = \text{SiO}_2 \tag{4.19}$$

$$\frac{4}{3}\text{Al} + \text{O}_2(\text{g}) = \frac{2}{3}\text{Al}_2\text{O}_3 \tag{4.20}$$

Equation (4.18) represents the formation of an oxide from elements, for which ΔG^0 is the *standard free energy of formation* (ΔG_f^0) *of oxide per mole* O_2.

For equilibrium calculations, the values of ΔG_f^0 as function of temperature are required. A precise functional form is

$$\Delta G_f^0 = A + BT + CT \ln T \tag{4.21}$$

where, A, B and C are empirical constants, and T is the temperature in kelvin. However, for practical applications, the following simpler equation is often employed, viz.

$$\Delta G_f^0 = A + BT \tag{4.22}$$

Figure 4.1 presents ΔG_f^0 for formation of oxides of importance in iron and steelmaking as a function of temperature. The unit of ΔG_f^0 is joules (J) per mole. Table 4.1 compiles the values of A and B for these oxides. In Figure 4.1, the elements and oxides are at their respective standard states (i.e. pure). For such a situation, the activities of both M and M_XO_Y are 1, by *convention.*

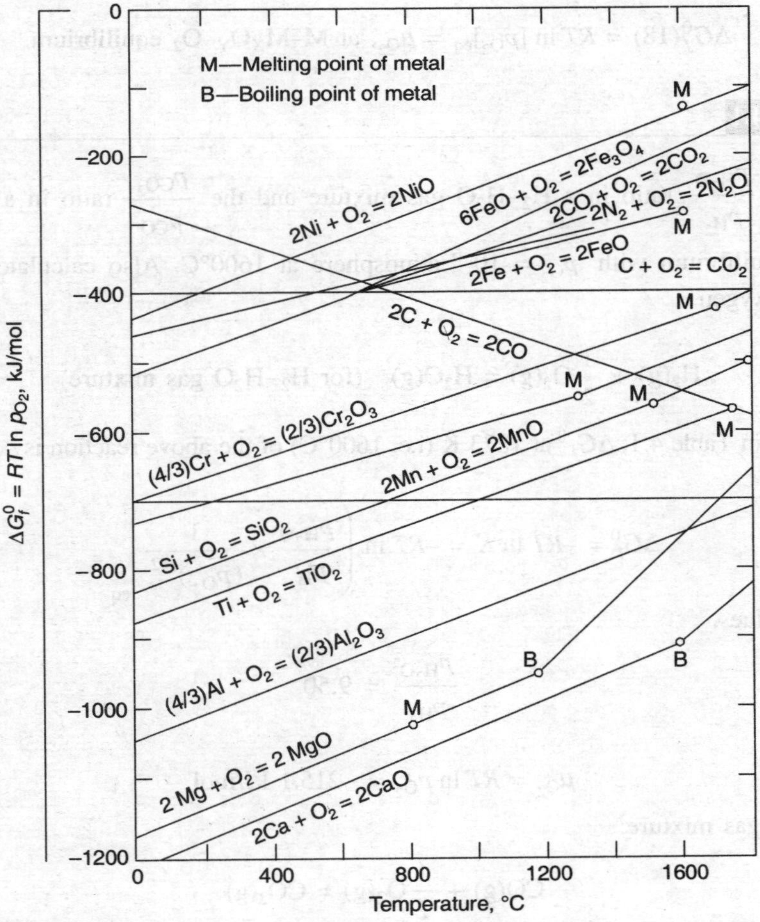

Figure 4.1 Standard free energy of formation of some oxides as function of temperature.

On the basis of Eq. (4.17), the equilibrium relations for reaction (4.18) would be

$$\Delta G_f^0\,(18) = -RT \ln K_{18} = -RT \ln \left[\frac{(a_{M_xO_y})^{2/Y}}{(a_M)^{2X/Y} \cdot a_{O_2}} \right]_{eq}$$

$$= -RT \ln \left(\frac{1}{1 \cdot p_{O_2}} \right)_{eq}$$

$$= -RT \ln \left(\frac{1}{p_{O_2}} \right)_{eq} = RT \ln [p_{O_2}]_{eq} \qquad (4.23)$$

since, $a_M = 1 = a_{M_xO_y}$, and $a_{O_2} = p_{O_2}$, oxygen behaving as an ideal gas.

Again, on the basis of Eq. (4.10),

$$\Delta G_f^0(18) = RT \ln [p_{O_2}]_{eq} = \mu_{O_2}, \text{ at M–M}_X\text{O}_Y\text{–O}_2 \text{ equilibrium.} \qquad (4.24)$$

EXAMPLE 4.1

Calculate the $\frac{p_{H_2O}}{p_{H_2}}$ ratio in a H_2–H_2O gas mixture and the $\frac{p_{CO_2}}{p_{CO}}$ ratio in a CO–CO_2 gas mixture at equilibrium with $p_{O_2} = 10^{-6}$ atmosphere at 1600°C. Also calculate the chemical potential of oxygen.

Solution:

$$H_2(g) + \frac{1}{2} O_2(g) = H_2O(g) \quad \text{(for } H_2\text{–}H_2O \text{ gas mixture)} \qquad \text{(Ex. 4.1)}$$

From the data in Table 4.1, $\Delta G_f{}^0$ at 1873 K (i.e. 1600°C) of the above reaction is –142,625 J/mol. Now,

$$\Delta G_f^0 = -RT \ln K = -RT \ln \left(\frac{p_{H_2O}}{p_{H_2}} \times \frac{1}{(p_{O_2})^{1/2}} \right)_{eq}$$

Putting the values,

$$\frac{p_{H_2O}}{p_{H_2}} = 9.50$$

Also,

$$\mu_{O_2} = RT \ln p_{O_2} = -215.1 \text{ kJ/mol}$$

For CO–CO_2 gas mixture:

$$CO(g) + \frac{1}{2} O_2(g) = CO_2(g) \qquad \text{(Ex.4.2)}$$

Table 4.1 Standard free energy of formation ($J \cdot mol^{-1}$) of some compounds as a function of temperature (at the indicated temperature range)

$$\Delta G_f^0 = A + BT$$

Reaction	Temperature, K	A, $J \cdot mol^{-1}$	B, $J \cdot mol^{-1} \cdot K^{-1}$
$2Al(l) + (3/2)O_2(g) = Al_2O_3(s)$	1500–2000	–1679876	321.79
$Ba(l) + (1/2)O_2(g) = BaO(s)$	1500–1910	–552288	92.47
$Ca(l) + (1/2)O_2(g) = CaO(s)$	1500–1765	–6395242	107.86
$Ca(g) + (1/2)O_2(g) = CaO(s)$	1765–2000	–786173	191.21
$C(gr) + (1/2)O_2(g) = CO(g)$	1500–2000	–111700	–87.65
$C(gr) + O_2(g) = CO_2(g)$	1500–2000	–394100	–0.84
$2Ce(l) + (3/2)O_2(g) = Ce_2O_3(s)$	1500–2000	–1826316	336.65
$Ce(l) + O_2(g) = CeO_2(s)$	1500–2000	–1029264	214.22
$2Cr(s) + (3/2)O_2(g) = Cr_2O_3(s)$	1500–2000	–1131981	256.69
$H_2(g) + (1/2)O_2(g) = H_2O(g)$	1500–2000	–251877	58.33
$Fe(l) + (1/2)O_2(g) = FeO(l)$	1809–2000	–238070	49.45
$Fe(s) + (1/2)O_2(g) = FeO(s)$	298–1642	–259600	62.55
$3Fe(s) + 2O_2(g) = Fe_3O_4(s)$	298–1642	–1102720	307.5
$2Fe(s) + (3/2)O_2(g) = Fe_2O_3(s)$	298–1800	–814512	250.7
$Mg(g) + (1/2)O_2(g) = MgO(s)$	1500–2000	–731154	205.40
$Mn(l) + (1/2)O_2(g) = MnO(s)$	1500–2000	–408149	88.78
$2P_2(g) + 5O_2(g) = P_4O_{10}(g)$	1500–2000	–3140929	964.83
$Si(l) + O_2(g) = SiO_2(l)$	1883–2000	–936379	192.80
$Si(l) + O_2(g) = SiO_2(\beta\text{-crist})$	1686–1986	–947676	198.74
$Ti(s) + O_2(g) = TiO_2(s)$	1500–1940	–935124	173.85
$Zr(s) + O_2(g) = ZrO_2(s)$	1500–2000	–1079472	177.82

Combining free energies of formation of CO and CO_2 from Table 4.1, ΔG^0 for the above reaction at 1873 K is –119,805 J/mol. Noting that K is $\left(\frac{p_{CO_2}}{p_{CO}} \times \frac{1}{(p_{O_2})^{1/2}}\right)_{eq}$,

$$\frac{p_{CO_2}}{p_{CO}} = 2.194$$

EXAMPLE 4.2

Predict whether solid FeO can be reduced to metallic iron by these gas mixtures at $\frac{p_{H_2O}}{p_{H_2}}$ and $\frac{p_{CO_2}}{p_{CO}}$ ratios calculated in Example 4.1, at a temperature of 1000°C.

Solution: $FeO(s) + H_2(g) = Fe(s) + H_2O(g);\ \Delta G^0 = \Delta G_f^0(H_2O) - \Delta G_f^0(FeO)$ (Ex.4.3)

From data in Table 4.1, ΔG^0 for reaction at 1000°C is

$$\Delta G^0 = 3734 \text{ J/mol} = -RT \ln \left(\frac{p_{H_2O}}{p_{H_2}}\right)_{eq}$$

This gives, $\left(\frac{p_{H_2O}}{p_{H_2}}\right)_{eq} = 0.70$. Since this value is lower than $\left(\frac{p_{H_2O}}{p_{H_2}}\right)_{actual}$ (i.e. 9.50 as calculated in Example 4.1), reduction is not possible. A similar calculation gives $\left(\frac{p_{CO_2}}{p_{CO}}\right)_{eq} = 0.466$, which is lower than the $\left(\frac{p_{CO_2}}{p_{CO}}\right)_{actual}$. Hence, reduction is not possible.

4.3 ACTIVITY VS. COMPOSITION RELATIONSHIPS

4.3.1 Introduction

In the equations given earlier, *activity* is an abstract thermodynamic parameter, and is of no practical significance. What is important is to know the compositions of various phases—metal, slag, gas, etc. which would co-exist at chemical equilibrium. This requires knowledge of activity as a function of composition in various phases of importance in ironmaking and steelmaking at high temperatures.

Roughly speaking, activity is a measure of 'free concentration'. In ideal gases, molecules are free, and hence activity of a species i (i.e. a_i) = p_i, as already noted in the earlier section.

Pyro-metallurgical processing is quite fast and gets completed in a reasonably short period of time (of the order of hours/minutes). Solid reactants and reagents in these processes are compounds (either pure or mixture). Solid products are also either almost pure metals or compounds, since with solid-state diffusion being very slow, there is almost no opportunity for solid solution formation. Hence, all participating solids are assumed to be *pure* and by convention, are at their respective standard states, and hence, their activities are to be taken as 1.

Therefore, the main concern is with activity-versus-composition relations in liquid slags and liquid alloys. From a thermodynamic viewpoint, molten slags are *solutions of oxides*. Liquid alloys are *metallic solutions*.

4.3.2 Ideal, Non-ideal and Regular Solutions

An ideal solution obeys Raoult's law, which may be stated as

$$a_i = X_i \tag{4.25}$$

In practical applications, the weight percent constitutes the composition scale. The X_i is related to W_i by the following equation:

$$X_i = \frac{W_i/M_i}{\sum_{i=1}^{k}(W_i/M_i)} = \frac{W_i/M_i}{(W_1/M_1)+\cdots+(W_i/M_i)+\cdots+(W_k/M_k)} \tag{4.26}$$

where, W_i and M_i are the weight percent and molecular mass respectively of component *i*.

Most real solutions do not obey Raoult's law. They exhibit either *positive* or *negative* deviations from it. For a binary solution, this is illustrated in Figure 4.2 (Ward 1963) for some Fe–B liquid binary alloys at 1600°C (i.e. 1873 K). In this figure, B is Cu, Mn or Si. The Fe–Mn solution obeys Raoult's law, the Fe–Cu exhibits strong positive deviation and the Fe–Si strong negative deviation from Raoult's law. In binary liquid oxides, FeO–MnO behaves ideally, whereas most binary silicates (i.e. CaO–SiO_2, FeO–SiO_2, MgO–SiO_2, MnO–SiO_2, etc.) exhibit strong negative deviations from Raoult's law.

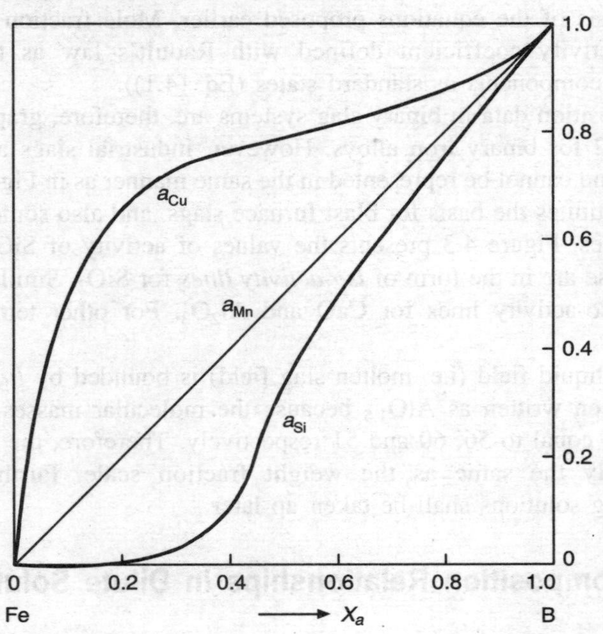

Figure 4.2 Raoultian activities of copper, manganese and silicon in solution in molten iron at 1600°C.

Departures from Raoult's law are quantified using a thermodynamic parameter, known as the *activity coefficient*, which is defined as

$$\gamma_i = \frac{a_i}{X_i} \tag{4.27}$$

where, γ_i is the activity coefficient of component i in a solution.

Over the past several decades, various attempts have been made to propose analytical correlations between activity and composition for *non-ideal solutions*. None of them, however, can be taken as valid for all types of solutions, since they invariably contain some simplifying assumptions. The simplest of all of these solution models is the *regular solution model*. For a binary solution with components A and B, it predicts

$$RT \ln \gamma_A = \alpha X_B^2; \qquad RT \ln \gamma_B = \alpha X_A^2 \tag{4.28}$$

where, α is a constant at constant temperature. It may be noted further that α varies inversely with T, and that $X_A + X_B = 1$.

4.3.3 Activities in Molten Slag Solutions

Molten slags are, by definition, concentrated solutions since the minimum concentration of any component oxide is more than a few weight percent. Hence, their activity–composition relations are handled on the basis of the equations proposed earlier. Mole fraction is the composition scale, activity and activity coefficient defined with Raoult's law as the reference state [Eq. (4.27)], and pure components as standard states (Eq. (4.1)).

Activity vs. composition data in binary slag systems are, therefore, graphically represented as shown in Figure 4.2 for binary iron alloys. However, industrial slags are generally multi-component solutions, and cannot be represented in the same manner as in Figure 4.2. The ternary $CaO–SiO_2–Al_2O_3$ constitutes the basis for blast furnace slags, and also some slags encountered in steelmaking processes. Figure 4.3 presents the values of activity of SiO_2 in this system at 1550°C (1823 K). These are in the form of *iso-activity lines* for SiO_2. Similary, there would be diagrams presenting iso-activity lines for CaO and Al_2O_3. For other temperatures, separate diagrams are required.

In Figure 4.3, the liquid field (i.e. molten slag field) is bounded by *liquidus lines*. In this diagram, Al_2O_3 has been written as $AlO_{1.5}$ because the molecular masses of CaO, SiO_2 and $AlO_{1.5}$ are close, being equal to 56, 60 and 51 respectively. Therefore, the mole fraction scale becomes approximately the same as the weight fraction scale. Further discussions on thermodynamics of slag solutions shall be taken up later.

4.3.4 Activity–Composition Relationships in Dilute Solutions

Activities with one weight percent standard state

Liquid steel and to a reasonable extent liquid pig iron primarily fall in the category of dilute solutions, where concentrations of solutes (carbon, oxygen, silicon, manganese, sulphur, phosphorus, etc.) are mostly below 1 wt. % or so, except for high-alloy steels.

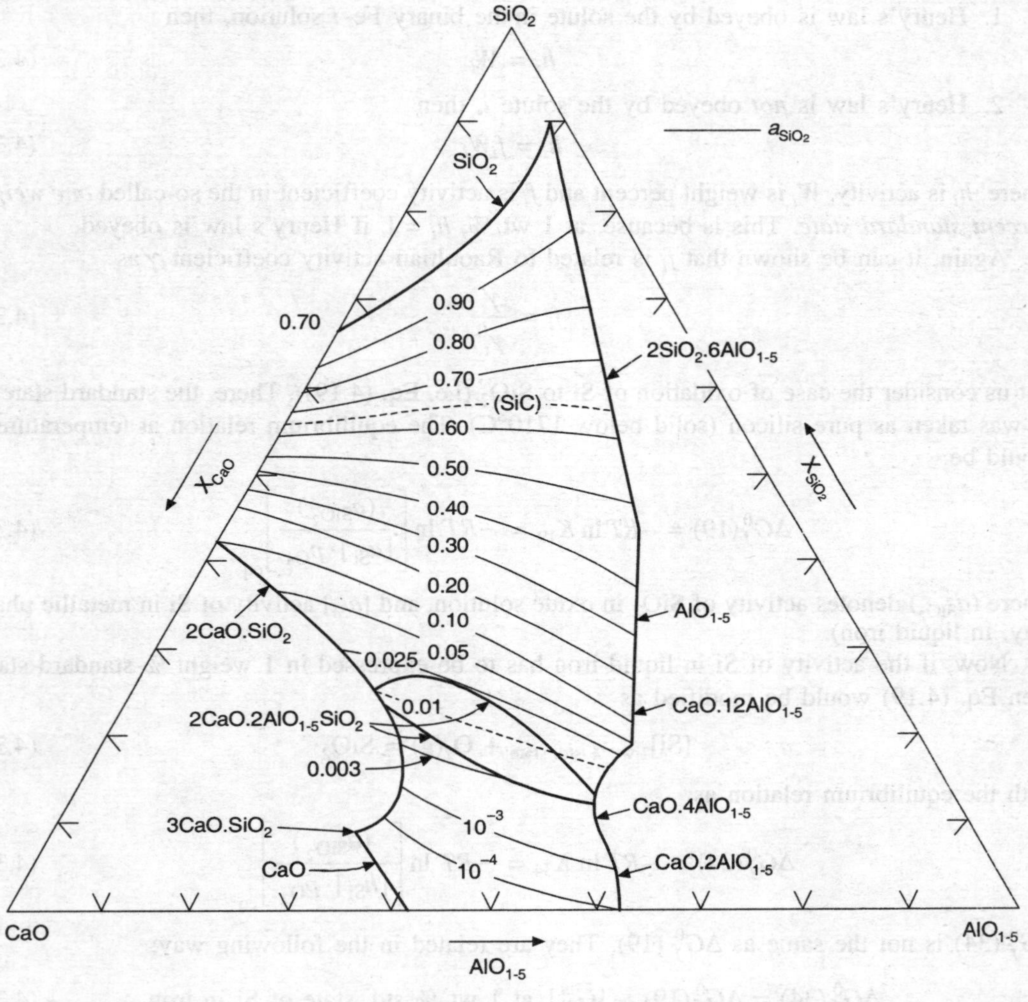

Figure 4.3 Iso-activity lines of SiO_2 in $CaO–SiO_2–Al_2O_3$ ternary at 1823 K; the liquid at various locations on the liquidus is saturated with compounds as shown.

Solutes in dilute binary solutions obey Henry's law, which is stated as follows:

$$a_i = \gamma_i^0 X_i \tag{4.29}$$

where, γ_i^0 is a constant, known as the Henry's law constant. Deviation from Henry's law occurs when the solute concentration increases.

Therefore, activities of dissolved elements in liquid steel are expressed with reference to Henry's law, and not Raoult's law. Since it is the intention to find values directly in weight percent, the composition scale is weight percent. With these modifications, i is in solution with Fe as solvent in the binary Fe–i solution. If:

1. Henry's law is obeyed by the solute in the binary Fe–*i* solution, then

$$h_i = W_i \tag{4.30}$$

2. Henry's law is *not* obeyed by the solute *i*, then

$$h_i = f_i W_i \tag{4.31}$$

where, h_i is activity, W_i is weight percent and f_i is activity coefficient in the so-called *one weight percent standard state*. This is because, at 1 wt. %, $h_i = 1$, if Henry's law is obeyed.

Again, it can be shown that f_i is related to Raoultian activity coefficient γ as

$$f_i = \frac{\gamma_i}{\gamma_i^0} \tag{4.32}$$

Let us consider the case of oxidation of Si to SiO_2 (i.e. Eq. (4.19)). There, the standard state of Si was taken as pure silicon (solid below 1710°C). The equilibrium relation at temperature T would be:

$$\Delta G_f^0(19) = -RT \ln K_{19} = -RT \ln \left[\frac{(a_{SiO_2})}{[a_{Si}] \cdot p_{O_2}} \right]_{eq} \tag{4.33}$$

where (a_{SiO_2}) denotes activity of SiO_2 in oxide solution, and $[a_{Si}]$ activity of Si in metallic phase (say, in liquid iron).

Now, if the activity of Si in liquid iron has to be expressed in 1 weight % standard state, then Eq. (4.19) would be modified as

$$[Si]_{1\text{ wt. \% std. state}} + O_2(g) = SiO_2 \tag{4.34}$$

with the equilibrium relation as

$$\Delta G_f^0(34) = -RT \ln K_{34} = -RT \ln \left[\frac{(a_{SiO_2})}{[h_{Si}] \cdot p_{O_2}} \right]_{eq} \tag{4.35}$$

ΔG_f^0 (34) is not the same as ΔG_f^0 (19). They are related in the following way:

$$\Delta G_f^0(34) = \Delta G_f^0(19) - [\bar{G}_{Si}^m] \text{ at 1 wt. \% std. state of Si in iron} \tag{4.36}$$

Therefore, for equilibrium calculations involving solution in liquid iron in 1 wt. % standard state, the values of partial molar free energies of mixing $(\bar{G}_i^m)$ of solutes in liquid iron are required as well. Some of these are tabulated in Table 4.2 (Engh 1992).

Solute–solute interactions in dilute multi-component solutions

Molten steel and iron as well as other impure metals (Cu, Pb , etc.) have several dissolved solutes in dilute state. For example, steel has C, Mn, S, P, etc. It has been found that solutes in a multi-component solution interact with one another and thus influence activities of other solutes. If Fe is the solvent, and 1, 2, ..., *i*, *j*, ..., *k* are solutes in dilute state, then it has been derived that

$$\log f_i = \sum_{j=1}^{k} e_i^j \cdot W_j = e_i^1 \cdot W_1 + \cdots + e_i^i \cdot W_i + e_i^j \cdot W_j + \cdots + e_i^k \cdot W_k \tag{4.37}$$

Table 4.2 Free energy of mixing of some elements at 1 wt. % standard state in liquid iron ($\bar{G}_i^m$) as function of temperature ($\bar{G}_i^m = C + DT$)

Element, *i*	*C*, J · mol⁻¹	*D*, J · mol⁻¹ · K⁻¹
Al(l)	63180	27.91
B(s)	65270	21.55
C(graphite)	22590	42.26
Ca(g)	−39460	49.37
Co(l)	1000	−38.74
Cr(s)	19250	−46.86
Cu(l)	33470	−39.37
(1/2)H_2(g)	36480	30.46
Mn(l)	4080	−38.16
Mo(s)	27610	−52.38
(1/2)N_2(g)	3600	23.89
Nb(s)	23010	−52.30
Ni(l)	−20920	−31.05
(1/2)O_2(g)	−117150	−2.89
(1/2)P_2(g)	−122170	−19.25
Pb(l)	212550	−106.27
(1/2)S_2(g)	−135060	23.43
Si(l)	−131500	−17.24
Sn(l)	15980	−14.43
Ti(l)	−46020	−37.03
Ti(s)	31130	−44.98
V(s)	−20710	−45.61
W(s)	−31380	−63.60
Zr(l)	−51050	−42.38
Zr(s)	−34730	−50.00

where, the values of e are constants. e_i^j is called *interaction coefficient* describing the influence of solute j on the activity coefficient of solute i. It is defined as

$$e_i^j = \left[\frac{\delta(\log f_i)}{\delta W_j}\right]_{W_j \to 0} \tag{4.38}$$

It can be derived further that

$$e_j^i = \left[\frac{\delta(\log f_j)}{\delta W_i}\right]_{W_i \to 0} = e_i^j \frac{M_j}{M_i} + 0.434 \times 10^{-2}\left(\frac{M_i - M_j}{M_i}\right) \tag{4.39}$$

where, M is the molecular mass. Equation (4.39) allows the estimation of e_j^i from e_i^j. Table 4.3 presents some values of interaction coefficients in liquid iron at 1600°C (1873 K) (Sigworth et al. 1974; *Steelmaking Data Sourcebook* 1988).

Table 4.3 Interaction coefficients (e_i^j) of some common elements in liquid iron at or near 1600°C (1873 K)

i↓ \ j→	Al	B	C	Cr	Mn	Mo	N	Si
Al	0.043	–	0.091	–	–	–	−0.015	0.056
C	0.043	0.24	0.243	−0.023	−0.012	−0.008	0.11	0.08
Cr	–	–	−0.114	−0.0003	0.004	0.002	−0.182	−0.004
H	0.013	0.058	0.06	−0.0024	−0.002	0.003	–	0.027
Mn	–	−0.024	−0.054	0.004	0	0.005	−0.091	−0.033
Mo	–	–	−0.14	0	0.005	0.0121	0	0.048
N	0.1	0.094	0.130	−0.046	−0.020	−0.011	0	0.048
Ni	–	–	0.032	0	−0.008	–	0.015	0
O	−1.17	−0.31	−0.421	−0.055	−0.021	0.005	−0.14	−0.066
P	0.037	0.015	0.13	−0.018	−0.032	0.001	0.13	0.099
S	0.041	0.134	0.111	0.010	−0.026	0.003	0.01	0.075
Si	0.058	0.20	0.18	−0.0003	−0.015	2.36	0.092	0.103
Ti	–	–	–	−0.055	−0.043	–	−2.06	2.1
V	–	–	−0.14	0.012	0.006	–	−0.4	0.042

All the preceding discussions and equations along with the required thermodynamic data constitute the basis for equilibrium calculations. Their applications will be illustrated in the later chapters and through the worked-out examples.

EXAMPLE 4.3

Determine the activity of SiO_2 in the $CaO–SiO_2–AlO_{1.5}$ system at 1823 K at $X_{CaO} = 0.5$, and $X_{SiO_2} = 0.4$. Consider the equilibrium of this slag with an Fe–Si liquid alloy and a gas mixture of $CO + CO_2$ at this temperature. Calculate the (p_{CO_2}/p_{CO}) ratio in gas at equilibrium.

Given: In the alloy, $X_{Si} = 0.02$; $\gamma_{Si} = 1.6 \times 10^{-3}$.

Solution:

$$[\text{Si}] + 2\text{CO}_2(\text{g}) = (\text{SiO}_2) + 2\text{CO}(\text{g}); \quad \Delta G_4^0 \qquad \text{(Ex. 4.4)}$$

$$\Delta G_4^0 = \Delta G_f^0(\text{SiO}_2) + 2[\Delta G_f^0(\text{CO}) - \Delta G_f^0(\text{CO}_2)]$$

From data of Table 4.1, at 1823 K, $\Delta G_4^0 = -337179$ J/mol $= -R \times 1823 \ln K_4$

Hence,
$$K_4 = 4.60 \times 10^9 = \left[\left(\frac{p_{CO}}{p_{CO_2}}\right)^2 \times \frac{(a_{SiO_2})}{[a_{Si}]}\right]_{eq}$$

From Figure 4.3, a_{SiO_2} in slag = 0.1; a_{Si} (alloy) $= X_{Si} \cdot \gamma_{Si} = 0.02 \times 1.6 \times 10^{-3} = 3.2 \times 10^{-5}$
Substituting the values, $(p_{CO_2}/p_{CO}) = 8.24 \times 10^{-4}$.

EXAMPLE 4.4

(i) What is the value of h_{Si} (i.e. activity of Si in 1 wt. % standard state) at the alloy composition in Example 4.3?

(ii) Calculate $\bar{G}_{Si}^{m}$ at 1 wt. % std. state for Si in liquid iron.

Given: Henry's Law constant for Si in liquid iron (i.e. γ_{Si}^{0}) = 1.3×10^{-3}

Solution: On the basis of Eq. (4.26), and noting that atomic masses of Si and Fe are 28 and 56 respectively, wt. % Si (W_{Si}) at the above alloy composition = 1.01%

$$h_{Si} = f_{Si} \cdot W_{Si}; \text{ From Eq. (4.32), } f_{Si} = \frac{\gamma_{Si}}{\gamma_{Si}^{0}} = \frac{1.6 \times 10^{-3}}{1.3 \times 10^{-3}} = 1.23$$

Hence, $h_{Si} = 1.01 \times 1.23 = 1.24$

(ii) On the basis of Eq. (4.3), $\bar{G}_{Si}^{m} = RT \ln [\gamma_{Si}^{0} \times (X_{Si})_{1\,wt.\,\%}]$

On the basis of Eq. (4.26), X_{Si} = 0.0198 at 1 wt. % Si. Calculations yield

$$\bar{G}_{Si}^{m} = -160.1 \text{ kJ/mol Si}$$

EXAMPLE 4.5

An Fe–Mn solid solution having 0.001 mole fraction of Mn, is at equilibrium with an FeO–MnO solid solution and an oxygen containing atmosphere at 1000 K. Calculate the composition of the oxide solution. Both metallic and oxide solutions are ideal.

Given: $Mn(s) + \frac{1}{2} O_2(g) = MnO(s); \Delta G_f^0 = -384700 + 72.8\,T$ J/mol

Solution: $[Fe] + (MnO) = [Mn] + (FeO); \Delta G_5^0 = \Delta G_f^0(FeO) - \Delta G_f^0(MnO)$ (Ex.4.5)

From data on ΔG_f^0 for formation of FeO in Table 4.1, and that for MnO given above, at 1000 K, ΔG_5^0 = 114850 J/mol, giving $K_5 = 10^{-6}$.

Noting that $a_{FeO} = X_{FeO}$, $a_{MnO} = X_{MnO}$, $X_{FeO} + X_{MnO} = 1$, calculations yield $X_{FeO} = 10^{-3}$, and X_{MnO} = 0.999.

EXAMPLE 4.6

Calculate the chemical potential of nitrogen gas at equilibrium with liquid steel at 1600°C. The steel contains 0.01% N, 0.5% C, 0.5% Mn.

Given: $[N]_{\text{ppm std state in iron}} = K_N \times p_{N_2}^{1/2}$, where $\log K_N = -\frac{581}{T} + 2.937$

(*Note:* 1 wt. % = 10^4 ppm)

Solution: At equilibrium, $\mu_{N_2}(gas) = \mu_{N_2}(steel) = RT \ln p_{N_2}$

$$\log p_{N_2} = 2\,[\log h_N - \log K_N], \text{ where } h_N \text{ is in ppm.}$$

At 1873 K, $\log K_N = 2.6268$; also from Eqs. (4.31) and (4.37),

$$\log h_N = \log [N]_{ppm} + e_N^N \cdot W_N + e_N^C \cdot W_C + e_N^{Mn} \cdot W_{Mn}$$

Substituting values of interaction coefficients from Table 4.3, calculations yield $\log h_N = 2.055$, and thus, $\log p_{N_2} = -3.1436$, and $\mu_{N_2} = 2.303 \times 8.314 \times 1873 \times (-3.1436) \times 10^{-3} = -112.7$ kJ/mol N_2

4.4 STRUCTURE AND PHYSICOCHEMICAL PROPERTIES OF MELTS

The melts of interest in ironmaking and steelmaking are liquid iron, steel and molten slags. In the liquid state, there is neither perfect order nor perfect disorder. It contains a large concentration of voids, known as *holes* contributing to its flowability.

In ironmaking and steelmaking, the physicochemical properties that are of primary interest are:

- Melting point as low as possible
- Viscosity as low as possible, i.e. high fluidity
- Appropriate reactivity as measured by thermodynamic activities of components
- Solubilities of components in the melts which govern the limits of reactions/processes.

The densities of liquid iron alloys and liquid slags of interest do not vary to any appreciable extent with composition, and hence, it is not generally necessary to consider density. Surface tension is another physicochemical property; however, it is also not normally considered except in some special situations, such as foaming of slag, slag–metal emulsion, etc.

4.4.1 Properties of Liquid Iron and Steel

Solid pure iron occurs in two crystalline modifications, namely, body-centred cubic (BCC) denoted as α-Fe and δ-Fe, and face-centred cubic (FCC), denoted as γ-Fe. The phase transformation for pure iron occurs as

$$\alpha\text{-Fe} \xrightarrow{910°\text{C}} \gamma\text{-Fe} \xrightarrow{1392°\text{C}} \delta\text{-Fe} \xrightarrow{1537°\text{C}} \text{Liquid Fe} \xrightarrow{2870°\text{C}} \text{Gaseous Fe}$$

The vapour pressure of iron at steelmaking temperatures is approximately 0.01 mm Hg (10^{-4} to 10^{-5} atmosphere). Solutes dissolved in liquid iron lower its melting point depending on the nature and concentration of the solute. Carbon and phosphorus, for example, significantly lower the melting point of iron. Liquidus temperature (T_L) of steel can be calculated with the following formula,

$$T_L\ (°\text{C}) = 1537 - 88W_C - 30W_P - 25W_S - 5W_{Cu} - 8W_{Si} - 5W_{Mn} - 2W_{Mo} - 4W_{Ni} - 15W_{Cr} - 18W_{Ti} - 2W_v \quad (4.40)$$

where, W denotes the weight percent of the solute. Hence, in Fe–C alloy,

$$T_L = 1449°\text{C and } 1185°\text{C respectively at 1 and 4 wt. \% carbon}$$

The density of pure liquid iron (ρ_{Fe}) varies with temperatures as

$$\rho_{Fe} = 8.30 - 8.36 \times 10^{-4}\ T \tag{4.41}$$

where, T is temperature in °C and ρ_{Fe} is in $g \cdot cm^{-3}$ (i.e. $kg \cdot m^{-3} \times 10^{-3}$).

From Eq. (4.41), $\rho_{Fe} = 7.0$ and 6.9 at 1550°C and 1700°C respectively, i.e. there is negligible variation at steelmaking temperatures. Liquid iron from blast furnace contains about 4 wt. % C. For this at 1600°C, ρ = 6.75 in contrast to 6.95 for pure Fe. This difference is also not significant, for most purposes.

Figure 4.4 shows the dependence of viscosity (η) of Fe and Fe–C liquids on temperature (Barfield and Kitchener, 1995). The overall variation is from 0.05 to 0.08 poise (i.e. 0.005 to 0.008 $kg \cdot m^{-1} \cdot s^{-1}$). The quantity η/ρ is known as *kinematic viscosity* and is inversely proportional to fluidity, i.e. the ease with which a fluid can flow. Higher η/ρ means that the fluidity is lower. For liquid iron, η/ρ is approximately 0.01 in cgs units. This value for liquid iron is approximately the same as that of water and hence, liquid iron is as fluid as water.

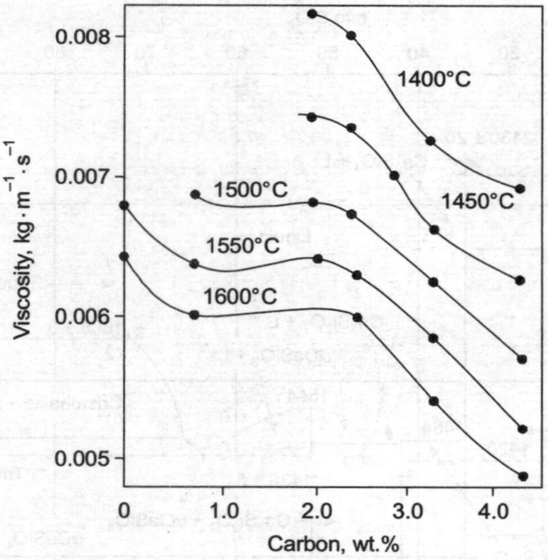

Figure 4.4 Composition dependence of viscosity in iron–carbon melts.

The surface tension of liquid iron (σ_{Fe}) varies with temperature in the following way:

$$\sigma_{Fe} = 2367 - 0.34T \tag{4.42}$$

where T is in °C, unit of σ is $dynes \cdot cm^{-1}$, i.e. $N \cdot m^{-1} \times 10^{-3}$. This gives a value of 1823 at 1600°C. Solutes generally lower σ. Most solutes do not have much effect on surface tension of liquid iron, except sulphur, oxygen, tellurium and selenium. In other words, these elements are *surface active*. For example, at 1550–1600°C, the presence of 0.2% S or 0.1% oxygen in iron lowers the surface tension to about 1100.

4.4.2 Structure and Physicochemical Properties of Slag Melts

Melting points of a few common oxides are (in °C): Al_2O_3—2050, CaO—2600, FeO—1371, MgO—2800, MnO—1785, SiO_2—1710. Fundamental studies on liquid slags have been mostly carried out on binary systems: MO–SiO_2, where SiO_2 is the acidic oxide and MO is a basic oxide (CaO, Na_2O, MgO, FeO, etc.). In actual ironmaking and steelmaking operations, the principal flux addition is CaO in the form of CaO or $CaCO_3$ with the traditional objective of fluxing acidic oxides (SiO_2, Al_2O_3, etc.) so as to obtain a liquid slag at a reasonably low temperature (above approximately 1300°C).

Figure 4.5 presents the binary CaO–SiO_2 phase diagram. Low liquidus temperatures are obtained around the mid-composition ranges. The solid-state comprises a series of crystalline CaO-SiO_2 compounds. Figure 4.3 has already presented the SiO_2 isoactivity lines in the liquid field of CaO–SiO_2–Al_2O_3 ternary at 1550°C. Considerable enlargement of the liquid field in the ternary over that in the binary CaO–SiO_2, or CaO–Al_2O_3 may be noted. Some additional points are worth mentioning.

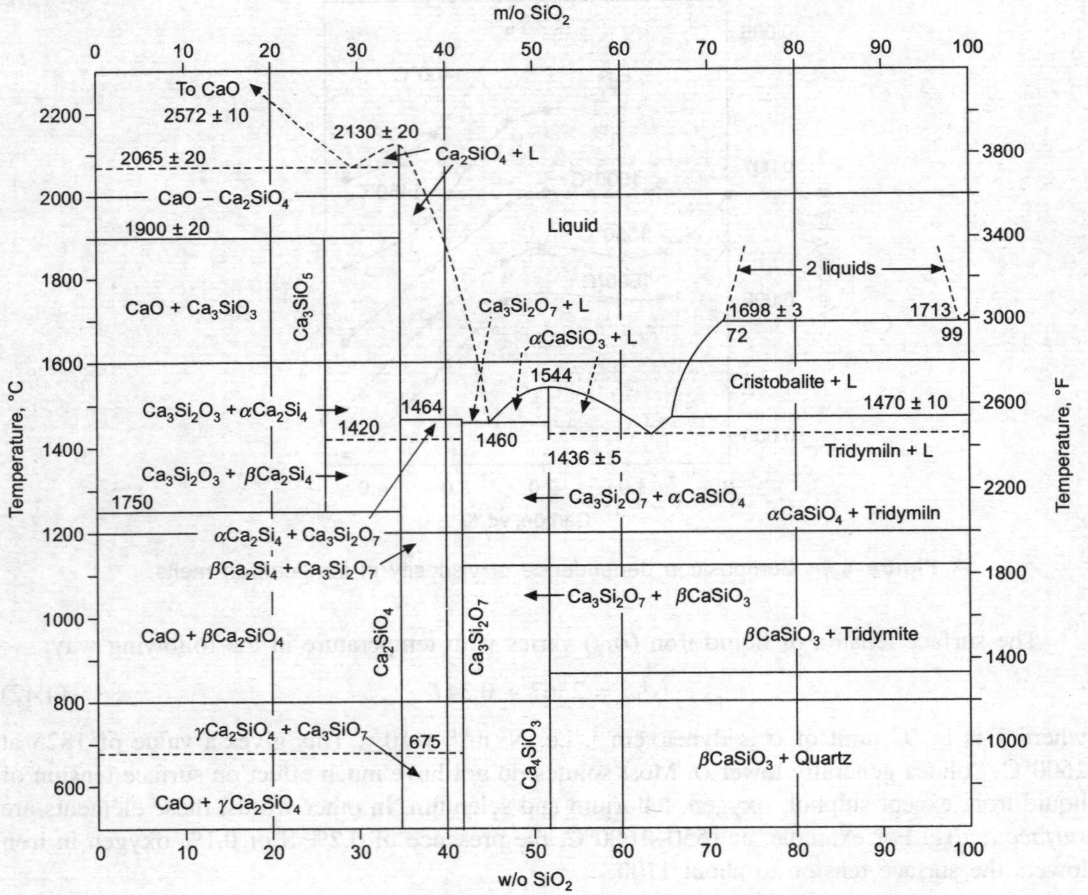

Figure 4.5 Phase diagram for CaO–SiO_2 system.

Further lowering of liquidus temperature is possible in a multi-component slag by suitable additions. Blast furnace slag is an example, where the presence of oxides such as MgO, TiO_2 in the $CaO–SiO_2–Al_2O_3$ can result in lower liquidus temperatures. Further:

- Very low liquidus temperature (minimum 1175°C) is possible in the $FeO–SiO_2$ system at high FeO contents
- Decrease in temperature shrinks the liquid field.

A variety of physicochemical measurements have been carried out on molten slags, especially on binary metal silicates over a period of several decades through X-ray diffraction, electrical conductivity, transport number, viscosity, density, surface tension and spectroscopic studies. In addition, some conclusions and deductions have been arrived at on the basis of atomic physics and physical chemistry. As a result, the following general conclusions have been arrived at.

- The basic building block in SiO_2 and silicates is the *silicon-oxygen tetrahedron* with one atom of Si at the centre of the tetrahedron bonded to four oxygen atoms, located at the four corners (Figure 4.6).

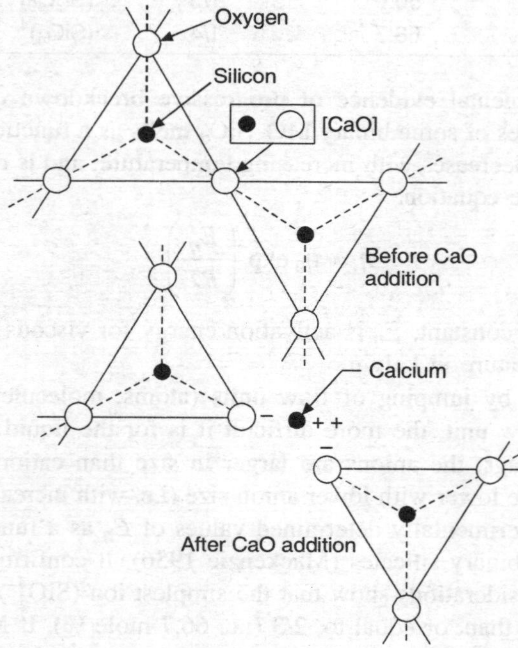

Figure 4.6 Illustration of network breaking following the addition of CaO to SiO_2.

- In solid pure SiO_2 these tetrahedra are linked together by a three-dimensional crystalline network.
- Upon melting of pure SiO_2, short-range order remains, but long-range order is destroyed.
- Oxides are ionic in both solid and liquid states.

- Molten slags are polymeric ionic melts. The cations (Ca^{2+}, Na^+, Mg^{2+}, Mn^{2+}, Fe^{2+}, etc.) are free and mobile, whereas anions (SiO_4^{4-}, AlO_4^{5-}, PO_4^{3-}, etc.) are complex and less mobile.
- Therefore, basic oxides (CaO, etc.) are also called *network breakers.* They break the SiO_2 network, as illustrated in Figure 4.6. Based on this classification, the acidic oxides (SiO_2, etc.) are *network formers.*
- Al_2O_3, Fe_2O_3, Cr_2O_3 behave as basic oxides at high concentrations and acidic oxides at low concentrations. Hence, they are *amphoteric* oxides in nature.

With the addition of more and more metal oxide (MO) to SiO_2, there is progressive breakdown of the silica network. Hence, the complex anions become smaller and smaller in size (Table 4.4).

Table 4.4 Dominant discrete silicate ions at some compositions

Composition	Molar % MO	Si/O ratio	Discrete ion
$2SiO_2 + MO$	33.3	2/5	$(Si_6O_{15})^{6-}$ or $(Si_8O_{20})^{8-}$
$SiO_2 + MO$	50.0	1/3	$(Si_3O_9)^{6-}$ or $(Si_4O_{12})^{8-}$
$SiO_2 + 2\ MO$	66.7	1/4	$(SiO_4)^{4-}$

An important experimental evidence of progressive breakdown of network comes from measurements of viscosities of some binary $MO–SiO_2$ melts as a function of MO concentration. The viscosity of a liquid decreases with increasing temperature, and is related to temperature by the following approximate equation:

$$\eta = \eta_0 \exp\left(\frac{E_\eta}{RT}\right) \tag{4.43}$$

where, η_0 is an empirical constant, E_η is activation energy for viscous flow, R is universal gas constant, and T is temperature in kelvin.

Viscous flow occurs by jumping of flow units (atoms, molecules, ions) into holes. The bigger the size of the flow unit, the more difficult it is for the liquid to flow, and hence, the higher is E_η. In liquid slags, the anions are larger in size than cations and therefore, govern viscous flow. E_η should be lower with lower anion size (i.e. with increasing MO concentration). Figure 4.7 shows the experimentally determined values of E_η as a function of the metal oxide content in several liquid binary silicates (Mackenzie 1956). It confirms this expectation.

Simple structural considerations show that the simplest ion (SiO_4^{4-}) only occurs if the mole fraction of MO is greater than, or equal to, 2/3 (i.e. 66.7 mole %). If MO is more than 66.7%, then the excess oxygen of MO is expected to be present as free oxygen ions (O^{2-}) through ionisation as

$$MO = M^{2+} + O^{2-} \tag{4.44}$$

Although stoichiometrically O^{2-} is not expected if the fraction of MO is less than 2/3, some free O^{2-} will always be present to satisfy reactions of the type

$$2(Si_2O_7)^{6-} = (Si_4O_{12})^{8-} + 2O^{2-} \tag{4.45}$$

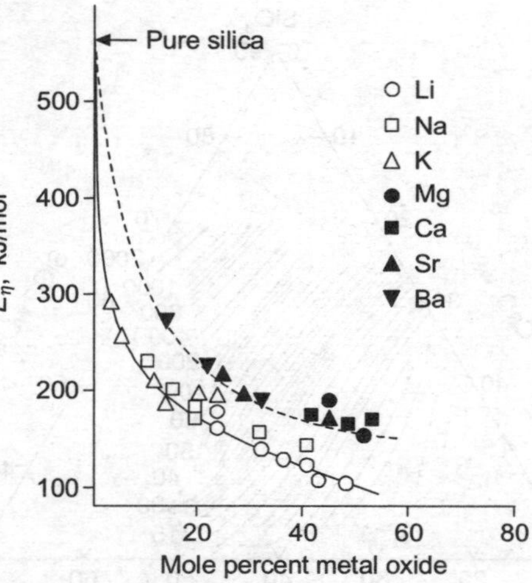

Figure 4.7 Variation of activation energy for viscous flow with increasing metal oxide content in liquid binary silicates.

The above conclusions can be extended to more complex slag melts. The only difference would be that $(AlO_4)^{5-}$, $(PO_4)^{3-}$, $(FeO_4)^{5-}$ anions would also be present in addition to $(SiO_4)^{4-}$ above 66.7 mole % MO.

As stated in Section 4.4.1, the density and the viscosity of liquid steel do not vary much with composition and temperature. The overall variation in density of molten ironmaking and steelmaking slags is also not very appreciable (approximately 2.5–2.8 $g \cdot cm^{-3}$). However, this is not the case with viscosity, which varies by orders of magnitude, depending on composition and temperature of the slag melt. This is illustrated in Figure 4.8 by the iso-viscosity lines for CaO–SiO_2–Al_2O_3 slags at 1500°C (Machin and Lee, 1948), where the overall variation is from 2.5 to 2000 poise (i.e. 0.25 to 200 $kg \cdot m^{-1} \cdot s^{-1}$).

The surface tension of liquid oxides and slags varies in the range of 200–600 $m \cdot N \cdot m^{-1}$. For slag–metal reactions, the slag–metal interfacial tension is a more relevant parameter than the surface tension and hence, many measurements have been made (not discussed further).

4.4.3 Slag Basicity and Capacities

A slag is not only a collector of gangue, but also acts as a refining agent. This is the origin of the age-old statement *good steelmaking is nothing but good slagmaking*. The basicity of a slag increases with increased percentages of basic oxides. It is an important parameter governing refining, and steelmakers always pay attention to this aspect.

CaO is the common fluxing agent. It is also a powerful basic oxide for the removal of sulphur and phosphorus from molten iron and steel. Therefore, in practice, an index of basicity, the so-called *Vee Ratio* (*V*) is used, where:

$$V = \frac{\text{wt. \% CaO}}{\text{wt. \% SiO}_2} \text{ in slag} \tag{4.46}$$

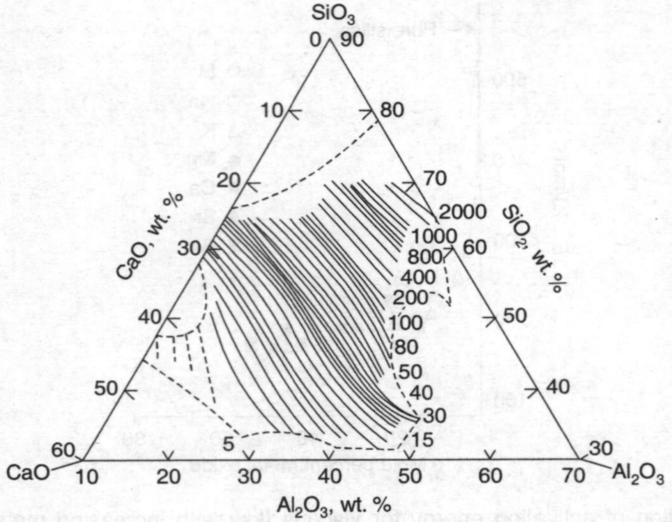

Figure 4.8 Iso-viscosity lines for CaO–SiO_2–Al_2O_3 slag at 1500°C; values in poise (i.e. 0.1 $kg \cdot m^{-1} \cdot s^{-1}$).

The modified *V*-ratios incorporating other basic and acidic oxides are also in use, depending on actual practice. Another index that is often referred to is known as *excess base* (*B*), where

$$B = MO - 2SiO_2 - 4P_2O_5 - 2Al_2O_3 - Fe_2O_3 \tag{4.47}$$

It assumes the formation of compounds like $2MO \cdot SiO_2$, $4MO \cdot P_2O_5$, etc. Free concentration of MO, which is assumed to participate in reactions, is therefore, obtained by deducting those tied-up as compounds.

In terms of weight percent,

$$B = \text{wt. \% CaO} - 1.86 \text{ wt. \% } SiO_2 - 1.19 \text{ wt. \% } P_2O_5 \tag{4.48}$$

Since a basic oxide tends to dissociate into cation and oxygen ions, the concentration of free O^{2-} increases with increasing basicity (Eq. (4.44)). Therefore, from a thermodynamic point of view, the activity of oxygen ions ($a_{O^{2-}}$) may be taken as an appropriate measure of the basicity of slag. However, there is no method available for experimental determination of $a_{O^{2-}}$.

A breakthrough came with the development of the concept of *optical basicity* (Λ) in the field of glass chemistry by Duffy and Ingram in 1975–76, which was subsequently applied to metallurgical slags. Experimental measurements of Λ in transparent media such as glass and aqueous solutions were carried out by employing Pb^{2+} as the probe ion. In an oxide medium, electron donation by oxygen brings about a reduction in the 6s – 6p energy gap, and this, in turn, produces a shift in the frequency (ν) in the UV spectral band.

$$\Lambda = \frac{\nu_{free} - \nu_{sample}}{\nu_{free} - \nu_{CaO}} \tag{4.49}$$

where ν_{free}, ν_{CaO} and ν_{sample} are frequencies at peak for free Pb^{2+}, Pb^{2+} in CaO, and Pb^{2+} in sample respectively. Therefore, $\Lambda = 1$ for pure CaO by definition. Hence, Λ is an expression for *lime character*, even though there may not be any CaO in the sample.

Slags are opaque. Hence, Λ is estimated for slags and there are controversies regarding the values for some oxides as well as correlations with reaction such as desulphurisation. In view of this problem, the concept of optical basicity has not been universally accepted in industrial applications.

Along with basicity, another concept that is important is that of *slag capacity*. This has evolved over a period of time, and has become quite widely used. Richardson and Fincham in 1954 first defined *sulphide capacity* (C_S) as the potential capacity of a slag melt to hold sulphur as sulphide. Mathematically,

$$C_S = (\text{wt. \% } S^{2-} \text{ in slag}) \times (p_{O_2}/p_{S_2})^{1/2} \tag{4.50}$$

where p_{O_2}/p_{S_2} are partial pressures of O_2 and S_2 in the gas at equilibrium with the slag. Noting that the reaction is:

$$\frac{1}{2}S_2(g) + (O^{2-}) = \frac{1}{2}O_2(g) + (S^{2-}) \tag{4.51}$$

it can be shown that

$$C_S = \frac{K_{51} \cdot a_{O^{2-}}}{\phi_{S^{2-}}} \tag{4.52}$$

where K_{51} is the equilibrium constant for the reaction in Eq. (4.51) and $\phi_{S^{2-}}$ is the activity coefficient of S^{2-} in the slag in an appropriate scale.

C_S is a function of slag composition and temperature only. Therefore, its values can be tabulated or presented graphically for use by all. This is an important advantage. Subsequently, several other capacity terms have been proposed and reported in literature. For example, if the slag–metal phosphorus reaction is written as

$$\frac{1}{2}P_2(g) + \frac{5}{4}O_2(g) + \frac{3}{2}(O^{2-})_{slag} = (PO_4^{3-})_{slag} \tag{4.53}$$

then the phosphate capacity of a slag may be defined as

$$C_P = \frac{(\text{wt. \% } PO_4^{3-})}{(p_{P_2})^{1/2}\,(p_{O_2})^{5/4}} \tag{4.54}$$

where the values are at equilibrium of reaction (4.53).

4.4.4 Slag Models

The basic features of activity vs. composition data of binary and oxide melts have been briefly presented in Section 4.3.3. For application, however, this sort of graphical presentation is quite unsatisfactory, since:

- Slags are multi-component, and graphical presentation is very cumbersome
- Thermodynamic calculations can only be performed if the activity vs. composition data can be expressed in the form of equations, which allow easier interpolation and extrapolation of laboratory experimental data as well.

With the above objectives, many attempts have been made to represent either slag activity or slag–metal equilibrium by analytical relations. These attempts have made assumptions about the structure of slags. The earlier models had assumed that slags consist of oxide compounds (the so called *molecular models*). The later models have treated slag melts as ionic liquids. However, this is an advanced area, and hence will not be dealt with further, except for mentioning that the following models have found some industrial applications:

- Flood and Forland model
- Kapoor and Frohberg model
- Regular solution model.

EXAMPLE 4.7

A slag of CaO, SiO_2 and Al_2O_3, having mole fraction of alumina as 0.1, has $Si_2O_7^{6-}$, AlO_4^{5-} anions. Calculate the slag composition.

Solution: Take 1 gmol of slag. Therefore, the mole fraction X is same as the number of moles n. Hence,

$$n_{CaO} + n_{SiO_2} + n_{Al_2O_3} = 1 \qquad \text{(Ex. 4.6)}$$

From oxygen balance,

$$n_O = n_{CaO} + 2n_{SiO_2} + 3n_{Al_2O_3} \qquad \text{(Ex. 4.7)}$$

Again, since anions are $Si_2O_7^{6-}$, AlO_4^{5-},

$$n_O = \frac{7}{2} n_{SiO_2} + 8 n_{Al_2O_3} \qquad \text{(Ex. 4.8)}$$

Noting that $n_{Al_2O_3} = 0.1$, and solving the above equations, the mole fractions of CaO, SiO_2 are 0.74 and 0.16 respectively.

EXAMPLE 4.8

Calculate the activation energy for viscosity for a liquid slag, whose viscosities are 10 and 2 $kg \cdot m^{-1} \cdot s^{-1}$ at 1500 and 1600°C respectively.

Solution: From Eq. (4.43),

$$\ln \eta = \ln \eta_0 + \frac{E_\eta}{RT} \qquad \text{(Ex. 4.9)}$$

Substituting the values for the given temperatures in the above equation, and combining them, gives

$$\ln \eta \,(\text{at } 1873 \text{ K}) - \ln \eta \,(\text{at } 1773 \text{ K}) = \ln\left(\frac{2}{10}\right) = \ln 0.2 = \frac{E_\eta}{R}\left(\frac{1}{1873} - \frac{1}{1773}\right)$$

Calculations give, $E_\eta = 4.45 \times 10^5$ J/mol = 445 kJ/mol

EXAMPLE 4.9

(a) A liquid slag has 50 wt. % CaO, 10 wt. % MgO, 25 wt. % SiO_2, and 15 wt. % Al_2O_3. Calculate its sulphide capacity at 1900 K with the help of the following equation:

$$\log C_S = 3.44(X_{CaO} + 0.1X_{MgO} - 0.8X_{Al_2O_3} - X_{SiO_2}) - \frac{9894}{T} + 2.05 \qquad \text{(Ex. 4.10)}$$

(b) Consider equilibrium of the above slag with a gas mixture consisting of 75% H_2, 15% H_2O, and 10% H_2S (of course volume % as per convention for gases), at 1900 K and 1 atmosphere total pressure. Calculate wt. % S in slag at equilibrium.

Solution: (a) Conversion of wt. % into mole fraction with the help of Eq. (4.26), and noting the atomic masses of Ca, Mg, Si, Al and O as 40, 24, 28, 27 and 16 respectively, gives

$$X_{CaO} = 0.523, \quad X_{MgO} = 0.146, \quad X_{SiO_2} = 0.244, \quad X_{Al_2O_3} = 0.087$$

Substituting the values of these in Eq. (Ex. 4.10), at 1900 K, $\log C_S = -2.384$, i.e. $C_S = 4.1 \times 10^{-3}$.

(b) From Eq. (4.50), $\quad C_S = (\text{wt. \% } S^{2-} \text{ in slag}) \times \left(\dfrac{p_{O_2}}{p_{S_2}}\right)^{1/2}$

From Example 4.1, $\quad H_2(g) + \dfrac{1}{2}O_2(g) = H_2O(g)$

From data in Table 4.1, ΔG_f^0 at 1900 K of the above reaction is –141,050 J/mol.

$$\Delta G_f^0 = -RT \ln K = -RT \ln \left(\frac{p_{H_2O}}{p_{H_2}} \times \frac{1}{(p_{O_2})^{1/2}}\right)_{eq}$$

Substituting values, and solving,

$$p_{O_2} = 7.0 \times 10^{-10} \text{ atmosphere}$$

For the reaction: $H_2(g) + \dfrac{1}{2}S_2(g) = H_2S(g)$

$$\Delta G_f^0 = -246{,}000 + 54.8\, T \text{ J/mol}$$

$$\Delta G_f^0 = -RT \ln K = -RT \ln \left(\frac{p_{H_2S}}{p_{H_2}} \times \frac{1}{(p_{S_2})^{1/2}}\right)_{eq}$$

Substituting values and solving,

$p_{S_2} = 2.81 \times 10^{-10}$ atmosphere and wt. % S in slag $= 1.65 \times 10^{-3}$

4.5 KINETICS, MIXING AND MASS TRANSFER

4.5.1 Introduction

Ironmaking and steelmaking processes are carried out at high temperatures where the reactions proceed rapidly. Therefore, chemical equilibria are closely attained in some reactions; but there are some other reactions and processes which do not attain equilibrium. The subject of *Kinetics* is to be taken help of both for process improvement as well as for a better understanding. This aspect is covered in brief in the subsequent paragraphs.

Reactions in ironmaking and steelmaking are *heterogeneous* in nature, i.e. they involve more than one phase, like slag and metal, gas and solid, etc. The chemical reactions between such phases occur at the phase boundaries (i.e. at *interfaces)*. The rate of reactions, therefore, would be proportional to the interfacial areas. At the same time, for these heterogeneous reactions to proceed, it is necessary to transport the reactants to the interface and the products of reaction away from the interface. This is achieved by the process of *mass transfer*. Mass transfer may be further subdivided into the following categories:

1. Mass transfer in the bulk phase away from the interface. This step is sufficiently rapid only in fluids, and that too, when the flow is turbulent in nature. The terminology *mixing* is commonly used in this connection.
2. Mass transfer at or near the interface, which depends on the concentration at the interface, temperature, total area available, etc.

As a result, all heterogeneous reactions take place through a series of *kinetic steps*, which may be classified into:

- Interfacial chemical reaction
- Mixing in the bulk fluid
- Mass transfer at/near the interface.

As already stated in Section 4.3.1, solids may be assumed to be pure in pyro-metallurgical processes since solid-state diffusion is extremely slow and can be neglected. However, a large variety of *porous solids* (e.g. iron ore, sinter, coke, lime, etc.) involved in these processes react fast owing to easy diffusion of gases through these materials, and in some cases, even liquids flowing through their pores.

Often new phases form as a result of these reactions, for example, the formation of carbon monoxide bubbles during decarburisation and deoxidation products following the addition of deoxidants. Theoretically, the formation of such products requires *nucleation* and *growth*. However, it has been established that nucleation is not required in industrial processing and only growth is involved.

4.5.2 Interfacial Chemical Reaction

Laws of chemical kinetics were proposed/derived for *homogeneous reactions* such as reactions in gases or in aqueous solutions. The same laws with modifications/additions are applied to interfacial chemical reactions. According to the *law of mass action,* for the *interfacial reaction*:

$$\mathrm{A + B = C + D} \tag{4.55}$$

$$r = A(k_f C_\mathrm{A} C_\mathrm{B} - k_\mathrm{b} C_\mathrm{C} C_\mathrm{D}) = Ak_f\left(C_\mathrm{A} C_\mathrm{B} - \frac{C_\mathrm{C} C_\mathrm{D}}{K}\right) \tag{4.56}$$

where r is the rate of reaction, A is the interfacial area, k_f, k_b are the forward and backward rate constants, K is the equilibrium constant for reaction (4.55) and C refers to concentrations per unit volume.

In ironmaking and steelmaking, generally speaking, first-order reversible reactions, such as A = C are involved. In this situation, Eq. (4.56) can be modified to

$$r = Ak_f\left(C_{\text{A}} - \frac{C_{\text{C}}}{K}\right) \tag{4.57}$$

k_f increases with temperature as per Arrhenius equation, namely

$$k_f = A\exp\left(-\frac{E}{RT}\right) \tag{4.58}$$

where, E is the activation energy and A is pre-exponential factor. T is the temperature in kelvin.

Interfacial chemical reactions occur in the following steps:

- Adsorption of reactants into the interfacial layer
- Chemical reaction amongst the adsorbed species
- Desorption of the products into the bulk material.

At high temperatures, adsorption and desorption involve chemical bond formation/breakage. This is what is known as *chemisorption*. Adsorption equilibria are governed either by *Langmuir adsorption isotherm* or *Gibbs adsorption isotherm*.

4.5.3 Diffusion

Diffusion (i.e. molecular diffusion) is governed by the *Fick's first law of diffusion* as follows:

$$\text{Molar flux} = \frac{\frac{dn_i}{dt}}{A} = -D_i \cdot \frac{\delta C_i}{\delta x} \tag{4.59}$$

$$\text{Mass flux} = \frac{\frac{dm_i}{dt}}{A} = -D_i \cdot \frac{\delta C_i^*}{\delta x} \tag{4.60}$$

for diffusion of species i along the x-direction. C_i is the concentration of i in moles/volume, C_i^* is the concentration of i in mass/volume and D_i is the *diffusion coefficient* (i.e. diffusivity) of i having the unit of $\text{cm}^2 \cdot \text{s}^{-1}$ or $\text{m}^2 \cdot \text{s}^{-1}$. Values of D (in $\text{m}^2 \cdot \text{s}^{-1}$) at ironmaking and steelmaking temperatures are of the order of 10^{-2} to 10^{-3} for gases, 5×10^{-8} to 5×10^{-9} for liquid steel, and 5×10^{-10} to 5×10^{-11} for liquid slags.

As stated in Section 4.5.1, ironmaking and steelmaking are concerned with molecular diffusion only inside the pores of a porous solid. Extensive studies have been carried out on this subject, both in chemical and metallurgical engineering. It is agreed that diffusion of gases or liquids through pores can be mathematically treated by the usual diffusion equations. Only special consideration is required for estimation of the value of D. For this purpose the equation:

$$D_i\ (\text{in pores}) = D_i\ (\text{in bulk gas/liquid}) \cdot \frac{\varepsilon}{\tau} \tag{4.61}$$

can be used, where ε is volume fraction of pores in the solid and τ is the *tortuosity factor*. The value of the tortuosity factor may be taken to be approximately 2, for estimation purposes (this is a source of uncertainty). Although the above equation can be employed for diffusion of liquids through a porous solid, further uncertainty is involved when it comes to the *wettability* of the liquid. If the liquid does not wet the solid, it cannot penetrate into the pores properly, and the role of wettability is thus obvious.

4.5.4 Turbulence and Mixing in Fluids

Although the term fluid includes both liquid and gas, in ironmaking and steelmaking, turbulence and mixing in liquid iron and steel and sometimes in liquid slag is involved.

The general equation for mass transfer for species *i* in the *x*-direction is

$$\frac{\frac{dn_i}{dt}}{A} = J_{ix} = -D_i \cdot \frac{\delta C_i}{\delta x} + C_i \cdot v_x - E_D \cdot \frac{\delta C_i}{\delta x} \tag{4.62}$$

where, J_{ix} is the flux of *i* along *x*, v_x is the convective velocity of the fluid in *x*-direction and E_D is the *eddy diffusivity* (only in turbulent flow).

Since $E_D >> D_i$, for turbulent flow, molecular diffusion can be ignored. Therefore, mixing in the bulk fluid occurs by *convection* and *eddy diffusion*. Whenever any addition is made to a liquid, it takes a long time for complete (i.e. perfect) mixing. Therefore, for all practical purposes, the *mixing time* (t_{mix}) is defined as the time required for a degree of mixing of 95%, i.e. 95% of perfect mixing.

Creation of turbulence and motion requires agitation of the fluid by stirring. The greater the extent of stirring, the faster is the mixing, and the lower is t_{mix}.

Extensive measurements of mixing time have been carried out in the context of processing of molten steel in gas-stirred ladles and converters, primarily using water models and mathematical modelling. It has been established that, in general,

$$t_{mix} = BP^{-m} f(\text{geometry, size of vessel}) \tag{4.63}$$

where, *P* is the *specific* stirring power input, *B* and *m* are empirical constants.

4.5.5 Convective Mass Transfer at Interface

Mass transfer at fluid–solid interface

At fluid–solid interfaces, the fluid can be assumed to be stagnant. Therefore, the convection and eddy diffusion terms in Eq. (4.62) can be ignored. This gives rise to a significant concentration gradient for the species which is being transferred in the fluid layer adjacent to a solid surface. This is the so-called *concentration boundary layer,* schematically shown in Figure 4.9. Since only molecular diffusion is involved, Eq. (4.62) is modified as

$$\left(\frac{\frac{dn_i}{dt}}{A}\right)_{\text{surface}} = -D_i \left(\frac{\delta C_i}{\delta x}\right)_{x=0}$$

$$= D_i \cdot \frac{(C_i^S - C_i^0)}{\delta_{C,\text{eff.}}} = k_{m,i}\,(C_i^S - C_i^0) \tag{4.64}$$

where, $\delta_{C,\text{eff}}$ is the effective concentration boundary layer thickness

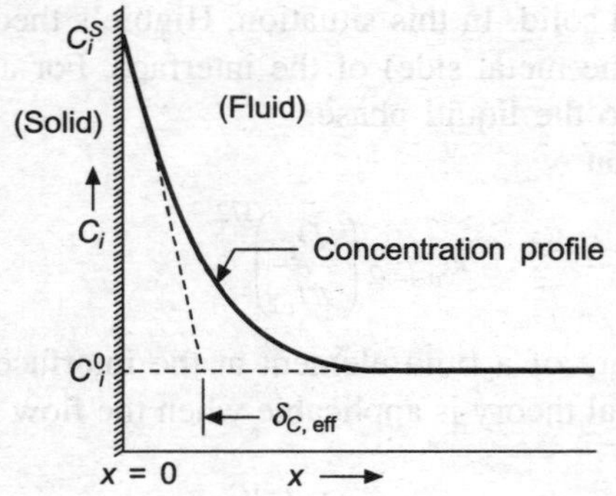

Figure 4.9 Concentration boundary layer in fluid adjacent to a solid surface during mass transfer.

and $\quad k_{m,\,i}$ = mass transfer coefficient for $i = \dfrac{D_i}{\delta_{C,\mathrm{eff}}}$

The more intense the stirring (agitation), the lower is $\delta_{C,\,\mathrm{eff}}$, and the higher is $k_{m,\,i}$. Therefore, mass transfer increases with increasing fluid convection and agitation. Experimental data have been correlated through *dimensionless numbers* using empirical equations of the type

$$\mathrm{Sh} = \mathrm{B\,Re}^m\,\mathrm{Sc}^n \quad \text{for forced convection} \tag{4.65}$$

and

$$\mathrm{Sh} = \mathrm{B'\,Gr}_m^{m'}\mathrm{Sc}^{n'} \quad \text{for free convection} \tag{4.66}$$

where Sh, Re, Sc, Gr stand for the Sherwood, Reynolds, Schmidt and Grassoff numbers respectively.

$$\mathrm{Sh} = \frac{k_{m,i}\;L}{D_i}$$

where L is a characteristic dimension of the system.

Mass transfer between two fluids

The reaction between two fluids is exemplified by those of molten metal and molten slag or gas. The salient differences between a fluid–fluid interface and a fluid–solid interface are as follows:

- The fluid layer is stagnant at the solid–fluid interface, but the possibility of flow and consequent renewal of interfacial layers is to be considered for a two-fluid situation.
- There may be turbulence at the fluid–fluid interface.

Many so-called *surface renewal theories* of mass transfer have, therefore, been proposed. Out of these theories (or models), two theories are generally employed—*Higbie's surface renewal theory* and *Danckwerts' surface renewal theory.*

Higbie's theory is applicable when the flow is laminar at the interface and there is no velocity gradient normal to the interface. For example, in the case of slag–metal interactions, the liquid slag is much more viscous than the liquid metal. Therefore, in a laminar flow situation, the velocity gradient in the slag layer normal to the interface would be negligible, i.e. the slag layer would behave like a rigid solid. In this situation, Higbie's theory may be applied to mass transfer on the slag side (not the metal side) of the interface. For a gas–liquid interface under laminar flow, it is applicable to the liquid phase.

Higbie's theory predicts that

$$k_{m,i=2}\left(\frac{D_i}{\pi t_e}\right)^{1/2} \tag{4.67}$$

where, t_e is the time of exposure of a fluid element at the interface.

Danckwerts' surface renewal theory is applicable when the flow is turbulent at the interface. It predicts

$$k_{m,i} = (D_i S)^{1/2} \tag{4.68}$$

where S is known as the *surface renewal factor*, and varies from 20 per second for very mild turbulence, to about 300 per second under strongly turbulent conditions. Sometimes, t_e can be estimated theoretically, but in most cases S has to be determined experimentally or by making an *educated guess*.

4.5.6 Enhancement of Process Rates

The reaction rates between solids, liquids, gases can be increased by:

(i) Increasing the surface area of the solid by grinding it to a fine powder or creating drops, bubbles and emulsions. These methods are very effective and the rates can be enhanced by several orders of magnitude.

(ii) Ensuring that the solids should have sufficient porosity.

(iii) Increasing the fluidity of the liquid and the extent of agitation. Both these factors lead to enhanced mixing and mass transfer.

Although temperature does have a strong influence on reaction rates, in most cases, it is not possible to increase it to any significant extent owing to various other technological reasons (refractory attack, vapour formation, etc.).

EXAMPLE 4.10

A bubble of nitrogen gas of diameter, $d = 0.5$ mm, at a pressure of 1.5 atm, is rising through a stagnant melt of steel of composition and temperature as in Example 4.6. Assuming mass transfer in the melt to be rate controlling, and Higbie's theory to be applicable, calculate the rate of transfer of nitrogen from gas to melt.

Solution: Rate of N transfer = $r_N = Ak_{m,i}\,(C_i^S - C_i^0)$, where i stands for atomic N.

$$A = \text{bubble surface area} = \pi d^2 = 78.5 \times 10^{-6}\ \text{m}^2$$

$k_{m,N}$ is given by Higbie's Eq. (4.67); Diffusivity of N in liquid steel at 1600°C = 3.8×10^{-9} m²/s. Exposure time, $t_e = d/v_t$, where v_t is the rising velocity of the bubble (according to Stokes' law, Eq. (20.9)).

Noting that, $g = 9.81$ m/s^2, $\rho_l = 6.73 \times 10^3$ kg/m^3, $\rho_g \cong 0$, and $\eta_l = 5 \times 10^{-3}$ N · m^{-2} · s^{-1}, $v_t = 18.34$ m/s, thus giving $t_e = 2.73 \times 10^{-4}$ s, and $k_{m,N} = 3.28 \times 10^{-7}$ m/s.

Assume the bulk concentration of N (C_N^0) = 0; the surface concentration (C_N^S) is at equilibrium with the N_2 gas. With reference to Example 4.6, wt. % N at equilibrium may be calculated as follows:

$[h_N]_{ppm} = K_N \cdot p_{N_2}^{1/2}$; at nitrogen pressure of 1.5 atmosphere, therefore, $[h_N]_{ppm} = 560.3$. Again, $\log [h_N]_{ppm} = 4 + \log W_N + \log f_N$.
On the basis of data in Example 4.6, $W_N = 0.0494$ wt. %.

C_N^S = mass of N per m^3 of melt = wt. fraction N in melt × density of liquid iron = $0.0494 \times 10^{-2} \times 6.73 \times 10^3 = 3.325$ kgN/m^3.
Therefore, the rate of N transfer = $3.28 \times 10^{-7} \times 3.325 = 1.09 \times 10^{-6}$ kg/s.

EXAMPLE 4.11

Consider the following slag–metal reaction at 1600°C.

$$[Si] + 2(MnO) = (SiO_2) + 2[Mn] \qquad \text{(Ex. 4.11)}$$

Compare the maximum rates of transfer of Si and Mn in liquid iron at the slag–metal interface. Assume validity of Danckwerts' surface renewal theory (Eq. (4.68)).
Given: D_{Si} (in liquid iron) = 2.5×10^{-9} m^2/s; D_{Mn} (in liquid iron) = 4.0×10^{-9} m^2/s at 1600°C. The composition relation in iron, at equilibrium with the slag, is: $[W_{Si}]/[W_{Mn}]^2 = 0.23$. Liquid iron contains 0.3 mole % Si and 0.5 mole % Mn.

Solution: Rate of transfer of Si = $Ak_{m,Si}\,[C_{Si}^0 - C_{Si}^S]$;

$$\text{Rate of transfer of Mn} = Ak_{m,Mn}\,[C_{Mn}^S - C_{Mn}^0]$$

$$\frac{Ak_{m,Si}}{Ak_{m,Mn}} = \frac{(D_{Si} \cdot S)^{1/2}}{(D_{Mn} \cdot S)^{1/2}} = \left(\frac{D_{Si}}{D_{Mn}}\right)^{1/2} = 0.79$$

At maximum rate for Si, the concentration of Mn in liquid iron is uniform at 0.5 mole %. Si concentration at the slag–metal interface is given by the chemical equilibrium relation as:

$$0.23 \times [\text{mole\% Mn}]^2 = 0.23 \times 0.5^2 = 0.0575$$

Since C is proportional to mole %, the maximum rate of Si transfer = $k_{m,Si}\,[0.3 - 0.0575] \times B$, where B is the constant of proportionality.

In a similar way, the maximum rate of transfer of Mn = $k_{m,Mn}\,[(0.3/0.23)^{1/2} - 0.5] \times B$. From the above, the ratio of the rates of Si and Mn transfer = 0.298.

REFERENCES

Barfield R.N. and J.A. Kitchener, JISI (1955), Vol. 180, p. 324.

Engh, T.A., *Principles of Metal Refining*, Oxford University Press, UK (1992).

Machin, J.S. and T.B. Lee, J. American Ceramic Soc. (1948), Vol. 31, p. 200.

Mackenzie, J.D., J.Chem. Rev. (1956), Vol. 5, p. 455.

Sigworth, G.K. and G.F. Elliott, Metal Science, 8, 1974, p. 298.

The Japan Society for the Promotion of Science, the 19th Committee on Steelmaking, *Steelmaking Data Sourcebook*, Gordon and Breach Science Publishers, New York, Revised ed., 1988, pp. 180–291.

Ward R.G., *An Introduction to the Physical Chemistry of Iron and Steelmaking*, Edward Arnold, London (1963), p. 25.

Part B

Blast Furnace Ironmaking

- Physical Chemistry of Blast Furnace Reactions
- Thermal and Chemical Features of the Blast Furnace
- Internal Zones and Gas Flow in Blast Furnaces
- Raw Materials I: Coke
- Raw Materials II: Iron Ore and Agglomerates
- Blast Furnace Productivity, Fuel Efficiency and Modern Developments
- Blast Furnace Products and Their Utilisation
- Blast Furnace Modelling and Control

5

Physical Chemistry of Blast Furnace Reactions

Chapter 2 presented chemical reactions in various zones of a blast furnace along with the approximate temperature levels (Figure 2.1). It also contained a brief description of the process as well as the internal structure of various regions (Figures 2.1, 2.2 and 2.3). The following regions were identified:

- The upper region, i.e. *Stack* or *Shaft*
- The middle portion of the furnace, i.e. *Belly and Bosh*
- The lower region, i.e. *Hearth*.

The lower region again can be subdivided into various zones—*Cohesive zone*, *Deadman zone* and *Combustion zone* (or *Tuyere zone/Raceway*).

Reactions take place in all these regions, and their control has a major influence on the quality of hot metal produced. An understanding of the reactions is therefore important.

5.1 THERMODYNAMICS OF THE CARBON–OXYGEN REACTION

In Chapter 4, the basics of physical chemistry, i.e. thermodynamics and kinetics of reactions as well as other physicochemical properties of liquid iron and slags of importance to ironmaking and steelmaking were presented. Based on the above, this chapter and some other subsequent chapters shall deal with physicochemical aspects of the reactions and processes of specific interest. In this chapter, the blast furnace reactions are covered.

5.1.1 Combustion of Coke in the Tuyere Zone

Coke is the principal source of carbon in the blast furnace and the principal reducing agent. Carbon combusts with oxygen in the pre-heated air blast at the tuyere zone at temperatures of approximately 1900–2000°C. Carbon is thus also the principal source of heat. The hot gas consisting primarily of CO, N_2 and some CO_2 travels upwards through the bed of solids, which gets heated up and melts. Various reactions take place—the principal ones being the reduction of iron ore and the gasification of coke.

The reactions of carbon with oxygen include:

$$C(s) + O_2(g) = CO_2(g) \tag{5.1}$$

$$\Delta H_1^0 = -393.7 \times 10^3 \text{ J}\cdot\text{mol}^{-1} \text{ at 298 K}$$

$$\Delta G_1^0 = -394{,}100 - 0.84T \text{ J}\cdot\text{mol}^{-1}$$

$$C(s) + \frac{1}{2}O_2(g) = CO(g) \tag{5.2}$$

$$\Delta H_2^0 = -110.6 \times 10^3 \text{ J}\cdot\text{mol}^{-1} \text{ at 298 K}$$

$$\Delta G_2^0 = -111{,}700 - 87.65T \text{ J}\cdot\text{mol}^{-1}$$

From the above, it may be noted that the combustion of carbon to CO_2 releases much more heat than the conversion to CO. Hence, from the point of view of thermal efficiency, the formation of CO_2 to the maximum possible extent is preferable.

Coke is a mechanical mixture of carbon and ash, which consists of inorganic compounds. From Chapter 4, Section 4.2, it may be noted that for pure carbon, the activity of carbon is 1. Also the activities of gaseous species are equal to their respective partial pressures (in standard atmosphere units). Therefore, on the basis of Eq. (4.17), for reaction (5.1):

$$\Delta G_1^0 = -RT \ln K_1 = -RT \ln\left(\frac{p_{CO_2}}{p_{O_2}}\right)_{eq.} \tag{5.3}$$

and for reaction (5.2),

$$\Delta G_2^0 = -RT \ln K_2 = -RT \ln\left(\frac{p_{CO}}{(p_{O_2})^{1/2}}\right)_{eq.} \tag{5.4}$$

In the tuyere region of a modern blast furnace, the total pressure is as high as about 4 atmosphere. Since air contains about 79% N_2 by volume, the sum of partial pressures of CO, CO_2 and O_2 will be approximately 1 atmosphere. Taking the tuyere temperature as 1900°C (2173 K), and from values of ΔG_1^0 and ΔG_2^0, $K_1 = 3.24 \times 10^9$ and $K_2 = 1.75 \times 10^6$. These are large values. Therefore, at equilibrium, from Eqs. (5.3) and (5.4), p_{O_2} is negligible. In other words, oxygen is almost completely converted into CO and CO_2 at the tuyere level. It will be shown later in the following section that the product is essentially CO rather than CO_2 at the tuyere level.

5.1.2 C–CO_2–CO Reaction

On the basis of the above, for reactions in the stack and bosh, O_2 can be ignored and only the following reaction needs to be considered:

$$CO_2(g) + C(s) = 2CO(g) \tag{5.5}$$

Reaction (5.5) is a combination of reactions (5.1) and (5.2). Using Hess' law,

$$\Delta G_5^0 = 2\Delta G_2^0 - \Delta G_1^0 = 170{,}700 - 174.46T \text{ J}\cdot\text{mol}^{-1} \tag{5.6}$$

Therefore,
$$\ln K_5 = \ln\left(\frac{p_{CO}^2}{p_{CO_2}}\right)_{eq.} = \ln\left(\frac{X_{CO}^2}{X_{CO_2}}\right)_{eq.} \cdot P_T$$

$$= -\frac{\Delta G_5^0}{RT} = -\frac{20532}{T} + 20.98 \tag{5.7}$$

where $P_T = p_{CO} + p_{CO_2} = 1$ atmosphere, and X_{CO}, X_{CO_2} are mole fractions of CO and CO_2 respectively. For ideal gases, X is the same as its volume fraction (refer Chapter 4).

Since,
$$X_{CO} + X_{CO_2} = 1, \quad K_5 = \frac{X_{CO}^2}{1 - X_{CO}} \tag{5.8}$$

On the basis of Eqs. (5.7) and (5.8), volume fractions (or volume percent) of CO and CO_2 for C–CO–CO_2 equilibrium at any temperature can be calculated. Figure 5.1 presents such calculated volume fraction of CO in CO–CO_2 mixture as a function of temperature. In the above equations, T is in kelvin but for convenience of users the unit of temperature in Figure 5.1 is given in °C. Reaction (5.5) is the famous *Boudouard Reaction*. In blast furnace ironmaking the forward reaction is known as the *Solution Loss Reaction*. In general, it is referred to as the *Gasification Reaction*.

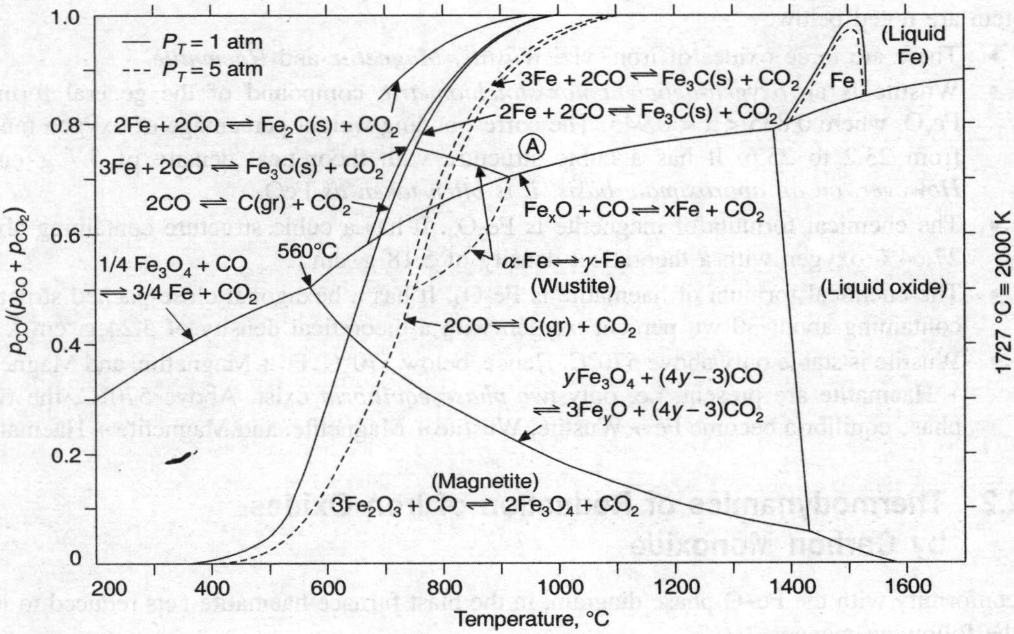

Figure 5.1 Equilibrium $p_{CO}/(p_{CO} + p_{CO_2})$ ratios in gas as a function of temperature for reactions in the Fe–C–O system. The lines are for equilibria of reactions as indicated.

Figure 4.1 shows that CO becomes more and more stable compared with CO_2 as the temperature is increased. This is also demonstrated in Figure 5.1. Therefore, at the tuyeres where the temperatures are the highest, CO is the only stable oxide of carbon and this gas passes through a bed of coke. By neglecting the effects of hydrocarbons or any other tuyere injectants, the composition of the gas as it enters the bottom of the stack can be calculated assuming that air contains 21% O_2, 79% N_2 and that the entire amount of O_2 gets converted into CO. For 100 moles of air, therefore, the number of moles of N_2 and CO would be 79 and 42 respectively. Hence,

$$\text{Volume \% CO} = \frac{42}{79+42} \times 100 = 34.7$$

$$\text{Volume \% } N_2 = 100 - 34.7 = 65.3$$

5.2 GAS–SOLID REACTION EQUILIBRIA IN THE BLAST FURNACE STACK

5.2.1 The Fe–O System

Figure 5.2 shows the Fe–O phase diagram (Darken and Gurry, 1946). The salient features of this system are noted below.

- There are three oxides of iron, viz. *Wustite, Magnetite* and *Haematite.*
- Wustite is an *oxygen-deficient non-stoichiometric* compound of the general formula Fe_xO, where $0.835 < x < 0.945$. The corresponding weight percentage of oxygen ranges from 23.2 to 25.6. It has a cubic structure with theoretical density of 5.7 $g \cdot cm^{-3}$. *However, on an approximate basis, it is often taken as* FeO.
- The chemical formula of magnetite is Fe_3O_4. It has a cubic structure containing about 27.64% oxygen with a theoretical density of 5.18 $g \cdot cm^{-3}$.
- The chemical formula of haematite is Fe_2O_3. It has a hexagonal close-packed structure containing about 30 wt. percent oxygen with a theoretical density of 5.24 $g \cdot cm^{-3}$.
- Wustite is stable only above 570°C. Hence, below 570°C, Fe + Magnetite, and Magnetite + Haematite are present, i.e. only *two-phase equilibria* exist. Above 570°C, the two-phase equilibria become Fe + Wustite, Wustite + Magnetite, and Magnetite + Haematite.

5.2.2 Thermodynamics of Reduction of Iron Oxides by Carbon Monoxide

In conformity with the Fe–O phase diagram, in the blast furnace haematite gets reduced to iron in the following manner:

$$Fe_2O_3 \rightarrow Fe_3O_4 \rightarrow Fe_xO \rightarrow Fe$$

About 75% of oxygen in Fe_2O_3 gets removed at the $Fe_xO \rightarrow Fe$ stage.

Any gas–solid reaction is much faster than a reaction between two solid species, in this case, solid iron oxide and solid carbon. Therefore, reduction of solid iron oxides in a blast furnace occurs through reaction primarily with carbon monoxide in the stack.

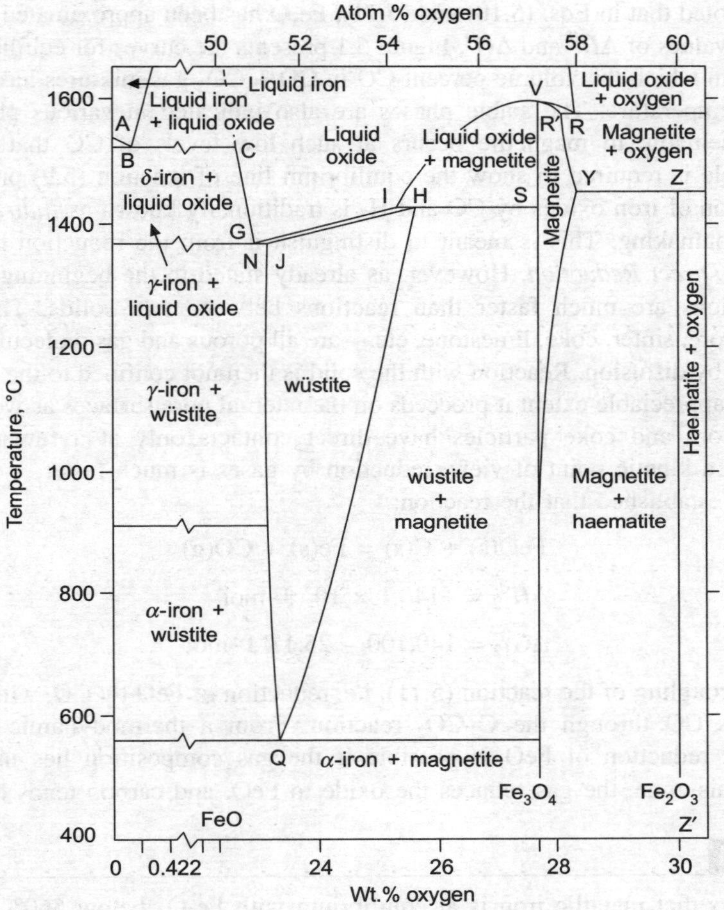

Figure 5.2 Iron–oxygen phase diagram.

Using Hess' law, and from Table 4.1 (for ΔG^0 only),

$$3Fe_2O_3(s) + CO(g) = 2Fe_3O_4(s) + CO_2(g) \tag{5.9}$$

$$\Delta H_9^0 = -52.8 \times 10^3 \text{ J} \cdot \text{mol}^{-1}$$

$$\Delta G_9^0 = -44{,}300 - 39.89T \text{ J} \cdot \text{mol}^{-1}$$

$$Fe_3O_4(s) + CO(g) = 3FeO(s) + CO_2(g) \tag{5.10}$$

$$\Delta H_{10}^0 = +36.3 \times 10^3 \text{ J} \cdot \text{mol}^{-1}$$

$$\Delta G_{10}^0 = 29{,}860 - 38.29T \text{ J} \cdot \text{mol}^{-1}$$

$$FeO(s) + CO(g) = Fe(s) + CO_2(g) \tag{5.11}$$

$$\Delta H_{11}^0 = -17.3 \times 10^3 \text{ J} \cdot \text{mol}^{-1}$$

$$\Delta G_{11}^0 = -22{,}800 - 24.26T \text{ J} \cdot \text{mol}^{-1}$$

(*Note:* Since the values of ΔH^0 and ΔG^0 could not be collected from the same source, some minor discrepancies may be present).

It may be noted that in Eqs. (5.10) and (5.11), Fe_xO has been approximated to FeO in order to use concrete values of ΔH^0 and ΔG^0. Figure 5.1 presents the curves for equilibria of reactions (5.9) to (5.11), in which the volume percent CO in CO + CO_2 gas mixtures has been plotted as a function of temperature. The stable phases are also indicated in various phase fields. The reduction of haematite to magnetite occurs at such low levels of CO that a different gas composition scale is required to show the equilibrium line of reaction (5.9) properly.

The reduction of iron oxides by CO and H_2 is traditionally known as *Indirect Reduction* in blast furnace ironmaking. This is meant to distinguish it from the reduction by solid carbon, which is called *Direct Reduction*. However, as already stated in the beginning of this section, gas–solid reactions are much faster than reactions between two solids. The solid burden materials—iron ore, sinter, coke, limestone, etc.—are all porous and gas molecules can penetrate into these pores by diffusion. Reaction with the solid is then not confined to the external surface alone, but to an appreciable extent it proceeds on the internal pore surfaces as well. On the other hand, adjacent ore and coke particles have direct contacts only at a few point locations. Therefore, from a kinetic point of view, reduction by gases is much faster.

It has been established that the reaction:

$$\text{FeO(s)} + \text{C(s)} = \text{Fe(s)} + \text{CO(g)} \tag{5.12}$$

$$\Delta H^0_{12} = +140.1 \times 10^3 \text{ J}\cdot\text{mol}^{-1}$$

$$\Delta G^0_{12} = 140{,}100 - 25.1T \text{ J}\cdot\text{mol}^{-1}$$

occurs through coupling of the reaction (5.11), i.e. reduction of FeO by CO, with reaction (5.5), which generates CO through the C–CO_2 reaction. From a thermodynamic point of view, therefore, direct reduction of FeO is possible if the gas composition lies in region (A) of Figure 5.1. In this zone, the gas reduces the oxide to FeO, and carbon tends to form CO.

EXAMPLE 5.1

Figure 5.1 shows that metallic iron is at equilibrium with Fe_3O_4 below 560°C and with FeO above 560°C. Justify this through thermodynamic considerations.

Solution: Since gas phase is also involved, according to phase rule, $F = C - P + 2$, where F is degrees of freedom, C is the number of components, P is the number of phases.
At 560°C, $P = 4$ (i.e. Fe, FeO, Fe_3O_4, gas), $C = 2$ (i.e. Fe and O), since the role of CO and CO_2 mixture is essentially to control oxygen potential in gas. Hence, $F = 0$ at 560°C (i.e. it is an invariant point).
Consider the reaction:

$$\text{Fe(s)} + \text{Fe}_3\text{O}_4\text{(s)} = 4\text{FeO(s)};\ \Delta G^0 \tag{Ex.5.1}$$

From data in Table 4.1, or from Eqs. (5.10) and (5.11), it is obtained that

$$\Delta G^0 = 4\Delta G^0_f(\text{FeO}) - \Delta G^0_f(\text{Fe}_3\text{O}_4) = 52{,}325 - 62.58T \text{ J}\cdot\text{mol}^{-1} \tag{Ex.5.2}$$

Since, in reaction (Ex. 5.1), the reactants and the product are pure solids, the feasibility criterion for the reaction is ΔG^0 itself and not ΔG. See Chapter 4 for further clarification.
Let the temperature at which reaction (Ex. 5.1) is at equilibrium be T_0. Then, at T_0, $\Delta G^0 = 0$. This gives T_0 = 836 K = 563°C, which is slightly different from that in Figure 5.1, due to different thermodynamic data sources.

5.2.3 Dissociation of Limestone

Limestone in lump form often constitutes one of the burden materials (in many cases, the entire lime requirement is met through sinter). Limestone decomposes in the stack region of the furnace through the reaction

$$CaCO_3(s) = CaO(s) + CO_2(g) \tag{5.13}$$

$$\Delta H^0_{13} = 179 \times 10^3 \text{ J}\cdot\text{mol}^{-1} \text{ at } 298 \text{ K}$$

$$\Delta G^0_{13} = 168{,}500 - 144T \text{ J}\cdot\text{mol}^{-1}$$

Consider a temperature of 850°C, which is typical in the lower part of the stack. p_{CO_2} in the gas in this region of a blast furnace may be assumed to range between 0.3 and 0.4 atmosphere. Based on the value of ΔG^0_{13}, p_{CO_2} in equilibrium with $CaCO_3$ and CaO is 0.48 atmosphere.

Since p_{CO_2} (actual) < p_{CO_2} (eq.), calcium carbonate should completely decompose at this level. But this does not happen because of kinetic limitations, and, in a blast furnace, significant decomposition occurs only at 1000–1100°C. Decomposition of limestone is endothermic and requires heat to be supplied. During the progress of decomposition, a layer of porous CaO forms on the outer layer of limestone. This layer has very poor thermal conductivity, and consequently, slows down heat transfer into the interior of the limestone lumps. This factor also affects the rate of decomposition.

5.2.4 Reactions of Hydrogen in the Stack

In the tuyere area, steam has been traditionally injected to control the flame temperature. Injection of hydrocarbon in the form of natural gas or oil was also resorted to in some blast furnaces around the world. A recent development is the injection of pulverised coal. The coal decomposes at the tuyere level liberating hydrocarbons and volatile H–C–O compounds. All these compounds become a source of hydrogen in the furnace.

Hydrocarbons are unstable at a high temperature and readily decompose into carbon and hydrogen. Also steam reacts with carbon in coke, thus generating more hydrogen.

$$H_2O(g) + C(s) = H_2(g) + CO(g) \tag{5.14}$$

$$\Delta H^0_{14} = 131.4 \times 10^3 \text{ J}\cdot\text{mol}^{-1} \text{ at } 298 \text{ K}$$

$$\Delta G^0_{14} = 134300 - 142.45T \text{ J}\cdot\text{mol}^{-1}$$

Again,
$$\Delta G^0_{14} = -RT \ln K_{14} = -RT \ln\left(\frac{p_{CO} \times p_{H_2}}{p_{H_2O}}\right)_{eq.} \tag{5.15}$$

At the tuyere level, assuming T = 2173 K (i.e. 1900°C), p_{CO} = 1 atmosphere, a sample calculation shows that at equilibrium, p_{H_2}/p_{H_2O} ratio is 1.63×10^4: 1, i.e. H_2O would be almost completely converted into H_2. Therefore, the gas mixture in the lower part of the stack (typically at a temperature of 1000°C or so) would consist of CO, CO_2, H_2 and N_2. In the stack, the following reaction needs to be considered.

$$H_2(g) + CO_2(g) = H_2O(g) + CO(g) \tag{5.16}$$

This is known as the *Water Gas Reaction*, since it occurs during generation of water gas.

For reaction (5.16),

$$\Delta H^0_{16} = 32.0 \times 10^3 \text{ J} \cdot \text{mol}^{-1} \text{ at } 298 \text{ K}$$

$$\Delta G^0_{16} = 30{,}470 - 28.48T \text{ J} \cdot \text{mol}^{-1}$$

At 1000 K (i.e. 727°C), $K_{16} = 0.8$. Hence, the equilibrium ratios of H_2/H_2O and CO/CO_2 are approximately the same at 1000 K.

The rates of all gaseous reactions are very high at high temperatures (say, above 700–800°C). Hence, the general assumption is that equilibrium is attained at such temperatures. The water gas reaction is no exception. As far as the blast furnace is concerned, it has been observed that this equilibrium exists above 800–1000°C, but in the upper stack (below a temperature of 600–700°C), equilibrium does not exist.

H_2 is a reducing agent like CO, and equations analogous to Eqs. (5.9)–(5.11) can be written for the reduction of iron oxides by hydrogen. For example, the reduction of FeO would occur as

$$FeO(s) + H_2(g) = Fe(s) + H_2O(g) \tag{5.17}$$

$$\Delta H^0_{17} = 8.0 \times 10^3 \text{ J} \cdot \text{mol}^{-1} \text{ at } 298 \text{ K}$$

$$\Delta G^0_{17} = 7800 - 4.22T \text{ J} \cdot \text{mol}^{-1}$$

It may be noted that the reduction of FeO by CO is exothermic, while that by H_2 is endothermic. The equilibrium relations for iron oxide reduction by H_2 as a function of temperature are plotted in Figure 5.3 as volume fraction H_2 in $H_2 + H_2O$ mixtures. The slope of the FeO–Fe equilibrium line is just opposite to that for reduction by CO. Therefore, hydrogen is thermodynamically a better reductant than carbon monoxide at higher temperatures.

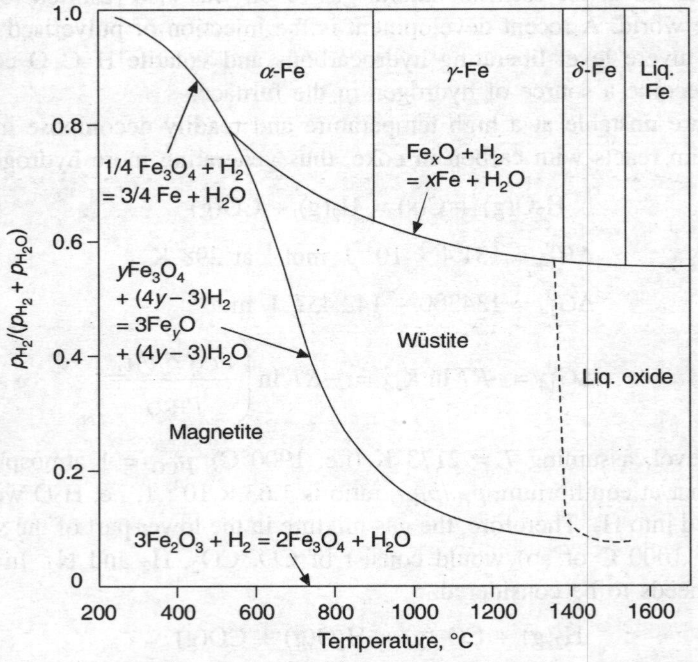

Figure 5.3 Equilibrium $[p_{H_2}/(p_{H_2} + p_{H_2O})]$ ratios in gas as a function of temperature for reactions in Fe–H–O system. The lines are for equilibria of reactions as indicated.

EXAMPLE 5.2

A gas mixture containing 50% CO_2 and 50% H_2, is introduced into a furnace at 1000 K. Assuming that it attained equilibrium at the furnace temperature quickly, predict whether it will deposit carbon as solid. Assume total pressure (P_T) = 1 atmosphere.

Solution: Consider equilibrium of the reaction

$$H_2(g) + CO_2(g) = H_2O(g) + CO(g) \tag{5.16}$$

From the data given, ΔG^0 for the above reaction at 1000 K = 1990 J·mol^{-1}

So,
$$1990 = -R \times 1000 \ln \left(\frac{p_{H_2O} \cdot p_{CO}}{p_{H_2} \cdot p_{CO_2}} \right)_{eq.} \tag{Ex.5.3}$$

Assume that initially 1 gmol of $H_2 + CO_2$ mixture was introduced into the furnace. Let x moles of each react, before equilibrium is reached. Then the number of gmol of H_2, CO_2, H_2O and CO are $0.5 - x$, $0.5 - x$, x and x respectively. Since partial pressures are proportional to number of moles,

$$1990 = -R \times 1000 \ln \left[\frac{x^2}{(0.5 - x)^2} \right]$$

Calculations give $\dfrac{p_{CO_2}}{p_{CO}} = \dfrac{X_{CO_2}}{X_{CO}} = \dfrac{0.5 - x}{x} = 3.20$

Noting that $p_{CO_2} + p_{CO} = (0.5 - x) + x = 0.5$ atmosphere, the values of p_{CO_2} and p_{CO} are 0.381 and 0.119 atmosphere respectively.
Now, consider the reaction,

$$CO_2(g) + C(s) = 2CO(g) \tag{5.5}$$

From Eq. (5.7), at 1000 K, K for reaction (5.5) is 1.565.

$$J = \frac{p_{CO}^2}{p_{CO_2}} \text{(actual)} = \frac{0.119^2}{0.381} = 0.037$$

$\Delta G = RT \ln (J/K) = -31{,}095$ J·mol^{-1}. Since it is negative, reaction (5.5) shall proceed in the forward direction. Therefore, carbon deposition shall not occur.

5.3 KINETICS OF REACTIONS IN THE STACK

The major reactions are:

- Reduction of iron oxides by CO and H_2
- Gasification of carbon by CO_2
- Reduction of FeO by carbon.

The first two are gas–solid reactions while the last reaction is a combination of the first two reactions as mentioned earlier.

5.3.1 Kinetics of Reduction of Iron Oxides by CO and H_2

General features

The general features of kinetics and mechanism of iron oxide reduction by CO and H_2 are similar. Hence, they will be discussed together. Straightway it needs to be pointed out that the major difference is that reduction by H_2 is 5–10 times faster than that by CO. Numerous fundamental investigations carried out in the laboratory over a period of six decades have confirmed this finding.

Lump ores, sinter and pellets contain iron oxide mostly as Fe_2O_3, but in some ore bodies, the oxide is in the form of magnetite. The gangue minerals contain primarily SiO_2 and Al_2O_3 besides other minor compounds. In the stack region, CO and H_2 can reduce only the oxides of iron. The fundamental measure of the extent of reduction is the *Degree of Reduction* (F_0) defined as

$$F_0 = \frac{\text{loss of mass of the ore due to removal of oxygen}}{\text{total mass of removable oxygen in ore}} \tag{5.18}$$

Figure 5.4 shows the relationship between F_0 and time t for the reduction of iron oxide pellets by hydrogen at 900°C (Bogdandy and Engell, 1971). Salient kinetic features that need to be noted are as follows:

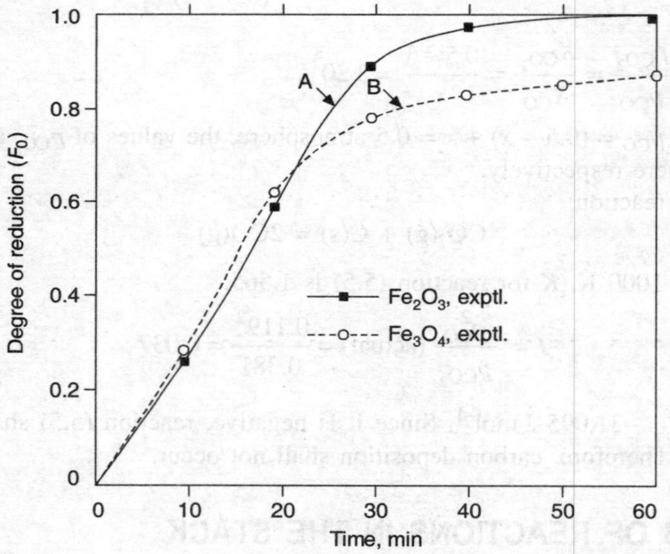

Figure 5.4 F_0 vs. t plots for reduction of Fe_2O_3 and Fe_3O_4 in H_2 at 900°C.

- Lump ore, sinter and pellets are porous solids.
- Reduction is characterised by the formation of a porous product layer.
- Fe_2O_3 is reduced in stages, viz. $Fe_2O_3 \rightarrow Fe_3O_4 \rightarrow Fe_xO \rightarrow Fe$.
- Additional porosity develops during reduction owing to density differences of the product solids. The relative volumes per unit mass of Fe are:

$$Fe : Fe_xO : Fe_3O_4 : Fe_2O_3 = 1 : 1.79 : 2.08 : 2.14$$

As a result, when haematite is reduced to magnetite, additional porosity develops, enhancing the rate of further reduction of haematite. Hence, as shown in Figure 5.4, haematite is more reducible than magnetite.

- A measure of the rate of reduction (r_0) is dF_0/dt, where t is the time after reduction starts.
- The term *Reducibility* is popular in technical literature. The higher the reducibility of an iron oxide bearing solid, the faster is the rate of reduction. Hence, dF_0/dt may be considered as a measure of reducibility.
- Figure 5.4 shows that dF_0/dt is a function of time, which gives rise to problems in assigning a characteristic value to reducibility. Different conventions have been adopted, out of which the following alternatives are popular.

$$r_0 = \frac{dF_0}{dt} \text{ at } F_0 = 0.4 \text{ or } 0.5$$

$$r_0 = \frac{[1-(1-F_0)^{1/3}]}{t} = \text{constant} \tag{5.19}$$

With respect to gas composition, the rate is first order, reversible, i.e.

$$\text{for CO reduction of FeO,} \qquad r_0 = k_C\left(p_{CO} - \frac{p_{CO_2}}{K_{11}}\right) \tag{5.20}$$

$$\text{for } H_2 \text{ reduction of FeO,} \qquad r_0 = k_H\left(p_{H_2} - \frac{p_{H_2O}}{K_{17}}\right) \tag{5.21}$$

where k_C, k_H are rate constants, and K_{11} and K_{17} are equilibrium constants of reactions (5.11) and (5.17) respectively.

Mechanism of reduction

If the reduction of FeO in any ore proceeds in the manner depicted in Figure 5.5, the kinetic

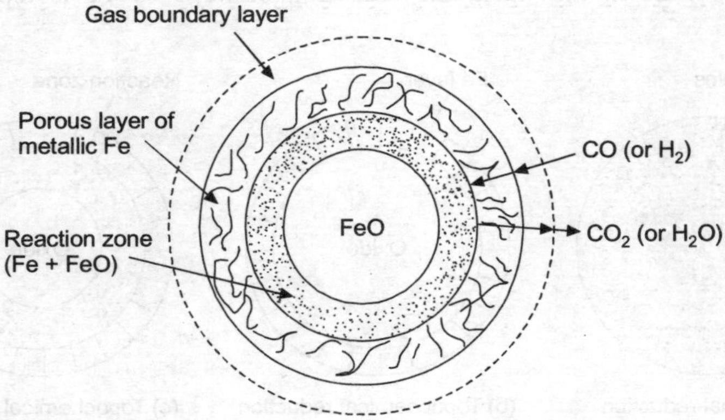

Figure 5.5 Sketch of a partially reduced sphere of FeO showing layers and kinetic steps.

steps involved are:

- Transfer of reactant gas to the solid surface (CO or H_2) across the gas boundary layer around the piece of solid
- Inward diffusion of reactant gas through the pores of the solid
- Chemical reaction (5.11) or (5.17)
- Outward diffusion of the product gas (CO_2 or H_2O) through the pores
- Transfer of the product gas from the solid surface into the bulk gas across the boundary layer.

It has been established by laboratory investigations that the rates of all these steps are comparable. Therefore, generally speaking, all of them have to be considered as partially rate controlling steps. The overall rate would depend on:

- Temperature
- Gas composition
- Size of the particle
- Nature of the solid in terms of its structure and composition.

Depending on the situation, the pattern of ore reduction has been classified into the following:

1. *Uniform internal reduction* is obtained when diffusion through the pores is faster than chemical reaction (smaller particles, lower temperature, slower reduction, higher porosity).
2. *Topochemical* reduction with a sharp interface is obtained when pore diffusion is slower than chemical reaction (large particles, higher temperature, low porosity).
3. Topochemical reduction with a diffused interface is obtained when the chemical reaction rate is comparable with the pore diffusion rate.

These phenomena are illustrated in Figure 5.6. In the blast furnace, reduction of $Fe_2O_3 \rightarrow Fe_3O_4 \rightarrow Fe_xO$ (i.e. stagewise reduction) occurs in the upper part of stack at lower temperature. The pattern is basically internal reduction, and thus stagewise reduction occurs throughout the entire particle. Lower down the stack, the reduction of $Fe_xO \rightarrow Fe$ is topochemical with a diffused interface.

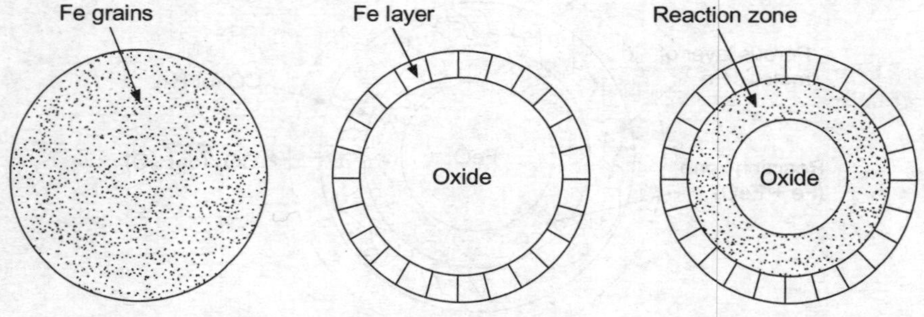

(a) Internal reduction (b) Topochemical reduction with sharp interface (c) Topochemical reduction with diffused interface

Figure 5.6 Sketches of sections of partially reduced iron ore pellets, showing three patterns; (Fe_2O_3, Fe_3O_4 and FeO have not been shown separately).

It is interesting to note that at a fixed temperature and gas composition, and for any type of ore/sinter/pellet burden of a given size range, the reducibility values do not differ by more than a small factor.

The overall kinetics of iron ore reduction is complex because of:

- Dependence of the rate on the structure of the solid, especially its porosity and pore structure
- Changes in the structure of the solid during reduction on account of swelling/contraction, recrystallisation and grain growth
- Comparable rates of chemical reaction, pore diffusion and in many cases, boundary layer mass transfer.

Several rate equations have been proposed, and mathematical modelling exercises have been reported in the literature. The best results are obtained by a combination of (i) experimental rate measurements, (ii) characterisation of the ore-pore size distribution, pore surface area, mineralogical details, etc., and (iii) quantitative analysis/mathematical modelling.

In a blast furnace, as the solid burden moves downwards, it undergoes changes in the surrounding environment (in terms of temperature, gas composition, overlying load, etc.). In view of this as well as complex kinetics, in actual practice, integrated tests are preferred where the blast furnace situation is simulated in the laboratory for small batches of ore/sinter/pellets. On this basis, an attempt is made to assess the overall performance.

5.3.2 Kinetics of Gasification of Carbon by CO_2

Blast furnace coke has 80–90% carbon, the rest is ash, which consists of various inorganic oxides. The gasification reaction is also of significant interest in carbothermic reduction of some other metals as well as in several chemical industries. Therefore, the kinetics of this reaction has been a subject of intense study from as early as the 1920s, initially by physical chemists, and later by chemical/metallurgical engineers and fuel technologists. A large amount of literature is available on this topic.

The degree of gasification of carbon (F_C) is given as

$$F_C = \frac{\text{mass loss of carbon in the sample}}{\text{total mass of carbon in the sample}} \tag{5.22}$$

The term *Reactivity* is commonly used to denote the speed of the gasification reaction. The higher the reactivity of the sample, the faster is the gasification. The reactivity (r_C) can be defined as

$$r_C = \frac{dF_C}{dt} \tag{5.23}$$

where t is the time of reaction. In contrast to ore reduction, F_C has been found to vary approximately linearly with t, up to about F_C = 0.3 to 0.4. In this region, therefore, r_C is a constant.

The kinetic steps involved in the gasification of a piece of carbon are:

- Transfer of CO_2 across the gas boundary layer to the surface of the particle
- Inward diffusion of CO_2 through the pores
- Chemical reaction on the pore surfaces
- Outward diffusion of CO through the pores
- Transfer of CO into the bulk gas by mass transfer across the boundary layer.

Laboratory experiments have demonstrated that the chemical reaction is much slower compared with the other steps; hence it constitutes the principal rate controlling step. Such a conclusion has been arrived at on the basis of the large activation energy involved, strong retarding influence of CO on the rate, significant catalytic enhancement of the rate in the presence of metallic iron, alkalies, etc., and retardation by sulphides.

Since the chemical reaction is the rate controlling step, the reaction occurs internally as in Figure 5.6(a). Therefore, the rate increases with increase in pore surface area (S). It so happens that S varies from 0.1 $m^2 \cdot g^{-1}$ to 10^3 $m^2 \cdot g^{-1}$, depending on the nature of carbon. Therefore, the rate of gasification is strongly dependent on the nature and source of carbon as indicated in Figure 5.7 (Turkdogan et al. 1970).

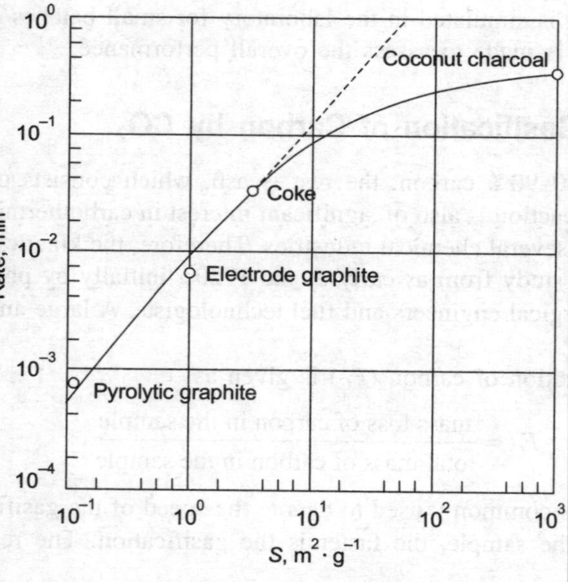

Figure 5.7 Rate of oxidation of carbon samples in CO_2 at 1100°C as a function of internal pore surface area.

5.3.3 Kinetics of Reduction of FeO by Carbon

As discussed in Section 5.2.2, reduction actually occurs via the gas phase through coupling of reaction (5.5), i.e. gasification of carbon with reaction (5.11), which is the reduction of FeO by CO. Laboratory experiments have confirmed that the net rate of this reaction is primarily controlled by the rate of the gasification reaction. As in the case of the gasification reaction, it is characterised by large activation energy and is catalysed/inhibited by the reagents which influence the gasification reaction in a similar way.

When the molar rates of reactions (5.5) and (5.11) become equal, then, reaction (5.12) takes place stochiometrically. This equality is expressed as

$$\text{mass of ore} \times \text{fraction of oxygen in ore} \times r_O \times \frac{1}{16}$$

$$= \text{mass of coke} \times \text{fraction of carbon in coke} \times r_C \times \frac{1}{12} \quad (5.24)$$

The factors 16 and 12 denote the atomic masses of oxygen and carbon respectively.

The calculated rates of generation of CO by gasification and consumption of CO by the reduction reaction as a function of temperature for a sample of 1500 kg ore and 500 kg coke are plotted in Figure 5.8 (Turkdogan 1978). At lower temperature, the gasification rate is much lower than the reduction rate, but with the increasing temperature, they tend to equalise. This happens because the rate of the gasification reaction increases rapidly with the increase in temperature because of large activation energy. That is why direct reduction in a blast furnace takes place only in the bosh and lower stack regions.

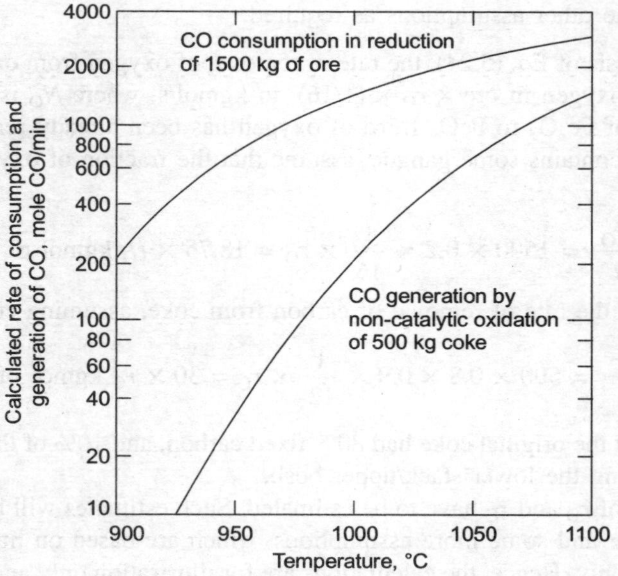

Figure 5.8 Rates of reduction of lump haematite ore (1500 kg, 1 cm dia.) and non-catalytic internal oxidation of coke (500 kg) at simulated blast furnace gas composition and pressure.

5.3.4 Direct and Indirect Reduction in the Blast Furnace

The carbon in coke charged into a blast furnace has two functions, namely *chemical* (i.e. as a reducing agent) and *thermal* (i.e. as a provider of heat).

When the carbon burns at the tuyeres and generates CO, the gas reduces iron oxide by indirect reduction, and only one oxygen atom of the oxide is removed by one atom of carbon. On the other hand, if the oxide is also reduced directly by carbon in the lower part of the furnace, the resulting CO again reduces the oxide. Thus, one carbon atom removes two atoms of oxygen from the ore. Therefore, direct reduction improves the chemical utilisation of carbon. However, since direct reduction is strongly endothermic, it lowers the thermal efficiency. Hence, it is normally desirable that there should be a balance between direct and indirect reduction—about 66% indirect and the remainder direct reduction is considered to be the optimum.

To achieve this objective, the following are required:

- The reducibility of the iron oxide used should be as high as possible.
- The reactivity of coke should have an optimum value (opinions vary on what is the optimum).

EXAMPLE 5.3

Calculate the rate of oxygen removal due to reduction of FeO in iron ore by CO, and the rate of gasification of carbon in coke by CO_2, for a situation prevailing at the lower stack/upper bosh of a blast furnace. Assume the temperature as 1100°C, pressure of $CO + CO_2$ as 0.7 atmosphere, of which 90% is CO and 10% CO_2. Calculate for 1500 kg of original ore before reduction, and 500 kg of coke. Make other assumptions as required.

Solution: On the basis of Eq. (5.24), the rate of removal of oxygen from ore $(-dN_O/dt)$ = mass of ore × fraction of oxygen in ore × r_O × (1/16), in kgmol/s, where N_O is kgmol of O.

After reduction of Fe_2O_3 to FeO, 1/3rd of oxygen has been already removed. Considering this and that the ore contains some gangue, assume that the fraction of oxygen remaining with the ore is 0.2. Hence,

$$-\frac{dN_O}{dt} = 1500 \times 0.2 \times \frac{1}{16} \times r_O = 18.75 \times r_O \text{ kgmol of O/s} \qquad \text{(Ex. 5.4)}$$

Proceeding similarly, the rate of removal of carbon from coke, assuming coke to have 80% C,

$$-\frac{dN_C}{dt} = 500 \times 0.8 \times 0.9 \times \frac{1}{12} \times r_C = 30 \times r_C \text{ kgmol of C/s} \qquad \text{(Ex. 5.5)}$$

This assumes that the original coke had 80% fixed carbon, and 10% of that has been gasified already before reaching the lower stack/upper bosh.

Now, the values of r_O and r_C have to be estimated. Such estimates will be done on the basis of data in this chapter and some more assumptions, which are based on literatures in this area and are approximate only. Hence, the calculations are for illustration only and are not necessarily representative of a real blast furnace.

Estimation of r_O

From Eq. (5.20), $r_O = (dF_O/dt)$. Figure 5.4 presents F_O vs. t curves for reduction by H_2 at 900°C for two ores. Let us take ore A. The curve is approximately linear in the middle ranges. The values of F_O after 10 and 20 minutes from the start of reduction are 0.24 and 0.6 respectively. This gives

$$r_O = \frac{0.6 - 0.24}{20 - 10} \times \frac{1}{60} = 6 \times 10^{-4}\ s^{-1}$$

On an average, reduction by CO is lower by a factor of 6 than that by H_2. This gives a value of $10^{-4}\ s^{-1}$ for reduction by pure CO at 900°C.

Taking an approximate value of activation energy of reduction as 30 kJ/mol, calculations give r_O for pure CO = $1.57 \times 10^{-4}\ s^{-1}$. The influence of gas composition on rate is

for reduction of FeO by CO–CO_2 mixture, $r_O = k_C\left(p_{CO} - \frac{p_{CO_2}}{K_{11}}\right)$ (5.20)

From data provided, p_{CO} and p_{CO_2} are 0.63 and 0.07 atmosphere respectively. At 1100°C, K_{11} = 0.4.

Substituting the values in Eq. (5.20), $r_O = 0.714 \times 10^{-4}\ s^{-1}$.

Estimation of r_C

From Eq. (5.23), $r_C = dF_C/dt$. Figure 5.7 presents the values of r_C for some carbonaceous materials at 1100°C in pure CO_2. For coke, the value is $3.2 \times 10^{-2}\ min^{-1}$, i.e. $5.33 \times 10^{-4}\ s^{-1}$.

In CO–CO_2 atmosphere, the rate of reaction can be expressed as

$$r_C = r_C \text{ in pure } CO_2 \times [p_{CO_2} - (p_{CO_2})_{eq}] \quad \text{(Ex. 5.6)}$$

where the equilibrium refers to reaction (5.5), for which K is given in Eq. (5.7). At 1100°C, i.e. 1373 K, K = 6.0. At the given gas composition, and for total pressure of CO + CO_2 = 0.7 atmosphere, calculations give the value of partial pressure of CO_2 at equilibrium with p_{CO} = 0.63, as 0.066 atmosphere.

Inserting values in Eq. (Ex. 5.6), $r_C = 5.33 \times 10^{-4}(0.07 - 0.066) = 2.13 \times 10^{-6}\ s^{-1}$

Therefore, from Eq. (Ex. 5.4), the rate of reduction of 1500 kg of ore,

$$-\frac{dN_O}{dt} = 13.4 \times 10^{-4} \text{ kgmol of O/s}$$

and rate of carbon gasification of 500 kg of coke,

$$-\frac{dN_C}{dt} = 30 \times 2.13 \times 10^{-6} = 0.63 \times 10^{-4} \text{ kgmol of C/s}$$

5.4 REACTIONS AND PHENOMENA IN THE BLAST FURNACE BOSH AND HEARTH

The composition of hot metal produced in blast furnaces operating around the world lies within the following overall range (weight percent): Carbon: 3.5–4.3, Silicon: 0.2–1.5, Sulphur: 0.020–0.050, Phosphorus: 0.1–2.0, Manganese: 0.2–1.5, Titanium: 0.15 maximum. The composition differs from country to country and even from region to region in the same country because of the compositions of raw materials used and the ironmaking practice adopted.

As far as hot metal composition control in the blast furnace is concerned, the following need to noted.

- Some amount of manganese is desirable in hot metal.
- Control of carbon, phosphorus and titanium are not possible.
- Sulphur and silicon can be and should be controlled. Silicon should be maintained below 0.6%, if possible. However, this is not always possible on account of raw materials/ operating practice (this is the case in India). As far as sulphur is concerned, though normally speaking, it should be as low as possible, often when going in for increased productivity, the sulphur content is allowed to increase, since external desulphurisation of hot metal (Chapter 16) is now a standard practice.

In view of the above, no further discussion on carbon and phosphorus is included.

The formation of a slag of desirable properties is of considerable importance in order to:

- Control the hot metal composition
- Obtain sufficiently fluid stag at as low a temperature as possible
- Make the slag suitable for use in cement-making.

The subsequent sections shall briefly discuss some of these issues.

5.4.1 Blast Furnace Slag—Composition and Viscosity

In Section 4.4.1 the properties of liquid iron and steel have been presented. In a blast furnace, metallic iron starts absorbing carbon in the lower part of the stack owing to the presence of coke, and it becomes liquid at as low a temperature as approximately 1300°C. In the hearth, molten hot metal contains about 4% C with a liquidus temperature lower than 1200°C (see Section 4.4.1).

The structure and physicochemical properties of slag melts have already been dealt with in Section 4.4.2. The major constituents of blast furnace slag are CaO, Al_2O_3, SiO_2, and in most cases, some amount of MgO is also present. The minor constituents are: MnO, TiO_2, FeO, alkali oxides, etc. SiO_2 and Al_2O_3 come from the gangue contained in iron ore and from the coke ash, while CaO and MgO come from the fluxes (limestone and dolomite).

Figure 4.3 has presented the iso-activity lines of SiO_2 in the liquid field of the ternary CaO–SiO_2–Al_2O_3 system at 1550°C (1823 K). It will be noted that the liquid field is fairly large; however, with decreasing temperature, it becomes smaller and smaller, and disappears completely at around 1250°C. It has also been mentioned in Section 4.4.2 that liquid slag is much more viscous than liquid iron. Furthermore, the viscosity varies by orders of magnitude depending on the composition and temperature. In Figure 4.8, the iso-viscosity lines for CaO–SiO_2–Al_2O_3 slags at 1500°C have been shown. The overall variation is from 2.5 to 2000 poise (i.e. 0.25 to 200 $kg \cdot m^{-1} \cdot s^{-1}$).

For proper furnace operation, the liquid slag should have as low a viscosity as possible, preferably lower than 2 poise. Viscous slags:

- Pose difficulties during slag–metal separation in the hearth
- Slowdown the rates of slag–metal reactions
- Do not flow down properly from the bosh to the hearth
- Hinder smooth upward flow of gas through the burden.

Extensive viscosity measurements have been carried out in the laboratory for 'synthetic' blast furnace liquid slags, and enough data are available on this subject.

Slag basicity is another important parameter (see Section 4.4.3). Acceptable levels of transfer of both sulphur and silicon from the metal to slag are facilitated if the slag is basic. But, highly basic slags have higher viscosity as well. These two contradictory requirements are met in the blast furnace by maintaining a V-Ratio (see Eq. (4.46)) of the *Hearth slag* between 1.0 and 1.25.

Nowadays it has become a standard practice to use slags containing 4–10% MgO in the blast furnace since MgO lowers both the liquidus temperature as well as the viscosity. The gangue of Indian iron ore has high Al_2O_3/SiO_2 ratios, resulting in high Al_2O_3 in blast furnace slag in Indian furnaces. In this situation, addition of larger amounts of MgO to arrive at a hearth slag composition of about 30–32% CaO, 30% SiO_2, 25–30% Al_2O_3 and 7–10% MgO is resorted to.

At any given composition of slag, its viscosity decreases with increasing temperature. Figure 5.9 (Coudurier et al., 1985) shows viscosity (η) vs. temperature (T) curves for blast furnace-type slags at three different basicity ratios. To obtain a fluid, free-running slag, a minimum hearth temperature is required. This is known as the *Critical Hearth Temperature*. It should be as low as possible in order to cut down the heat requirement as well as to increase the hearth lining life. Typically, it is maintained at 1400–1450°C. At this temperature $CaO–SiO_2–Al_2O_3–MgO$ containing slags become sufficiently fluid owing to the presence of the minor constituents (MnO, TiO_2, alkali oxides, etc.).

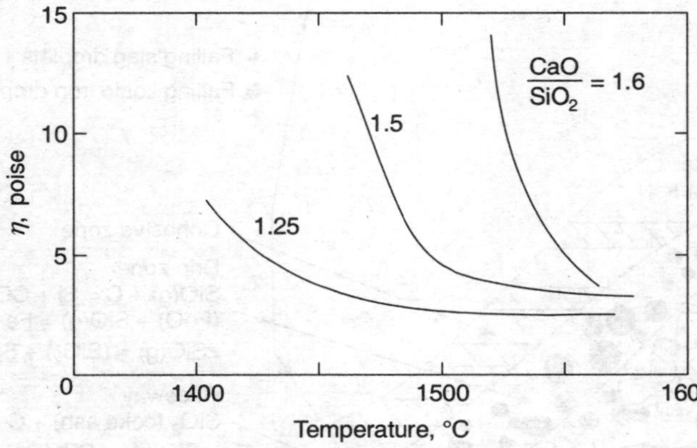

Figure 5.9 The relationship between viscosity and temperature for basic blast furnace slags.

In modern blast furnaces, *prepared sinter* constitutes a large percentage of the iron oxide burden. The sinter may be acid sinter, self-fluxed sinter, or super-fluxed sinter, having CaO/SiO_2 ratios less than 1, approximately equal to 1 and above 2, respectively. The first slag that forms in the belly region at around 1200–1300°C may or may not contain any CaO. As stated in Section 4.4.2, melting at such a low temperature is only possible because of the formation of $FeO–SiO_2$ compounds in large amounts. These compounds have very low liquidus temperatures when they react with the reduced FeO to form what is known as the *primary slag*.

As the primary slag trickles down through the bed of solids, its temperature rises. Moreover, FeO gets reduced and the slag dissolves more CaO. At the tuyere level, the coke burns thereby releasing coke ash consisting of SiO_2 and Al_2O_3. This makes the slag at the tuyere level high in SiO_2 (acid slag). The slag at the bosh region is known as *Bosh slag*. Final composition adjustments occur during the passage of the bosh slag into the hearth, during which the FeO content becomes very low.

5.4.2 Reaction of Silicon

Reaction in raceway and bosh

Figure 5.10 schematically shows the mechanism of reduction of SiO_2, pick up of metallic Si by liquid iron, etc. in the blast furnace raceway, bosh and hearth. The coke burns in the blast furnace raceway in front of the tuyeres, thus releasing coke ash containing SiO_2. Some molten slag

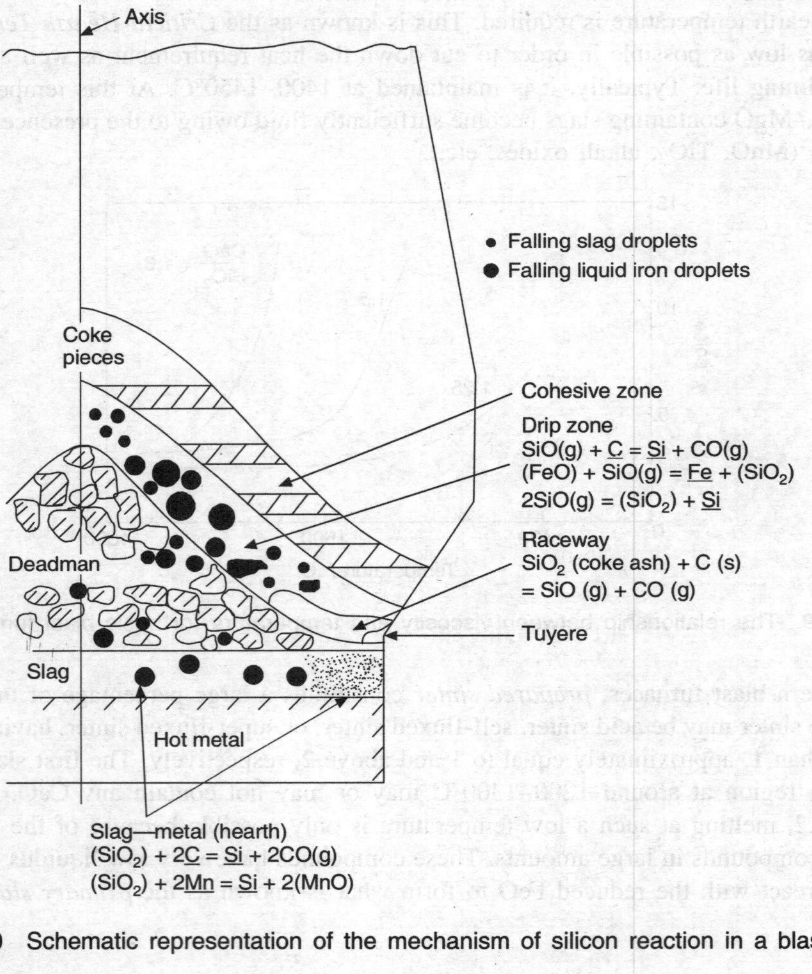

Figure 5.10 Schematic representation of the mechanism of silicon reaction in a blast furnace.

containing high SiO_2 and FeO also drips down through the raceway. The temperature in the raceway zone is 1900–2000°C (2200 K approximately). In the presence of carbon and depending on the activity of silica, SiO vapour is generated by one of the following reactions:

$$SiO_2 \text{ (in coke ash or slag)} + C(s) = SiO(g) + CO(g) \tag{5.25}$$

Or, SiO_2 initially forms SiC, which then forms SiO:

$$SiO_2(s) + 3C(s) = SiC(s) + 2CO(g) \tag{5.26}$$

$$SiC(s) + CO(g) = SiO(g) + 2C(s) \tag{5.27}$$

The values of ΔG_f^0, i.e. standard free energy of formation for CO and SiO_2 are given in Table 4.1. From thermodynamic data sources, ΔG_f^0 for SiO and SiC are –253250 and –7565 J at 2173 K (i.e. 1900°C). At $a_{SiO_2} = 1$ and $p_{CO} = 1$ atmosphere, calculations yield $p_{SiO} = 4.4$ and 0.044 respectively for reaction (5.25) and (5.27). Hence, for SiO formation, the dominant reaction is (5.25).

At 1500°C (1773 K), p_{SiO} at equilibrium with reaction (5.25) is approximately 10^{-4} atmosphere. This makes SiO vapour unstable when it rises upwards in the bosh. Therefore, in this region Si gets transferred into liquid Fe by the reaction of SiO with C dissolved in liquid iron in the following way.

$$SiO(g) + [C] = [Si] + CO(g) \tag{5.28}$$

Or, by decomposition as

$$2SiO(g) = (SiO_2) + [Si] \tag{5.29}$$

Other reactions have been proposed, such as:

$$(FeO \text{ in slag}) + SiO(g) = [Fe] + (SiO_2) \tag{5.30}$$

In whichever way it is formed, SiO_2 joins the slag phase.

Recent investigations on the mechanism of the reaction of silicon in the blast furnace have shown that:

- The percentage of Si in liquid metal is as high as 6–8% within 1 metre of the raceway, decreasing to about zero towards the furnace axis, indicating that large-scale Si absorption by metal takes place in the raceway.
- The percentage of Si in metal increases with increase in *RAFT* (i.e. *Raceway Adiabatic Flame Temperature*).

As early as the 1950s and 1960s, investigators quenched running blast furnaces by using a cold nitrogen blast. This froze the liquids in the bosh and tuyere regions. Samples collected from the frozen metal demonstrated the pattern of variation in Si dissolved in iron which is shown in Figure 5.11. The maximum value was at the tuyere level.

Reactions in hearth

Molten metal droplets react with the slag in hearth while passing through the slag layer. Extensive laboratory and plant investigations have been carried out on several blast furnace reactions in the hearth.

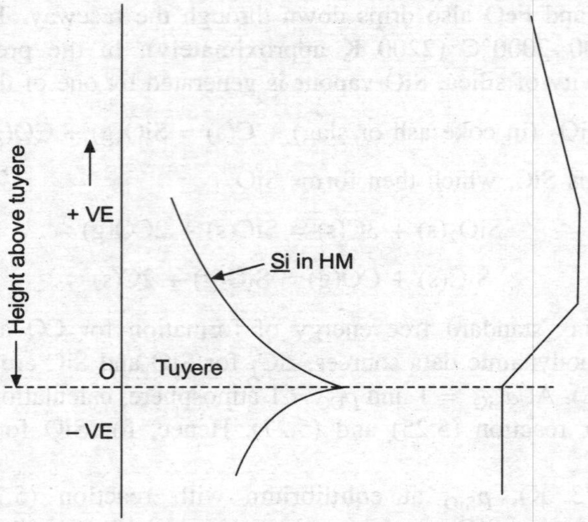

Figure 5.11 Schematic representation of the profile of silicon concentration in liquid iron near the tuyere level.

For silicon, the slag–metal reaction is:

$$(SiO_2) + 2[C] = [Si] + 2CO(g) \tag{5.31}$$

for which,

$$K_{31} = \frac{[\%Si][f_{Si}]}{(a_{SiO_2})}\left(\frac{p_{CO}}{a_C}\right)^2 \tag{5.32}$$

and

$$\log K_{31} = -\frac{30,935}{T} + 20.455 \tag{5.33}$$

(*Note:* [%Si] is another way of representing wt. % Si dissolved in metal. It is used in most of the books; but in this book, the symbol $[W_{Si}]$ has been chosen. However, the symbol chosen is inconsequential.)

Based on the above as well as the empirical relations of a_{SiO_2} in slag with slag composition, an empirical correlation can be obtained, as illustrated in Figure 5.12 (Fruehan (Ed.) 1998). The assumption in all such cases is that the hot metal is saturated with graphite (i.e. $a_C = 1$).

It has been further observed that the Si–Mn reaction, which is a slag–metal reaction, also occurs in blast furnace hearth, i.e.

$$2(MnO) + [Si] = 2[Mn] + (SiO_2) \tag{5.34}$$

It has been proposed that the experimental data for graphite saturated melts at 1400–1600°C may be represented by the following equation:

$$\log K_{34} = 2.8\left(\frac{\%CaO + \%MgO}{\%SiO_2}\right)_{\text{in slag}} - 1.16 \tag{5.35}$$

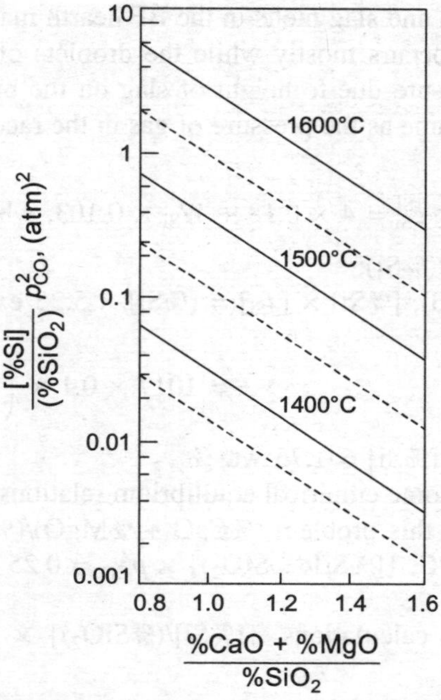

Figure 5.12 Silicon distribution ratio for graphite-saturated melts for blast furnace type slags containing about 10% MgO and 10% Al_2O_3.

Controversies exist as to whether reactions of Si–SiO_2 with carbon (Eq. (5.31)) or with Mn (Eq. (5.34)) attain equilibrium in the blast furnace hearth. From a variety of evidence, it can be concluded that equilibrium is not attained. The actual silicon content of hot metal is a few times higher than that predicted by the slag–metal equilibria. This is in conformity with Figure 5.11, which indicates that Si content of metal decreases from the tuyere to the hearth level.

EXAMPLE 5.4

For the reaction (5.31), i.e. $(SiO_2) + 2[C] = [Si] + 2CO(g)$, calculate the weight percent. Si in liquid iron at equilibrium with the slag in a blast furnace hearth at 1500°C. Assume that the iron contains 4% carbon besides Si, and the slag consists of 49 wt. % CaO, 42 wt. % SiO_2, and 9 wt. % Al_2O_3. Make other assumptions as necessary.

Solution: The equilibrium relation for reaction (5.31) is given as

$$K_{31} = \frac{[\%\text{Si}][f_{\text{Si}}]}{(a_{\text{SiO}_2})}\left(\frac{p_{\text{CO}}}{a_{\text{C}}}\right)^2 \tag{5.32}$$

Here a_C may be taken as 1, since the liquid iron may be assumed to be saturated with graphite.

The activity of SiO_2 in slag may be found out from Figure 4.3, Chapter 4. Although the figure is for 1550°C, it is approximately valid for 1500°C as well. For this the conversion of wt. % into mole fractions is required. It can be done using Eq. (4.26) in Chapter 4. Calculations give the values of mole fractions (X) of CaO, SiO_2 and $AlO_{1.5}$ as 0.50, 0.40 and 0.15 respectively. From Figure 4.3, $a_{SiO_2} = 0.1$. From Eq. (5.33), $K_{31} = 1017$.

The gas bubbles inside iron and slag melts in the BF hearth may be assumed to be pure CO. Since the slag–metal reaction occurs mostly while the droplets of liquid iron are going down through the slag melt, the pressure due to height of slag on the bubbles may be ignored. This makes p_{CO} approximately the same as the pressure of gas in the raceway. On this basis, p_{CO} may be taken as 3 atmosphere.

$$\log f_{Si} = W_C \times e_{Si}^{C} + W_{Si} \times e_{Si}^{Si} = 4 \times 0.18 + W_{Si} \times 0.103, \text{ where } W \text{ is same as wt. \%.}$$

Hence, $f_{Si} = 5.25 \exp (0.103 \times \%Si)$.
Substituting values in Eq. (5.33), $[\%Si] \times [f_{Si}] = [\%Si] \times 5.25 \exp (0.103 \times \%Si)$

$$= 1017 \times 0.1 \times \left(\frac{1}{3}\right)^2 = 11.3$$

Trial and error solution gives, $[\%Si] = 1.75$ wt. %

Figure 5.12 has presented some empirical equilibrium relations for the above reaction based on many experimental data. In this problem (%CaO + %MgO)/(% SiO_2) in slag is 1.117. For this slag composition, at 1500°C, $\{[\%Si]/(\%SiO_2)\} \times p_{CO}^2 = 0.25 - 0.3$, an approximate range obtained from Figure 5.12.

Based on our equilibrium calculations, $\{[\%Si]/(\%SiO_2)\} \times p_{CO}^2 = 0.375$. Agreement is therefore fairly good.

Strategy for production of low silicon hot metal

As mentioned earlier, hot metal with a low silicon content is desirable for efficient steelmaking. The strategy for achieving the same can be devised on the basis of the mechanism of silicon reaction, which was discussed in the previous section. The strategy would involve several steps.

1. Decreasing the extent of SiO formation by:
   - Lowering ash in coke, and the coke rate
   - Lowering RAFT
   - Lowering the activity of SiO_2 in coke ash by lime injection through the tuyeres.
2. Decreasing Si absorption by liquid iron in the bosh by enhancing the absorption of SiO_2 by the bosh slag. This can be achieved by:
   - Increasing the bosh slag basicity
   - Lowering the bosh slag viscosity by operating at lower basicities.
3. Removal of Si from metal by slag–metal reaction at the hearth by:
   - Lowering the hearth temperature
   - Producing a slag of optimum basicity and fluidity.

5.4.3 Reaction of Sulphur

Most of the sulphur (say about 80%) enters the blast furnace through coke as CaS and FeS in coke ash as well as in the form of organic sulphur. The remainder comes through the other burden materials. In any blast furnace, about 80–90% of the sulphur input leaves the furnace with the slag, 10–15% reports to flue dust and top gas, while 2–5% gets dissolved in hot metal.

Earlier most steel grades required sulphur contents of less than 0.040%. Subsequent to the adoption of continuous casting, the upper limit was brought down to 0.025%. Earlier all sulphur removal had to be completed within the blast furnace; however, with the current practice of external desulphurisation of hot metal as well as some desulphurisation during secondary steelmaking, blast furnaces have greater flexibility with regard to the final sulphur content in hot metal.

Reactions in raceway and bosh

Figure 5.13 (Biswas 1984) shows the variation of weight percentages of metal sulphur and slag sulphur at various heights from the tuyeres, as measured in different investigations. The behaviour of sulphur is qualitatively similar to that of silicon (Figure 5.11), i.e. the highest sulphur in metal is at the tuyere level.

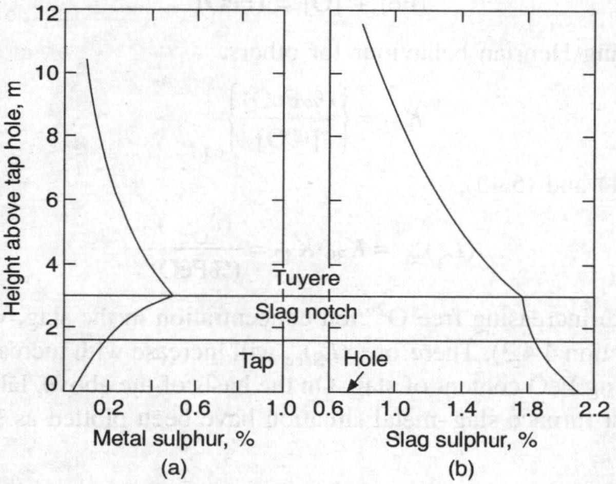

Figure 5.13 Variation of (a) metal sulphur, (b) slag sulphur, above and below the tuyeres.

Recent investigations have established that the dominant mechanism involved in sulphur reactions is broadly similar to that of silicon (Figure 5.10). The sulphur in coke ash undergoes the following reactions in the raceway:

$$CaS \text{ (in coke ash)} + SiO(g) = SiS(g) + CaO \tag{5.36}$$

$$FeS \text{ (in coke ash)} + SiO(g) + C(s) = SiS(g) + CO(g) + [Fe] \tag{5.37}$$

In the bosh and belly regions, SiS decomposes as

$$SiS(g) = [Si] + [S] \tag{5.38}$$

Small amounts of sulphur are also absorbed by the bosh slag. It should be mentioned here that sulphur forms some other volatile compounds—COS, CS, which are also carried up into the gas stream and undergo reactions. However, it needs to be emphasised that SiS is the dominant vapour species.

Reactions in hearth

In the hearth, the slag–metal sulphur reaction may be written in general ionic form as

$$[S] + (O^{2-}) = (S^{2-}) + [O] \tag{5.39}$$

Assuming Henrian behaviour for all species except (O^{2-}),

$$K_{39} = \frac{(\%S)[\%O]}{[\%S](a_{O^{2-}})} \tag{5.40}$$

i.e. $(L_S)_{eq}$ = Equilibrium partition coefficient for sulphur

$$= \left(\frac{(\%S)}{[\%S]}\right)_{eq.} = K_{39}\frac{(a_{O^{2-}})}{[\%O]} \tag{5.41}$$

Now,

$$[Fe] + [O] = (FeO) \tag{5.42}$$

Since $a_{Fe} \simeq 1$, assuming Henrian behaviour for others,

$$K_{42} = \left\{\frac{(\%FeO)}{[\%O]}\right\}_{eq.} \tag{5.43}$$

Combining Eqs. (5.41) and (5.43),

$$(L_S)_{eq.} = K_{39} \cdot K_{42} = \frac{(a_{O^{2-}})}{(\%FeO)} \tag{5.44}$$

$a_{O^{2-}}$ increases with increasing free O^{2-} ion concentration in the slag, which again increases with slag basicity (Section 4.4.3). Therefore, $(L_S)_{eq}$ will increase with increasing basicity and will decrease with increasing FeO content of slag. On the basis of the above, laboratory experimental data of $(L_S)_{eq}$ for blast furnace slag–metal situation have been plotted as shown in Figure 5.14 (Biswas 1984).

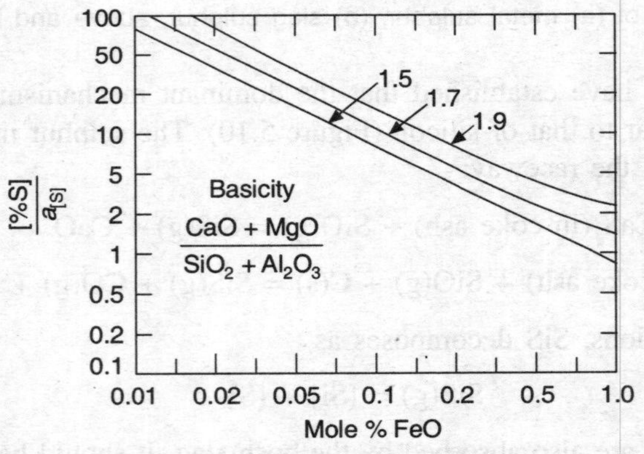

Figure 5.14 Influence of basicity and iron oxide content of slag on equilibrium partition of sulphur between slag and metal in the blast furnace temperature range.

It should be mentioned that CaO is a much more powerful base and desulphuriser than MgO—about 100 times stronger. It is also to be noted that for adequate desulphurisation, the oxygen content of the metal should be very low. This is achieved in the blast furnace hearth by the reaction of dissolved oxygen in the hot metal with strong oxide formers: C, Si, Mn (reference Figure 4.1) dissolved in liquid metal. On this basis, the following reactions in terms of compounds can be written

$$(CaO) + [S] + [C] = (CaS) + CO(g) \tag{5.45}$$

$$(CaO) + [S] + [Mn] = (CaS) + (MnO) \tag{5.46}$$

$$(CaO) + [S] + \frac{1}{2}[Si] = (CaS) + \frac{1}{2}(SiO_2) \tag{5.47}$$

On the basis of reaction (5.45), *an empirical correlation* that has been proposed in Tata Steel (Gupta 1991) is:

$$\log (L_S)_{eq} = 1.35\frac{1.79(\%CaO) + 1.24(\%MgO)}{1.66(\%SiO_2) + 0.33(\%Al_2O_3)} - \log p_{CO} - \frac{8130}{T} + 4.15 \tag{5.48}$$

It appears that reaction (5.46) also attains equilibrium in the blast furnace hearth. On the basis of above, the strategy for making low sulphur hot metal is the same as that for silicon, except that higher hearth temperatures promote better desulphurisation.

5.4.4 Reactions of Manganese and Titanium

Reactions of manganese

Whereas the lowest contents of silicon and sulphur in hot metal are desired, it is necessary to maximise manganese recovery in hot metal. Manganese is an input into blast furnaces through iron ore, and sometimes through the deliberate addition of manganese ore. It is present as MnO_2, which gets reduced to Mn_3O_4, and subsequently to MnO in the blast furnace stack by indirect reduction.

Figure 4.1 shows that MnO is more stable than FeO, but less stable than SiO_2. The figure also shows that MnO is reduced by C, which occurs as

$$(MnO) + C(s) = [Mn] + CO(g) \tag{5.49}$$

This reaction is possible only above 1400°C; therefore, MnO reduction by carbon occurs primarily in the hearth region, either when the liquid slag containing MnO flows down through the coke bed or during reaction in the hearth between metal and slag.

The earlier sections have already presented Mn–Si coupled reactions as well as Mn–S reaction at the hearth. The manganese content of hot metal ranges between 0.2% and 1.5%, and the MnO content of the slag is also approximately the same.

Recovery of manganese in the hearth can be increased by:

- Increasing γ_{MnO} (i.e. a_{MnO}) in the slag by using higher slag basicity
- Increasing the slag and metal temperatures
- Increasing the silicon content of hot metal.

The typical range of recovery of manganese varies between 60% and 70% for basic slags (i.e. (CaO/SiO2) > 1), and between 50% and 60% for acid slags.

Reactions of titanium

Titanium is usually present in blast furnace raw materials as Ilmenite ($FeO.TiO_2$) and occasionally as Rutile (TiO_2). Figure 4.1 illustrates that TiO_2 is more stable than SiO_2, and is therefore reduced to a much lesser extent at any given hearth temperature. Titanium also forms stable carbide, nitride and carbo-nitride. These compounds have high melting points and low solubilities in liquid iron (0.3% for carbides and 0.2% for carbo-nitrides) and they separate to form encrustations on the bosh walls, hearth walls and the hearth bottom, resulting in accretion build-up on the blast furnace bottom region lining. This can often lower the furnace campaign life since the highest temperatures prevail in this region.

For the reaction,

$$(TiO_2) + 2C(s) = Ti(s) + 2CO(g) \tag{5.50}$$

the equilibrium constant can be calculated from data in Table 4.1. Both laboratory and plant data have shown that the Ti content of hot metal increases with greater reduction of SiO_2 and MnO, as expected theoretically. While the wt. % Ti in metal is less than 0.15, the wt. % TiO_2 in slag may be in the range of 0.3–1.

REFERENCES

AISE Steel Foundation, *The Making Shaping and Treating of Steel*, 11th ed., Vol. 2, (Ed.) R.J. Fruehan (1998), p. 110.

Biswas, A.K., *Principles of blast furnace ironmaking*, SBA publications, Kolkata (1984), p. 352 and p. 354.

Bogdandy, Von L. and H.J. Engell, *The Reduction of Iron Ores*, Springer Verlag, Berlin (1971), p. 181.

Coudurier, L., D.W. Hopkins and I. Wilkomirsky, *Fundamentals of Metallurgical Processes*, 2nd ed., Pergamon Press, Oxford, (1985), p. 221.

Darken, L.S. and R.W. Gurry, J. American Chem. Soc., 68(1946) 798.

Gupta, S.S., *Blast Furnance Ironmaking*, in S.S. Gupta and Amit Chatterjee (Eds.), Tata Steel Jamshedpur (1991), p. 145.

Turkdogan, E.T., Met Trans. B, 9B (1978) 163.

Turkdogan, E.T., R.G. Olsson, and J.V. Vinters, Carbon, 8 (1970) 545.

6

Thermal and Chemical Features of the Blast Furnace

6.1 INTRODUCTION

Chapter 2 briefly presented the chemical reactions at various zones in the blast furnace along with the approximate temperature levels at different heights (Figures 2.1–2.3). In Chapter 5 the thermodynamics, the mechanisms and kinetics of important reactions in the tuyere zone, stack, bosh and hearth areas have been discussed.

The processing of solid burden in the blast furnace requires an enormous amount of heat not only to heat and melt the hot metal and the slag, but also to cater to heat demands of various endothermic reactions as well as to provide for heat losses. The total heat requirement of a modern blast furnace is approximately 8–11 gigajoules (i.e. 10^9 joules) per thm (i.e. per tonne of hot metal). Out of this total heat, approximately 60–70% is required for the reduction of iron oxides, the remainder for other endothermic reactions, heating of the solid burden as well as melting of metal and slag. About 8–10% of the total heat is lost through the top gas and through the walls. About 80–85% of heat input comes from the exothermic combustion reaction of carbon and hydrocarbons, and the remainder from the sensible heat of the hot air blast.

6.1.1 Mass and Heat Balances

In chemical engineering terminology, the blast furnace is a *continuous countercurrent reactor* and it is at steady state. By convention, all balances are done on the basis of per thm. Hence, the balances may be generalised as

$$\text{Inputs per thm} = \text{Outputs per thm} \tag{6.1}$$

Table 6.1 provides an example of mass balance for a simplified blast furnace process (Walker 1986). Here 1 mole iron has been taken as the basis. The mass balance exercise consists of solving a set of simultaneous linear equations equating the input and the output of individual elements (or compounds, if they do not decompose in the process itself, such as CaO and Al_2O_3). An additional equation can be formulated based on the balance of the total mass input with the mass output.

Table 6.1 Simple overall mass balance for a blast furnace producing hot metal containing one mole of iron

	Inputs		Outputs	Proportion (%)
Burden		**Top gas**		
Fe_2O_3	0.5 mole	N_2	4.04 mole	(58.2)
$CaCO_3$	0.1 mole	CO_2	1.31 mole	(18.9)
SiO_2	0.12 mole	CO	1.31 mole	(18.9)
C	2.71 mole	H_2O	0.24 mole	(3.5)
H_2O	0.2 mole	H_2	0.04 mole	(0.5)
		Total	6.94 mole	(100.0)
Hot blast		**Slag**		
O_2	1.075 mole	CaO	0.1 mole	
N_2	4.044 mole	SiO_2	0.1 mole	
H_2O	0.08 mole			
		Hot metal		
		Fe	1.0 mole	(95.0)
		C	0.19 mole	(4.0)
		Si	0.02 mole	(1.0)

For heat balance, the equation would be

$$\text{Heat input per thm} = \text{Heat output per thm} \tag{6.2}$$

Equation (6.2) is based on the First Law of Thermodynamics, where a *reference temperature* needs to be selected. The conventional *Universal* reference temperature is 298 K; however, other reference temperatures can also be chosen, if so desired.

For the blast furnace process,

Heat input = Sensible heat (i.e. heat contents) of the input materials (including ΔH for changes in the states of aggregation) + Heat evolved by the exothermic reactions (measured at the reference temperature and states) (6.3)

Heat output = Sensible heat of the output materials (including ΔH for changes in the states of aggregation) + Heat absorbed by the endothermic reactions (measured at the reference temperature and states) + Heat loss to the surroundings (6.4)

The terms included in the sensible heat of any substance depend on its state at 298 K and its state at the final temperature in the process. The most common way that is adopted is to consider a solid at 298 K, first becoming liquid, and then becoming gas at the final temperature. Then, the *sensible heat* of the substance in question at temperature T (solid at 298 K → gas at T) is given as

$$H_T - H_{298} = \int_{298}^{T_m} C_p(\text{s})\,dT + \Delta H_m + \int_{T_m}^{T_b} C_p(\text{l})\,dT + \Delta H_v + \int_{T_b}^{T} C_p(\text{g})\,dT \tag{6.5}$$

where $$C_p = a + bT + cT^{-2} \tag{6.6}$$

Here, C_p(s), C_p(l), C_p(g) are *heat capacities* of solid, liquid, and gas respectively. T_m, T_b are melting and boiling points respectively. ΔH_m and ΔH_v are the *latent heats* of melting and vaporisation. a, b and c are empirical constants and T is temperature in K. The universal convention is to prepare the thermodynamic data tables on the basis of 1 mole of the substance.

Heat of a reaction (i.e. change in enthalpy owing to reaction) may be designated as ΔH_r, where by Hess' law,

$$\Delta H_r = \sum \Delta H_f \text{ (products)} - \sum \Delta H_f \text{ (reactants)} \tag{6.7}$$

Here, ΔH_f is the *heat of formation of a compound from elements*. The values of C_p, ΔH_f at *standard states* are available in thermodynamic data tables. Some values for the important reactions have been noted in Chapter 5.

For easy application, Biswas (1984) has proposed a simple heat balance (in kilojoules per thm) as follows:

$$3.5 \times 10^3 C + 1.4 V_b T_b = 8.8 \times 10^6 + 1465 S + 14.1 V_g T_g + 126.4 V_g \cdot \% \text{ CO}_g \tag{6.8}$$

where, C and S refer to mass of carbon and slag respectively in kg, V_b and V_g are volumes of the air blast and top gas respectively in Nm^3, and T_b and T_g are temperatures of the air blast and top gas respectively in °C. The constant term 8.8×10^6 represents the lump sum approximate value of the heat of dissociation of ferric oxide + heat of liquid iron + cooling losses, etc. and % CO_g is % of CO in top gas.

EXAMPLE 6.1

A blast furnace makes hot metal containing 3.6 wt. % C, 1.4% Si, the remainder being Fe (i.e. 95%). Other data are:

- The ore contains 85% Fe_2O_3, the remainder being 15% gangue of SiO_2 and Al_2O_3.
- The coke contains 85% fixed carbon and 15% ash.
- Coke consumption is 800 kg per tonne of hot metal.
- Flux contains 95% $CaCO_3$ and the remainder is SiO_2, and its consumption is 400 kg/tonne hot metal.
- The blast furnace top gas contains a ratio of $CO/CO_2 = 28/12$.

Calculate (per tonne of hot metal) (i) the weight of ore used (W_{ore}), (ii) the weight of slag made (W_{slag}), and (iii) the volume of BF gas (V_g).

Solution: Modern blast furnace practice employs prepared burdens besides ore. It has also other features such as coal injection, etc. However, in order to illustrate the material balance calculation, a simplified situation of old practice has been assumed here.

Note that all quantities in the following material balances are in kg per tonne of hot metal produced.

(i) Fe-Balance: W_{Fe} in ore = W_{Fe} in hot metal = $1000 \times 0.95 = 950$ kg

$$W_{ore} = 950 \times \frac{M_{Fe_2O_3}}{2M_{Fe}} \times \frac{100}{85}, \qquad \text{where } M \text{ denotes the atomic mass.}$$

Noting that M of Fe_2O_3 is 160 and M of Fe is 56, $W_{ore} = 1597$ kg

(ii) W_{slag} = Weight of gangue in ore + Weight of ash in coke + Weight of CaO in flux + Weight of gangue in flux – Weight of SiO_2 equivalent of Si in hot metal.

$$= \left(\frac{1}{100}\right)\times\left[1597\times15+800\times15+400\times95\times\frac{M_{CaO}}{M_{CaCO_3}}\right.$$

$$\left.+400\times5-1000\times1.4\times\left(\frac{60}{28}\right)\right]$$

$$= 562.4 \text{ kg}$$

(iii) Carbon going out through BF gas = Carbon input through coke – Carbon in hot metal. So, carbon going out through BF gas as CO and CO_2 = 800 × 0.85 – 1000 × (3.6/100) = 644 kg = 644/12 = 53.67 kgmol.

Out of the above, molar fractions of CO = 28/(28 + 12), and of CO_2 = 12/(28 + 12). Calculations yield kgmol of CO and CO_2 as 37.57 and 16.10 respectively.

Oxygen (as O_2) required to be supplied with air blast = Oxygen required to produce CO + CO_2 – Oxygen supplied through iron ore = {37.57 × 1/2 + 16.10} – W_{Fe} in ore × $\left(\frac{48}{112}\cdot\frac{1}{32}\right)$ = 22.16 kgmol of O_2, since W_{Fe} in ore = 950 kg

N_2 in air blast = 22.16 × 79/21 = 83.37 kgmol

Hence, the total BF gas = 37.57 + 16.10 + 83.37 = 137 kgmol = 137 × 22.4 = 3070 Nm^3

6.1.2 Regionwise Heat and Mass Balances

The heat balance of the entire blast furnace has its own utility. However, for understanding and process control, *sectoral heat balances*, i.e. heat balance of the tuyere region, stack, hearth, etc. separately, are popular. The solid burden is charged at the top of the furnace at room temperature. The final products are: liquid iron, slag and top gas. Similarly, the gas is at a very high temperature in the raceway, but leaves the furnace from the top typically at 200–300°C. Within the furnace, both the temperature and the composition of the gas vary along the furnace height as well as in the radial direction. Thus, the nature of this variation in temperature can be understood only through sectoral heat balances.

The vertical temperature profile along the height of the furnace can be considered in a simple fashion, if the radial variations in temperatures are ignored and only the average temperature at a particular height is considered. All phenomena in the furnace—reaction equilibria and rates, softening, melting, and gasification—are dependent on temperature. Hence, the thermal profile governs both the chemical and physicochemical features of the furnace at various heights.

The solid burden descending from the top and the hot reducing gas flowing upwards interact with each other. This interaction can be generalised in terms of the following:

(a) *Heat exchange*, i.e. heat transfer from gas to solid
(b) *Oxygen exchange*, i.e. oxygen transfer from solid to gas.

As a result of extensive experimental measurements over the years, a fairly deep knowledge of the internal state of a running blast furnace has been gathered. The techniques that are used to gather data include the following:

- Measurement of temperature, composition and pressure of the gas at various heights
- Sampling as well as chemical-physical characterisation of the burden material, mostly in laboratories, by simulated blast furnace tests, and occasionally, by inserting tuyere probes into a running furnace
- Quenching a running furnace using cold nitrogen as the blast followed by sectioning the furnace, and determining the physicochemical characteristics of the solids and frozen liquids
- Visualisation and temperature measurement in the raceway of actual furnaces using infrared cameras.

6.2 TUYERE FLAME TEMPERATURE

In Section 5.4.1 of Chapter 5 it was pointed out that a fluid, free-running slag is required for efficient blast furnace operation, and for this, a minimum hearth temperature has to be maintained. This minimum temperature is known as the *Critical Hearth Temperature*, and is about 1400–1450°C. The source of heat is the *raceway*, i.e. the combustion zone in front of the tuyeres. In order to ensure rapid transfer of heat the combustion zone temperature has to be maintained at a much higher temperature—normally in the range of 1800–2000°C. This temperature is known as the *Tuyere Flame Temperature* (TFT). While the requirement of free-running, fluid slag sets the lower limit of TFT, the upper limit is dictated by other requirements such as the following:

1. Extremely high TFT would result in the formation of FeO-rich slag at a somewhat upper level of the furnace, before the entire FeO gets reduced. As the burden descends, the FeO in the slag gets reduced, and the slag becomes richer in CaO. It thus becomes more viscous and even tends to freeze, effectively cementing pieces of solids. This phenomenon causes erratic burden movement and is thus undesirable.
2. Chapter 5, Section 5.4.2 presented discussions on reduction of SiO_2 through the formation of SiO gas in the raceway. For efficient steelmaking, lower silicon in hot metal is desirable and this requires that the TFT be kept low.
3. Higher TFT encourages the vaporisation of alkalis and thereby aggravates the problem of alkali vapour recirculation.

Therefore, TFT should be maintained within a range, which is decided by the experience gathered by operating a specific furnace and from some theoretical guidelines. A reliable, direct measurement of TFT is difficult and, therefore, reliable data are not always available. Hence, calculations are resorted to, assuming the raceway to have an adiabatic enclosure. In that case, the heat balance equation becomes:

$$\text{Heat input through exothermic combustion of carbon and sensible heat of hot air blast} - \text{Heat output due to endothermic decompositions of compounds} = \text{Heat content of the flame} \tag{6.9}$$

6.2.1 RAFT Calculations

From the heat content (i.e. sensible heat) of the flame, its temperature can be calculated. This is known as *Raceway Adiabatic Flame Temperature* (RAFT). As a first approximation, it can be taken that,

$$\text{Heat content of flame} = \text{Mass of gas in the flame} \times \text{Average specific heat of gas} \times (\text{RAFT} - 298) \quad (6.10)$$

The calculation of RAFT is a very useful tool for furnace control. It is known that all inputs through the tuyeres influence the RAFT. The moisture in the air blast causes reaction with carbon (Eq. (5.14)), which is endothermic, and thus lowers RAFT. The same is the effect of endothermic decomposition of injectants such as gaseous hydrocarbons and pulverised coal. On the other hand, oxygen enrichment of the air blast increases RAFT, since the volume of gas in the flame is less because of less nitrogen. This consequently lowers the mass of gas in the flame.

Biswas has suggested a simple heat balance equation for calculating the RAFT approximately, with only air blast and no injectants. It is as follows:

$$9628 + 2260 + 4.44 \times 1.4T_b = 5.376 \times 1.41T_f \quad (6.11)$$

where

9628 = heat of combustion of C to CO, kJ/kg
2260 = heat content of carbon at 1400°C, kJ/kg
1.4 = specific heat capacity of air, kJ/Nm^3/°C
1.41 = specific heat capacity of flame gas, kJ/Nm^3/°C
T_b and T_f are the blast and flame temperatures in °C respectively.

Rigorous calculation of RAFT might be performed on the basis of Eqs. (6.5)–(6.7). Detailed procedures are available elsewhere (Peacy and Davenport, 1978). Observations have indicated that the calculated values of RAFT are about 100–200°C higher than the actual TFT. Hence, the RAFT should be maintained between 1900°C and 2100°C, depending on the operational practice adopted. Figure 6.1 (Peacy and Davenport, 1978) shows the influence of the blast temperature

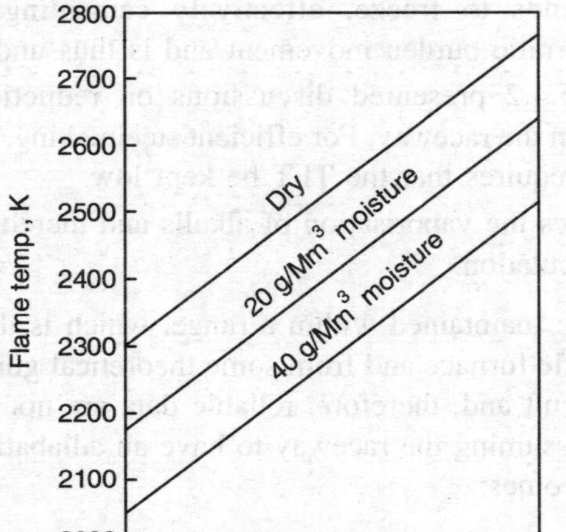

Figure 6.1 Raceway adiabatic flame temperature following combustion of coke at 1800 K with air to form CO, as a function of blast temperature and moisture content of air.

and moisture content of the air blast on RAFT, whereas Table 6.2 shows the effect of changes in furnace conditions on RAFT (Walker, 1986).

Table 6.2 Effects of changes in furnace conditions on RAFT

Change in operating variable	Change in RAFT (°C)
Blast temperature raised by 100°C	+82
Blast oxygen raised by 1%	+53
Blast moisture raised by 5 g/Nm^3	–28
1% methane added to blast	–56

EXAMPLE 6.2

Calculate RAFT in a blast furnace.

Given: Blast temperature (T_b) = 1000°C; Coke contains 83% carbon, remainder being ash; Coke consumption is 800 kg per tonne of hot metal; Coke enters the raceway at 1400°C.

Solution: Equation (6.11) gives an empirical equation for thermal calculation from literature, and it is as follows (for 1 kg carbon):

$$9628 + 2260 + 4.44 \times 1.4T_b = 5.376 \times 1.41T_f$$

Substituting the given values in the above equation,

$$9628 + 2260 + 4.44 \times 1.4 \times 1000 = 5.376 \times 1.41T_f \qquad \text{(Ex.6.1)}$$

This gives RAFT = T_f = 2388°C, which is somewhat high.

To determine T_f, heat balance calculation is done by the procedure given below.

Material and heat balance per tonne hot metal

Oxygen (O_2) required for coke combustion to produce CO = (800 × 0.83 × 16)/12 = 885.3 kg, which is equivalent to 885.3/32, i.e. 27.67 kgmol O_2

Quantity of N_2 in the air blast = 27.67 × 79/21 = 118.9 kgmol N_2

kgmol of carbon in coke = (800 × 0.83)/12 = 55.33

From (Peacey and Davenport, 1978), sensible heats ($H_T - H_{298}$), in kJ/kgmol are as follows:

$$\text{C}: 23.5T - 11800;\ \text{CO}: 35.3T - 14000;\ N_2: 34.4T - 13000;\ O_2: 36.2T - 13500$$

Standard heat of formation of CO (ΔH_f^0) at 298 K = –111000 kJ/kgmol

Heat Balance (reference temperature = 298 K)

Heat liberation ($-\Delta H_f^0$) due to formation of CO at 298 K + Sensible heat of air blast (at 1000°C) + Sensible heat of coke (at 1400°C) = Sensible heat of flame (at T_f) (Ex. 6.2)

i.e. 55.33 × 111000 + 118.9 × [34.4 × 1273 – 13000] + 27.67 × [36.2 × 1273 – 13500] + 55.33 × [23.5 × 1673 – 11800] = 118.9 × [34.4T_f – 13000] + 55.33 [35.3T_f – 14000]

The solution of the above equation gives RAFT = T_f = 2407 K = 2134°C

[*Note:* Some simplifying assumptions have been made. For example, some carbon of coke will be gasified before reaching the tuyere zone, making the heat generated by CO formation lower. Also, the sensible heat of ash has been ignored. All these will lower the heat input and thus make the RAFT somewhat lower.]

6.2.2 Tuyere Coal Injection

Metallurgical coke is expensive constituting more than 60% of the total burden cost. Moreover, coke ovens are considered to be a major source of pollution in steel plants. Furthermore, in some countries (e.g. India), proper quality coal to manufacture high-quality coke is not available. Hence, injection of natural gas or oil through the tuyeres to partially replace coke as the fuel/reductant, is often resorted to in many countries.

Injection of hydrocarbons through the tuyeres generates H_2 and CO in the combustion zone. H_2 gives several additional benefits, such as the following:

- Faster gaseous reduction of iron oxides
- Better bed permeability in the furnace, since hydrogen has a much lower density than CO and N_2
- Higher thermal conductivity of the gas and consequently, faster heat transfer to the solid burden.

However, the oil crisis in the 1970s led to a large increase in the price of oil and natural gas, especially oil, making such injection commercially unviable. In this situation, in its place the injection of pulverised coal through the tuyeres became very popular. More and more furnaces around the world have adopted this technique. In pulverised coal injection, non-coking coal, which is far less expensive than metallurgical coking coal, is used. ROM coal is fed into a grinding mill, where it is dried and pulverised. The coal + gas stream from the mill then passes through a cyclone, where the primary separation of solids and gases is made. The pulverised coal is then stored in storage bins for eventual injection through the tuyeres using nitrogen gas. An inert atmosphere must be maintained in the system to avoid the danger of spontaneous combustion of finely ground coal.

Typically, coal is ground to about 80% below 75 micron (0.075 mm). In order to maintain the RAFT within the desirable temperature range, coal injection is normally accompanied by suitable oxygen enrichment of the air blast. Coal injection rates above 100 kg coal per thm are quite common nowadays and some modern furnaces have reached a level as high as 250 kg per thm. It has been found that in most cases, 1 kg coal replaces 1 kg coke. The choice of the appropriate coal in terms of its ability to combust easily in the raceway, which in turn, depends on the nature of the coal (particularly its volatile matter content), its particle size distribution and mode of injection are important parameters that influence this *replacement ratio*.

Pulverised coal injection (PCI) is a topic of considerable current interest in blast furnaces all over the world and there is considerable literature available on the theory and practice of coal injection.

6.3 THERMAL AND CHEMICAL RESERVE ZONES

6.3.1 Concept of an Ideal Blast Furnace

As stated in Section 6.1, the temperature and the composition of gas in the stack and in the bosh not only vary along the height of the furnace, but also in the radial direction. However, radial variation will be ignored in this chapter (taken up in the next chapter), in order to develop a better understanding of the interior state of the furnace. In this connection, the concept of an *ideal blast furnace* has been found to be useful, not only for easy understanding of some gross features, but also for quantitative analysis. In the ideal furnace concept, radial variations are ignored.

An ideal blast furnace is characterised by a well-developed *thermal reserve zone* (TRZ) and a *chemical reserve zone* (CRZ). Several investigators have experimentally determined the temperature and composition profiles of the gas phase in the stack and the bosh by inserting thermocouples and sampling probes at various locations. For solids, data are more difficult to collect and hence are limited. Figure 6.2 (Biswas 1984) presents an idealised sketch of the

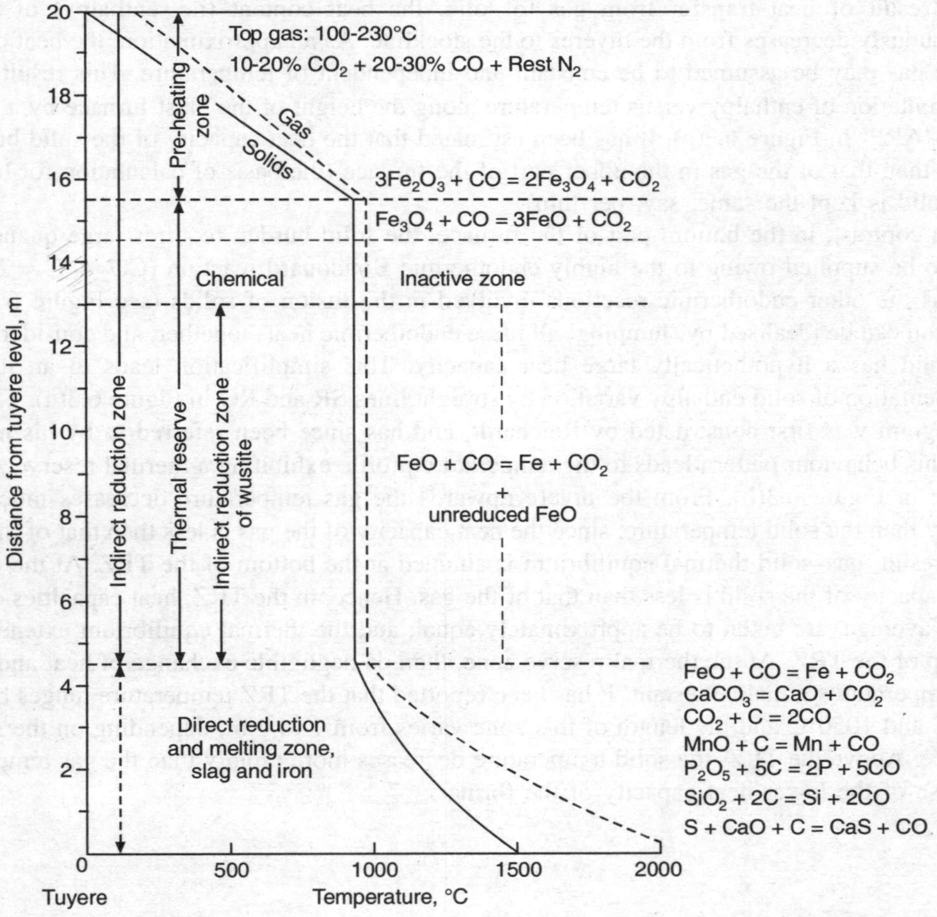

Figure 6.2 An idealised scheme of temperature distribution of gas and solids along the height of a blast furnace showing the chemical reactions occurring in the three main temperature zones.

temperature distribution of gas and solid along the height of a blast furnace, and shows the chemical reactions occurring in the three main temperature zones. The CRZ consists of the chemically inactive zone as well as indirect reduction zone of wustite, and is a part of the TRZ.

The salient features of an ideal blast furnace are as follows.

- It consists of three zones, namely preheating zone, TRZ and CRZ, direct reduction and melting zone.
- The gas temperature is always higher than the solid temperature, thus allowing gas-to-solid heat transfer.
- The gas temperature decreases rapidly going vertically upwards from the bottom and becomes constant at the TRZ, before it begins to decrease.
- The temperature of the solids also remains constant at the TRZ.

6.3.2 Reichardt's Diagram and Thermal Reserve Zone

As a result of heat transfer from gas to solid, the heat content (i.e. enthalpy) of the gas continuously decreases from the tuyeres to the stockline. As an approximation, the heat capacity of the gas may be assumed to be constant and independent of temperature. This results in the representation of enthalpy versus temperature along the height of the blast furnace by a straight line—'ARF' in Figure 6.3(a). It has been estimated that the heat capacity of the solid burden is lower than that of the gas in the upper part of the furnace (the basis of calculation for both gas and solid is kept the same, say, per thm).

In contrast, in the bottom part of the furnace, the solid burden requires large quantities of heat to be supplied owing to the highly endothermic Boudouard reaction ($CO_2 + C = 2CO$) as well as the other endothermic reactions involved in the fusion of solids (see Figure 6.2). The situation can be idealised by 'lumping' all these endothermic heats together, and considering that the solid has a hypothetically large heat capacity. This simplification leads to an idealised representation of solid enthalpy variation by straight lines SR and RO in Figure 6.3(a). This type of diagram was first constructed by Reichardt, and has since been referred to by his name.

This behaviour pattern leads to the temperature profile exhibiting a thermal reserve zone, as shown in Figure 6.3(b). From the tuyere upwards the gas temperature decreases much more rapidly than the solid temperature, since the heat capacity of the gas is less than that of the solid. As a result, gas–solid thermal equilibrium is attained at the bottom of the TRZ. At the top, the heat capacity of the solid is less than that of the gas. Hence, in the TRZ, heat capacities of both, on an average, are taken to be approximately equal, and the thermal equilibrium extends up to the top of the TRZ. At the thermal reserve zone, there is negligible exchange of heat and hence, the temperatures remain constant. It has been reported that the TRZ temperature ranges between 900°C and 1050°C and the length of this zone varies from 1 to 4 m, depending on the specific furnace. Above the TRZ, the solid temperature decreases more rapidly than the gas temperature because of the lower heat capacity of the former.

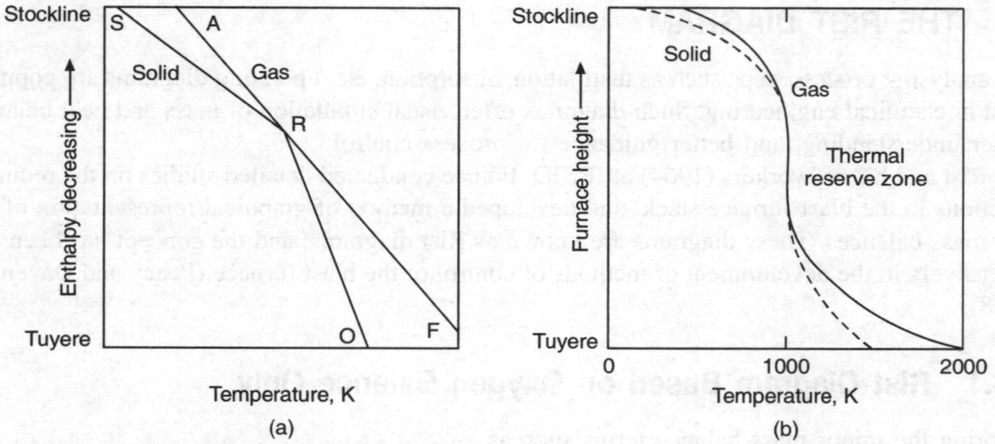

Figure 6.3 Simplified sketch of (a) Reichardt's diagram, and (b) Thermal reserve zone.

6.3.3 Chemical Reserve Zone

Figure 6.2 shows the chemical reserve zone in an ideal blast furnace. It is a part of the thermal reserve zone. At the CRZ, iron is present as a mixture of wustite (Fe_xO) and metallic Fe. The gas phase has a constant composition. In an ideal blast furnace, Fe-wustite-gas equilibrium is attained in the CRZ. Some well-operated modern blast furnaces with basic sinter as the major iron-bearing burden, do exhibit attainment of this chemical equilibrium at the CRZ. This is shown in Figure 6.4 (Turkdogan 1978), where the top curve with the solid line represents the Fe–Fe_xO equilibrium.

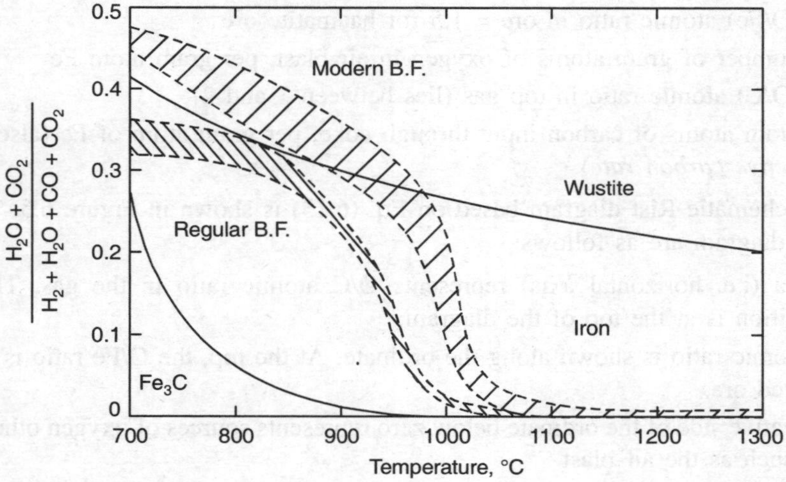

Figure 6.4 Variation in temperature and gas composition profiles with blast furnace practice.

6.4 THE RIST DIAGRAM

For analysing process steps such as distillation, absorption, etc. operating diagrams are popularly used in chemical engineering. Such diagrams offer visual simulation of mass and heat balances, easier understanding, and better guidance for process control.

Rist and his co-workers (1964) at IRSID, France conducted detailed studies on the reduction reactions in the blast furnace stack, and developed a method of graphical representation of heat and mass balances. These diagrams are known as Rist diagrams; and the concept has been used extensively in the development of methods of control of the blast furnace (Peacy and Davenport, 1978).

6.4.1 Rist Diagram Based on Oxygen Balance Only

Ignoring the minor mass balance terms such as

- Reduction by hydrogen
- Dissolution of carbon in hot metal
- Reduction of SiO_2, MnO, etc.

the following oxygen balance can be written for the entire blast furnace:

Oxygen input through air blast and iron oxide of burden = Oxygen going out as CO and CO_2 with the top gas (6.12)

The oxygen balance *per gram atom of iron* may be written as

$$\left(\frac{\text{O}}{\text{Fe}}\right)^x + n_\text{O}^B = n_\text{C}^g \cdot \left(\frac{\text{O}}{\text{C}}\right)^g \tag{6.13}$$

where

$(\text{O/Fe})^x$ = (O/Fe) atomic ratio in ore = 1.5 for haematite ore

n_O^B = number of gram atoms of oxygen in air blast, per gram atom Fe

$(\text{O/C})^g$ = (O/C) atomic ratio in top gas (lies between 1 and 2)

n_C^g = gram atoms of carbon input through coke, per gram atom of Fe (also known as *active carbon rate*).

A simple schematic Rist diagram based on Eq. (6.13) is shown in Figure 6.5. The salient features of the diagram are as follows:

1. Abscissa (i.e. horizontal axis) represents O/C atomic ratio in the gas. The top gas composition is at the top of the diagram.
2. O/Fe atomic ratio is shown along the ordinate. At the top, the O/Fe ratio is that of the unreduced ore.
3. The negative side of the ordinate below zero represents sources of oxygen other than iron oxide, such as the air blast.
4. The slope of the line is n_C^g. The rotation of the line along the arrow means lower value of n_C^g, i.e. more efficient blast furnace operation with lower coke rate.
5. PA indicates the extent of indirect reduction of iron oxide, and PE that of direct reduction.

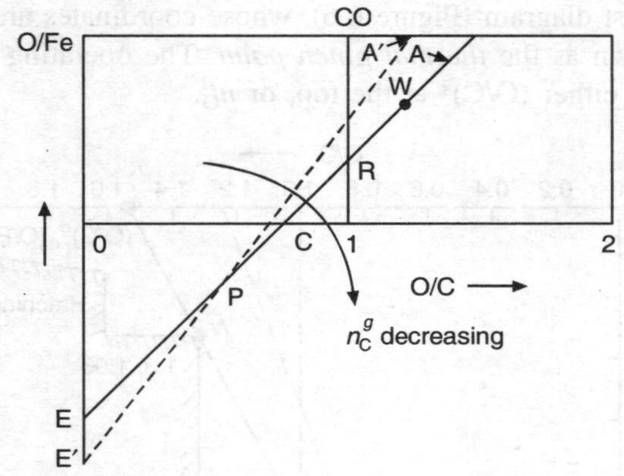

Figure 6.5 The Rist diagram based on oxygen balance (schematic).

6.4.2 Rist Diagram Based on Mass and Heat Balance

In a simplified approach, only the oxygen balance may be considered in the mass balance. Combined heat and mass balance gives a more realistic representation than that based on mass balance alone. Besides Eq. (6.13), additional equations come from heat balance (Peacy and Davenport, 1978).

$$\text{Heat demand } (D) = \text{Heat supply } (S) \tag{6.14}$$

The most simple relations (with approximations) are:

$$D = n_{Fe_2O_3}(-\Delta H^0_{298})_{Fe_2O_3} + (H^0_{1800} - H^0_{298})_{Fe(l)} \tag{6.15}$$

$$S = n^g_{CO} \cdot (-\Delta H^0_{298})_{CO} + n^g_{CO_2} \cdot (-\Delta H^0_{298})_{CO_2} \tag{6.16}$$

Combining the above equations and using the values of heats of formation, the combined mass and heat balance equation becomes

$$\left[\left(\frac{O}{Fe}\right)^x - \frac{D}{283000}\right] + n^B_O = n^g_C \cdot \frac{172000}{283000} \tag{6.17}$$

where D and S are in kJ per kgmol. Since D can be fixed in a straightforward manner, and x has a fixed value depending on the nature of ore, (e.g. for Fe_2O_3, $x = 1.5$),

$$\left(\frac{O}{Fe}\right)^x - \frac{D}{283000} = \text{a fixed quantity for a blast furnace}$$

$$= \left(\frac{O}{Fe}\right)_H \tag{6.18}$$

Again, let

$$\frac{172000}{283000} = 0.61 = \left(\frac{O}{C}\right)_H \tag{6.19}$$

Then the point H in the Rist diagram (Figure 6.6), whose coordinates are $(O/C)_H$ and $(O/Fe)_H$, is an *invariant* and is known as the *thermal pinch point*. The operating line rotates around H depending on the value of either $(O/C)^g$ at the top, or n_O^B.

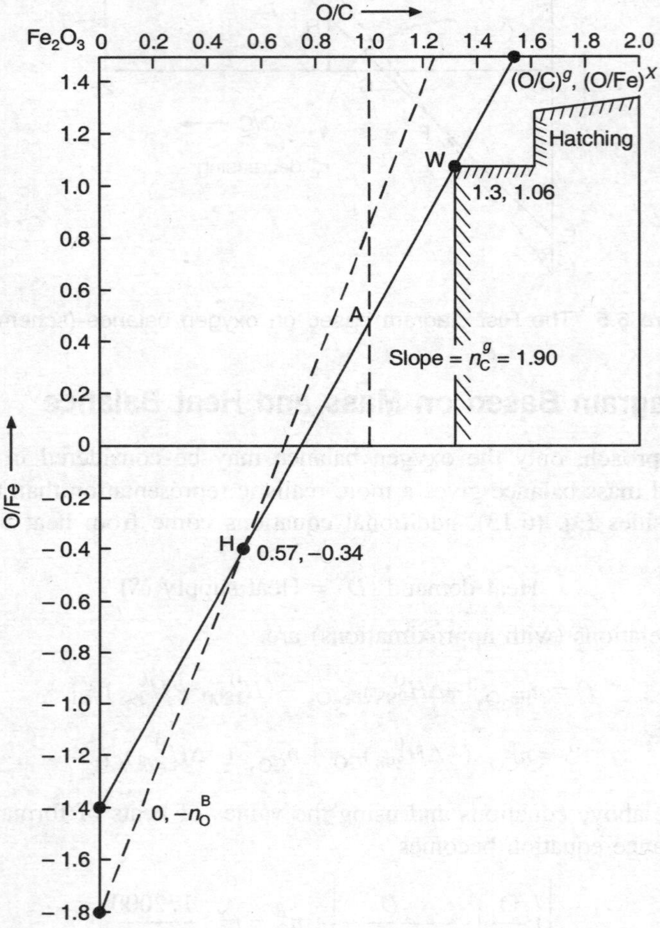

Figure 6.6 The Rist diagram based on mass and heat balance, and Fe–Fe_xO–gas equilibrium at the chemical reserve zone.

6.4.3 Rist Diagram Based on Oxygen and Heat Balance, and Fe–Fe_xO–Gas Equilibrium

Section 6.3.3 discussed the attainment of Fe–Fe_xO–gas chemical equilibrium at the chemical reserve zone in well-operated modern blast furnaces. Assuming a temperature of 950°C in the CRZ and on the basis of the Fe–C–O phase stability diagram (Figure 5.1), it is possible to represent the equilibria of Fe_2O_3, Fe_3O_4 and Fe_xO with gas in a Rist diagram. This is shown by the hatched lines in Figure 6.6. The minimum permissible value of the slope n_C^g is obtained at the operating line HW. W is known as the *chemical pinch point*. It corresponds to Fe–Fe_XO–gas equilibrium. Hence, the line WAH represents the best possible operating practice with a minimum coke rate. This corresponds to the concept of an ideal blast furnace (Section 6.3). *Hence, an ideal blast furnace has the highest efficiency*.

REFERENCES

Biswas, A.K., *Principles of Blast Furnace Ironmaking*, SBA Publications, Kolkata (1984).

Peacy, J.G. and W.G. Davenport, *The Iron Blast Furnace*, Pergammon Press, Oxford (1978).

Rist, A. and N. Meysson, Rev. Met., 61 (1964) 121–126.

Turkdogan, E.T., Met. Trans B, 9B (1978) 164.

Walker, R.D., *Modern Ironmaking Methods*, The Institute of Metals, London (1986).

7

Internal Zones and Gas Flow in Blast Furnaces

7.1 INTRODUCTION

Chapter 6, Section 6.3 presented the concept of an *ideal blast furnace*, which has been found to be very useful, not only for easy understanding of some gross features, but also for quantitative analyses and process control. In such an ideal furnace, the temperature and composition of the gas and solid inside the furnace are assumed to vary only along the height of the furnace and all variations in the horizontal direction are ignored.

However, in an actual blast furnace, there are significant temperature and composition variations along the horizontal direction as well. Figure 7.1 illustrates this phenomenon—the

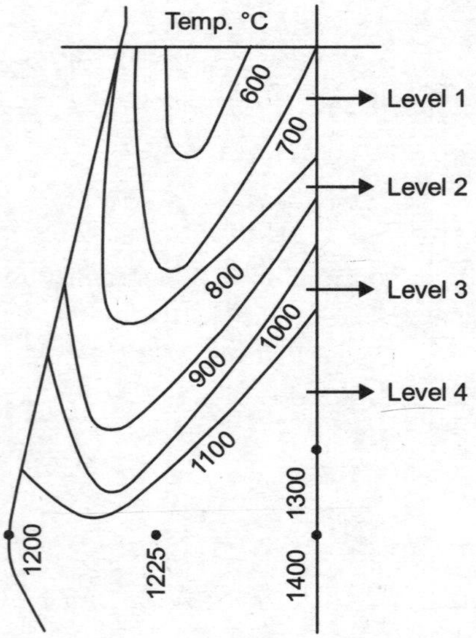

Figure 7.1 Radial temperature profiles in a 2000 m^3 Russian blast furnace at four vertical levels.

temperature *isotherms* are not horizontal (Nekrasov et al. 1969; 1970). The temperature rises from the periphery and reaches the maximum at the centre along any given horizontal plane. Figure 7.2 shows the variation in gas composition in the horizontal direction.

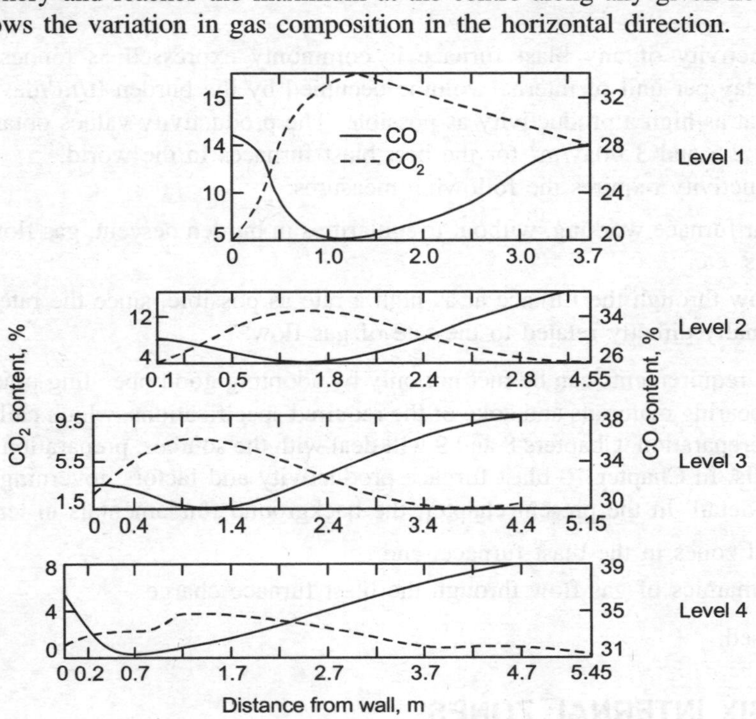

Figure 7.2 Radial variations in CO and CO_2 content of gas at four levels for the investigation reported in Figure 7.1.

The basic reasons for horizontal non-uniformity are as follows:

1. The hot air blast introduced through the tuyeres assists in localised combustion in the tuyere area. The resulting gases flow upwards and are not able to penetrate uniformly up to the furnace centre.
2. The solid burden charged from the top is heterogeneous—it consists principally of iron ore/sinter/pellets, and coke. The density of the oxide charge approximately ranges from 3.5×10^3 to 4.0×10^3 kg/m^3, and that of coke is about 1.0×10^3 kg/m^3. In addition, the burden constituents have different ranges of sizes—the optimum size range being 10–30 mm for ore, 6–15 mm for sinter, 6–25 mm for pellets and 40–80 mm for coke. Since the burden is charged from the top of the furnace, some non-uniformity in the size and density from the centre to the periphery cannot be avoided.

In Chapter 2, it was explained that this phenomenon leads to horizontal non-uniformity in the solids within the blast furnace at the belly and the bosh region, leading to formation of different internal zones in the furnace. The detailed structures of these zones have a major influence on the performance of the furnace. The structure of each zone depends on the *physical* (strength, abrasion resistance, etc.), *chemical* (reducibility/reactivity) and physicochemical (softening, melting, reduction-degradation) properties of the solid burden, besides the operating practice used.

The productivity of any blast furnace is commonly expressed as tonnes of hot metal produced per day per unit of internal volume occupied by the burden (t/m^3/day). The furnace operators aim at as high a productivity as possible. The productivity values obtained at present range between 2.5 and 3 t/day/m^3 for the best blast furnaces in the world.

High productivity requires the following measures:

- Regular furnace working, without irregularities in burden descent, gas flow, temperature patterns, etc.
- Gas flow through the furnace at as high a rate as possible, since the rate of production is normally directly related to the rate of gas flow.

The above requirements can be met not only by adopting good operating practices, but also by using iron-bearing materials and coke of the required specifications, which calls for extensive raw materials preparation. Chapters 8 and 9 will deal with the sources, preparation and properties of raw materials. In Chapter 10 blast furnace productivity and factors governing the same will be covered in detail. In the present chapter, the background fundamentals in terms of the

- Internal zones in the blast furnace, and
- Aerodynamics of gas flow through the blast furnace charge

will be discussed.

7.2 THE SIX INTERNAL ZONES

Besley et al. 1959, quenched an experimental blast furnace, sectioned it vertically, collected samples from various zones, and analysed them. This led to a valuable insight into the internal state of the furnace in terms of the existence of various zones, their structure and composition, as well as the reaction mechanisms involved. After this pioneering investigation, several other workers, especially in Japan, carried out similar sectioning studies in the decades of the 1960s and 1970s. All these studies have provided a huge amount of details on the internal state of a furnace and its influence on furnace behaviour.

It is now accepted that a blast furnace can be broadly divided into six zones, as shown schematically in Figure 7.3. This figure also indicates the probable gas flow path pattern (through the arrows). Before going any further, it needs to be pointed out that regarding the existence of six internal zones in a blast furnace, there is no generally accepted norm. Only some broad agreements among the different investigations exist, as far as the major divisions are concerned. As a result, even in the present text, there may be some differences in the terminologies used here and those used in the other chapters. However, too much emphasis need not be laid on these differences. What is more important is to arrive at an understanding of the phenomena taking place inside a blast furnace.

As stated in Section 7.1, the hot air blast is unable to penetrate right up to the centre of the furnace. This results in the occurrence of a *relatively inactive coke-zone* in the central region. Consequently, the zones immediately above the tuyeres have approximately inverse V-shapes, and the isotherms within the furnace also exhibit the same shape (refer to Figure 7.1).

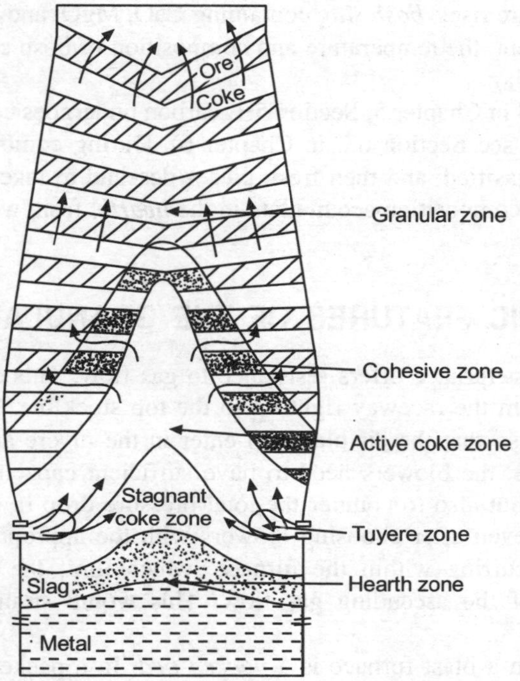

Figure 7.3 Schematic sectional diagram of the internal zones in a blast furnace.

Right at the top of the furnace is the *granular zone* that contains the coke and the iron-bearing materials charged, sometimes along with small quantities of limestone and other fluxes. The iron-bearing oxides charged get reduced to wustite and metallic iron towards the lower end of the granular zone. As the burden descends further, and its temperature rises on account of contact with the ascending hot gases, softening and melting of the iron-bearing solids takes place in the so-called *cohesive zone* (mushy zone). Further down the furnace, impure liquid iron and liquid slag are formed. It has already been stated in Chapter 1, and also in Chapter 4, Section 4.4.1, that the absorption of carbon lowers the melting point of iron drastically. For example, an iron alloy containing 4 wt. % carbon melts at only 1185°C. In the cohesive zone and below it, coke is the source of carbon for carburisation of liquid iron. However, carbon directly does not dissolve in liquid iron at this stage. The possible mechanism of carburisation of iron entails the formation of CO by gasification of carbon (Eq. (5.5)), followed by the absorption of carbon by the reaction:

$$2CO(g) = [C]_{\text{in Fe}} + CO_2(g) \tag{7.1}$$

This has also been explained in connection with the reduction of FeO by carbon in Section 5.3.3.

As discussed in Section 5.4.1, Chapter 5, the initial slag that is formed within a blast furnace has a low melting point because it contains large amounts of FeO. This is the type of slag that is formed in the cohesive zone. It is known as the *primary slag*. As the primary slag trickles down the furnace through the active and inactive coke bed, FeO gets progressively reduced by carbon. As the temperature rises, *bosh slag* containing CaO, MgO, and high percentages of silica gets formed. To this extent, the temperature and composition of bosh slag are radically different from those of primary slag.

As already discussed in Chapter 5, Section 5.1, carbon undergoes combustion in the *raceway of the tuyere zone* (also see Section 6.2 in Chapter 6). During combustion, coke pieces swirl around before they get gasified, and then fresh pieces descend to take their place. Finally, slag and metal of the desired composition accumulate in the *hearth*, from where they are periodically tapped.

7.3 AERODYNAMIC FEATURES OF THE GRANULAR ZONE

The charge within a blast furnace offers resistance to gas flow. This causes a pressure drop in the vertical direction from the raceway right up to the top stockline. Turbo-blowers supply air at the required pressure so that the air blast can enter in the tuyere area where the pressure is the maximum. Therefore, the blowers need to have sufficient capacity not only to supply the volume of air required, but also to counter the total pressure drop in the charge bed above the tuyere level. However, even after choosing blowers with the appropriate characteristics, there may be phenomena occurring within the furnace, which limit the rate of air blowing and consequently the rate of the ascending gas flow. This would straightaway hamper furnace productivity.

The granular zone in a blast furnace is a *packed bed*. In a packed bed, the solid particles are stationary. As the linear velocity of the gas generated (v) increases, the pressure drop across the bed (ΔP) also increases. Finally, a stage is reached when the upward force owing to ΔP becomes equal to the weight of the bed above it. Any further increase in velocity causes the solid particles to get fluidised to form a *fluidised bed*. This constitutes the upper limit to gas flow.

For a simple case of spheres of uniform size and density, fairly rigorous co-relationships of ΔP vs. v are available. However, as stated in Section 7.1, the solid burden in a blast furnace has a range of sizes as well as differences in density. This requires a more empirical and approximate quantitative approach that is presented in the following sections.

7.3.1 Ergun Equation for Packed Beds

For a packed bed of solid spheres of uniform size and density, the ΔP vs. v correlation is well-established. It is commonly known as the Ergun equation. The friction factor (ψ) vs. Reynolds Number (Re) correlation for *laminar flow* was derived assuming that the bed consists of a series of crooked channels of irregular cross section. The coefficient was adjusted and the equation extended to *turbulent flow* on the basis of extensive laboratory measurements.

Figure 7.4 shows the ψ vs. Re plot of the Ergun equation on a logarithmic scale. The equation is

$$\psi = \frac{150}{\text{Re}} + 17.5 \tag{7.2}$$

where

$$\psi = \text{friction factor} = \left(\frac{\Delta P \rho_g}{G_0^2}\right)\left(\frac{d_p}{H}\right)\left(\frac{\varepsilon^3}{1-\varepsilon}\right) \tag{7.3}$$

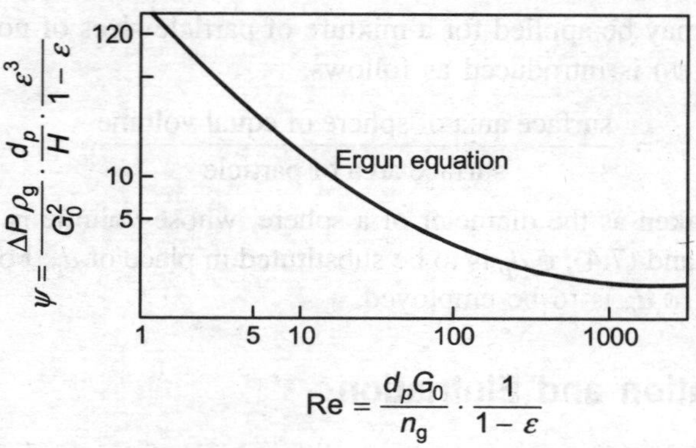

Figure 7.4 Friction factor plot for flow of gas through a packed bed of solids.

and

$$\text{Re} = \text{Reynolds number} = \frac{d_p G_0}{\eta_g(1-\varepsilon)} \tag{7.4}$$

Here,

ρ_g = gas density

d_p = particle diameter

H = bed height

η_g = viscosity of gas

$$\varepsilon = \text{void fraction in the packed bed} = \frac{\text{volume of empty space in bed}}{\text{volume of bed}} \tag{7.5}$$

G_0 = mass velocity of gas

= mass flow per unit cross sectional area of bed (7.6)

= $\rho_g v_0$

The velocity v_0 is known as the *empty-tube velocity* (i.e. the nominal gas velocity), since the actual gas velocity through the bed voids is unknown.

In Eq. (7.2), the factor 150/Re is for laminar flow, and 1.75 is for highly turbulent flow (Re > 2000). Gas flow in blast furnaces is turbulent in nature and hence Eq. (7.2) may be simplified as

$$\psi = 1.75 \tag{7.7}$$

For turbulent flow, the pressure gradient in the vertical direction can be obtained by combining Eq. (7.7) with Eq. (7.3). Then,

$$\frac{\Delta P}{H} = 1.75 \frac{G_0^2}{\rho_g} \frac{1}{d_p} \frac{1-\varepsilon}{\varepsilon^3} \tag{7.8}$$

From Eqs. (7.6) and (7.8),

$$\frac{\Delta P}{H} = 1.75\, \rho_g \frac{1}{d_p} \frac{1-\varepsilon}{\varepsilon^3} v_0^2 \tag{7.9}$$

The Ergun equation may be applied for a mixture of particle sizes of non-spherical shapes. For this, a *shape factor* (ϕ_s) is introduced as follows.

$$\phi_s = \frac{\text{surface area of sphere of equal volume}}{\text{surface area of particle}} \tag{7.10}$$

In Eq. (7.9), d_p is to be taken as the diameter of a sphere, whose volume is the same as that of the particle. In Eqs. (7.3) and (7.4), $\phi_s d_p$ is to be substituted in place of d_p. For a mixture of sizes the arithmetic average of $\phi_s d_p$ is to be employed.

7.3.2 Bed Fluidisation and Elutriation

As stated earlier, with increasing gas velocity, solid particles in a packed bed start getting fluidised. This is known as the *onset of fluidisation.* At this stage, ΔP and v_0 have critical values given by

$$\left(\frac{\Delta P}{H}\right)_{\text{crit}} = \text{weight of unit bed volume} = (1-\varepsilon)(\rho_s - \rho_g)\, g \tag{7.11}$$

where ρ_s is density of solid, and g is acceleration due to gravity.

Combining Eq. (7.11) with Eq. (7.9),

$$v_0^2(\text{crit}) = \frac{1}{1.75}\,\frac{(\rho_s - \rho_g)g}{\rho_g}\,\varepsilon^3 d_p \tag{7.12}$$

If the gas velocity is increased even further, a stage comes when the individual particles start escaping from the bed, and are conveyed into the gas. This is known as *Elutriation.* The minimum elutriation velocity (v_t) is given by the famous Stokes equation, viz.

$$v_t = \frac{1}{18}\,\frac{g d_p^2}{\eta_g}(\rho_s - \rho_g) \tag{7.13}$$

7.3.3 Gas Flow Through the Granular Zone of a Blast Furnace

As noted in Section 7.1, the granular zone of a blast furnace contains particles of non-uniform sizes and shapes. Moreover, the densities of ore, coke and other materials are also different. In such a situation, quantitative applications of the above equations are difficult and would at best be approximate. However, a qualitative understanding of the behaviour pattern is relatively straightforward, and the same is presented in the paragraphs below.

The bed void fraction (ε) is lower for mixed particle size compared with those for uniform sizes. Figure 7.5(a) schematically shows the nature of packing for the following situations:

- Large spheres of uniform size
- Small spheres of uniform size
- Mixture of large and small spheres.

That ε should be lower for the mixed size is obvious.

Figure 7.5(b) presents the quantitative data for the same diameter ratios of the solid particles in which d_s and d_l are the diameters of small and large particles respectively (Jeschar 1975). On the left and right boundaries, uniform sizes can be seen in between the mixtures of various size proportions. Equations (7.8) and (7.9) show that ΔP is proportional to $(1 - \varepsilon)/\varepsilon^3$, if other factors are kept constant. At $\varepsilon = 0.45$, $(1 - \varepsilon)/\varepsilon^3 = 6.0$, and at $\varepsilon = 0.3$, $(1 - \varepsilon)/\varepsilon^3 = 26.0$. Hence, ΔP will be larger with lower ε. In other words, with lower voidage in the case of particles with mixed sizes, the *bed permeability* will decrease. At the same value of ΔP, the gas flow rate (and thus productivity) will then go down. This is a very undesirable effect, that has to be avoided. The following summary focuses on these issues:

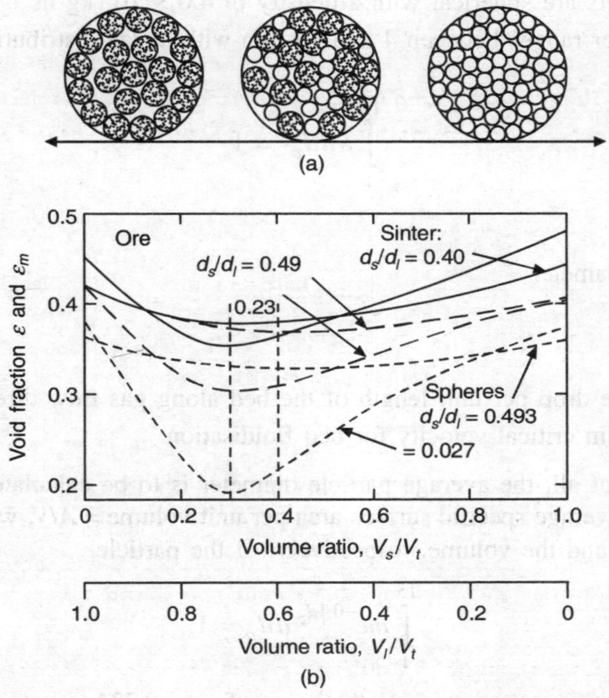

Figure 7.5 (a) Figures on the extreme left and right show the packings of uniform large and small spheres, and the middle that of a mixed bed of large and small spheres. (b) Void fractions of mixtures of two sizes of ores, sinter and spheres of different size ratios.

1. From Eq. (7.9), $\Delta P/H$ decreases as d_p increases. As a consequence, the critical fluidisation velocity increases with increase in d_p (Eq. (7.12)). Therefore, for higher permissible gas flow rates, d_p should also be as large as possible. Hence, d_l is better than d_s.
2. There is a tendency towards size segregation, and consequent non-uniformity of gas flow in a horizontal plane of the furnace.
3. At the furnace stockline, small particles tend to escape with the gas, thus causing dust losses.

EXAMPLE 7.1

Examples of packed bed reactor in ironmaking are the blast furnace stack, the sinter strand for sintering of iron ore, the shaft furnace for sponge ironmaking by gaseous reduction of iron ore pellets, etc. Consider the aerodynamics of such a reactor.

Given:

(i) Nominal velocity of gas through the bed is 2 $m \cdot s^{-1}$ at 500 K

(ii) The gas consists of 60% N_2, 20% CO_2 and 20% CO; gas viscosity = 3×10^{-5} $kg \cdot m^{-1} \cdot s^{-1}$

(iii) Bed void fraction is 0.35

(iv) Iron ore pellets are spherical with a density of 4.0×10^3 $kg \cdot m^{-3}$

(v) Pellet diameter ranges between 4 and 15 mm with a size distribution function, defined as

$$\int_4^{15} S\,dd_p = 1$$

where

$S = me^{-0.1d_p}$

d_p = the pellet diameter

m = a constant.

Calculate:

(a) The pressure drop per unit length of the bed along gas flow direction

(b) The minimum critical velocity for bed fluidisation.

Solution: (a) First of all, the average particle diameter is to be calculated from the relation, $d_p = 6/a$, where a = average specific surface area per unit volume = A/V, where A and V are the average surface area and the volume, respectively, of the particle.

Now,
$$\int_4^{15} me^{-0.1d_p}\,dd_p = 1 \qquad \text{(Ex. 7.1)}$$

The solution of the above equation gives the value of m = 0.224.

$$A = \int_4^{15} 0.224e^{-0.1d_p}(\pi d_p^2)\,dd_p \qquad \text{(Ex. 7.2)}$$

The integral is of the form: $\int x^2 e^{ax} dx = \dfrac{e^{ax}}{a^3}(a^2x^2 - 2ax + 2)$, from Table of integrals.

On solving Eq. (Ex. 7.2), it is obtained, $A = 0.178 \times 10^3$ mm^2

Again,
$$V = \int_4^{15} 0.224e^{-0.1d_p}\left(\frac{\pi}{6} \cdot d_p^3\right)dd_p \qquad \text{(Ex. 7.3)}$$

Solving this with the help of Table of integrals, gives $V = 0.275 \times 10^3$ mm^3.
From values of A and V, the average value of $d_p = 9.28$ mm.

From Eq. (7.4), $\text{Re} = \dfrac{d_p G_0}{\eta_g (1-\varepsilon)}$, where $G_0 = \rho_g v_0$

Gas density $= \rho_g = [28 \times (0.6 + 0.2) + 44 \times 0.2] \times \dfrac{273}{22.4 \times 500} = 0.76$ kg·m^{-3}

Putting in values in Eq. (7.4), Re = 724.

Figure 7.4 shows that the flow is turbulent. Hence, Eq. (7.9) is applicable for pressure drop calculation.

$$\frac{\Delta P}{H} = 1.75 \rho_g \frac{1}{d_p} \frac{1-\varepsilon}{\varepsilon^3} v_0^2$$

Calculations give the value of $\Delta P/H = 5.24 \times 10^4$ N·m^{-3}.

(b) For the calculation of the critical fluidisation velocity, Eq. (7.12) was used.

$$v_0^2(\text{crit}) = \frac{1}{1.75} \frac{(\rho_s - \rho_g)\, g}{\rho_g} \varepsilon^3 d_p$$

Fluidisation first starts with the smallest particle size, which in this case is of 4 mm diameter. Putting in values and solving Eq. (7.12), gives $v_0^2(\text{crit}) = 5.05$, i.e. $v_0(\text{crit}) = 2.25$ m·s^{-1}.

7.4 GAS FLOW IN WET ZONES

Wet zones consist of the coke beds in the bosh and belly regions, i.e. inactive coke zone, active coke zone, and the coke slits in the cohesive zone. Here molten iron and molten slag flow downwards through the bed of coke. This reduces the free cross section available for gas flow, thus offering greater resistance, thereby increasing the pressure drop. An extreme situation arises when, at high gas velocity, the gas prevents the downward flow of liquid. This is known as *loading*. With further increase in gas velocity, the liquid gets carried upwards mechanically, causing *flooding*.

The relation between the gas and the liquid flow in a packed column was first investigated by Sherwood et al. 1938. Other investigators subsequently worked in the same field. *Sherwood equations* have been applied to the blast furnace wet coke zones. However, there are controversies and uncertainties about their applicability to blast furnaces. Nonetheless, an attempt will be made to illustrate this type of effort.

The Sherwood correlation is

$$\log \psi' = -0.559 \log m - 1.519 \tag{7.14}$$

where, ψ' = flooding (i.e. hanging) factor

$$= \frac{v_{tu}^2}{g} \frac{a_c}{\varepsilon^3} \frac{\rho_g}{\rho_l} \eta_l^{0.2} \tag{7.15}$$

and

$$m = \text{fluid ratio} = \frac{L}{G_{tu}} \left(\frac{\rho_g}{\rho_l} \right)^{1/2} \tag{7.16}$$

where

L = superficial mass flow rate of bosh slag, kg/m^2/h
v_{tu} = superficial tuyere gas velocity (empty tube), m/s
a_c = specific surface area of coke particles, m^2/m^3
G_{tu} = superficial mass flow rate of tuyere gas, kg/m^2/h.

Here, the subscript l refers to liquid bosh slag.

$$\text{Flooding occurs, if } \psi'^2 m > 0.001 \tag{7.17}$$

Since, $\psi' \propto (\eta_l^{0.2}/\rho_l)$, liquid slag would be responsible for flooding because:

- Viscosity of liquid slag is greater than that of liquid metal, and
- Liquid slag has lower density than liquid metal.

Figure 7.6 shows the ψ' vs. m relationship for flooding (Eq. (7.17)) in a log–log plot (Beer and Heynert, 1964). It also presents some values collected from the data of several blast furnaces. The Sherwood diagram (Figure 7.6) suffers from the drawback that both the co-ordinates have gas terms, and the ordinate is not dimensionless. Later, another loading and flooding diagram was proposed by Mersmann, 1965, in connection with gas and liquid counterflow in packed and irrigated beds. This has also been employed for the analysis of blast furnace gas flowing through the wet zone. However, the conclusion has been the same qualitatively, i.e. flooding limits the flow of gas through the inactive coke zone and the cohesive zone of a blast furnace.

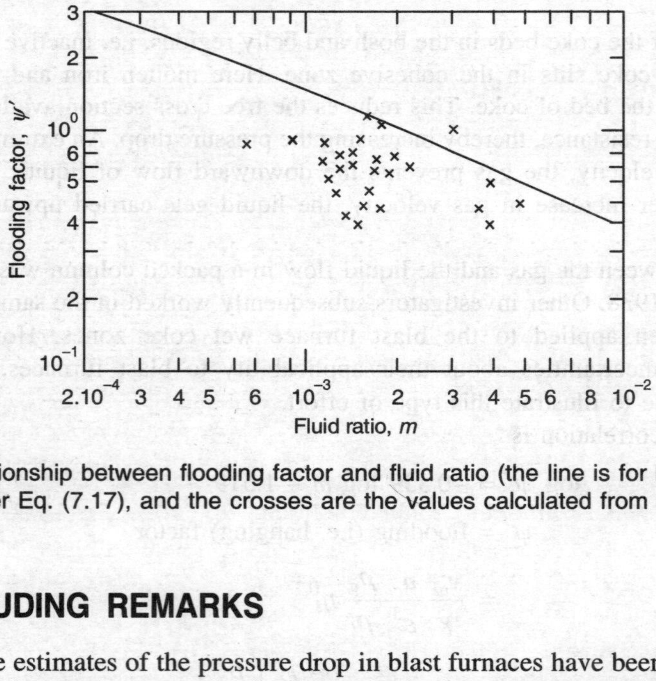

Figure 7.6 Relationship between flooding factor and fluid ratio (the line is for limiting flooding curve as per Eq. (7.17), and the crosses are the values calculated from some blast furnaces).

7.5 CONCLUDING REMARKS

Some quantitative estimates of the pressure drop in blast furnaces have been attempted based on the theory and semi-empirical correlations that were presented in the earlier sections. However, they are approximate. Moreover, they are only for the granular zone and coke zones. The situation in the cohesive zone is very complex, and reliable theoretical estimates are extremely difficult to come by.

Therefore, for practical applications in blast furnaces, an empirical parameter, called *Flow Resistance Coefficient* (FRC) has become popular. The FRC for a bed is given as

$$\text{Gas flow rate} = \frac{\Delta P}{\text{FRC}} \tag{7.18}$$

where the gas flow rate is for unit cross section of the bed, i.e. either mass flow velocity (G_o), or volumetric flow velocity (v_o).

Hence,

$$\text{FRC} = \frac{1}{\text{bed permeability}} \tag{7.19}$$

The FRC for a furnace can be empirically determined from measurements of pressure drop and gas flow rate. Since it is possible to measure pressures at various heights within a furnace, the values of FRC for individual zones can also be determined.

$$(\Delta P)_{\text{overall}} = \sum_{\substack{\text{zones} \\ \text{1 to 5}}} \Delta P = (\text{gas flow rate}) \times \sum_{\substack{\text{zones} \\ \text{1 to 5}}} \text{FRC} \tag{7.20}$$

These measurements have indicated that FRCs for the granular, cohesive, coke + tuyere zones are approximately 20%, 50% and 30% of the overall furnace FRC. This means that the cohesive zone is responsible for the maximum flow resistance and pressure drop, to a very large extent.

As stated in Section 7.1, the furnace productivity is approximately proportional to the mass flow rate of gas. Therefore, for high productivity, the total FRC for the entire furnace should be as low as possible. The role of various operating parameters and burden properties in this situation will be discussed in more detail in Chapter 10.

REFERENCES

Beer, H. and G. Heynert, Stahl u. Eisen (1964), Vol. 84, pp. 1353–1365.

Besley, J.J., N.B. Melcher and M.M. Harris, J. Metals (1959), Vol. 11, pp. 610–615.

Jeschar, R. et al., in: *Blast furnace aerodynamics*, Proc. Symp. Aus. IMM, (Ed.) N. Standish, Wollongong (1975).

Mersmann, A., Chem. Ing. Tech., Vol. 37 (1965), pp. 218–226.

Nekrasov, Z.J. and M.T. Buzoverya, Stahl in Eng., Feb. 1969, pp. 141–147; July 1970, pp. 502–509.

Sherwood, T.K. et al., Ind. Eng. Chem. (1938), Vol. 30, pp. 765–769.

8

Raw Materials I: Coke

8.1 INTRODUCTION

Coke is one of the most important raw materials for hot metal production through the blast furnace route. It often accounts for almost 60% of the cost of producing hot metal in blast furnaces, and hence, attention to coke is extremely important. Coke plays three major roles in a blast furnace, viz. supplies energy for the chemical reactions to occur; supports the burden, particularly at the lower region when the charge melts, thereby providing permeability for the gases to pass through a packed bed of solids; and finally, it carburises the hot metal bath prior to steelmaking.

Cokemaking involves *carbonisation* (destructive distillation) of coal under controlled conditions in a *coke oven.* The quality of coke—expressed in terms of its room temperature and high temperature strength, reactivity, ash content and chemistry—has a major influence in determining the *coke rate* and *productivity* of a blast furnace. The quality of coke primarily depends on the quality of coal (or, more often, coal blend) used to make coke and the pre-carbonisation techniques adopted prior to charging coal into the coke ovens. To a much lesser extent, coke quality is also influenced by the actual carbonisation conditions adopted during cokemaking, as well as by any post-carbonisation technique that is practised before the coke made is sent to the blast furnaces.

8.1.1 Availability of Coking Coal

The vital raw material for cokemaking is, of course, *coking coal*. The total world proven coal reserves exceed 1 trillion tonnes, half of which is hard coking coal suitable for making blast furnace grade coke. The largest reserves are in the USA (23% of the world reserves), erstwhile Soviet Union (23%) and China (11%). Today, China is the world's leading coal producer, followed by the USA, while India ranks third. In 2004–05, India's coal production was about 375 million tonnes, which is expected to reach around 430 million tonnes by 2006–07.

India's reserve is limited to the extent of 7.6% of the world, and out of this limited amount, the coking coal proportion is only 15% (Table 8.1). The meagre amount of coal that is available in India has also problems of high ash content (up to 30%) and low rank (MMR 0.8–1.1), both of which are important parameters governing the quality of coal used to make blast furnace

Table 8.1 Total coal reserves in India

Coal type	Reserves, billion tonnes	Reserves, down to 600 m depth
Coking coal	30	24
Non-coking superior grade	47	43
Non-coking inferior grade	124	112
Total non-coking coal	171	156
Total coal available	**201**	**180**

(metallurgical) coke. Besides poor quality, Indian coal, both coking and non-coking, has adverse washability characteristics, i.e. even after undergoing extensive crushing before washing, removal of ash from these coals becomes difficult, without encountering large losses in yield. Yields higher than 55% are difficult even for removing one-third of the ash present in the coal that is mined. At the same time, because of the inordinately high ash content, all coking coal has to be washed to yield clean coal with 15–18% of ash. For this purpose, India has many coal washeries (currently 19, with a total capacity of 27.2 Mtpa).

The coal deposits in India occur mostly in thick seams and at shallow depths. The non-coking coal reserves aggregate 172.1 billion tonnes (85%) while the coking coal reserves are 29.8 billion tonnes (the remaining 15%). The reserves are fairly widely distributed over 13 states in India located as far apart as Gujarat and Rajasthan in the West, Madhya Pradesh and Chattisgarh in Central India, Tamil Nadu in the South, Jammu and Kashmir in the North and Assam in the Northeast (Ray et al. 2005). However, the eastern states of Bengal, Bihar, Jharkhand, etc. are the principal coal-bearing areas.

Around 0.8 million tonnes of coal on an average is extracted daily in India, and at this rate, the reserves are likely to last just over 100 years. This does not augur well, particularly since the energy derived from coal in India is about twice that of the energy from oil, as against the rest of the world, where energy from coal is about one-third lower than that from oil. Thus, coal is no doubt a cause for concern for Indian industry as a whole, particularly when it comes to steel production using the classical BF–BOF route.

8.1.2 Types of Coal Available

Geochemical metamorphosis of plant matter over several ages has given rise to different degrees of coalification with time. During this prolonged metamorphosis, the carbon content has gradually increased. In addition, the degree to which the coalification reactions have been completed for a given coal deposit also determines its rank, i.e. its pedigree.

Progressive metamorphism of coal and its effect on the increase in rank can be depicted as:

$$\text{Peat} \rightarrow \text{Lignite} \rightarrow \text{Bituminous coal} \rightarrow \text{Anthracite} \rightarrow \text{Graphite}$$

8.2 CHEMICAL CHARACTERISTICS OF COALS FOR COKEMAKING

8.2.1 Proximate Analysis

The proximate analysis of coal is a convenient and effective means of determining the distribution of products obtained by heating coal under a set of standard conditions. The analysis includes determination of *moisture, ash, volatile matter* and *fixed carbon* contents, all of which have an important bearing on the coking potential of a particular coal. However, since it is a fairly standard procedure, it is not discussed in any greater detail here.

Figure 8.1 schematically represents the variation in fixed carbon, volatile matter and moisture contents for different types of coal. An important point to note is that ash, to a very large extent, decides the physical characteristics of coke, and this, in turn, has a major impact on blast furnace performance. The use of high ash coke increases the coke rate and the slag volume in blast furnaces, both of which are detrimental.

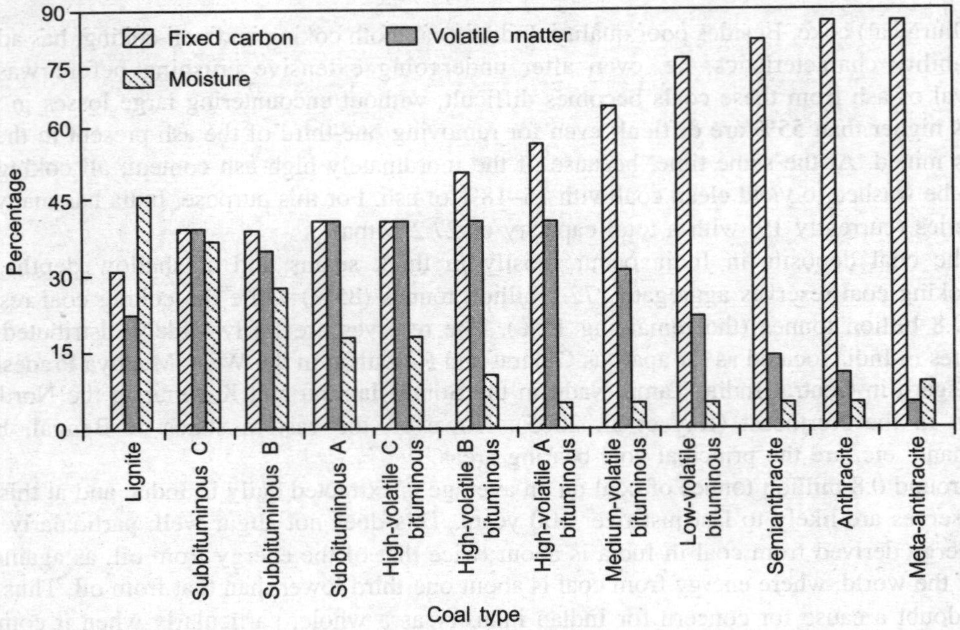

Figure 8.1 Proximate analysis data for different types of coals.

It has been established that every 1% increase in coke ash increases the coke rate by 23–25 kg/thm under Indian conditions, where coke with 18–22% ash made from a coal blend with 14–18% ash is normally used, compared with 8–13 kg/thm elsewhere, where coke with ash lower than 12–15% made from coal with 10–12% ash is considered suitable for use in efficient blast furnaces. Calculations have also indicated that every 1% increase in the ash content of coke typically raises the total silica input into blast furnaces by about 7% and decreases the productivity by around 3%. This explains why the coke rate is higher and the productivity lower, even in efficiently run blast furnaces in India.

Another important property of ash in coal is its ash fusion temperature since it influences the temperature at which the ash begins to become plastic. Here again, Indian coals normally have low initial ash fusion temperatures (1200–1250°C). While this may not be of major significance in cokemaking, it plays a vital role in coal used for blast furnace tuyere injection as well as for direct reduction (dealt with in Chapter 13).

Since volatile matter in coal is almost completely expelled during cokemaking, low-volatile coals yield higher amounts of coke from the same amount of coal, thereby providing more carbon to the blast furnace, and vice versa. However, coal with less than 14% volatile matter (dry mineral matter-free basis) will not coke, while coal with an extremely high volatile matter is also not desirable, since such coals either do not coke at all or make coke of poor quality with very low fixed carbon contents. Although it is somewhat arbitrary, coals with volatile matter less than 18% or greater than 38% are not normally considered suitable for cokemaking. However, like ash in coal, proper blending of different coals can be carried out to formulate a blend having the desired level of volatile matter.

8.2.2 Ultimate Analysis

The ultimate analysis indicates the chemical composition of coal in terms of its hydrogen, carbon, nitrogen, oxygen, phosphorus and sulphur contents. Usually, ultimate analysis is reported either on a dry-basis, or on a moisture-and-mineral matter-free basis, to avoid inclusion of hydrogen and oxygen present in water or as constituents of mineral matter. Sulphur and phosphorus are harmful impurities for steel and have to be removed during ironmaking or steelmaking.

Carbon: Carbon is obviously the most important component of any coal. The actual carbon that is available in coke to carry out reduction of iron oxide to hot metal in a blast furnace (after deducting the amount of coke required for simultaneous smelting of the gangue constituents present in any iron ore), is termed 'effective carbon'. The 'effective carbon' required for producing one tonne of hot metal in different blast furnaces operating with varying types of coke and oxide feed is a measure of their relative performance. It needs to be stressed here that despite the high coke rates in Indian blast furnaces, the effective carbon rates are not very unfavourable, and, in some cases, globally comparable.

Sulphur: Sulphur is present in coal, both as organic and inorganic (pyritic) sulphur. In Indian coals with total sulphur contents of 0.5–0.6% (except Assam coal which has 1.5–2.5% sulphur), 70% of the sulphur is in inorganic form and 30% is organic sulphur. Pyritic sulphur decomposes completely to hydrogen sulphide and ferrous sulphide during cokemaking, while only half of the organic sulphur decomposes to hydrogen sulphide. Approximately 75–80% of the sulphur in coal thus ends-up in coke.

Sulphur in coke has a detrimental effect on blast furnace operation, since increased slag volume is required to remove it as a sulphur-bearing compound in blast furnace slag. This automatically reduces the productivity and increases the coke rate. Therefore, in recent years, recourse has been taken to external desulphurisation of blast furnace hot metal to bring down the sulphur levels to say 0.030% maximum, prior to the use of hot metal in BOF steelmaking (details given in Chapter 16). In order to restrict the sulphur content in hot metal to within reasonable limits (say 0.060–0.080%) even if external desulphurisation is practised, the upper limit for sulphur in coals suitable for cokemaking is generally placed at 1%. Sulphur in coal does not normally pose problems in India.

Phosphorus: The entire amount of phosphorus that enters a blast furnace through the burden materials gets reduced under the conditions used, and is present in the hot metal. Removal of phosphorus is carried out during steelmaking. A safe limit for phosphorus in coal would be 0.050 to 0.060%, and many coals fall well within this range.

Alkalis: Alkalis are present in coal in the form of sodium and potassium oxides (Na_2O and K_2O) to the extent of typically 0.20–0.35%. The alkali content of iron ore, in comparison, is normally very small. Blast furnace operation gets seriously affected if the alkali content of raw materials is high (say beyond 2 kg/thm) because alkalis keep re-circulating between the tuyere area and the upper stack. Normally, half of the total alkali input comes from coke ash. Fluxes like limestone and dolomite contribute the remainder. Therefore, the alkali content in any coal is a parameter used for its selection in cokemaking.

8.3 PETROGRAPHIC CHARACTERISTICS OF COALS FOR COKEMAKING

8.3.1 Macerals and Mineral Matter

Macerals are the microscopically recognisable individual organic constituents of any coal. They are distinguishable under a microscope on the basis of their reflectance and morphology. A given maceral may differ significantly in composition and properties from one coal to another. For some macerals, the variation depends mainly on the rank of the coal (see Section 8.3.2). There are three main maceral groups—vitrinite, exinite and inertinite.

Vitrinite: Vitrinite is the most common and important maceral group in bituminous coals. Vitrinite is considered a reactive maceral that burns readily during combustion.

Exinite: The exinite group is normally a minor maceral component in any coal. It is, however, the most reactive maceral group, since it contains more hydrogen than the others.

Inertinite: As the name suggests, the inertinite group of macerals is generally not reactive at all.

Mineral matter: Mineral matter comprises the inorganic components of coal. During combustion of any coal, the composition of the mineral matter gets altered because of the evolution of the water of hydration of the minerals, and the expulsion of other components such as carbon dioxide and sulphur oxides. The end product of combustion of coal is ash, which then has a different composition compared to the original mineral matter.

8.3.2 Reflectance (Rank) of Coal

Reflectance is measured by microscopic examination of vitrinite using a special reflectance microscope. For this purpose, fine coal is made into a small sample using an adhesive, and the top face of the sample is polished before it is placed under the reflectance microscope. Oil having a refractive index of 1.585 is spread on the polished surface, and then the objective of the microscope is allowed to come in contact with the oil layer. When light impinges on the polished surface, the extent by which the incident light gets reflected from the surface of the coal sample is a measure of the rank of the coal. An average of 100 such reflectance readings is usually reported as the *average reflectance of coal in oil*—R_o (average) (the subscript o denotes oil). Since vitrinite is bireflective, the reflectance varies as the microscope stage is rotated. Following complete rotation (360°), the two maximas of reflectance that are observed give the maximum reflectance of that particular coal particle. This procedure is repeated for 100 particles (to yield 200 maximas) and the mean of all these measurements of reflectance of separate vitrinite particles gives the *mean maximum reflectance* (MMR).

Both these methods are used to measure the quality of vitrinite present in any coal. Vitrinite reflectance increases with the rank of coal and is perhaps the most significant parameter influencing the cokemaking potential of any coking coal.

8.4 OTHER IMPORTANT CHARACTERISTICS

Caking property: All coals undergo chemical changes when heated, but some coals also exhibit physical changes. The latter group of coals is generally called coking coals, i.e. individual particles of such coals on heating form a mass or cake. This caking tendency of any coal is influenced by its volatile matter content, reaching a maximum in the range of 25–30% volatile matter. High caking tendency is mandatory for the production of metallurgical coke.

Free swelling index: The *free swelling index* (FSI) is a measure of the increase in the volume of any coal when it is heated under a given set of conditions without any external restrictions. In general, the FSI of bituminous coal generally increases with increasing rank, but the values may vary considerably even within a given rank. Therefore, though this parameter is of some importance in assessing the coking properties of any coal, absolute interpretation of this data is quite tricky and sometimes extremely difficult. The FSI values are lower for coals that are below bituminous coal in rank. The extreme is anthracite, which does not fuse at all, and shows no swelling.

Hardgrove grindability index: Before any coal is charged for cokemaking, it has to be crushed to at least 80% (sometimes even 90%) below 3 mm so that:

(i) Adequate bulk density is obtained when the coal is charged into the coking chamber (typically 800–900 kg/m^3)

(ii) Sufficient surface area is exposed when the coal begins to liquefy during the heating cycle thereby producing strong coke at the end of carbonisation.

The *Hardgrove grindability index* (HGI) of any coal gives an idea of its relative grindability or ease of pulverisation. In comparison with any coal used as a standard, the index is determined in terms of the amount of that sample coal which passes through 200 mesh after grinding in a special Hardgrove grinding machine. This percentage is given an index number—the higher the number, the softer is the coal, i.e. the easier it is to grind that coal. The HGI values higher than 55 indicate that the coal is soft. The values less than 45 are for hard coals. Therefore, coals with a minimum HGI of 50–52 are considered suitable for economical cokemaking.

Crucible swelling number: The *crucible swelling number* (CSN), similar to FSI, is an important factor in determining whether a coal will coke or not. The method is rapid and is particularly sensitive to the extent of oxidation of any coal. Therefore, it is often used in exploration audits to ascertain the extent of oxidation that has taken place in any deposit, or the amount of oxidation (weathering) of any coal during storage after mining and before use. The values range from 0 (no caking characteristics at all) to 9, and beyond 9+ (superior coking properties). Generally, coals with CSN of 3½ minimum are required for cokemaking.

Fluidity: When coals used for cokemaking are heated during carbonisation, they pass through successive stages of softening, swelling, becoming semi-plastic and completely plastic, before finally solidifying into coke. Therefore, any way of measuring these alterations in the state of coal is of considerable significance in cokemaking. High-quality coking coals melt and get fused into a hard coke mass, i.e. the fluid constituents in such coals combine with the non-melting fractions to form a strong solid mass. Some coals may have inadequate plasticity, while others may be too fluid for this to happen. In both extremes, blending is required before coals exhibiting this type of behaviour can to be used. In fact, very few coals by themselves make high-grade blast furnace coke. In all such cases, optimum coal blends have to be formulated and knowledge of the fluid/plastic behaviour of the individual coals becomes necessary.

Several *plastometers* (Gieseler, Sapozhnikhov, etc.) are available for measuring the plastic properties of coal, and each of these has its respective optima for assessing the coking potential of a coal.

Dilatometric properties: At the temperature at which fusion of any coal mass occurs, there is significant evolution of volatile matter in gaseous form. The bubbles originating within the pasty region exert pressure on the remaining coal, thereby resulting in swelling of the entire coal mass. Instruments have been designed to measure this dilation/swelling properties, thereby giving some idea of what would occur when such coals are charged into a coking chamber. There are two types of dilatometers, viz. Audibert-Arnu and Ruhr that are available to measure the *dilatometric properties* of any coal. The former is more commonly used.

8.5 SELECTION OF COALS FOR COKEMAKING

The criteria used for the selection of coals for cokemaking are as follows:

- Chemical properties—proximate and ultimate analysis
- Rheological properties—assessed by Gieseler plastometer, Sapozhnikov plastometer, etc.
- Dilatometric properties—determined by Audibert Arnu or Ruhr dilatometer
- Agglomerating properties—caking index, CSN, FSI, etc.
- Petrographic analysis—which determines the coal rank, the maceral make-up, and the mineral composition.

All these properties have been used with varying degrees of success to predict the quality of coke that can be expected from any coal. These parameters are also utilised in formulating suitable coal blends, and the interaction between the individual properties is often a decisive factor in determining the quality of coke made. It must be mentioned that among these characteristics, perhaps the most useful feature in selecting and blending coals is the petrographic analysis. The Japanese researchers have developed a relationship between Gieseler fluidity and vitrinite reflectance obtained from petrographic analysis to formulate blends for cokemaking in terms of what has become the well known *MOF diagram,* shown in Figure 8.2 (Amit Chatterjee 1991). Since the area suitable for cokemaking can be clearly delineated in such a diagram, the construction of the MOF diagram often is the first step in selecting coking coal blends in many coke plants.

In the case of some methods of carbonisation that have a marked effect on the bulk density of the charge (such as stamp-charging), the dilation characteristics of the individual coals and those of the blend also become an additional criterion for formulating a blend. The variations in dilation and coking pressure as a function of reflectance as summarised in Figure 8.3 (Amit Chatterjee 1991), indicate that beyond the R_o (mean) values of 1.1–1.2%, the 'coking pressure' and 'volume change' increase rapidly. This shows that if such techniques are practised, some precautions need to be taken to avoid high pressure and insufficient contraction during carbonisation.

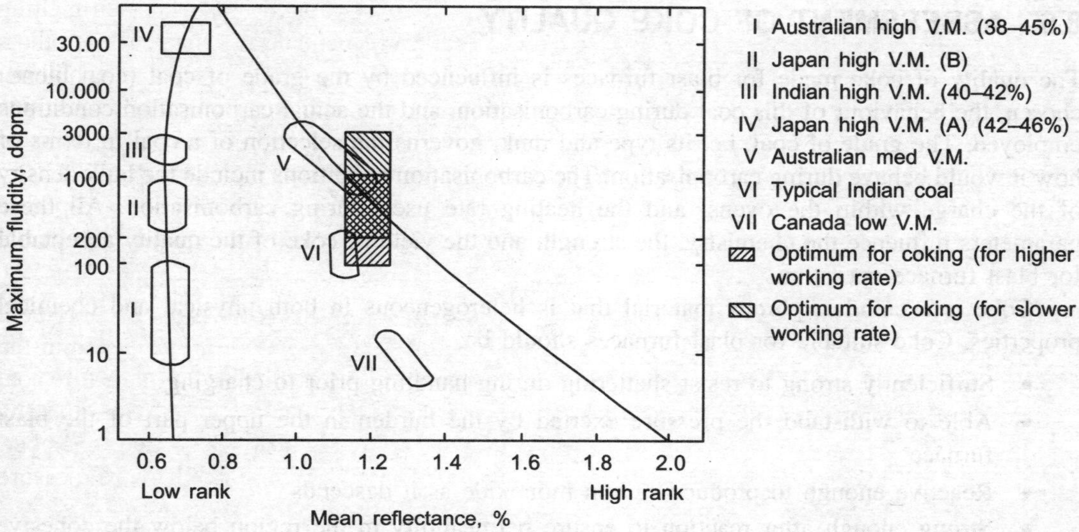

Figure 8.2 Relationship between maximum Gieseler fluidity and rank of coal (MOF diagram).

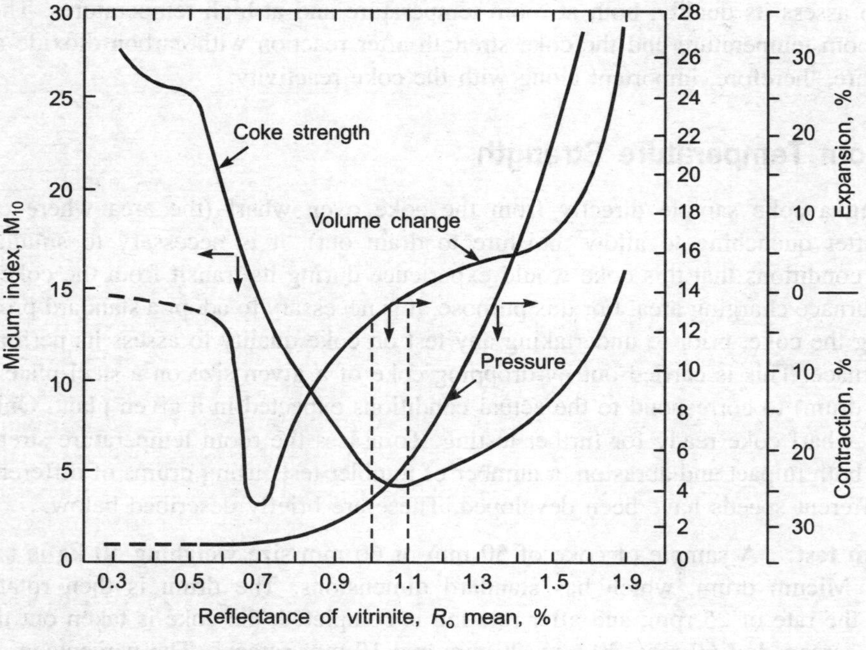

Figure 8.3 Relationship between reflectance and coke strength, volume change (expansion and contraction), and pressure for an individual coal.

8.6 ASSESSMENT OF COKE QUALITY

The quality of coke made for blast furnaces is influenced by the grade of coal (coal blend) chosen, the behaviour of this coal during carbonisation, and the actual carbonisation conditions employed. The grade of coal, i.e. its type and rank, governs the selection of a coal in terms of how it would behave during carbonisation. The carbonisation conditions include the bulk density of the charge within the ovens, and the heating rate used during carbonisation. All these parameters influence the chemistry, the strength and the yield of coke of the quality acceptable for blast furnace operation.

Coke is a cellular, porous material that is heterogeneous in both physical and chemical properties. Coke suitable for blast furnaces should be:

- Sufficiently strong to resist shattering during handling prior to charging
- Able to withstand the pressure exerted by the burden in the upper part of the blast furnace
- Reactive enough to produce carbon monoxide as it descends
- Strong enough after reaction to ensure permeability in the region below the cohesive zone.

Therefore, in order to evaluate the suitability of coke for use in blast furnaces, it becomes mandatory to assess its quality, both at room temperature and at high temperatures. The coke strength at room temperature and the coke strength after reaction with carbon dioxide at high temperature are, therefore, important along with the coke reactivity.

8.6.1 Room Temperature Strength

After drawing a coke sample directly from the coke oven wharf (the area where coke is discharged after quenching to allow moisture to drain out), it is necessary to simulate the approximate conditions that this coke would experience during its transit from the coke wharf to the blast furnace charging area. For this purpose, it is necessary to adopt a standard procedure for stabilising the coke, prior to undertaking any test on coke quality to assess its performance in a blast furnace. This is carried out by dropping coke of a given size on a steel plate (or by rotation in a drum) to correspond to the actual conditions expected in a given plant. Only then is coke oven wharf coke ready for further testing. To assess the room temperature strength of coke against both impact and abrasion, a number of tumbler tests using drums of different sizes rotated at different speeds have been developed. These are briefly described below.

Micum drum test: A sample of coke of 50 mm or 60 mm size weighing 50 kg is taken in a mild steel Micum drum, which has standard dimensions. The drum is then rotated for 4 minutes at the rate of 25 rpm, and after rotation is completed, the coke is taken out through the door and screened at 60 mm, 40 mm, 20 mm and 10 mm screens. The percentage of coke retained on the 40 mm screen and that passing through the 10 mm screen are designated as the *Micum indices*—M_{40} and M_{10} respectively. The former gives an idea of the resistance of coke to breakage by impact, and the latter its resistance to abrasion. Therefore, high M_{40} and low M_{10} indices are desirable in all blast furnace coke.

IRSID test: The IRSID test initially suggested by IRSID's laboratory in France and later adopted by The International Organisation for Standardisation (ISO), determines the strength of smaller-sized coke (say up to 20 mm). The drum used is identical to the Micum drum. The quality parameters assessed by this test are the *IRSID indices*:

I_{20} = the percentage weight of coke that is above 20 mm size after rotation

I_{10} = the percentage weight of coke passing through 10 mm screen after rotation.

ASTM tumbler test: This test also shows the abrasion characteristics of coke and is a modified version of the Micum test. The percentage of coke retained on a 25.4 mm screen is reported as the stability factor, and that on a 6.35 mm screen is reported as the hardness factor.

8.6.2 High Temperature Characteristics

In Chapter 7, gas flow through the bed of solids in a blast furnace has been discussed. As mentioned earlier, coke is a porous solid consisting of carbon and ash. The physical chemistry (thermodynamics and kinetics) of combustion of coke, gasification of carbon by CO_2 and reduction of iron oxide by carbon in blast furnaces have been discussed in Chapter 5. Chapter 6 gave the details of the thermal aspects of reaction of coke/carbon in blast furnaces.

Coke reactivity is a measure of the rate at which coke carbon reacts with the oxidising gases like carbon dioxide, oxygen, air, or steam. The rates of the reactions depend upon the characteristics of the coke surface, the total surface area of coke exposed, and the chosen test conditions (gas composition, velocity, concentration, and temperature). The reactivity of coke has a direct relationship with the resistance that coke offers to CO_2 attack during the *solution loss reaction* ($C + CO_2 \rightarrow 2CO$). Too high a reactivity would lead to high solution loss, thereby giving rise to disadvantages like:

- Loss of carbon from the stack region of the blast furnace, resulting in high coke rate
- Degradation of the coke owing to gas produced by the solution loss reaction
- Decrease in the hot strength of coke after reaction
- Reduction in the size of the coke in the lower part of the furnace, and its consequent effect on the permeability of the coke bed in the furnace hearth.

Various coke reactivity tests have been developed. They are all empirical in nature varying from test-to-test in terms of the prescribed conditions, such as the amount and size of coke used in the test, the geometry and dimensions of the reaction chamber used, the duration of the test during which coke is exposed to the gas, and the composition, the pressure, and the temperature of the gas that is used in the test. The Japanese method developed by Nippon Steel Corporation (NSC) is universally accepted for measuring coke reactivity. The NSC coke reactivity test is similar to the standard iron ore reducibility test, with appropriate alterations made in the apparatus dimensions and the test conditions to make it amenable for measuring the reactivity of coke. For any given sample of coke, the test yields two parameters—the *coke reactivity index* (CRI) and the *coke strength after reaction* (CSR).

Determination of CRI and CSR involves taking 200 g of 20 ± 1 mm coke in a tube, and reacting it with a stream of CO_2 at a flow rate of 5 lpm for two hours at a temperature of (1100 ± 5)°C. The material left after cooling (i.e. the residue), is weighed, and the CRI is calculated:

$$CRI = \frac{\text{original weight} - \text{weight of residue}}{\text{original weight}} \times 100 \tag{8.1}$$

The residue is tested for its strength by tumbling it in an I-Drum (130 mm diameter × 700 mm length), rotated at 20 rpm for 30 minutes. The CSR is calculated in the following manner:

$$CSR = \frac{\text{weight of +10 mm coke after tumbling}}{\text{initial weight of coke}} \times 100 \tag{8.2}$$

Though the two values obtained by using Eqs. (8.1) and (8.2) are independent, and should not really be compared, it is agreed that coke with a high CRI value generally has a low CSR, and coke with a low CRI has a high CSR, as shown in Figure 8.4 (Arendt et al. 2000). However, the adoption of pre-carbonisation (Section 8.9) or the use of alternative cokemaking technologies like non-recovery ovens (Section 8.7) play a role in altering the co-relationship between CRI and CSR. A minimum CSR of 60 and maximum CRI of 28 are considered desirable for high-quality coke used in large blast furnaces.

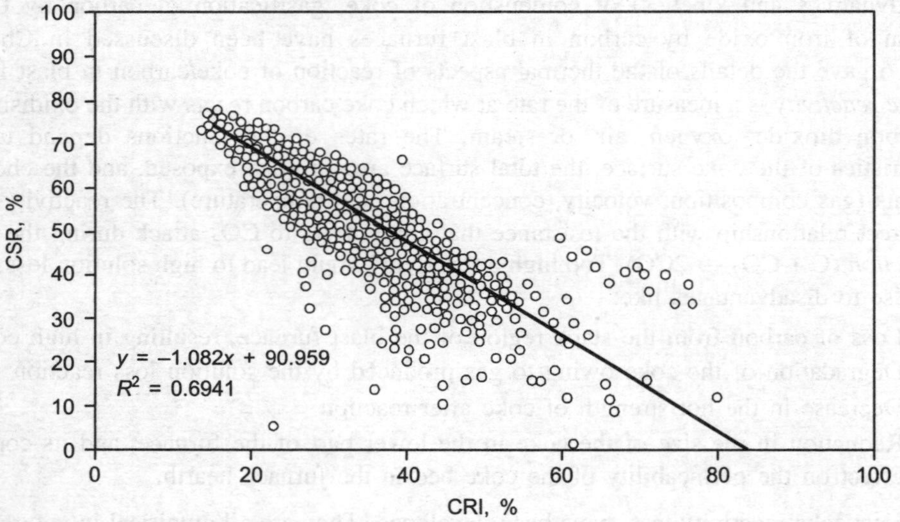

Figure 8.4 Correlation between CSR with CRI for different cokes.

8.7 PROCESSES USED FOR COKEMAKING

In the introduction it was mentioned that cokemaking involves carbonisation or *destructive distillation of coal* under controlled conditions, and in the absence of air. Therefore, the carbonisation conditions used in the coke ovens are of great importance in determining the coke properties. The recent usage of larger-sized blast furnaces (volumes greater than 2500 m^3) accompanied by increasing pulverised coal injection (PCI) have resulted in a greater demand for stronger and more consistent quality coke.

The cokemaking processes that are in commercial use all over the world to cater to blast furnace requirements are now discussed.

8.7.1 Conventional By-product Coke Ovens

The first *slot-type oven* chamber was built during the mid-19th century, and the design of the ovens has been progressively improved throughout the twentieth century to arrive at the design in use today in all conventional slot-type coke ovens. Figure 8.5 shows a sketch of a modern by-product coke plant consisting of a number of ovens built in series. Each oven is a relatively narrow, vertical, rectangular chamber. Since the ovens are heated from outside, and the heat required for carbonisation is transmitted through the side walls, oven widths are restricted in order to achieve uniform heating within each oven chamber. Similarly, convenience of charging and handling limits the length of each oven chamber. As a result, the only option left to increase the capacity of slot ovens is to make them taller, and oven heights have increased considerably over the years.

Individual ovens are typically 400–600 mm wide, 1300–1400 mm long, and vary in height from 4 m to 7 m. Each oven has two adjacent heating chambers on either side for gas firing to raise the oven temperature to the desired centre coke mass temperature of around 1350°C at the end of the carbonisation period. All the ovens are charged with fine coal (at least 80% below 3 mm) through ports (normally 3) provided on the top using a mechanically operated charging car; following which the charge is levelled along the length of each oven from one side. When carbonisation is complete, typically in 16–20 hours, red hot coke is carefully pushed out through the opposite side.

A series of slot-ovens in tandem (typically 15–55 ovens) forms a coke battery. The ovens are referred to as by-product recovery coke ovens since along with coke, both gas and liquids (like tar) are produced as by-products. These products are recovered and processed in a by-products recovery plant, which is normally located adjacent to a slot-oven coke battery. Some of the gas recovered is burned and used to heat the ovens, while the remainder, after cleaning, is exported as a fuel for other heating applications. Before using coke oven gas as fuel, many other constituents in the gas are recovered as by-products.

One tonne of coal will yield approximately:

- 750–800 kg of coke for blast furnace use
- 45–90 kg of coke breeze (below 6 mm size)
- 285–345 m^3 of coke oven gas (COG)
- 27–34 litres of tar
- 55–135 litres of ammonia liquor
- 8–12.5 litres of light oil.

A typical conventional slot-type coke oven battery along with the auxiliary facilities for charging, coke quenching and by-product recovery, is shown in Figure 8.6. Conventional slot-type coke ovens have silica brick walls, which must be able to withstand temperatures in excess of 1300°C with little structural support. Exposure to high temperatures for long lengths of time makes the walls susceptible to damage. The silica-based bricks are also required to retain their shape and position despite repeated heating and cooling in successive cokemaking operations. In order to minimise cracking and distortion of the bricks, ovens once heated, have to be kept permanently hot, i.e. slot-ovens cannot normally be stopped/started as and when required.

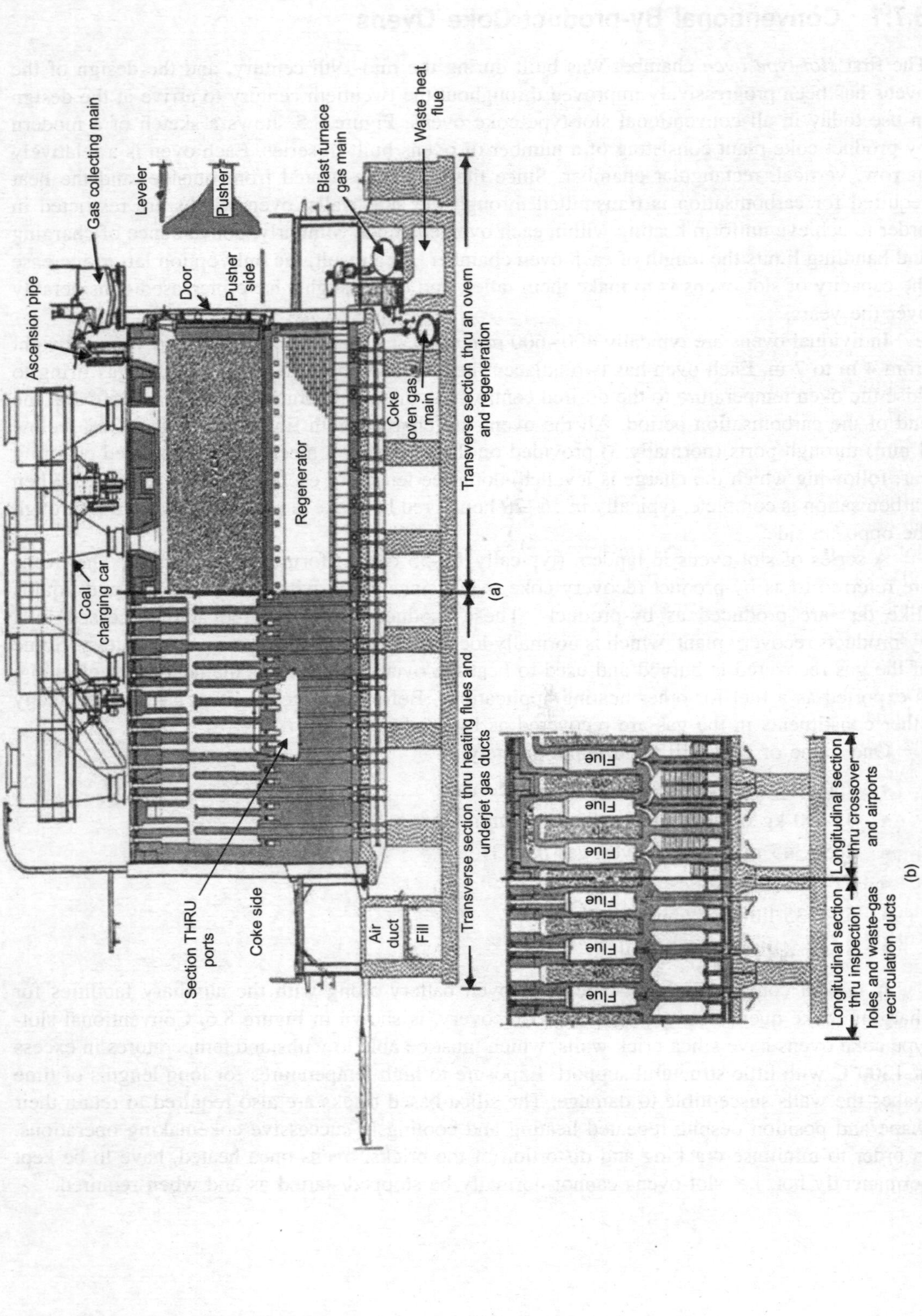

Figure 8.5 (a) Transverse and longitudinal sections through an underjet-fired low-differential combination by-product coke oven. (b) Enlarged section of waste-gas recirculation ducts in each individual oven.

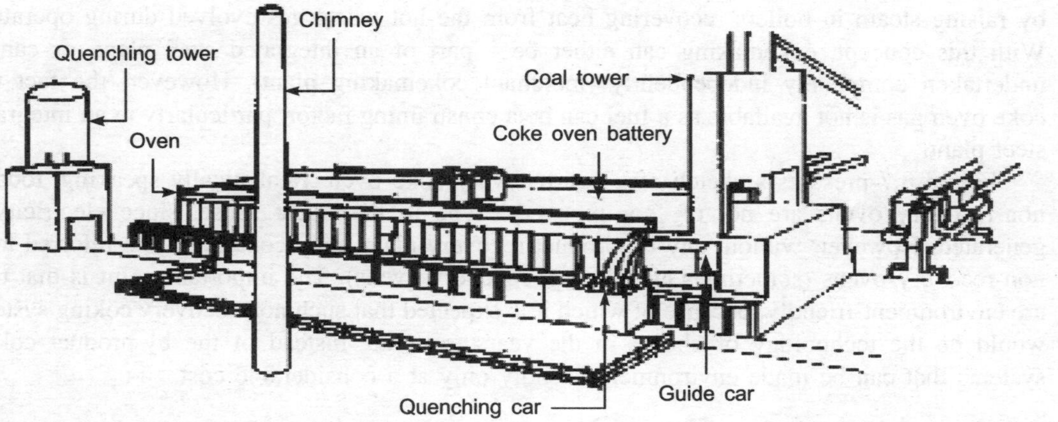

Figure 8.6 Schematic diagram of a top-charged conventional by-product coke oven battery.

8.7.2 Non-recovery Ovens

Utilisation of the gas emanating from slot-type coke ovens has become a major problem since the operations involved are not always environment-friendly. Huge capital is required to make slot-type coke oven batteries capable of fulfilling the stringent environmental norms that exist today. Taller and wider ovens are a partial solution to this problem of utilising the exit gas, combined with more complex gas-treatment units. However, constant efforts are still being made to evolve oven enclosure designs that would prevent emissions. For the above reasons, non-recovery type ovens are becoming popular in recent years. Such ovens are an extension of beehive technology of cokemaking, which has been known since long. Beehive technology originally attempted to increase the operational efficiency and the product yields by making the individual ovens flatter and wider, rather than narrower and taller. Such ovens were directly heated from the top instead of indirect heating through the side refractory walls, as is the case in slot-ovens.

The early beehive ovens vented the gases evolved during cokemaking directly to the atmosphere causing immense pollution. For this reason, beehive ovens were almost abandoned, at least in the developed countries. In the 1920s, further development in beehive ovens took place giving birth to non-recovery cokemaking technology. Kembla Coal & Coke Company in Australia introduced the concept of combusting coke oven gas in the sole flues, located beneath the coal charge. This development resulted in carbonisation of coal to coke in beehive ovens in a bidirectional mode, similar to that in vertical slot-ovens. No further development occurred in non-recovery cokemaking technology for the next 50 years (1920s to 1970s), essentially because of the favourable economics of the by-product coking system where the sale of by-products (benzol, toluene, ammonium sulphate, etc.) added to the total revenue. This state of affairs was acceptable until ecological considerations exerted pressure on by-product plant effluents. During the 1970s, new developments took place in the USA at Jewell Coke Company and Pennsylvania Coke Technology to incorporate the recovery of by-products from beehive ovens. In the modified system, while coke is the main product, electricity is generated as a secondary product by raising steam in boilers recovering heat from the hot waste gas evolved during operation. With this concept, cokemaking can either be a part of an integrated steel plant, or can be undertaken completely independently (merchant cokemaking plant). However, the fact that coke oven gas is not available as a fuel can be a constraining factor, particularly in an integrated steel plant.

Figure 8.7 presents a sketch of a non-recovery coke oven. Realistically speaking, today's non-recovery ovens are not of 'non-recovery' type in the truest sense, since electricity is generated. However, without any by-product recovery plant, they continue to be referred to as non-recovery ovens (sometimes also as heat recovery ovens). The important point is that they are environment-friendly, because of which it is expected that such non-recovery coking systems would be the technology of choice in the years to come, instead of the by-product coking systems that can be made environment-friendly only at a considerable cost.

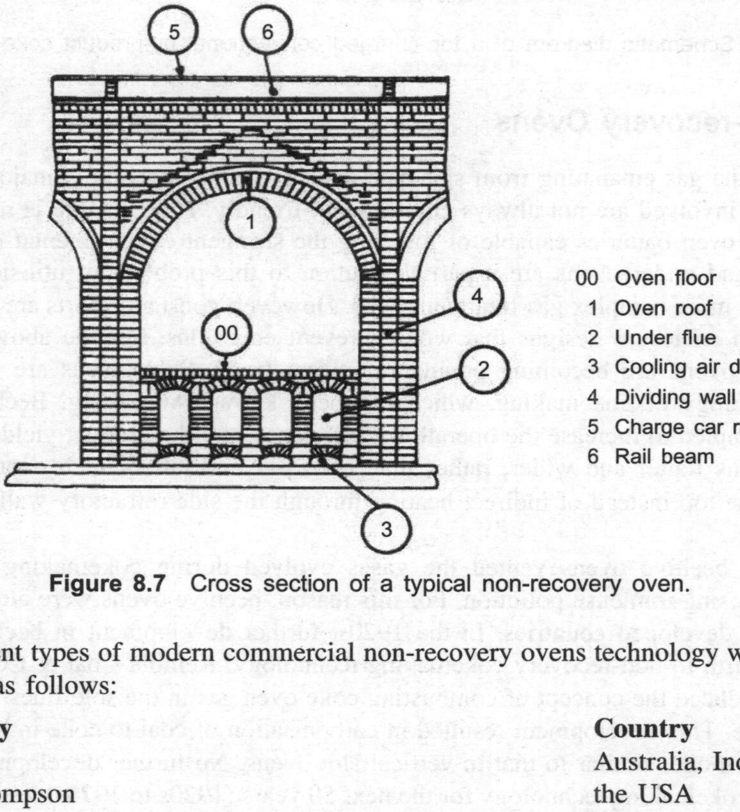

Figure 8.7 Cross section of a typical non-recovery oven.

The different types of modern commercial non-recovery ovens technology which are in use at present are as follows:

Technology	**Country**
Kembla	Australia, India
Jewell Thompson	the USA
PACTI	Mexico
Kumbraj	India
Dasgupta	India
SPDCI (Shangxi Province Development Coking Institute)	China

In non-recovery beehive ovens, the coking process instead of moving horizontally from the sides as in the case of slot ovens, proceeds vertically from the top of the coal charge downwards and from the bottom upwards. This makes the coking chambers horizontal with limited height. As a result, they are simple in design and are modular individual units, thereby reducing the capital costs of a battery of ovens considerably. Water quenching of red hot coke in a quenching tower is carried out, in the same way as in slot ovens. Volatile matter from the coal supplements the heat necessary for coking. However, the horizontal space requirement is at least 30–40% more than in the case of slot-oven batteries of the same capacity, and this is sometimes a drawback.

Because 'non-recovery' ovens operate under negative pressure and the by-products of carbonisation are burned within the ovens, the door emissions are greatly reduced, and sometimes, totally eliminated. In addition, any problems associated with coke pressure when using swelling-type coals are eliminated, since there are no constraining side walls in such ovens. There are, however, some disadvantages (enumerated earlier) that include:

- Reduced output of blast furnace quality coke from each oven
- No generation of coke oven gas, which can be of value in large integrated steelworks as a fuel in subsequent processing
- Low productivity rates per specific chamber volume on account of extended carbonisation times
- Requirement of more land for a given coke output
- Unavoidable partial burning of the coal charged inside the ovens owing to the presence of air—leading to at least 1–2% lower coke yield from a given amount of coal.

Figure 8.8 compares the modes of heat supply to slot-oven and beehive oven. Carbonisation in non-recovery ovens is, in principle, quite different from that in by-product ovens. Heat is supplied above the coal charge directly by partial combustion of the evolving flue gases and part burning of the top surface of the coal charge. While a part of the exit gas is sent to boilers for power generation, complete post-burning of the remaining flue gases in the oven sole heating flues provides heat directly beneath the coal charge.

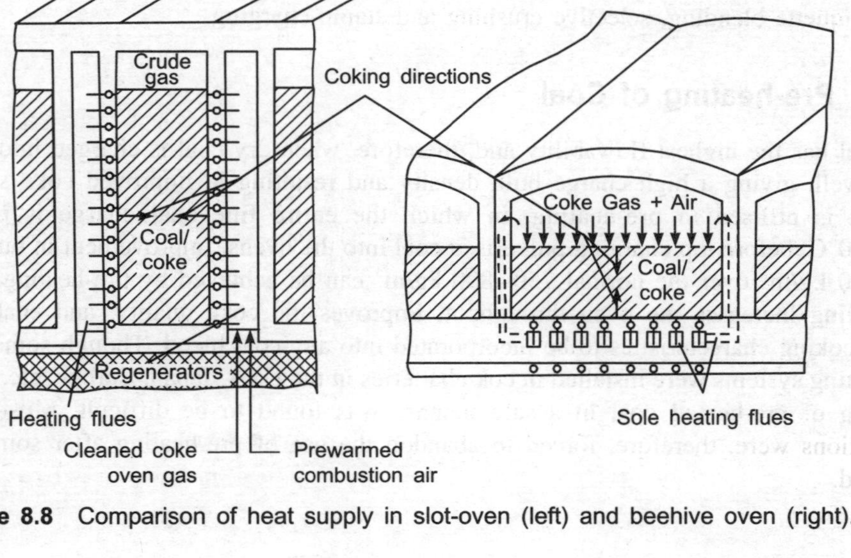

Figure 8.8 Comparison of heat supply in slot-oven (left) and beehive oven (right).

The first set of non-recovery coke ovens were built in Vansant, USA, in the year 1989 and more ovens were added in the next ten years, both in Vansant and other places in the USA, for example, by Inland Steel in Chicago. Other non-recovery installations exist in Australia, Mexico and India. These installations incorporate the concept of heat recovery. After the waste gas is combusted at 1000–1200°C, the heat is used to generate both steam and power. Once carbonisation begins and gases are evolved, they are partially combusted. This is done by introducing primary air through ports located on the top/sides of the oven chamber in the free space above the coal mass. The partially combusted gases leave the oven chamber through the downcomers in the oven walls, and enter the sole heating flues underneath the oven after more air is introduced so that combustion can be completed. At the end of the carbonisation cycle when the coke mass is at a temperature of about 1150°C, the doors are removed and the charge is pushed in the horizontal position by a pusher into the quench car.

Coke of high-quality with CSR exceeding 72 can be made in non-recovery ovens, owing to the higher bulk density of the charge (more so if the charge is compacted before insertion into the oven), higher operating temperatures particularly in terms of higher sole temperatures, and slower coking rates (longer coking times). Many of the properties of the non-recovery oven coke cannot be economically achieved in slot ovens.

8.8 PRE-CARBONISATION TECHNIQUES

Conventionally coke ovens are charged from the top with fine coal at ambient temperature and a moisture content of around 4–8%. During charging, compaction automatically takes place owing to the weight of coal. As a result, the charge within any oven tends to be most dense at the bottom of the oven, immediately below the charge holes and least dense at the top of the oven between the holes. Such density differences inevitably result in some variation in the properties of the coke made in different parts of the oven. Techniques have been developed to tailor the coal charge to increase and/or make the bulk density of the charge more uniform—these developments are referred to as pre-carbonisation techniques, which include pre-heating of coal, briquette blending, selective crushing and stamp-charging.

8.8.1 Pre-heating of Coal

Dry coal has the highest flowability and, therefore, when dry coal is charged into any oven, it packs well, giving a high charge bulk density and resulting in improved coke strength. This concept is utilised in pre-heating, in which the entire fine coal charge is pre-heated to 180–250°C, before top charging pulverised coal into the ovens. Improvement in bulk density by 100–150 kg/m^3 over the normal 750–800 kg/m^3 can be achieved by pre-heating. As a result, pre-heating increases the oven throughput, improves the coke quality, and enables coals of poorer coking characteristics to be incorporated into any coal blend. Though some commercial pre-heating systems were installed in coke batteries in the USA, Japan, Europe, etc. in the 1970s, handling of pre-heated coal in a safe manner was found to be difficult. Most cokemaking installations were, therefore, forced to abandon the use of pre-heating after some explosions occurred.

8.8.2 Briquette Blending of Coal

Briquette blending was developed in Japan to utilise the beneficial effects of high charge-coal density of a coal blend that contained briquettes. This also controlled the swelling of the charge. In briquette blending, either a portion of the total coal charge or only the poorer coking constituent of the blend is hot formed into briquettes (50 mm × 30 mm × 20 mm, or any similar size) in a grooved roll press and then blended with the remaining portion of the coal charge before carbonisation. Coal tar and pitch in various proportions are used as the binder during the manufacture of the briquettes. Briquette blending increases the bulk density of the charge in the oven and this factor along with the presence of tar/pitch improves the cold as well as the hot strength of the coke produced.

Since the binder used is relatively expensive, attempts have been made to go in for binder-less briquetting. In this technique, the entire coal to be charged into any oven is briquetted immediately prior to taking it into the charging car, without using any tar/pitch. Since no binder is used, the briquettes are susceptible to disintegration. However, the fragments so generated become a part of the charge and also enter the oven. The technique is referred to as partial briquetting—not as efficient as briquetting but still superior to charging only fine coal.

8.8.3 Selective Crushing of Coal

Selective crushing aims at controlling the degree of crushing of the different constituents of coal. The reactive components of coal—primarily vitrinites—are the softest constituents of coal, and the mineral matter is the hardest. In conventional coal crushing mills, the vitrinites get crushed to a relatively finer size compared to mineral matter constituents when the entire coal is crushed together. However, for producing high-quality coke, it is desirable to crush the mineral matter to sizes finer than the coaly mass comprising essentially vitrinites, so that during cokemaking, when the coal charge softens, the former is assimilated better, leading to improved coke strength. Though selective crushing is based on sound theoretical footing, this technology has not found general acceptance in the industry because the additional capital cost of two-stage crushing often did not justify the benefits that accrued, and the maintenance of the machinery was found to be difficult.

8.8.4 Stamp-charging

In stamp-charging, the bulk density of the coal charged into any oven is increased by physically stamping the charge into a cake, outside the oven. The cake, which is almost similar in size to the oven, is then inserted into the oven. Stamping is carried out externally in a stamp-charging-pushing machine which uses drop hammers to increase the bulk density of the charge to around 1150 kg/m^3 before it introduces the cake into the slot oven. Crushing to more than 90% below 3 mm and 40–50% below 0.5 mm is required to produce stable cakes. No extraneous binder is added to the coal blend after crushing. Only around 10% moisture has to be maintained to provide the binder action. With stamp-charging, low-rank, weakly-caking and high-volatile coals can also be used, but because the charge is compacted to very high bulk densities, increased wall pressures can be a problem. To control the wall pressure within acceptable limits so that the oven refractory walls are not damaged, the coal blend used must be carefully chosen. An optimum balance between high and low volatile coal is necessary in order to ensure that high-quality coke is made without causing permanent damage to the oven walls and the oven supporting structure.

Stamp-charging has the following advantages:

- Significantly higher bulk density (1150 kg/m^3)
- Increased throughput (8–10%) owing to higher bulk density
- Improved coke strength owing to closer 'packing' of the individual coal particles during carbonisation
- Coke produced is denser, smaller and more uniform in size
- Less pollution during carbonisation since fine coal is not charged from the top of the ovens.

The primary disadvantage is that the preparation and handling of the stamped cake entails increased capital cost. Stamp-charging has been successfully used in France, Poland, the Czech Republic, and India.

8.9 ALTERNATIVE COKING METHODS

It is felt by many that today's most prevalent multi-chamber by-product oven system has probably reached the end of its development potential. Consequently, building new replacement units, would involve a substantial capital investment. Keeping this in view, work has been undertaken to assess both the technical and economic prospects of alternative methods of producing coke. The development of non-recovery ovens has already been discussed. Other options (like Jumbo coke reactors) are being pursued vigorously. Conventional slot-type ovens are unlikely to be installed in most places in the future owing to environmental pressures, and therefore, non-recovery ovens, jumbo coke reactor, etc. will find increasing application.

REFERENCES

Arendt, P., F. Huhn, H. Kuhl and G. Sbierczik, CRI and CSR—An Assessment of Influential Factors, *Cokemaking International*, 1 (2000).

Chatterjee, Amit, Tata Tech, June 1991.

Ray, H.S., B.P. Singh, S. Bhattacharjee and V.N. Mishra, *Energy in Minerals and Metallurgical Industries*, Allied Publishers, 2005.

9

Raw Materials II: Iron Ore and Agglomerates

9.1 INTRODUCTION

Of the many variables that affect the productivity and energy consumption of blast furnaces, the quality of raw materials is perhaps the most significant. All over the world, substantial improvements in blast furnace performance have been brought about by using superior quality raw materials. Consistency in quality is another key requirement for ensuring efficient blast furnace operation.

The most widely used raw materials in blast furnace iron production are coke, lump iron ore, sinter, pellets (*sinter* and *pellets* are together often referred to as *agglomerates*), and fluxes like limestone and dolomite. Coke has been dealt with in Chapter 8. The other raw materials mentioned will be covered in this chapter. The influence of the quality of the raw materials on productivity, fuel rate and other parameters controlling blast furnace performance will be discussed in Chapter 10.

9.2 OCCURRENCE OF IRON ORE

Details of the iron ore reserves in some of the key steel producing countries in the world are presented in Table 9.1 (Chatterjee 2005). Most of the global iron ore deposits occur in the form of hillocks that project above the ground. Iron ore is obtained by controlled blasting of these hillocks. The *run-of-mine* (ROM) ore thus excavated is crushed using different types of crushers, followed by screening to obtain three basic products as follows:

- 10–30 mm or 10–40 mm size fraction, which is used as lump ore in blast furnaces
- An intermediate fraction (all below 10 mm and with a large proportion typically below 8 or 6 mm and above 100 mesh) for sintermaking
- Fines below 100 mesh size, that is either rejected or used to make pellets, often after beneficiation to increase the iron content to over 65%, since the gangue in iron ore gets concentrated in the 'fines' fraction.

Table 9.1 World iron ore reserves (Mt)

Country	Recoverable reserves	Average Fe content, %
United States	6900	30
Australia	18000	61
Brazil	7600	63
Canada	1700	65
China	21000	33
India	13400	63
Kazakhstan	8300	40
Mauritania	700	57
Russia	25000	56
South Africa	1000	65
Sweden	3500	63
Ukraine	30000	30
World total	150000	47*

*This figure is for the entire world and not the average of the countries listed in this Table.

Lump ore, sinter and pellets ore thus become the feedstock for liquid iron production in blast furnaces. It needs to be mentioned that in most deposits, a maximum of 10% is hard lump ore, and around 15–20% of the ROM ore after processing is in a size that is suitable as feed for sintermaking. Because of several advantages of using sinter in blast furnaces, sintered iron ore has emerged as the preferred iron feedstock. Pellets have replaced sinter in certain cases on account of their higher purity and greater size consistency. In general, more and more agglomerates are being used in blast furnaces, with the result that the use of lump ore has decreased in many countries from 35% in 1970 to less than 10% at present. This has also helped in prolonging the life of the iron ore deposits in view of the fact that only a small fraction is fit for use as lump ore, as already mentioned. Sinter usage has increased to at least 50% in most blast furnaces, and pellets, which were virtually unknown before 1965, now constitute up to 30% of the charge. The global pellets production has crossed 300 Mt (India around 15 Mt). Pellets are made in large quantities (3–6 Mt) in one central location and then transported by sea or rail. Since sinter cannot be transported easily over long distances after it is made, sinter plants are normally located inside almost all integrated steel plants.

All the iron oxide feedstocks for blast furnaces either contain haematite (Fe_2O_3) or magnetite (Fe_3O_4), with iron contents ranging from 55% to as high as 66.5%. The higher the iron content in the feed, the lower is the slag volume generated in the blast furnace, which automatically increases the productivity and reduces the coke rate. Therefore, higher iron contents in the feed (60% and more) are preferred. For the same reason, lump iron ores that contain less than 55% iron are often beneficiated to enrich the iron content to acceptable levels.

9.2.1 Iron Ore Reserves of India

As shown in Table 9.1, India has the sixth largest reserves of iron ore in the world, and these are of high grade. India along with Ukraine, Russia, China, and Australia accounts for about three quarters of the world reserves of 150 billion tonnes iron ore, the average Fe content of which is as low as 47%. The proven reserves of haematite iron ore in India (without considering the probable/inferred reserves that could be 2–3 times higher) are around 12 billion tonnes. This figure keeps changing as more iron ore sources are found. Out of the total reserves, high-grade ore (min. 65% Fe) is 13%, medium-grade ore (62–65% Fe) is 47%, and the rest is low grade ore.

The deposits of iron ore in India are located mainly either in eastern India (especially in Jharkhand and Orissa) or in central India (Chattisgarh and Madhya Pradesh). While the reserves are apparently quite extensive, it needs to be emphasised that high-grade lumpy ore in most of these deposits constitutes only 6–7% of the total, i.e. blast furnace operation based only on lump ore cannot be a long-term option for India. Magnetite, to the extent of around 11 billion tonnes, is found in western India. This is the only major reserve of magnetite, virtually all other Indian reserves are haematite. These magnetite deposits contain around 40% Fe, and occur in very fine form. Therefore, this magnetite cannot be used without beneficiation and pelletisation.

At present, there are three large capacity pelletising plants in western India, located in Goa, Karnataka and Andhra Pradesh. The pellets made are largely exported. However, for conservation of India's iron ore, pelletising is likely to be adopted to a much greater extent in the future all over India.

9.3 BENEFICIATION OF IRON ORE

The steps involved in the beneficiation of iron ores differ from ore to ore, depending on the mineralogical constituents of a particular iron ore and the nature of the association of the gangue minerals with iron oxide in that ore. The extent to which beneficiation can be undertaken economically depends both on the amount and the nature of the gangue. The methods available for the beneficiation of iron ore include the following:

- Crushing and screening
- Wet screening followed by desliming
- Gravity concentration
- Magnetic separation
- Floatation
- Selective flocculation
- Bio-leaching of iron ore.

The first three methods listed above are suitable only for beneficiating high-grade lump ore. The inferior grades require upgrading by adopting one or more of the selective methods of concentration. For example, the beneficiation of low-grade ores containing haematite, goethite or siderite usually involves incorporation of gravity concentration or high intensity magnetic separation, while magnetite ores with similar iron contents can be directly upgraded by using magnetic separators. For upgrading the finer fractions of both haematite and magnetite ores, floatation and selective flocculation techniques are normally used.

9.4 THE SINTERMAKING PROCESS

9.4.1 Bedding and Blending

In sintermaking, various materials in fine form, and in given proportions have to be processed.

Therefore, one of the steps preceding sintermaking is bedding and blending so that uniformity in the feed to the sintering machine(s) can be ensured, which, in turn would guarantee that the sinter produced is of consistent chemistry.

For this purpose, the individual raw materials comprising iron ore fines, fluxes (limestone, pyroxenite, dolomite, etc.) and coke breeze are first crushed (fluxes are ground in a hammer mill, and coke breeze is ground in a roll crusher or a rod mill) and screened to the size required—typically, iron ore between 100 mesh and 10 mm, fluxes below 3.15 mm and coke breeze below 6 mm. These materials are then individually stored in bins. The materials are discharged from these bins in the prescribed amounts onto conveyor belts. At the last stage, a shuttle-type conveyor belt takes all the materials together to the bedding and blending yard. The discharge from the conveyor is heaped in the shape of triangular piles of the mixed materials on the ground. From each of these piles, the mix is then scooped by a reclaimer, which in its turn, helps to make long, horizontal layers.

Approximately 300 individual layers make up one bed and at least two such beds are provided in any sintering plant—one that is still being laid horizontally, and the other from which the mixed materials are in the process of being sent for sintering. Immediately before sintering, flux is added and minor adjustments are often made to the coke breeze amount in the sinter mix, depending on the requirements of sinter chemistry and the prevailing thermal conditions. More often than not, solid wastes from the plant that contain some amount of iron and/or flux constituents are added to the sinter mix. Sintering provides an easy way for recycling these 'waste' materials.

If the fluctuations in sinter chemistry are such that the standard deviation in CaO content is 1.8–2.0% and that in the Fe content is about 0.70–0.75% without any bedding and blending, these fluctuations can be minimised to 0.6% for CaO and 0.3% for Fe by adopting bedding and blending. Thus, the need for bedding and blending operations prior to sintering is obvious.

9.4.2 Granulation

The green mix after thorough mixing is transferred to a mixing drum. In this drum, water is sprinkled and the drum is rotated to encourage ball/granule formation. This is essential for maintaining the permeability in the sinter bed, particularly if deep-bed sintering (bed depth 600 mm and more) is resorted to.

Since it is widely accepted that deep-bed sintering gives superior quality sinter, the mechanism of granule formation has received considerable attention. The growth of the granules has been described in terms of two limiting cases, or postulates. In the *k-postulate*, the granule size is assumed to be proportional to the seed size. Hence,

$$y = kx \tag{9.1}$$

where y and x are the granule size and seed size, respectively, and k is a constant of proportionality. Recently, it has been shown that k can be calculated from the relationship

$$k = \left(\frac{g\varepsilon\rho_l + W\varepsilon\rho_s}{g\varepsilon\rho_l - W\rho_s + W\varepsilon\rho_s} \right)^{1/3} \tag{9.2}$$

where W is the moisture content of the granulating charge, g is a minor correction for any entrapped air bubbles in the layers and for the curvature of the liquid–air interface at the granule surface, ε is the void fraction of the layer, and ρ_l and ρ_s are average densities of liquid and solid, respectively.

In the second theory, the so-called *t-postulate*, the layer thickness t is assumed to be fixed and independent of the seed size. Hence

$$y = x + 2t \tag{9.3}$$

At present, no theoretical analysis exists for predicting the layer thickness, based on which the merits/demerits of these two postulates can be assessed.

9.4.3 Sintering

The technique of sintering, whereby the fine materials charged are partially fused at a high temperature to produce clustered lumps was developed in the 1890s, in the non-ferrous industry as a batch process. Continuous sintering of copper ore was undertaken between 1903 and 1906 by Dwight and Lloyd in Mexico, wherein, a moving-bed of fine ore particles and other additives, supported on a metallic chain type strand, was agglomerated by exposing the bed to high temperatures. The heat required was supplied primarily from external sources. The same idea was later adopted for iron ore sintering. Since then, *Dwight–Lloyd technology* has been used all over the world to produce iron ore sinter for blast furnaces. Sinter is typically 5 mm to 40 mm in size, made from feed ore fines of below 10 mm in size.

The layout of a Dwight–Lloyd iron ore sintering machine is shown in Figure 9.1. The sinter mix is fed at one end of an endless belt (or strand) that consists of a large number of hollow individual steel boxes (called *pallets*), which keep moving continuously like a chain at the desired rate, determined by the vertical sintering speed, from the feed end to the discharge end of the strand. Once the mix is fed into a pallet, heating is begun (referred to *as ignition*) by using external burners located in the ignition hood at the feed end of the machine. Individual wind

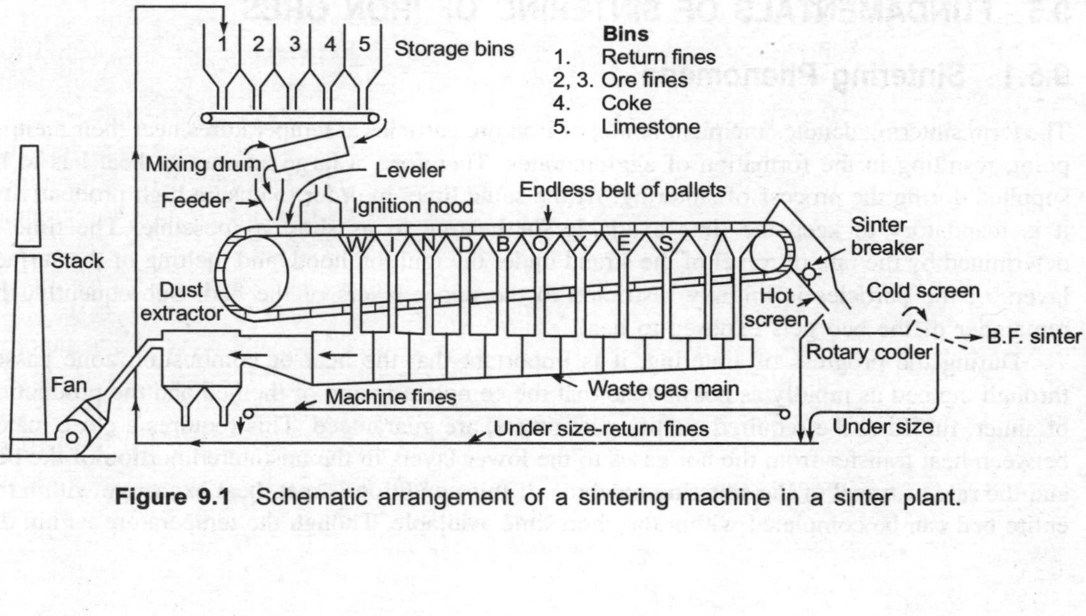

Figure 9.1 Schematic arrangement of a sintering machine in a sinter plant.

boxes located under the strand provide the suction as each pallet moves from the feed to the discharge end. Sintering is normally completed before the strand reaches the last two wind boxes at the discharge end. Suction of air through these two wind boxes cools the sinter on the strand.

9.4.4 Feed Preparation and Product Handling

The starting materials for making sinter are fine raw ore (less than 8–10 mm), coke breeze (coke that is between 3–6 mm in size), fine limestone/dolomite (less than 3 mm) and sand. An alternative to sand plus limestone/dolomite is dunite, i.e. magnesium silicate, which supplies both CaO and MgO along with silica, thereby helping to balance the sinter chemistry, without adding the three materials separately. Return sinter below 5 mm (normally referred to as *return fines*) and steel plant waste materials that contain some iron units, are also added. After mixing all the input materials, water is sprinkled for granule/nuclei formation as explained earlier (Section 9.4.2). These nuclei grow as mixing of the flux, carbon and iron ore fines is continued, but since the time available for granule formation is relatively short (3–4 minutes), the growth of the nuclei into large globules (more than 10 mm) is restricted. The granulated material is transferred to the sintering strand to form a bed (typically 400–600 mm deep). Burners, fired with blast furnace/coke oven gas or oil, are used to supply heat initially. Air is sucked at a fixed suction (usually 1.1–1.6 kPa) from under the strand so that the flame front after ignition travels through the entire bed of the sinter mix. The advance of the flame front is also supported by the combustion of coke breeze present in the bed.

The iron ore particles get agglomerated owing to partial melting at the surface and slag formation. The sinter thus produced is crushed and screened before charging into blast furnaces. For this purpose, the sinter cake from the machine is cooled and then broken to a suitable size (typically 6–40 mm) in a crusher, followed by screening to remove the below 5 mm size. Part of the original sinter (usually 30–40%) becomes return fines (generated both at the sinter plant and in the blast furnaces prior to charging).

9.5 FUNDAMENTALS OF SINTERING OF IRON ORES

9.5.1 Sintering Phenomena

The term sintering denotes incipient fusion of iron ore particles at temperatures near their melting point, resulting in the formation of agglomerates. Therefore, a large amount of heat has to be supplied during the process of sintering. At the same time, in order to ensure high productivity, it is mandatory to keep the time available for heating to as short as possible. The time is determined by the rate of travel of the strand under the ignition hood, and melting of the surface layers of the particles is initially restricted to the upper layers of the bed. Subsequently, the remainder of the bed gets exposed to heat.

During the progress of sintering, it is important that the heat or combustion zone passes through the bed as rapidly as possible so that the complete fusion of the bed and the production of sinter, fulfilling the required quality parameters, are guaranteed. This requires a close match between heat transfer from the hot gases to the lower layers in the unsintered portion of the bed and the rate of travel of the sintering machine. If this condition is met, heat exchange within the entire bed can be completed within the short time available. Though the temperature within the bed is as high as 1200–1300°C in the combustion zone, it decreases to 60°C quite quickly beyond the combustion zone. This is quite unlike the heat exchange that takes place in the upper part of a blast furnace, where almost 4 metres of descent is required to increase the material temperature from room temperature to 800–900°C. The large difference in the particle sizes involved and the difference in the suction conditions in the two cases are the essential reasons for the changed situation.

To monitor the conditions existing within the bed during sintering, it is important to know the positions of the *flame front* (maximum temperature zone) at any point of time. This can be achieved in practice by embedding thermocouples at different depths within the bed. This can easily be done in laboratory studies conducted in batch-type pot-grate set-ups, which simulate any one portion of the bed as it traverses through the entire sintering cycle—from ignition to cooling. For any thermocouple, positioned, say, at the centre of the bed, the time–temperature relationship would typically follow the pattern depicted in Figure 9.2 (Eketorp 1962). The temperature registered by the thermocouple will at first rise rapidly to about 60°C, then remain constant until the flame front passes through that portion of the bed, and finally, begin to decrease once the air gets sucked through that zone. After the combustion zone proceeds further to the lower regions of the bed, the products of combustion from the flame front further ahead also pass through the zone in question. As a result, within a few minutes, the thermocouple temperature, after rising to the sintering temperature of around 1200–1300°C, begins to decrease.

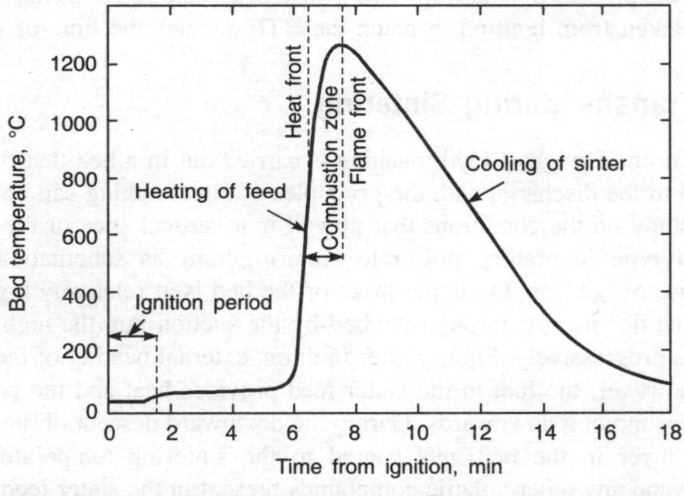

Figure 9.2 Temperature variation as a function of time in each layer of the sinter bed in a laboratory pot-grate sintering unit.

One striking feature of sintering is that the combustion zone (another name used to denote the flame front) travels so rapidly that it is possible to complete sintering of a bed of 500–600 mm depth within a span of around 25 minutes. The rapid dissipation of heat through the bed and the factors that influence the rate of travel of the flame front are, therefore, of key importance in sintering. From a fundamental standpoint, it can be envisaged that within the sinter bed, two fronts co-exist—the flame front and the heat front. While the flame front is the zone of maximum temperature in the bed at any point of time, the *heat front* is the zone that follows behind the flame front and absorbs the heat generated in the flame front. The heat front is, therefore, always located closer to the top surface of the bed than the flame front, and the lag between the two, has an influence on the process of sintering as well as the quality of sinter.

The rate of forward travel of the flame front is influenced by the moisture content in the sintering mix and the amount of fuel (coke breeze) it contains. Both these factors determine the total amount of heat generated per unit time in that portion of the bed. The exact trace of the time–temperature curve (typical case shown already in Figure 9.2) would thus be unique for a given set of operating conditions that also include the rate of air flow through the bed. The latter is an independent variable that is governed by the total depth of the bed, the bed permeability, and the extent of suction that is employed.

All these factors also have a role in determining the rate of upward travel of the cooling front, and, therefore, the position of the heat front. Only if a balance is struck between the rate of downward movement of the flame front and the movement of the heat front, would it be possible to make optimum use of the air that gets pre-heated by the approach of the combustion zone. If the speeds of these two fronts do not match, i.e. either one is slower or faster than the other, it would be manifested by widening of the combustion zone. Such a situation, however, would not increase its maximum temperature required for fusing the sinter mix. Most of the heat generated in the combustion zone is absorbed in the process of drying, calcining (if raw limestone/dolomite/dunite is used during trimming) and preheating of the lower layers of the bed. When the combustion zone reaches the grate bars, i.e. the lowest layer in the bed, it signifies the completion of the process of sintering. This is also often referred to as the *burn through point* (BTP). The time taken from ignition to reach the BTP denotes the time of sintering.

9.5.2 Heat Transfer during Sintering

Though sintering in the Dwight–Lloyd machine is carried out in a bed that travels horizontally from the feed end to the discharge end, the principles of sintermaking can be understood better by conducting a study on the conditions that prevail in a vertical slice of the bed. This is what is done in batch type laboratory pot-grate sintering unit as schematically illustrated in Figure 9.3. Because of ignition, the upper layer of the bed is at relatively higher temperatures; and as air is sucked downwards through the bed by the suction fan, the high temperature zone moves downwards progressively. Shortly after ignition, external heating of the bed from the top is discontinued; however, the fuel in the sinter feed provides heat and the combustion zone at 1200–1500°C keeps moving downwards. During the downward descent of the combustion zone, each subsequent layer in the bed gets heated to the sintering temperature. While this is happening, water (and any other volatile compounds present in the sinter feed) is driven off. By the time the combustion zone reaches the lower-most region of the bed, the bonding between the grains is completed throughout the entire bed. The agglomerates that are formed undergo cooling on the strand itself as discussed earlier. The final cooling of sinter before it is processed further is carried out in a separate sinter cooler that follows the sinter strand.

Figure 9.4 depicts the conditions existing within a vertical cross section of the bed in the Dwight–Lloyd sintering machine at any time during the progress of sintering. During the process of sintering beginning with the upper layers of the bed, the combustion front moves vertically downwards through the bed owing to the suction, until sintering is completed. Therefore, at any instant of time, within the bed, sinter is present at the top, and there is still some material that is yet to be sintered, since the combustion front has not travelled to that depth till that time.

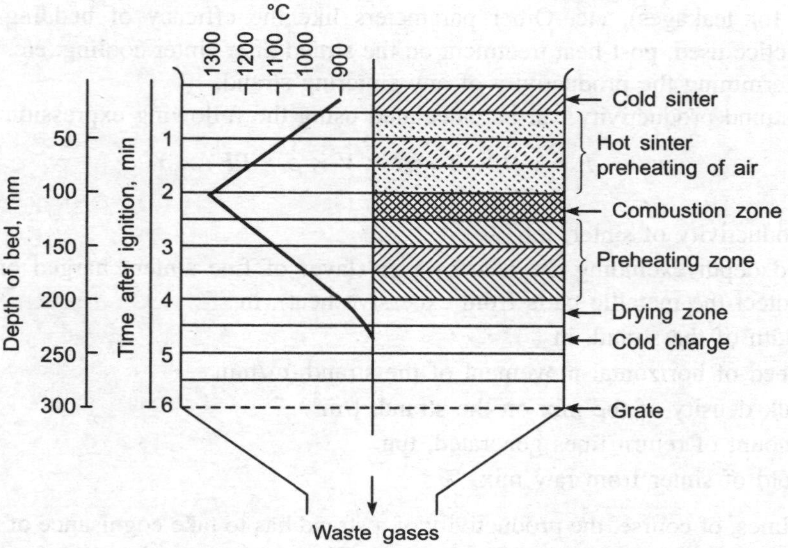

Figure 9.3 Vertical 'slice' through a sinter bed (300 mm deep) in a laboratory pot-grate sintering unit, few minutes after ignition of the top layer.

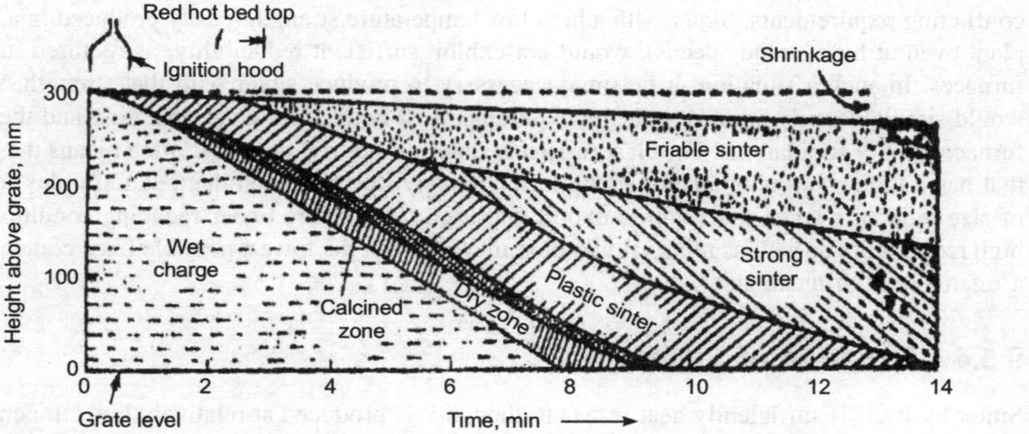

Figure 9.4 Vertical section through a sinter bed (300 mm depth) along the entire length of the bed showing the various zones existing in a Dwight–Lloyd sintering unit as a function of time.

9.5.3 Sinter Productivity

Sinter productivity, or the rate at which sinter is produced in a given sinter strand, depends on several factors such as the characteristics of the raw materials that are used, their preparation prior to charging on the strand (i.e. balling, trimming, addition, if any, etc.), the geometry of the sinter bed (width and depth), the suction applied, and effective suction under the strand (after accounting for leakages), etc. Other parameters like the efficacy of bedding and blending, ignition practice used, post-heat treatment on the strand after sinter cooling, etc. also contribute towards determining the productivity of any sintering strand.

Sinter strand productivity can be calculated using the following expression:

$$P = (60 \times B \times H \times V \times \rho - RF) \times Y \tag{9.4}$$

where

P = productivity of sinter, tph

B = bed depth excluding the hearth layer (layer of fine sinter charged on the strand to protect the metallic parts from excessive heat), m

H = width of the strand, m

V = speed of horizontal movement of the strand, m/min

ρ = bulk density of the mix on the strand, t/m^3

RF = amount of return fines generated, tph

Y = yield of sinter from raw mix, %

At all times, of course, the productivity of a strand has to take cognisance of the stipulations of sinter quality that is required by blast furnaces. The aim in most situations is to produce sinter with a high room temperature strength as well as a high low temperature (below 550°C) strength at the highest productivity of the strand. In some cases, blast furnace operation may demand a moderate low temperature strength combined with high reducibility of sinter. These are conflicting requirements. Sinter with a high low temperature strength (easily produced in a sinter plant even at high strand speeds), would not exhibit sufficient reducibility, as required in blast furnaces. In such a situation, it becomes necessary to produce sinter with that strength, which would simultaneously comply with the requirements of both sinter plant operation and the blast furnace quality stipulations. For blast furnaces, sinter of the 'right quality' often means the sinter that has a high room temperature strength, a relatively low reduction degradation index (extent of size reduction when the sinter is exposed to high temperature under reducing conditions), a high reducibility as well as minimal variation in chemistry, the lowest possible fines content, and a relatively high mean size.

9.5.4 Structure of Sinter

Sinter by itself is sufficiently heat resistant, though it is produced at relatively low temperatures (1050°C max.) without complete melting of the iron ore particles. Consequently, the microstructure of sinter, when viewed under a microscope consists of non-reacted ore particles bonded by fairly large amounts of complex SFCA (silico-ferrites of calcium and aluminium), as well as partially reduced haematite in the form of magnetite and wustite. Use of extra amount of flux or the selection of poorly sinterable ore fines can result in poor sinter quality. Furthermore, if all the materials in the sinter feed do not fuse within a narrow temperature range, sinter quality is also likely to suffer. This is one of the reasons why large amounts of wastes collected from different sources cannot often be added to the sinter mix.

Iron ore sinter is a product of recrystallisation following partial melting of iron ore fines and slag formation. The quality of the final sinter is governed by the nature of the minerals that are present after partial melting, fusion and subsequent recrystallisation. This can be assessed by studying and, if possible, controlling the mineralogical phases that constitute sinter. Mineralogical studies throw light on the type of mineral constituents and their texture. A wide variety of minerals is found in iron ore sinters such as magnetite, maghemite, wustite, troilite, ferrites and in silicates like fayalite, olivine, glass, etc. depending on the materials that are fed and the sintering conditions that are employed thereafter. It has been established that the type of iron ore minerals present in the feed influence the yield of sinter; on the other hand, the gangue minerals and the flux have a bearing on the physical strength of sinter. Therefore, the characteristics of the feed materials, including their composition, have to be carefully selected along with matching sintering conditions if high-quality sinter has to be produced.

9.5.5 Influence of Sinter Chemistry

Whenever the percentage of sinter used in the blast furnace is increased (and there is a constant need to do this on account of the superior properties of sinter compared with lump ore), the sinter chemistry has to be adjusted so that the total amount of fluxes (CaO/MgO) required in the blast furnace slag comes predominantly, if not wholly, through the sinter in the burden. The best situation exists when the entire flux requirement is catered to by sinter. In such a situation, the entire flux(es) that is required gets calcined during sintermaking, thereby reducing the total energy consumption in the blast furnace. It needs to be stressed that though this is always the ultimate goal, this goal is not always possible because there are limitations to the extent to which sinter basicity can be varied. In some basicity ranges (particularly at low basicities), the sinter properties get adversely affected, essentially on account of the amount and type of SFCA present in sinter under these conditions.

9.6 PELLETISATION

Pelletisation is a process that involves mixing very finely ground particles of iron ore of less than 325 mesh (45 micron) size with fluxes such as limestone, lime, dolomite, etc. as fines, and a binder like, bentonite (0.5–1%). After these materials are thoroughly mixed, the moisture level is generally adjusted to around 10% before the feed is taken for pelletising. Pelletising is carried out either in a rotating disc (typically 3.7–5.5 m in diameter) inclined at 45°, or in a drum (typically 9–10 m long and 2.5–3.0 m in diameter) rotating at 10–15 rpm. The green pellets that are made following rotation in either the disc or the drum are screened. The oversize (usually +9 mm) is sent for heat induration, while the undersize is returned to the feed circuit for re-grinding.

Figure 9.5 shows the principles of particle movement in drum and disc pelletisers. The paths of motion of the particles during rotation are shown by the arrows. Joining together or agglomeration of the fine particles in the feed into green balls/green pellets occurs by the *capillary forces* exerted by the moisture in the feed. The changes that take place gradually at various stages of ball formation are depicted in Figure 9.6. It is important to note that the amount of water used should not either be too little or be too much. Insufficient moisture would not generate enough capillary forces that are required for bonding, while *excessive wetting* would not also have the desired effect (see Figure 9.6(f)). Once nucleation has started, the pellets grow

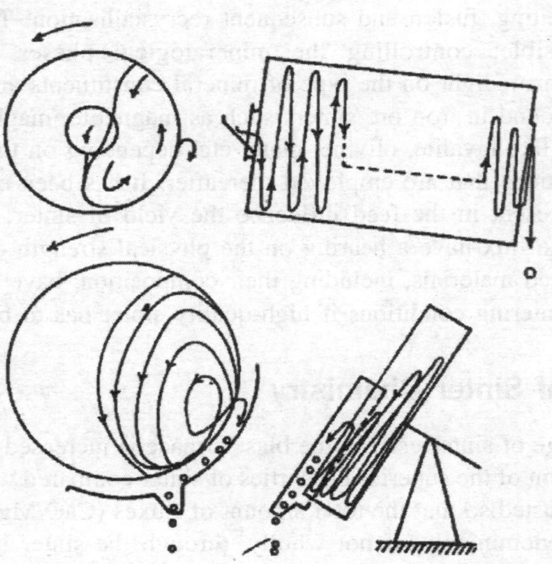

Figure 9.5 Principle of rotation of the charge in a drum (top) and disc (bottom) pelletiser.

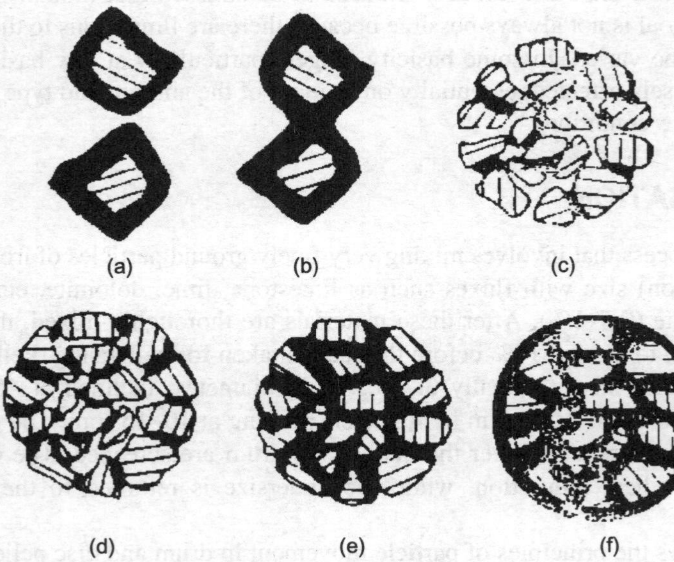

Figure 9.6 Stages in the formation of green balls: (a) initial wetting, (b) primary bonding, (c) formation of flocs, (d) agglomeration, (e) optimum balling, and (f) excessive wetting.

almost at an exponential rate. Depending on the extent of growth of the balls during rotation as well as the breakage that occurs owing to collision between the green balls already made, equilibrium is reached with respect to the size of pellets (generally restricted to 10–15 mm diameter). These green pellets are then dried and heat-hardened at a temperature of 1250–1300°C to produce pellets with acceptable strength.

Figure 9.7 shows the typical set-up of the equipment used for heat-hardening of green pellets comprising the following:

- A travelling grate where the green pellets are dried and pre-heated to around 600–700°C utilising the exit gases from the subsequent rotary kiln
- A rotary kiln operating at a maximum temperature of 1250–1300°C where the final heat-hardening takes place. The rotary kiln is heated by burners which use heavy oil/gas as the fuel positioned at the exit end.

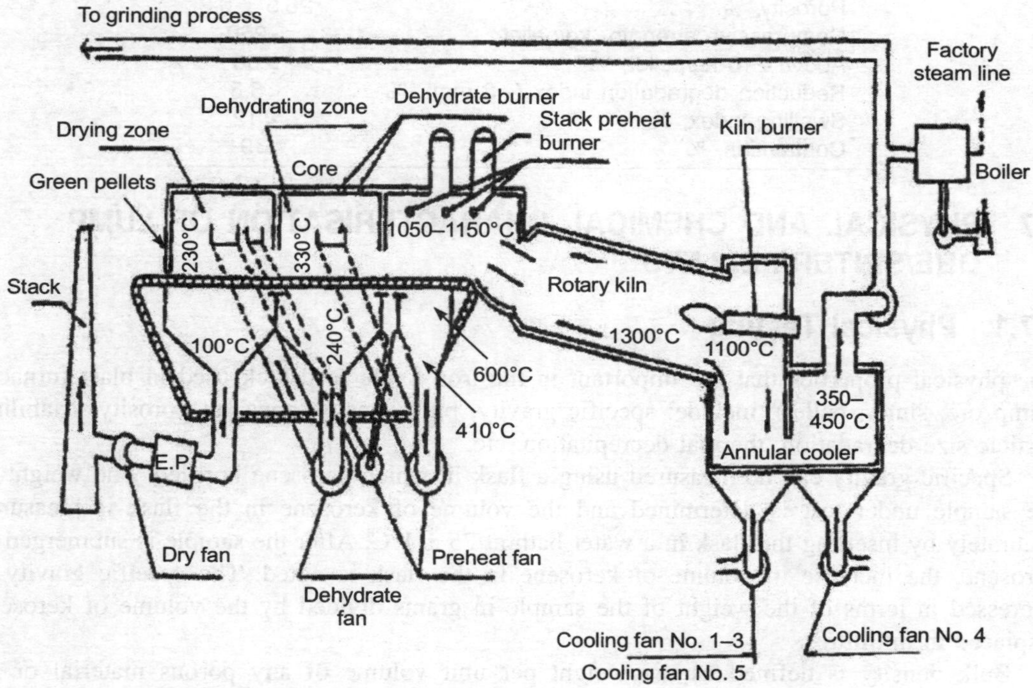

Figure 9.7 Induration of green pellets in a travelling grate-rotary kiln combination.

The temperatures in various zones of the grate–kiln combination are also indicated in Figure 9.7. In contrast to sintering, no incipient fusion occurs in the case of pelletising. The pellets develop strength by diffusion bonding and some amount of recrytallisation. Table 9.2 presents data on the typical properties of pellets suitable for blast furnaces.

In order to circumvent heat-hardening completely, attempts have also been made in several countries to produce cold-bonded pellets that possess sufficient strength without induration. However, so far, it has been possible to produce only limited tonnages of cold-bonded pellets. Nonetheless, since this technology holds considerable potential in terms of energy-saving, ability to utilise cheap fines and wastes, along with reduction in environmental pollution, cold-bonded pellets are likely to find wider applications in the future.

Table 9.2 Typical properties of pellets suitable for use in blast furnaces

Parameter	Target
SiO_2, %	2.8 ± 0.1
CaO/SiO_2	1.42 ± 0.05
MgO, %	2.1 ± 0.1
(Na_2O + K_2O), %	< 0.075
Mean diameter, mm	11.2 ± 1
Below 4 mm, %	< 0.5
Porosity, %	26.5 ± 0.3
Compressive strength, kg/pellet	> 260
Above 210 kg/pellet, %	> 80
Reduction degradation index (– 3 mm), %	< 5.5
Swelling index, %	< 12
Contraction, %	< 9

9.7 PHYSICAL AND CHEMICAL CHARACTERISATION OF LUMP ORE/SINTER/PELLETS

9.7.1 Physical Testing

The physical properties that are important in the iron oxide feedstock used in blast furnaces (lump ore, sinter, pellet), include: specific gravity, bulk density, apparent porosity, friability, particle size degradation, thermal decrepitation, etc.

Specific gravity can be measured using a flask in which kerosene is filled. The weight of the sample under test is determined and the volume of kerosene in the flask is measured accurately by inserting the flask in a water bath at 25 ± 1°C. After the sample is submerged in kerosene, the increase in volume of kerosene in the flask is noted. The specific gravity is expressed in terms of the weight of the sample in grams divided by the volume of kerosene displaced in millilitres.

Bulk density is defined as the weight per unit volume of any porous material or an assemblage of porous particles. Voids present both within and between the particles decrease the bulk density. To determine the bulk density, the material in question is filled into a metal container that has an internal diameter of 400 ± 2 mm and internal height of 250 ± 2 mm. The entire assembly is weighed at room temperature. Based on this measurement, the bulk density is calculated in terms of the weight per unit volume.

The apparent porosity of the feedstock has a direct influence on the maximum amount of water that it can absorb. To determine the apparent porosity, the material under test is weighed (S) before it is placed in distilled water, boiled for 2 hours and then allowed to cool to room temperature. The sample is then weighed again (W); dried at 105°C, and then finally weighed (D). From these three weighments, the apparent porosity is calculated using the following formula:

$$\text{Apparent porosity (vol. \%)} = \frac{W - S}{W - D} \times 100 \tag{9.5}$$

The friability of the oxide feedstock is determined by using a cast iron drum—177 mm in diameter and 177 mm long, closed at one end, with the other end fitted with a lid. The drum is also provided with three internal lifters of size 173 mm × 37 mm × 10 mm. One hundred grams of the sample in size 8–16 mm is inserted into the drum before it is rotated at 80 rpm for 4 hours. After tumbling, the sieve analysis of the product is carried out and the results reported as percentage fractions in various sizes. The friability index (FI) is calculated from the equation

$$\text{Friability index} = \frac{d_g}{d_0} \times 100 \tag{9.6}$$

where d_g is the mean geometric diameter of the sample after tumbling, and d_0 is the initial mean geometric diameter of the sample.

Some iron ores decrepitate on heating, thereby producing powdery fines. Decrepitation is measured in terms of the percentage of below 0.5 mm fines generated during heating of the oxide, particularly lump ore (size –25 + 19 mm) to temperatures of 400°C, 600°C and 800°C. Nitrogen at a standard flow rate is continuously passed for 1 hour, while the sample is maintained at the test temperature. The results obtained give an idea of the extent of thermal decrepitation. In case chemical decrepitation has to be determined, reducing gas has to be used when the sample reaches the required temperature.

9.7.2 Chemical Characterisation

The major constituents in all iron oxide feedstocks include: FeO, Fe_2O_3, silica, alumina, CaO, MgO, etc. along with trace elements like Cu, Ni, Co, Pb, Zn and Mn in the form of complex oxides. Chemical analysis can throw light on the behaviour of the particular feedstock in any blast furnace. It also helps in finding out the quantity of fluxes that need to be charged to obtain the slag of the appropriate chemistry. Thus, chemical analysis provides data on the quantity and the quality of hot metal and slag that would be produced in the blast furnace.

As far as important minor chemical constituents are concerned, Na_2O and K_2O are perhaps the most critical. Their amount should be maintained at as low a level as possible (0.05% maximum in iron ore and maximum total load of 2 kg/thm). Zinc is another minor element that needs careful control—the maximum allowable level is often as low as 0.02%. Other minor elements that require control in order to restrict their adverse effect on the environment include cadmium and lead—the maximum limit of each being 0.01%.

9.7.3 Thermal Analysis

Thermal analysis involves the study of the changes in the weight of the sample as a function of time and temperature. Thermal analysis can be carried out using different types of equipment. Thermal analysis conducted using a conventional *thermo-gravimetry* (TG) apparatus involves continuous measurement of the weight change of the iron oxide feedstock as a function of time and temperature. It gives an indication of its thermal stability, composition of the intermediate compounds that may be formed, and the final residue that is left behind after exposure to any given temperature for a given duration. In *derivative thermo-gravimetry* (DTG), the derivative of the weight change with respect to time is recorded as a function of time or temperature. *Differential thermal analysis* (DTA) involves a comparison of the temperature changes that occur in the sample under test with that of a thermally inert material, when the sample is heated/cooled at a uniform rate in a furnace. The changes that are recorded reflect the endothermic/exothermic enthalpy variations caused by moisture removal, phase changes, subsequent fusion (if any), etc.

Differential scanning calorimetry (DSC) is a technique that is employed to record the energy necessary to establish a given temperature difference between the material under test and a reference material, as a function of either time or temperature, as the two specimens are subjected to identical temperature regimes where heating/cooling are carried out at a controlled rate. DSC data is a direct representation of the enthalpy changes that occur. Evolved gas detection (EGD) and evolved gas analysis (EGA) are techniques used to detect whether or not any volatile product is formed during thermal analysis, and, if so, its nature and amount.

9.8 METALLURGICAL TESTS

Over the last few years, the International Organisation for Standardisation (ISO) has standardised procedures for conducting many tests on iron ores and agglomerates that are necessary to predict their metallurgical behaviour during smelting in a blast furnace. All the test procedures are basically empirical, and despite concerted efforts, no universally acceptable single standard has so far been evolved. For example, even for a property like reducibility of any iron oxide (a measure of its reduction potential), there are different standards adopted in different countries.

Table 9.3 summarises the different test conditions employed for assessing the metallurgical behaviour of iron oxides (Gupta and Chatterjee, 1995).

Table 9.3 Static tests on iron oxides

Test	Reducibility	Relative reducibility	Swelling index	Reduction under load	Reduction degradation index
Reducing gas, %					
CO	40 ± 0.5	30 ± 1	30 ± 0.5	40 ± 0.5	20 ± 0.5
N_2	60 ± 0.5	70 ± 1	70 ± 0.5	60 ± 0.5	60 ± 0.5
CO_2					20 ± 0.5
Flow rate, l/min	50 ± 0.5	15 ± 0.5	15 ± 1	85	20
Temperature, °C	950 ± 10	900 ± 10	900 ± 10	1050 ± 5	500 ± 10
Reduction time	O_2 loss 65% or 4 h	3 h	1 h	O_2 loss 80% or 4 h	1 h
Sample quantity	500 ± 1 g	500 ± 1g	18 pellets	1200 g	500 g
Size, mm	10–12.5	10–12.5	10–12.5	10–12.5	10–12.5
Load, kPa	–	–	–	50	–
Retort dia., mm	75	75	75	125	75 (130 mm dia., 200 mm length, 4 lifters, 30 rpm)
Property measured	Reducibility index	Degree of reduction	Degree of reduction, swelling index	Degree of reduction, change in height, pressure drop across the bed	Reduction degradation index, LTB index

The details of some of the important tests are discussed below.

9.8.1 Compression and Tumbler Strength

Compression strength is normally measured only in the case of pellets. Sixty pellets, in the size range of 10–12.5 mm are taken and load is applied using a universal testing machine at a cross-head speed of 15 ± 5 mm/min. The test values are reported as the mean crushing strength and the percentage under 200 daN/pellet (deca newton per pellet) and 150 daN/pellet. The acceptable values are as follows:

Average	min 250 daN/pellet
Below 200 daN/pellet	max 10%
Below 150 daN/pellet	max 5%

To determine the tumbler strength, a drum with a diameter of 1000 mm and length of 500 mm with two lifters of 50 mm height is used. 15 ± 0.15 kg of the sample (9–16 mm size pellets, or 6.3–40 mm size lump ore, or sinter of 10–40 mm) is subjected to 200 revolutions at 25 rpm. After the test, the material is screened; the percentage above 6.3 mm is designated as the *tumbler index*, and the percentage of below 0.25 (or sometimes 0.5) as the *abrasion index*.

The acceptable values of some of the properties mentioned above are as follows:

	Size, mm	Abrasion index, %	Swelling index, %	Tumbler index, %	Reducibility, R40
Pellets	−12.5 + 9.5 (below 5 mm, 4% max)	5	15 (max)	94	1.20 min for fluxed pellets and 0.80 min for acid pellets
Lump ore/Sinter	−10 + 40 (below 5 mm, 4% max)	5	Not important	65	1.24 min for lump ore

9.8.2 Reduction Behaviour

The objective of all the tests conducted to assess reduction behaviour is to determine the response of any iron oxide feedstock to the conditions prevailing in the stack and bosh of a blast furnace. Therefore, all the tests in this category are conducted with the iron oxide sample subjected to gas composition, temperature and external load conditions as close to a blast furnace as possible.

The following tests are commonly undertaken:

- Reduction at 500°C to assess disintegration at the beginning of reduction
- Reduction at around 900°C to assess the reducibility (as well as swelling only in the case of pellets)
- Assessment of permeability and the extent of softening that occurs when a bed of the material under testing is subjected to a temperature range of 1000–1100°C
- Melting and dripping in the temperature range of 1200–1500°C.

All the tests undertaken for measuring the above characteristics of iron oxide can be grouped into static or dynamic tests. Table 9.3 summarises the details of the various tests including the experimental conditions employed, and the methods used to evaluate the results.

Grain disintegration test

In the upper zone of a blast furnace, where the temperatures are relatively low, disintegration of the individual particles of the iron oxide charged can take place essentially because of the phase change from haematite to magnetite. The extent of disintegration can be assessed by undertaking reduction of the oxide at a low temperature followed by tumbling. The test is carried out in a vertical retort (the test conditions are summarised in Table 9.3). After reduction, the material is subjected to rotation at 30 rpm for 300 revolutions in a drum (130 mm diameter and 200 mm length). The material is then screened—the percentage over 6.3 mm is reported as the *disintegration strength*, and the percentage below 0.5 mm as the *abrasion index*.

A similar test is also carried out under dynamic conditions in a rotary furnace (refer Table 9.3 for details of the test conditions). The material after the test is screened and the percentage above 6.3 mm is called the *low temperature breakdown* (LTB) *index*, and the percentage below 0.5 mm, the *dynamic abrasion index*.

Swelling behaviour of pellets

The increase in the volume of pellets during reduction is measured in this test. The volume of the initial charge as well as that of the reduced material is measured by a mercury volumenometer. At the end of the test, the percentage increase in volume, the degree of reduction, and the compression strength of the pellets are reported.

9.8.3 Reducibility

For determining reducibility, two test procedures—relative reducibility and reducibility—are adopted. The results obtained from the first method indicate the degree of reduction as a relative rate compared with a standard sample; while in the second method, the rate of oxygen removal between 30% and 60% reduction is measured and the (*dR/dt*) at 40% reduction in per cent/minute is reported. Both the methods help to assess the reduction rate when the higher oxides present in any iron oxide sample under testing are reduced to FeO.

9.8.4 Reduction under Load

The test is conducted in a vertical retort of 125 mm diameter in which the sample is exposed to reducing conditions (30% CO + 70% N_2) at temperatures up to 1100°C as given in Figure 9.8. The test is particularly suitable for determining the stability of pellets, and other iron oxides, under these conditions. In addition to the extent of reduction, the shrinkage of the charge and its resistance to gas permeability are also measured. The differential pressure that is measured corresponding to 80% reduction gives an idea of the stability of the iron oxide during reduction.

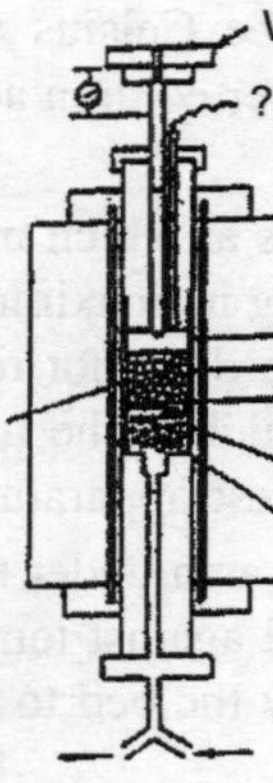

Parameter	Reduction under load	Softening–melting test
Sample		
Size, mm	9.5–12.7	9.5–12.7
Weight, g	500	200–300
Load, kg/cm^2	2	1
Reducing gas		
Flow rate, lpm	15	7.2
Composition, %	CO: 30 N2: 70	CO: 30 CO_2: If require N_2: 70
Heating rate	RT-800°C: 90 min. 800–1100°C: 180 min.	RT-1000°C: 10°C/min. 1000–1500°C: 5°C/min.

Figure 9.8 Schematic diagram of the reduction under load test (including test conditions).

9.8.5 Softening–Melting Test

In Japan and in the UK, in an effort to simulate the behaviour of iron oxides in the cohesive zone of a blast furnace, the test for reduction under load was extended up to 1500°C, using somewhat different test conditions, which are also included in Figure 9.9. This was necessary in order to study not only the reduction that takes place at low and medium temperatures in the solid state, but also the softening and melting behaviour of any iron oxide feedstock at higher temperatures in the cohesive zone of a blast furnace. The cohesive zone is the boundary between the two-phase (solid/gas) region in the upper part of the furnace, and the three-phase (solid/gas/liquid) region in the lower regions of the furnace.

Various parameters that are measured in the softening–melting test are shown schematically in Figure 9.9. Each of these parameters is defined below:

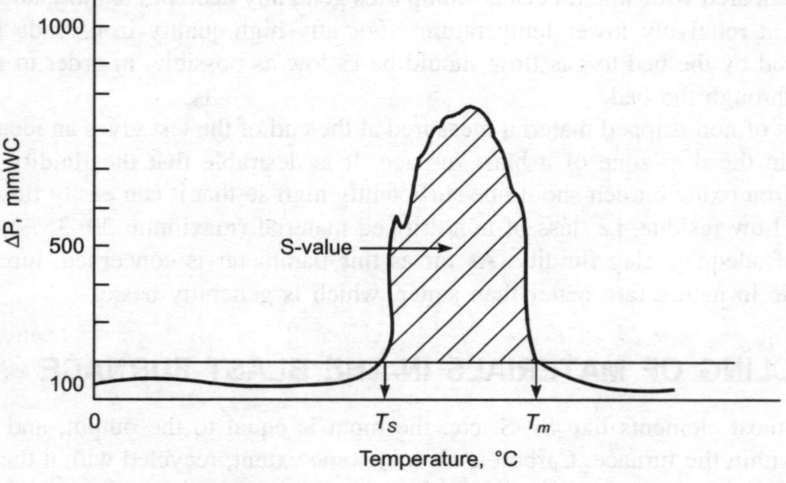

Figure 9.9 Depiction of various parameters measured in the softening–melting test.

(i) *Softening start temperature* (T_s): It is the temperature in degree Celsius at which softening begins denoted by a pressure differential of 100 mm water column across the bed.

(ii) *Melting temperature* (T_m): It is the temperature in degree Celsius at which melting is completed, i.e. when the pressure drop across the bed after reaching its maximum value again comes back to 100 mm water column. If the pressure drop does not reach this value after the test, T_m is assumed to be greater than 1550°C, which is the maximum temperature that the sample can reach in the softening–melting test apparatus.

(iii) *S value* (expressed in kPa°C): It is determined by measuring the area under the curve generated by plotting the pressure differential (ΔP) across the bed against temperature (shown in Figure 9.9). It is a measure of the resistance offered by the bed to gas flow in the furnace.

(iv) *Non-dripped material* (%): Non-dripped material is defined as the amount of residue that is left in the crucible after the test is completed, expressed as a percentage of the total weight of the sample less the oxygen associated with iron.

For lump iron ores, the softening start temperature (T_s) usually varies from 1150°C to 1200°C depending on its composition, whereas depending on the basicity and its gangue content, T_s of sinter is usually higher. High-quality sinter can have softening start temperatures as high as 1300–1320°C. The T_s values of mixed beds of lump iron ore and sinter are between the softening temperatures of the individual components. The final melting temperature (T_m) of iron ores and sinter varies between 1350°C and 1550°C. It is highly desirable to have as small a difference between T_m and T_s as possible, so that the mushy zone temperature range (T_m–T_s) is restricted. This temperature difference gives a direct indication of the span of the cohesive zone in a blast furnace. The narrower the cohesive zone, the easier it is for the gases to flow through the bed, resulting in better reduction kinetics of iron oxide. It is preferable to keep this difference in the range of 150–180°C, for optimum blast furnace performance.

The S-value, which indicates the resistance offered by the bed to gas flow, is usually higher for lump ore compared with sinter, because lump ores generally decrepitate more under reducing gas conditions at relatively lower temperatures. For any high-quality iron oxide burden, the resistance offered by the bed to gas flow should be as low as possible, in order to allow faster flow of gases through the bed.

The amount of non-dripped material measured at the end of the test gives an idea of the slag characteristics in the drip zone of a blast furnace. It is desirable that the fluidity of the slag formed by the iron oxide burden should be sufficiently high so that it can easily flow out of the cohesive zone. Low residue, i.e. less of non-dripped material (maximum 30–35%), is taken as an indication of adequate slag fluidity. As far as this parameter is concerned, lump iron ores which are acidic in nature fare better than sinter, which is generally basic.

9.9 RECYCLING OF MATERIALS IN THE BLAST FURNACE

In the case of most elements like Si, S, etc. the input is equal to the output, and there is no accumulation within the furnace. Carbon is also, to some extent, recycled within the furnace on account of the *Boudouard reaction* (Eq. (5.5)). Indirect reduction of iron oxide by CO produces CO_2. CO_2 further reacts with C to form CO at the bottom of the stack. CO in excess of equilibrium deposits carbon because of the backward reaction in the upper stack at a lower temperature (Eq. (5.5)). The fine carbon thus deposited travels downwards, and gets gasified into CO again. However, there is no net accumulation of carbon in the furnace.

In contrast, there are some elements/species that tend to accumulate inside the furnace over a period of time, since the output in these cases is less than the input. Alkalies and zinc fall in this category. The alkali metals enter the furnace as constituents of the fluxes, iron oxide and coke. They are found in many coal and iron ore deposits around the world. Therefore, the iron oxide used (lump ore or sinter/pellets) as well as the coking coal used to produce coke have to be carefully chosen with stringent limitations on their K_2O and Na_2O contents. Otherwise, the alkali oxides would generate large volumes of potassium and sodium vapour within a blast furnace by reaction with carbon above 1500°C. This occurs principally in the tuyere zone and, to some extent, in the bosh and hearth according to the overall reaction:

$$2K_2(Na_2)\ SiO_3(s) + 6C(s) = 4K\ (Na)(g) + 2Si + 6CO(g) \tag{9.7}$$

Of course, a part of the alkali silicates joins the slag phase. The vapour generated as per Eq. (9.7) travels upwards and reacts with the burden. Both potassium and sodium react in almost the same way and, hence, only one will be dealt with. The following reactions are of importance.

Formation of cyanides in the upper part of the stack. For example:

$$2K(g) + 2C(s) + N_2(g) = 2KCN(g) \tag{9.8}$$

The cyanide vapours get absorbed by the solid burdens and descend downwards.

Formation of carbonates in the upper part of the stack. For example:

$$2K(g) + 2CO_2(g) = K_2CO_3(s) + CO(g) \tag{9.9}$$

These carbonates deposit on the descending burden. At a higher temperature, they either get decomposed into the respective vapours through the reverse reaction, thereby causing excessive decrepitation, or alternatively, they dissolve in the slag (which is less detrimental to the process, but gives rise to problems of slag disposal).

Since alkali metals have negligible solubility in hot metal, they can be flushed-out only through the slag as oxides. Acid slags have the capability of absorbing more alkali oxide than basic slags, and hence SiO_2 in the form of quartzite and feldspar is occasionally charged into the furnace to flush-out excess alkalies.

Accumulation of alkalies in the elemental form or as cyanides is definitely harmful to efficient blast furnace operation owing to the following reasons.

1. Increased *productivity* of blast furnaces requires smooth gas flow and high burden permeability. Disintegration of the oxides or the coke into smaller pieces because of reduction and reaction lowers the permeability and therefore, decreases the productivity. Alkali metals make the coke more reactive besides leading to greater disintegration of ore, coke and sinter as shown in Figure 9.10 (Sasaki et al. 1977). The fact that the coke becomes more reactive can also have an adverse effect on productivity.

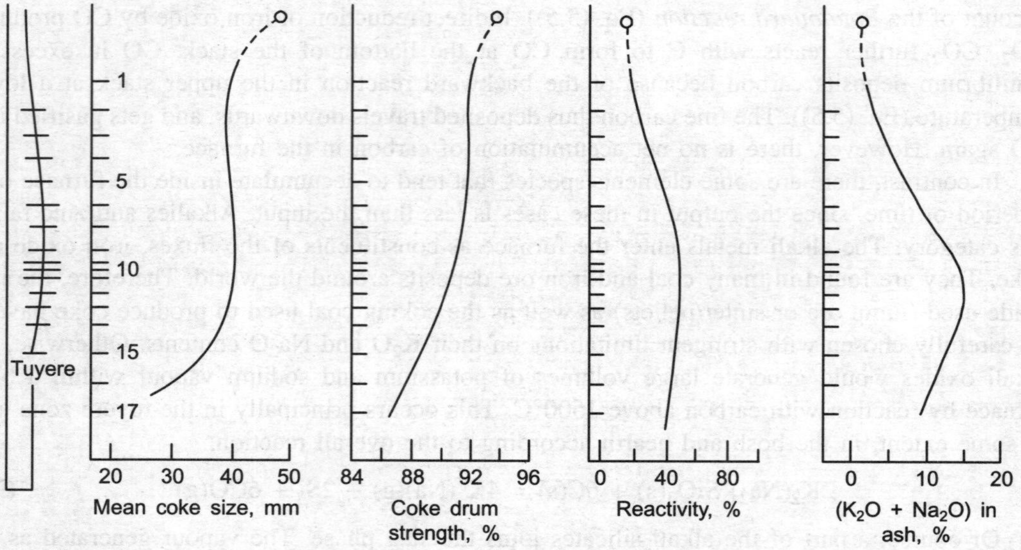

Figure 9.10 Variations in size, strength and reactivity of coke along the height of a blast furnace as a function of the alkali content of coke ash.

2. Alkalies and alkali cyanides enhance degradation and erosion of the refractory lining, particularly in the stack area.
3. Alkali cyanides tend to bind ore pieces forming accretions and thus cause operational problems (*scaffolds* in the stack which is dealt with in detail later in Chapter 10, Section 10.2.4).

Therefore, the best way to alleviate the problem of alkalies is to choose raw materials with low alkali contents to keep the alkali input below a maximum of 2 kg/thm.

REFERENCES

Chatterjee, Manoj, World Iron Ore Industry and Role of Indian Iron Ore Sector, *Steel Scenario*, Vol. 15 (2005) No. Q1.

Eketorp, S., Chipman Conference Proceedings, MIT Press, 1962.

Gupta, S.S. and Amit Chatterjee, *Blast Furnace Ironmaking*, SBA Publication, 1995.

Habishi, F., *Handbook of Extractive Metallurgy: Iron*, Vol. 1, Wiley–VCH, Weinhein, 1997.

Sasaki, K., et al., Trans. Iron Steel Inst. Jap., 17 (1977), 252.

10

Blast Furnace Productivity, Fuel Efficiency and Modern Developments

10.1 INTRODUCTION

Around the year 1960, the world's best blast furnaces were capable of producing about 2000 tpd (i.e. tonnes per day) of hot metal. Around the year 1980, the production in a few blast furnaces in Japan went up to 12,000 tpd, which was the maximum at that time. After 2000, the maximum production in the largest individual blast furnace (e.g. the Schwelgern furnaces of ThyssenKrupp in Germany) has touched 15,000 tpd. The world average per furnace is obviously lower, but has been going up steadily—for example, the average production in furnaces in Germany, which was about 1200 tpd in 1971 increased to 4700 tpd of hot metal in 1998. At the same time, it needs to be noted that the number of very large furnaces (greater than 3000 m^3 working inner volume) has not gone up substantially; instead, what has happened is that many furnaces of lower capacities have been shut down.

Large blast furnaces with working volumes more than 2000 m^3 which have recently been built in Asia include Baoshan No. 3 (4000 m^3) in China, POSCO Kwangyang No. 5 (3000 m^3) in Korea and China Steel, Kaoshung No. 4 (3000 m^3) in Taiwan. Two very large furnaces (3800–4200 m^3) are planned to be installed by Tata Steel over the next few years. Jindal South West Steel is also in the process of installing a similar capacity furnace. Since ironmaking and steelmaking capacity is predominantly going up in Asia, most of the twelve new blast furnaces built recently have been in Asia; whereas in the Western world, the number of furnaces in operation has been decreasing year by year.

It is interesting to note that in 1992, there were 555 blast furnaces existing in the Western world, 390 of which were in operation (around 70%) and the output amounted to 314 Mt or about 800,000 tonnes per furnace, i.e. production of 2250 tpd per furnace per year (assuming 355 days of operation, which is typical today). At present there are about 700 blast furnaces (including 300 in the Western world) in operation globally. During the past decade the number of blast furnaces available in the USA has also decreased from 83 to 43 and the operating furnaces from 48 to 40. Despite this decrease of 17% in the number of operating furnaces, the production has increased by 27% in the USA.

10.1.1 Efficiency of Operation

From the above discussion and from the data presented in Table 1.2 in Chapter 1 on the comparison of the best operating performance of blast furnaces in the year 1960 with those in the decade 1990–2000, it is evident that significant advances have taken place in blast furnace technology in the last few decades in terms of the rate of production. The principal reasons for this improvement include the following:

- The increase in the average inner volume of blast furnaces
- The increase in the *productivity* (per unit volume) of the furnaces.

The increase in furnace volume has been accomplished primarily by increasing the hearth diameter; the furnace heights have remained more or less constant and so has the tuyere-to-stock level height (i.e. *working height*) at about 25 m. The height has not been increased intentionally because otherwise, the burden would have a tendency to crumble to a greater extent on account of the increased burden weight. This would have adversely affected the furnace performance. Therefore, the increase in the hearth diameter was the only logical way of increasing the furnace production capability.

In 1960, the maximum hearth diameter was about 9 m, and the *working inner volume* (i.e. *from tuyere to stockline*) was about 2000 m^3. In 1980, the corresponding values were about 15 m and 5000 m^3 respectively. In all blast furnaces, the total inner volume is always greater than the working volume, since the former includes the volumes of liquid metal and slag in the hearth as well as the empty space (about 1 m high) at the furnace top above the stockline. In a typical case, for a total inner volume of 2000 m^3, the working volume would be around 1800 m^3. The furnace *productivity* (*P*) may be defined as

$$P = \frac{\text{rate of production } (R)\text{, thm/d}}{\text{working volume of furnace } (wV)\text{, m}^3} \tag{10.1}$$

So, $$R = P \times wV \tag{10.2}$$

The volume of the blast furnace (inner volume/working volume/tuyere-to-stockline volume) plays a major role in deriving figures for furnace productivity. This factor needs to be noted carefully while comparing the productivity figures of different furnaces, particularly from different steel plants. Equations (10.1) and (10.2) yielded a value of P of about 1 tonne/m^3/d of hot metal in 1960 and of about 2.6 tonnes/m^3/d in 1980 for the best operating furnaces. Today, the world's maximum corresponding value of P is slightly above 3.0, and the lowest is about 1.5.

An alternative definition of productivity adopted in some countries is the rate of production per day per m^2 of hearth area, but this is not very popular. Therefore, in this book the definition given by Eq. (10.1) has been adopted.

Several decades earlier, coke was the only fuel and reductant. Coke consumption in kg to produce one tonne of hot metal is known as the *coke rate* (CR). It is perhaps the most important index of furnace performance. The lower the CR, the better is the furnace performance. At present, when coal injection through the tuyeres has become a common practice, instead of coke rate, the term fuel rate (coke rate plus PCI (Chapter 6, Section 6.2.2) or for that matter any other injectant rate) is often taken as a measure of blast furnace performance. It reflects the overall fuel efficiency of blast furnace ironmaking. The silicon content in hot metal, which should be low for efficient steelmaking is another index of furnace performance. Over the years, the silicon content of hot metal has been reduced—from about 1% in 1960 in best operations to about 0.3% now. Both CR and silicon content are related to furnace productivity and shall be discussed later in this chapter.

Another factor that is taken as a measure of performance is the blast furnace refractory lining life. Though blast furnace ironmaking is a continuous process, all furnaces have to be shut down after some years of operation for complete relining (localised repairs are carried out during a campaign by going in for temporary stoppages). Earlier, each campaign lasted 5–6 years, but now, for modern furnaces the campaign length extends to more than 10 years and can often reach 20 years. Normally speaking, at the end of a campaign, the furnace is modernised (lines changed, top-charging gear altered, stoves attended to, etc.) besides the entire furnace getting relined.

10.2 FUNDAMENTALS OF BLAST FURNACE PRODUCTIVITY

Producing more hot metal from a blast furnace involves the following:

- Charging more raw materials
- Blowing more air through the tuyeres, more often than not, enriched with oxygen
- Tapping more hot metal and slag
- Handling increased amounts of top gas
- Maintaining stable operation of the furnace in terms of control over gas flow, and smooth burden descent
- Controlling lining wear in the stack, bosh and hearth.

Problems in one or more of the above areas can become bottlenecks in increasing the production. Such occurrences may be taken care of by adjustment of the operating practice, or through minor alterations in the equipment. Sometimes, capital investment during relining of the furnace may be called for either in the furnace itself or in the auxiliary facilities.

The use of the terminology modern developments varies depending on the context in which it is used. Often all the developments made from the decade of the 1950s, which are by no means modern in today's world of rapid technological change, are collectively referred to as 'modern developments' in textbooks for the ease of understanding. Here also, the same convention will be followed since all these developments in blast furnace ironmaking have contributed towards improvement in productivity.

The major developments that have taken place since the 1950s were listed in Chapter 1. These are being listed here again for ease of further discussions.

- Switch over from a large size range of lump iron ore to the use of prepared burdens (sinter and pellets)
- Better quality coke in a closer size range
- Injection of auxiliary fuels through the tuyeres—the latest being PCI
- Larger furnace volume
- Higher blast temperature

- Oxygen enrichment of the blast
- High top pressure operation
- Better burden distribution—the latest being through bell-less charging device
- Advances in the theory of ironmaking
- Much better understanding of the internal state of the furnace
- Computer-aided process control
- Online process simulation.

Chapters 5, 6 and 7 have dealt with the theoretical aspects of blast furnace ironmaking. Chapters 8 and 9 have discussed raw materials—coke, iron ore, sinter, and pellets. In Chapter 12, computer-aided process control will be discussed. In the following sections of this chapter, an attempt will be made to elucidate the fundamentals of productivity, and the factors that influence the productivity, fuel efficiency, and so forth.

10.2.1 The Concept of Productivity

The rate of iron production (R) may be related in a simple way to the rate of consumption of coke as

$$R = \frac{Q}{CR} \tag{10.3}$$

where Q is the rate of consumption of coke per day. The R and CR have already been defined.

Since coke is not the only fuel used nowadays and tuyere injection is common, a more relevant definition of R in today's context is

$$R = \frac{\text{total volume of gas blown through the furnace in m}^3\text{/day}}{\text{specific volume of gas required per tonne of hot metal}} \tag{10.4}$$

The gas consists of O_2, N_2, and decomposed hydrocarbons.

The definition provided in Eq. (10.4) leads to the conclusion that the furnace productivity which is proportional to R, can be increased by implementing the following measures:

- Lowering the specific volume of gas required per thm
- Increasing the rate of gas blowing
- A still better arrangement, i.e. a combination of both the above.

These factors will now be examined in the succeeding subsections.

10.2.2 Specific Gas Volume Requirement

In Chapter 6, Section 6.3, the existence of the thermal and chemical reserve zones, as well as the concept of an ideal blast furnace were discussed. It was pointed out that an ideal blast furnace is characterised by the following features:

- Uniform temperature and composition in the horizontal direction
- Well-developed thermal reserve zone (TRZ) and chemical reserve zone (CRZ) in the stack region.

Figure 6.2 gave a schematic representation of the TRZ and CRZ. At the CRZ (which is a part of the TRZ), the gas is at chemical equilibrium with wustite and metallic iron. As shown in Figure 6.4, equilibrium is found to exist in modern well-operated blast furnaces. Figure 6.6 contained the Rist diagram of a blast furnace based on oxygen and heat balance, as well as Fe–wustite–gas equilibrium. The slope of the line is n_c^g, i.e. gm.atoms of carbon input through coke per gm.atom Fe. n_c^g is proportional to coke rate. The minimum coke rate is depicted by the line HW. H is the thermal pinch point and depends on enthalpy balance, while W is the chemical pinch point and corresponds to Fe–wustite–gas equilibrium at the CRZ. From this, it follows that the minimum coke rate is obtained under the following circumstances:

- When the Fe–Fe_xO–gas equilibrium is attained at the CRZ, i.e. when a furnace is working ideally
- When point H is moved upwards as much as possible.

This requires the following:

- Minimisation of the heat loss through the wall and the top gas
- Optimum degree of direct reduction
- Higher blast temperature and greater oxygen enrichment of the blast.

At the raceway, the gas consists of CO, H_2 and N_2. Roughly speaking, the gas volume required per tonne hot metal (i.e. the specific gas volume) will be the minimum if the fuel requirement (coke + coal, etc.) is the minimum. For this to happen, Fe–Fe_xO–gas equilibrium at the CRZ is desirable, which calls for adequate reducibility of the iron-bearing burden (ore, sinter, pellets).

10.2.3 Gas Flow through the Furnace

As pointed out in Chapter 7, in any operating furnace, there are significant temperature and gas composition variations in the radial direction (see Figures 7.1 and 7.2). The entire furnace interior was subdivided into six zones for the convenience of discussions and Sections 7.3 and 7.4 presented the fundamental aerodynamic features of a blast furnace. The driving force for the upward gas flow is the difference of pressure (Δp) between the tuyeres and the furnace top. Adequate pressure of the gas at the tuyere level is required to overcome the resistance to gas flow offered by the burden.

The fundamental basis for any quantitative relationship between Δp and gas flow rate is the Ergun equation for the granular zone in the upper part of the furnace, and the Sherwood and other correlations in the wet zone in the lower part of the furnace. These are applicable to ideal situations, where there is no non-uniformity in the horizontal direction as elucidated in Sections 7.3 and 7.4. In the granular zone, when the upward force arising out of the pressure difference becomes equal to the bed weight, the bed becomes unstable, fluidisation begins and this limits the rate of gas flow. In order to increase the gas flow rate further, the bed permeability has to be improved and this can be done by increasing the bed void fraction (ε). Figure 7.5 shows that higher ε can be achieved if the solid burden comprises large- and uniform-sized particles. Under no circumtances is a mixed-size desirable.

At the same time, the size of the individual particles in the solid charges cannot be too large, since that would automatically decrease the rates of mass and heat transfer between the ascending gas and the solids. Hence, an optimum size has to be chosen for the highest productivity as illustrated schematically in Figure 10.1. As already noted in Section 7.1, the optimum size range for lump ore is 10–30 mm and for coke is 40–80 mm. The coke size is always 3–4 times larger than the ore size since coke is to be only partially burnt as it descends. It also has a lower density, and hence a greater tendency for fluidisation. Of course, in the lower bosh region of a blast furnace, coke is the only solid that remains, and which helps to support the burden.

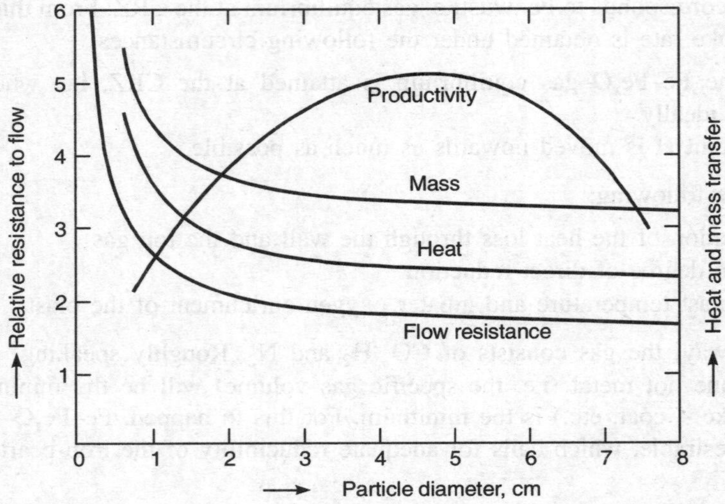

Figure 10.1 Influence of particle diameter on the resistance to flow, rates of heat and mass transfer as well as productivity.

Chapter 7, Section 7.5 introduced an empirical parameter, viz. *Flow Resistance Coefficient* (FRC), employed in operating blast furnaces. The higher the FRC, the greater is the resistance to flow. Figure 7.3 has schematically shown the various internal zones in a blast furnace and it is to be noted that the FRC is the highest in the cohesive zone. Therefore, the cohesive zone provides the maximum resistance to the gas flow. Several investigations have concluded that flooding in the cohesive and the deadman zones is the principal limiting factor governing gas flow, as illustrated in Figure 7.6.

Hartig et al. have reported data on the measurement of gas pressure at various locations inside a blast furnace. A summary of their findings is depicted in Figure 10.2 (Hartig et al. 2000). The pressure gradient along the furnace height ($\Delta p/h$) is 0.027 in the granular zone; but it is higher in the lower part of the furnace. Calculations based on these data show that $\Delta p/h$ is about 0.13 in the cohesive zone, i.e. about five times more than in the granular zone.

10.2.4 Furnace Irregularities

Even in well-operated blast furnaces, there are some day-to-day variations in hot metal composition and production. The monthly production averages also exhibit similar behaviour. These are random fluctuations caused by statistical variations in the composition and properties

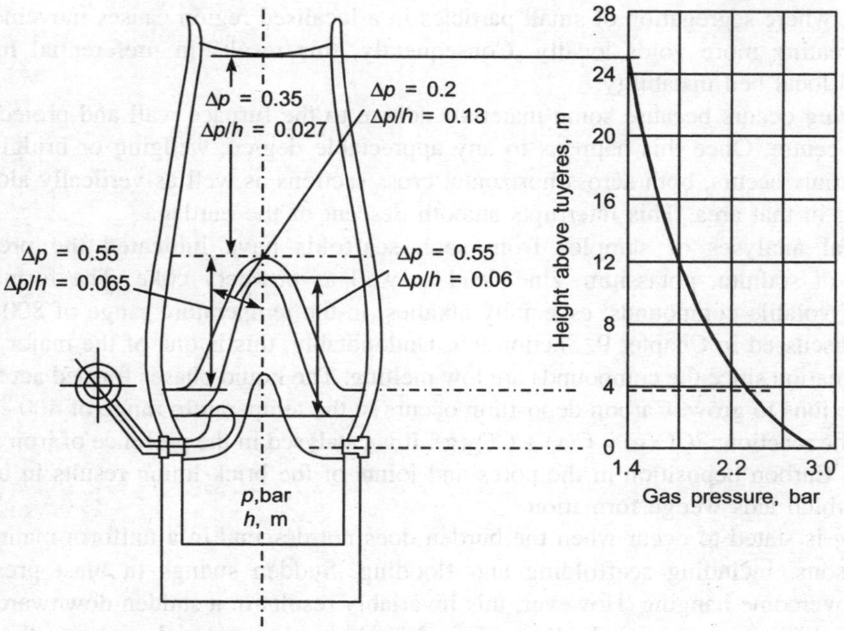

Figure 10.2 Typical gas pressure profile in a blast furnace.

of the input materials as well as in the control parameters. These variations are referred to as furnace irregularities. Earlier blast furnaces exhibited more severe irregularities, often leading to a considerable loss of production arising from the following sources.

- Malfunctioning or failure of the mechanical and electrical devices
- Faulty routine operations, like tapping, charging, etc.
- Malfunctioning or failure of any of the auxiliary facilities
- Abnormalities developed inside the furnace because of physicochemical phenomena.

To minimise irregularities, besides going in for regular maintenance and repair of the mechanical and electrical devices, immediate adoptions of short-range corrective procedures are undertaken by adjustments of the inputs. Alteration in the blowing procedure through the tuyeres has an immediate effect, whereas any change made in the amount/sequence of any of the constituents of the burden, takes at least 4–6 hours to manifest itself. Of course, with the use of sophisticated sensing devices and improved process control, the occurrence of serious irregularities is much less nowadays than what it was earlier. However, abnormalities caused by physicochemical phenomena inside the furnace still have to be taken care of and will be briefly described.

The flooding phenomenon has already been discussed in Chapter 7. In Section 10.2.3, it has already been mentioned that flooding is the principal limiting factor in increasing the production rate in blast furnaces. In the granular zone of the upper stack region, bed fluidisation constitutes the limiting factor for gas flow. However, fluidisation of the entire bed seldom occurs in an operating furnace. The more common irregularity related to this phenomenon is known as *channelling*, where segregation of small particles in a localised region causes movement of the particles, creating more voids locally. Consequently, this results in preferential higher gas velocity and local bed instability.

Scaffolding occurs because some materials adhere to the furnace wall and project towards the furnace centre. Once this happens to any appreciable degree, wedging or bridging of the charge materials occurs, both across horizontal cross sections as well as vertically along a part of the lining in that area. This interrupts smooth descent of the burden.

Chemical analyses of samples from such scaffolds have indicated the presence of compounds of sodium, potassium, zinc, lead as well as powdery coke. The formation and recycling of volatile compounds, especially alkalies, in the temperature range of 800–1100°C, have been discussed in Chapter 9, Section 9.9. Undoubtably, this is one of the major causes of scaffold formation since the compounds are low melting. The liquid phases formed act as binders for the accretions to grow. Carbon deposition occurs in the temperature range of 400–600°C on account of the reaction: $2CO(g) = C(s) + CO_2(g)$. It is catalysed in the presence of iron and alkali compounds. Carbon deposition in the pores and joints of the brick lining results in bulging of the bricks which aids wedge formation.

Hanging is stated to occur when the burden does not descend in a uniform manner. It has various reasons, including scaffolding and flooding. Sudden swings in blast pressure can sometimes overcome hanging. However, this invariably results in a sudden downward slippage of the solids. If as a result of such *slips,* relatively cold burden materials come to the hearth in substantial quantities, the liquid metal in the hearth may get chilled, thereby jamming the entire furnace.

10.3 EFFECT OF AGGLOMERATED IRON OXIDES ON PRODUCTIVITY

Chapter 9 dealt with lump iron ores as well as agglomerates (sinter and pellets). The primary purpose of burden preparation, i.e. use of agglomerates is to allow ore fines to be utilised. As discussed earlier, fines cannot be directly used since they do not allow proper gas flow through the furnace and are responsible for problems like fluidisation and flooding. While the optimum size range of lump ore is considered to be 10–30 mm, a large quantity of fines below 10 mm is produced, both during mining, subsequent beneficiation (if any) and handling. These fines can only be used after agglomeration. During agglomeration, fluxes can be added in order to produce pre-fluxed sinter or pellets. The use of pre-fluxed agglomerates improves furnace performance.

Large amount of literature is available on the improvement in production rate by the use of agglomerates in the burden and the elimination of oxide fines (from lump ore or sinter). An example is given in Figure 10.3 (McDonald 1962). In this case, fines below 9.5 mm size were screened out to various extents and its effect on the production rate was studied to reveal that the production rate increased steadily with increasing percentage of over 9.5 mm ore in the burden (i.e. with less fines).

10.3.1 Use of Sinter

As mentioned in Chapter 9, sintering is the dominant method of agglomeration. Many publications have reported improvements in furnace performance following the use of sinter.

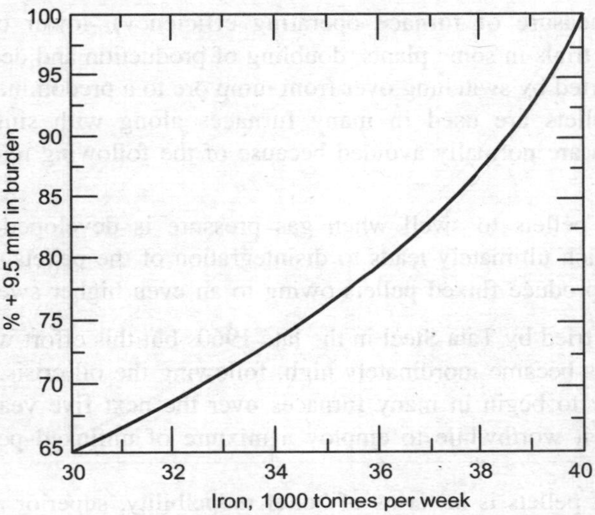

Figure 10.3 Increase in blast furnace output with increase in the degree of screening.

Increasing percentages of sinter in the burden, say from 20–30% to about 60–70% (often considered to be the optimum) have a marked beneficial influence on furnace performance. Use of higher percentages of sinter becomes difficult because at lower sinter basicity (basicity has to be lowered if higher amount of sinter is to be used in order to keep the flux input into the blast furnace constant), sinter properties like strength and reducibility tend to deteriorate appreciably. Depending upon the quality of ore and the physical and chemical properties of sinter, it is generally agreed that, on an average, in the range of 20–70% sinter, every 1% increase in the proportion of sinter increases the hot metal output by about 0.35% and reduces the coke rate by about 0.3%.

There is no doubt that with sinter of proper quality, at least up to 70% sinter in the burden, improves the blast furnace performance dramatically in terms of lower coke rate and higher productivity. As a result, there are no efficient blast furnaces in the world that do not use sinter.

10.3.2 Use of Pellets in Burden

As mentioned in Chapter 9, pelletising was resorted to in order to agglomerate very fine iron ore fractions, particularly beneficiated concentrates that are not amenable to sintering. Nowadays, fines below 0.15 mm in size are partly pelletised and partly used as a portion of the sinter feed by micro-pelletising the fines first at room temperature, or, by resorting to deep-bed sintering at high suction pressures (above 1300 mm Hg). Since in most cases, fines/concentrates are very rich in iron content (often almost pure haematite or magnetite), and the pellets are regular in shape (roughly spherical, diameter 9–16 mm) they form an ideal blast furnace burden.

Use of pellets gives rise to improved permeability in the granular zone in comparison to lump iron ore or sinter, as well as greater uniformity in the radial direction. This leads to virtual elimination of channelling, better gas-solid contact, and hence better utilisation of the thermal and chemical energies, leading to a lower temperature and lower CO/CO_2 ratio in the top gas (often taken as a measure of furnace operating efficiency), lower coke rate and higher productivity. In early trials in some plants, doubling of production and decrease in coke rate by about 20% were reported by switching over from lump ore to a predominantly pellet burden. At present, 15–25% pellets are used in many furnaces along with sinter/lump ore. Higher percentages of pellets are normally avoided because of the following reasons:

- High cost
- Tendency of pellets to swell when gas pressure is developed in the pores during reduction, which ultimately leads to disintegration of the pellets
- Difficulty to produce fluxed pellets owing to an even higher swelling tendency.

In India, pellets were tried by Tata Steel in the late 1960s but this effort was given up when the cost of making pellets became inordinately high, following the oil crisis. However, the use of pellets is again likely to begin in many furnaces over the next five years. Many steel plants overseas have found it worthwhile to employ a mixture of unfluxed pellets and superfluxed sinter.

The advantage of pellets is in terms of better reducibility, superior reduction–degradation index and improved softening–melting characteristics. The influence of these properties of iron-bearing materials on blast furnace performance will now be discussed (the procedure for measuring these values has been already given in Chapter 9).

10.3.3 Reducibility

Chapter 5, Section 5.3.1 discussed the salient features of kinetics of reduction of iron oxides by H_2 and CO. The fundamental studies were carried out primarily in the laboratory using single pellets owing to their uniform size and the consequent ease of using mathematical tools. It has been shown that the reducibility of pellets (and sinter) should be high because of the following reasons:

- To allow attainment of Fe–wustite–gas equilibrium in the CRZ with consequent decrease in fuel consumption, as discussed in Section 10.2.2
- To ensure complete reduction of wustite to Fe before the burden reaches the cohesive zone. If this does not happen, the residual FeO would tend to form low melting FeO–SiO_2 type slag, which would flow downwards into the adjacent coke layers causing loss of permeability.

As discussed in Section 5.3.1, the greater the porosity of the oxide, the higher is the reducibility. Fluxed sinter is produced by the addition principally of $CaCO_3$, which decomposes into CaO and forms various double compounds with SiO_2 and iron oxides. Figure 10.4 compares the degree of reduction of some of these sinters with that of haematite and magnetite for the case of hydrogen reduction at 800°C (Watanabe 1962). It may be noted that calcium ferrites have adequate reducibility; the least reducible phase is $CaO \cdot FeO \cdot SiO_2$ which is similar to *Fayalite* ($2FeO \cdot SiO_2$). It is well-established that Fayalite is a low-melting compound that is formed during sintering/pelletising as a glassy phase with very little porosity. Hence, it has a deleterious effect on reducibility. Laboratory measurements on self-fluxed pellets containing 5% CaO showed that the high temperature reducibility of pellets which had been partially reduced at 1000°C improved dramatically at 1300°C as shown in Figure 10.5 (Turkdogan 1978).

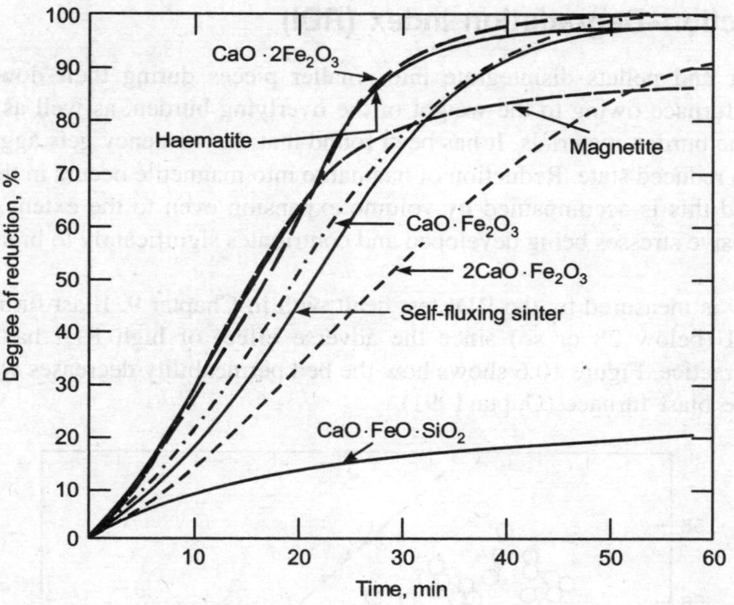

Figure 10.4 Reducibilities of various ores and sinter in hydrogen at 800°C.

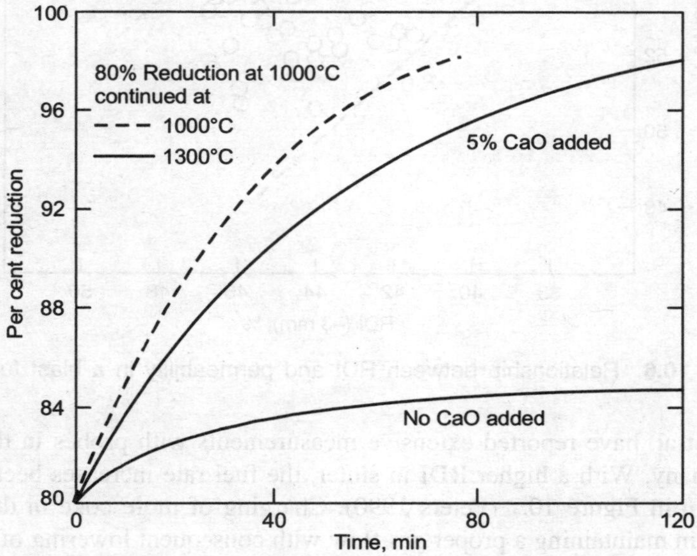

Figure 10.5 Effect of lime on the reducibility of sintered laboratory pellets at 1300°C after 80% reduction at 1000°C in CO/CO_2 = 9 at atmospheric pressure.

10.3.4 Reduction–Degradation Index (RDI)

Lump ores, sinter and pellets disintegrate into smaller pieces during their downward travel through the blast furnace owing to the weight of the overlying burden, as well as abrasion and impact between the burden materials. It has been found that this tendency gets aggravated when the oxides are in a reduced state. Reduction of haematite into magnetite occurs in the upper stack at 500–600°C, and this is accompanied by volume expansion even to the extent of 25%. This results in compressive stresses being developed and contributes significantly to breakdown of the iron oxides.

This tendency is measured by the RDI test dealt with in Chapter 9. Blast furnace operators prefer a low RDI (below 28 or so) since the adverse effect of high RDI has been clearly demonstrated in practice. Figure 10.6 shows how the bed permeability decreases with increasing RDI in a Japanese blast furnace (Gupta 1991).

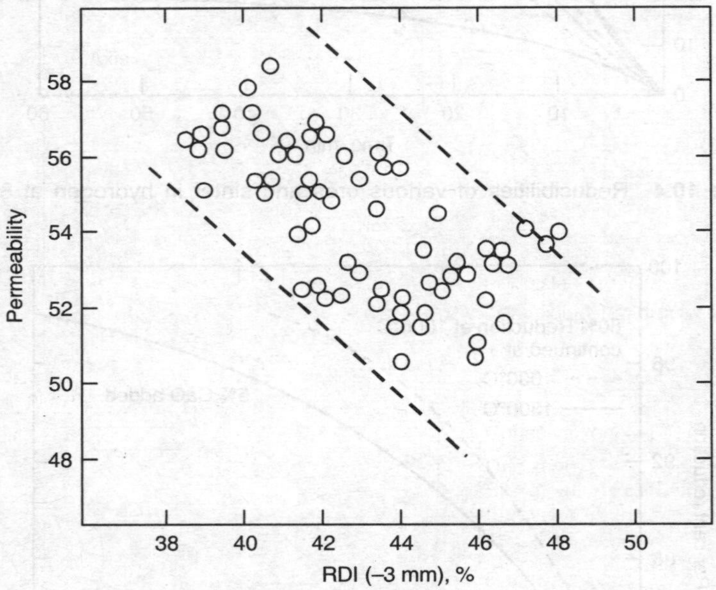

Figure 10.6 Relationship between RDI and permeability in a blast furnace.

K.H. Peters et al. have reported extensive measurements with probes in the blast furnaces of Thyssen, Germany. With a higher RDI in sinter, the fuel rate increases because of improper gas flow as shown in Figure 10.7 (Peters 1990). Charging of more coke in the central part of the furnace helps in maintaining a proper gas flow with consequent lowering of the fuel rate and improvement in productivity.

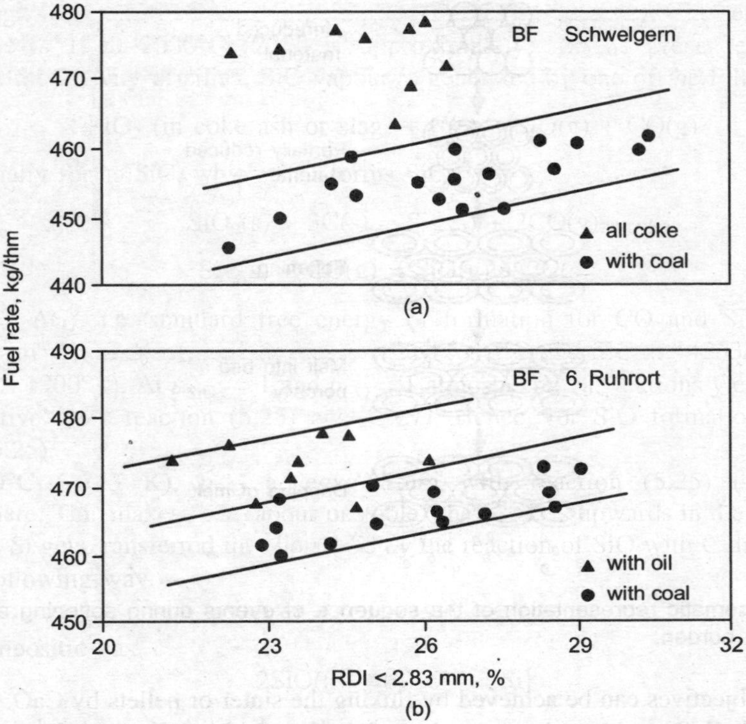

Figure 10.7 Influence of sinter RDI on the fuel rate in a blast furnace.

10.3.5 Softening–Melting Characteristics

Softening and melting of iron-bearing solid burden occurs in the cohesive zone over a range of temperature. The location of the cohesive zone, i.e. its height above the tuyere level as well as its thickness depends on the softening–melting characteristics of the burden materials. Regular measurements of softening temperature (T_s) and melting temperature (T_m) are carried out using a specialised apparatus (see Chapter 9).

The mechanism of the softening–melting phenomena is schematically illustrated in Figure 10.8. It is evident that with the onset of softening, the voidage in the bed decreases and the bed becomes more compact (origin of the terminology *cohesive*). As a consequence, further indirect reduction of iron oxide by gases becomes increasingly difficult. Upon melting, dripping of molten FeO-containing slag through the coke layers increases the flow resistance through the coke slits and the active (i.e. dripping) coke zone because of loss of permeability (see Figure 7.3).

As mentioned in Section 10.2.3 and shown in Figure 10.2, the cohesive zone has the lowest permeability. Hence, for proper gas flow:

1. T_s should be as high as possible
2. The thickness of the cohesive zone should be as small as possible. This thickness depends on the difference between T_s and T_m, ($T_m - T_s$), and therefore, the difference should be as low as possible.

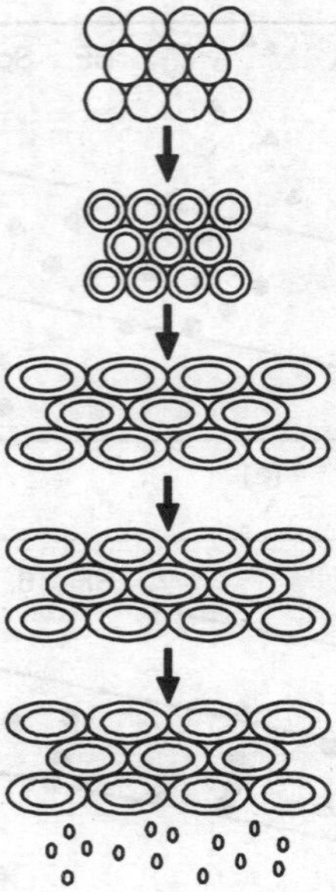

Figure 10.8 Schematic representation of the sequence of events during softening and melting of the burden.

Both these objectives can be achieved by fluxing the sinter or pellets by CaO. As discussed in Section 10.3.3, CaO prevents the formation of the low-melting fayalite phase and increases the extent of indirect reduction. This influences the quantity of slag formed in the dripping zone. Table 10.1 contains some laboratory data that illustrate this point (Clixby 1986). Further, the residual material left after testing consists of solid unmelted oxides and iron. The use of superfluxed sinter (CaO/SiO_2 = 2) results in 70% indirect reduction and 100% residual, and hence is the best from these points of view.

Table 10.1 Typical softening–melting characteristics of some burden materials

Material	Indirect reduction, %	T_s, °C	T_m, °C	$(T_m - T_s)$, °C	Residual material, %
Acid pellets	48.2	1215	1467	252	0
Hammersley lump iron ore	57.9	1352	1493	141	0
Fluxed sinter					
(i) CaO/SiO_2 = 1.65	66.4	1327	1523	196	23.7
(ii) CaO/SiO_2 = 1.96	69.3	1338	1515	177	100

10.4 COKE QUALITY FOR IMPROVED PRODUCTIVITY AND FUEL EFFICIENCY

For improved performance of a blast furnace including productivity and fuel efficiency, the coke should have low ash, moderate reactivity and high coke strength after reaction (CSR).

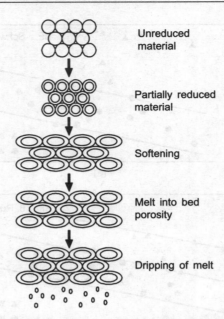

The benefits of using low ash coke are:

- Less inert burden and less slag, with consequent heat savings as well as increased burden throughout
- Lower silicon and sulphur in hot metal (see Chapter 5).

Highly reactive coke is undesirable since it promotes the solution loss reaction in the upper stack resulting in higher percentages of unutilised CO in the top gas. The aim is that coke should react primarily in the bosh and raceway zones so that the coke pieces remain relatively strong up to the stagnant (i.e. inactive) coke zone, thereby helping in supporting the overlying burden as well as preventing flooding. The coke CSR should be high in order to decrease the generation of coke fines in the lower part of the furnace. Samples collected from the inactive coke zone of some blast furnaces (Shimitzu et al. 1990, and Nicolle et al. 1990) have shown that the resistance to gas flow increases with increasing amounts of fine coke, and this also results in greater liquid hold-up (Figure 10.9(a) and (b)). Figure 10.10 shows the improvement in productivity with

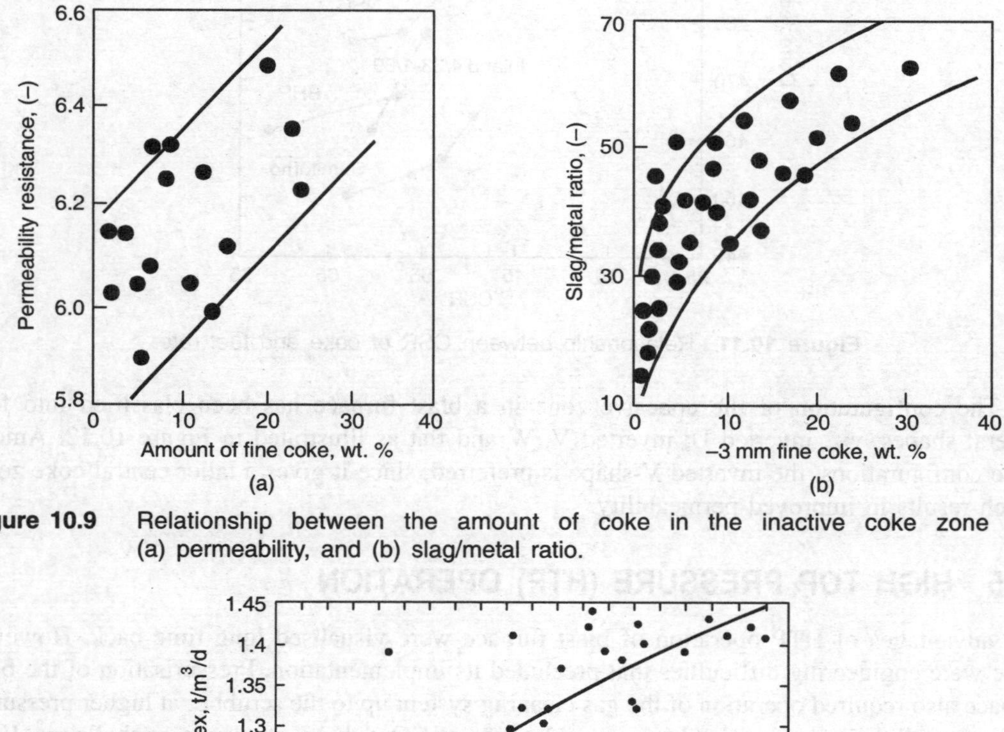

Figure 10.9 Relationship between the amount of coke in the inactive coke zone with (a) permeability, and (b) slag/metal ratio.

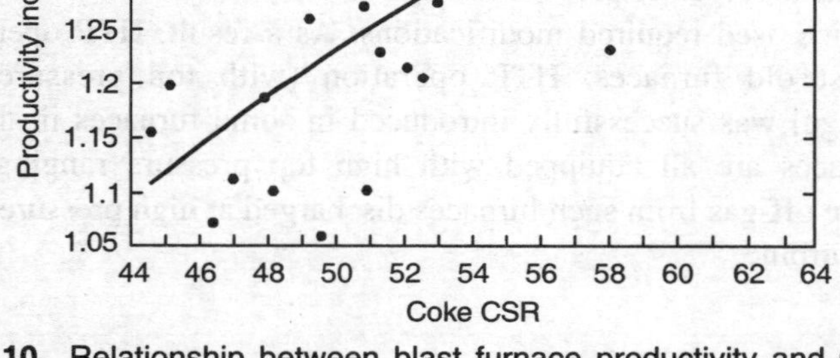

Figure 10.10 Relationship between blast furnace productivity and CSR of coke.

higher coke CSR (Kumar and Mukherjee, 1991) while Figure 10.11 (Kumar and Mukherjee, 1991) illustrates the decrease in the corrected fuel rates of several blast furnaces around the world with increasing CSR.

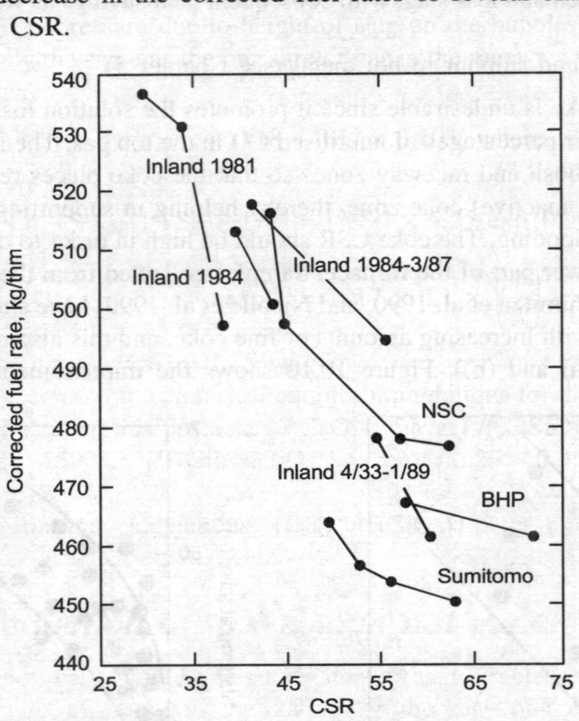

Figure 10.11 Relationship between CSR of coke and fuel rate.

The configuration of the cohesive zone in a blast furnace has been classified into four general shapes, viz. inverted U, inverted V, W and flat as illustrated in Figure 10.12. Among these configurations, the inverted V-shape is preferred, since it gives a taller central coke zone, which results in improved permeability.

10.5 HIGH TOP PRESSURE (HTP) OPERATION

The advantages of HTP operation of blast furnace were visualised long time back. However, there were engineering difficulties that precluded its implementation. Pressurisation of the blast furnace also required operation of the gas cleaning system up to the scrubber at higher pressures. Sealing of all the joints involved to prevent leakage of CO-rich gas was a major challenge. Even the top charging device used required modifications. As a result, HTP operation could not be incorporated in most old furnaces. HTP operation (with top pressure in the range of 0.7–0.85 kg/cm^2 gauge) was successfully introduced in some furnaces in the USA in the late 1940s. Modern furnaces are all equipped with high top pressure ranging between 1.0 and 3.0 kg/cm^2 gauge. The off-gas from such furnaces discharged at high pressure is used to generate power by driving a turbine.

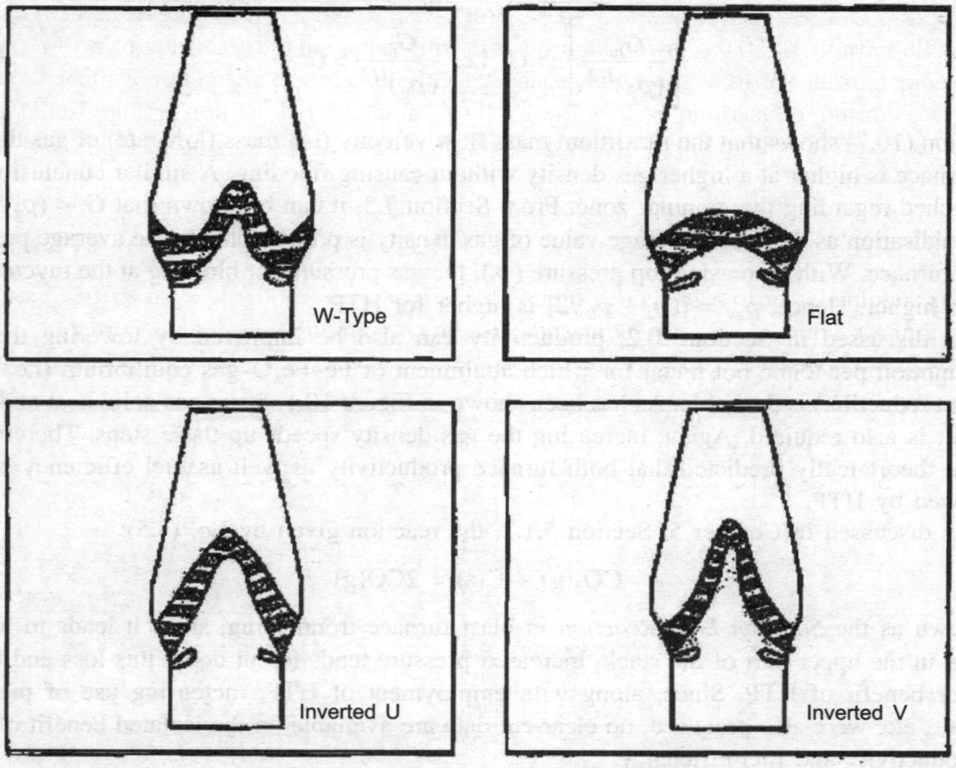

Figure 10.12 Schematic representation of different configurations of the cohesive zone.

10.5.1 Influence of HTP on Productivity and Fuel Efficiency

It has already been stated that productivity can be increased by increasing the gas flow in the furnace, which leads to decrease in fuel consumption (refer Section 10.2.1). Section 10.2.3 briefly discussed the fundamentals of gas flow through a blast furnace. It has been concluded that flooding in the cohesive zone and in the inert coke zone limits the rate at which gas flows. In Chapter 7, Section 7.4 provided the relevant equations, e.g. Eq. (7.17).

Flooding occurs, if $\psi'^2 m > 0.001$. Assuming that a_c, g, ε, ρ_l, η_L and L in Eqs. (7.15) and (7.16) are constants, Eq. (7.17) may be rewritten as

$$(v_{tu}^2 \cdot \rho_g)^2 \frac{(\rho_g)^{1/2}}{G_{tu}} > C \tag{10.5}$$

where C is a constant, and

$$G_{tu} = \rho_g v_{tu} \tag{10.6}$$

Combining Eqs. (10.5) and (10.6), and simplifying, the conditions for flooding can be written as

$$\left[\frac{G_{tu}}{(\rho_g)^{1/2}}\right]^3 > C, \text{ i.e, } \frac{G_{tu}}{(\rho_g)^{1/2}} > C^{1/3} \qquad (10.7)$$

Equation (10.7) shows that the maximum mass flow velocity (i.e. mass flow rate) of gas through the furnace is higher at a higher gas density without causing flooding. A similar conclusion can be reached regarding the granular zone. From Section 7.3, it can be shown that $G \propto (\rho_g)^{1/2}$ for bed fluidisation as well. The average value of gas density is proportional to the average pressure in the furnace. With increasing top pressure (p_t), the gas pressure for blowing at the tuyeres (p_b) is also higher. Hence, $p_{av} = [(p_t + p_b)/2]$ is higher for HTP.

As discussed in Section 10.2, productivity can also be improved by lowering the fuel consumption per tonne hot metal for which attainment of $Fe–Fe_xO$–gas equilibrium (i.e. faster indirect reduction) is desirable. As has been shown in Figure 10.1, faster gas-solid heat and mass transfer is also required. Again, increasing the gas density speeds up these steps. Therefore, it can be theoretically predicted that both furnace productivity as well as fuel efficiency can be improved by HTP.

As discussed in Chapter 5, Section 5.1.2, the reaction given by Eq. (5.5):

$$CO_2(g) + C(s) = 2CO(g)$$

is known as the *Solution Loss Reaction* in blast furnace ironmaking, since it leads to loss of carbon in the upper part of the stack. Increased pressure tends to cut down this loss and this is another benefit of HTP. Since, along with employment of HTP, increasing use of prepared burdens, etc. were also practised, no clear-cut data are available on the isolated benefit of HTP on productivity and fuel efficiency.

10.5.2 Some Other Performance Improvements through Use of HTP

Reduction of hot metal silicon

In Chapter 5, Section 5.4.2, reaction of silicon in the blast furnace was discussed. It was concluded that the dominant reaction given by Eq. (5.25) for formation of SiO vapour is

$$SiO_2 \text{ (in coke ash or slag)} + C(s) = SiO(g) + CO(g)$$

With HTP, the gas pressure at the tuyere level also increases. This raises p_{CO} and thus retards SiO formation. In the hearth too, increase in p_{CO} retards the reduction of SiO_2 from slag (Eq. (5.31)). Therefore, HTP operation is expected to lower the silicon content in hot metal, which is very desirable for better steelmaking. Such benefits have been obtained by ironmakers after their old furnaces were equipped with HTP facilities.

More uniform gas flow and burden descent

Attention is drawn to Eq. (7.8), Chapter 7. At constant mass flow velocity G_o, if d_p and ε are also constant, then

$$\frac{\Delta p}{H}\rho_g = \text{constant} \qquad (10.8)$$

Since $\rho_g \propto p$, then the differential form of this equation becomes

$$\frac{p\,dp}{dH} = B = \text{constant} \tag{10.9}$$

Integrating between limits, at tuyere, $H = 0$, $p = p_b$, and at top, i.e. $H = H_T$, $p = p_T$,

$$\frac{1}{2}(p_b^2 - p_T^2) = BH_T \tag{10.10}$$

i.e.

$$\Delta p = p_b - p_T = \frac{2BH_T}{p_b + p_T} = \frac{BH_T}{p_{av}} \tag{10.11}$$

where p_{av} = average furnace pressure = $\frac{1}{2}(p_b + p_T)$.

With HTP, p_{av} in the furnace is higher, which means that for the same G_O, Δp from tuyeres to stockline is lower (see Eq. (10.11)). Sample calculations show that for a situation in which Δp = 1.4 atm without HTP, it would be only 0.75 atm if the HTP = 2 atm gauge. The linear gas velocity decreases by 50%. Operating blast furnace data have confirmed this trend. Of course, the actual empirical equations are somewhat different from Eq. (10.11). This lowering of Δp and consequent lowering of linear gas velocity contributes to better gas distribution across the furnace cross section and consequently, smoother burden descent.

10.6 THE BELL-LESS TOP

Chapter 2 briefly narrated the devices for charging the solid burden at the top of a blast furnace. The traditional double-bell charging system was a standard feature in all furnaces built prior to 1970. It was improved by the incorporation of a rotating hopper, by means of which ore/sinter/pellets and coke could be charged alternately. The profiles of these layers, as obtained by charging through double bell, can be broadly divided into two patterns, viz. V-profile and M-profile, as shown schematically in Figure 2.6, Chapter 2.

As stated in Chapter 7, Section 7.1, the raw materials are neither of uniform size and shape and nor of the same density. For example, coke has a bulk density of about 1 tonne/m^3, whereas ore/sinter/pellets have bulk densities varying approximately in the range of 3–4 tonnes/m^3. When the big bell is lowered, the finer materials tend to fall vertically down, and hence, tend to get concentrated more towards the periphery. On the other hand, the larger particles tend to get deflected and segregate more near the centre. Figure 2.6 illustrated this schematically.

Since size segregation in the furnace cross section causes non-uniformity of gas flow and consequent irregularities like channelling, bed fluidisation, etc. burden descent in such a situation would become non-uniform and irregular. This affects productivity, fuel efficiency, and leads to control problems. Moreover, the two-bell arrangement posed difficulties for high top pressure operation as well.

In view of all these, as mentioned in Chapter 2, several improved top charging devices were developed at the beginning of 1970. The latest of these are the Paul–Wurth bell-less top (and the SIME TAL gimbal top charging technology) which have eliminated the above difficulties considerably. The burden distribution is much more uniform. Moreover, there is enough flexibility in the system to alter the charging pattern depending on the internal state of the furnace, e.g. coke can be preferentially charged at the centre or on the sides depending on the existing gas temperature profile. As a result, most modern blast furnaces are now equipped with bell-less tops and even the existing furnaces are likely to incorporate this facility during future shutdowns.

10.7 PULVERISED COAL INJECTION (PCI)

In connection with the calculation of RAFT in Chapter 6, Section 6.2.2, this topic was briefly presented. It was mentioned there that injection of hydrocarbons through the tuyeres in the form of oil and natural gas had been practised to various extents in order to cut down the consumption of coke in blast furnaces. The oil crisis starting in 1970s made such injections unattractive. Tuyere injection has come back now in the form of injection of pulverised non-metallurgical coal.

PCI is, without doubt, the most major development that has taken place in revolutionising blast furnace technology in the last twenty years or so. Starting from about 1990, several publications have come out. A few comprehensive ones are listed below:

1. B.D. Pandey: in *Blast Furnace Ironmaking*, Tata Steel, (1991), Ch. 16.
2. S. Zhang and X. Bi: Ironmaking and Steelmaking, Vol. 30 (2003), pp. 467–473.
3. W. Koen et. al.: Ironmaking Conf. Proc., ISS (1994), pp. 429–432.

PCI has become a standard feature of most modern blast furnaces. Figure 10.13 is a schematic representation of a typical tuyere injection system. Pulverised coal is injected with a stream of carrier gas (nitrogen/air) into the tuyere. Sometimes, auxiliary tuyeres are used for injection to improve the performance. Whatever be the system adopted, combustion of coal takes place in front of the tuyeres. The steps involved include:

- Heating
- Pyrolysis
- Ignition and combustion of the products of pyrolysis
- Combustion of the residual char.

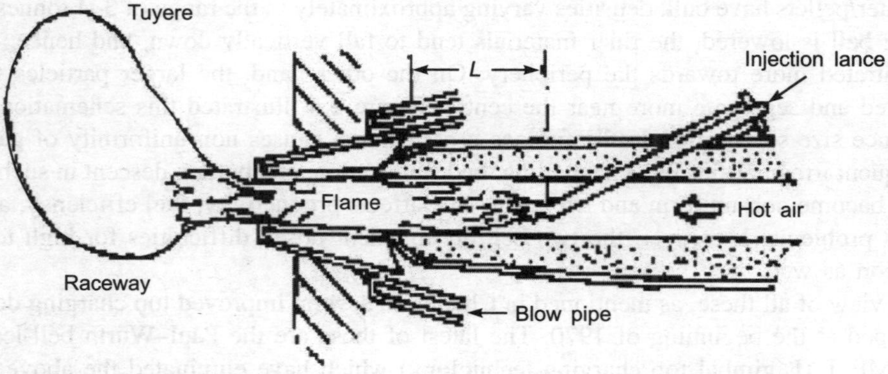

Figure 10.13 Coal injection system (schematic).

Since the residence time of the coal particles in the tuyere zone is a few seconds only, it has been inferred that the first three steps are very fast and require a maximum of 0.1 second. However, the combustion of char requires 1 to 4 seconds. Unless the combustion is completed in the tuyere zone, the fine char particles tend to block the bed voids, thereby increasing the resistance to gas flow. This has an adverse effect on productivity and fuel efficiency. It also enhances the solution loss reaction in the upper stack and increases the CO content of the top gas. Further, since these fines are easy to fluidise and elutriate, the dust losses tend to increase. Consequently, efforts are made to make sure that complete combustion of injected coal takes place in the tuyere zone. The factors that govern combustion efficiency and the overall efficacy of PCI are discussed below.

- The particle size of the coal injected should be as small as possible. However, this increases the grinding cost and can give rise to problems of flowability during injection. To avoid such problems, very fine grinding is avoided—ideally speaking the coal injected should consist of a mixture of fines and some relatively coarser particles. Figure 10.14 shows the coal pulverisation and preparation system used in the Fairfield Works of U.S. Steel (Oshnock 1995). The size distribution is also shown in this figure —about 80% of coal is below 200 mesh (–0.075 mm) in size. Coal of this size is conveyed to the storage bin(s) by heated inert gas. The purpose of using gas heated to above 100°C (150°C typically) is to remove moisture from coal. High moisture levels affect the flowability of the coal particles. It also gives rise to endothermic reactions in the raceway, which lowers the RAFT (see Table 6.2).

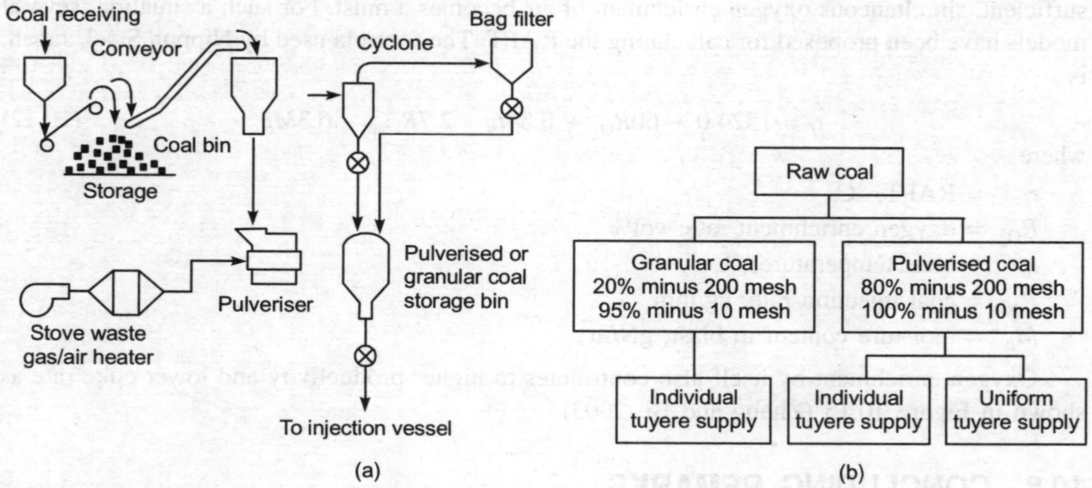

Figure 10.14 (a) Schematic representation of a coal pulverisation and preparation system, (b) Size range of pulverised coal and the types of injection systems.

- The hot blast temperature should be high. The rates of char gasification as well as oxidation of the volatiles are markedly speeded-up at higher temperatures. A minimum hot blast temperature of 1250°C is recommended for high PCI rates.

- Coals containing high volatile matter (VM) normally also exhibit superior combustibility owing to the fact that the char of high VM coal is more porous, and hence more reactive. However, very high VM levels lower the carbon available, and hence there is a maximum value of VM for PCI coals.
- Ash in coal is undesirable since it increases the slag volume and affects both fuel efficiency and productivity. High ash in PCI coal also tends to increase silicon content in hot metal. Hence, rigorous specifications have been evolved in terms of ash, VM and combustibility of PCI coals.

It is reported that at high rates of PCI (200 kg/thm and more), the maximum combustion efficiency is about 70–80%. This means that some unburnt char particles find their way into the upper regions of the furnace, thereby increasing the FRC (i.e. flow resistance coefficient). Operating data have confirmed that the FRC tends to increase with high rates of coal injection, particularly if the coal chosen is not appropriate. In such a situation, even burden descent can become irregular. Another important point to note is that PCI requires that the coke used in conjunction be of the highest quality. Otherwise, the coke would tend to disintegrate since a lower amount of coke has to support the burden. Further, with decreasing coke rate, the coke residence time in the furnace increases, thereby calling for better quality coke. The success of PCI also requires high-quality sinter. This has been demonstrated by blast furnace trials at several plants all over the world, including India (Bhilai and Tata Steel).

The endothermic decomposition of the injected coal lowers the RAFT. This is compensated, to some extent, by the increase in the blast temperature. However, since this is not always sufficient, simultaneous oxygen enrichment of air becomes a must. For such a situation, several models have been proposed for calculating the RAFT. The formula used by Nippon Steel, Japan, is

$$t_f = 1524.0 + 60R_{O_2} + 0.84t_b - 2.7R_{\text{coal}} - 6.3M_b \tag{10.12}$$

where

t_f = RAFT, °C
R_{O_2} = oxygen enrichment rate, vol%
t_b = blast temperature, °C
R_{coal} = coal injection rate, kg/thm
M_b = moisture content in blast, gN/m^3

Oxygen enrichment by itself also contributes to higher productivity and lower coke rate as shown in Figure 10.15 (Zhang and Bi, 2003).

10.8 CONCLUDING REMARKS

It has already been mentioned in Section 10.1 that improved blast furnace performance not only means higher productivity, but also lower fuel rate and lower silicon content in hot metal since all these parameters are strongly interrelated. As far as productivity and fuel rate are concerned, some examples have been cited. Some comments about hot metal silicon also have been made. Figure 10.16 summarises these improvements in the blast furnaces of the erstwhile British Steel in the period 1980 to1988 (Kumar and Mukherjee, 1991). It needs to be highlighted again that the extent of performance improvement following PCI also depends on the quality of the other raw materials.

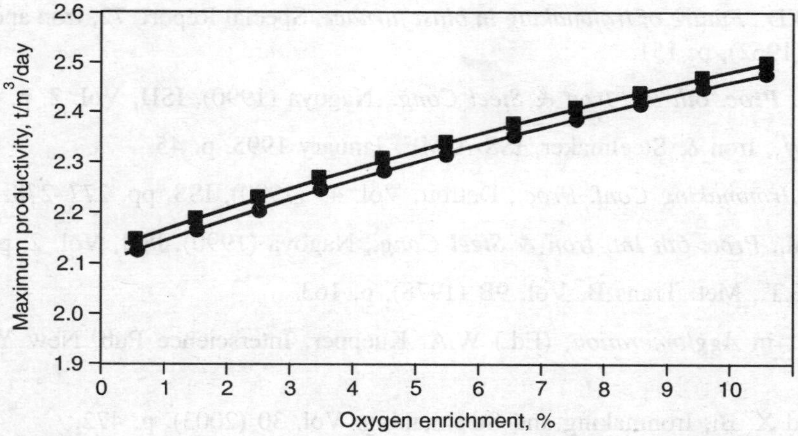

Figure 10.15 Effect of oxygen enrichment on maximum furnace productivity.

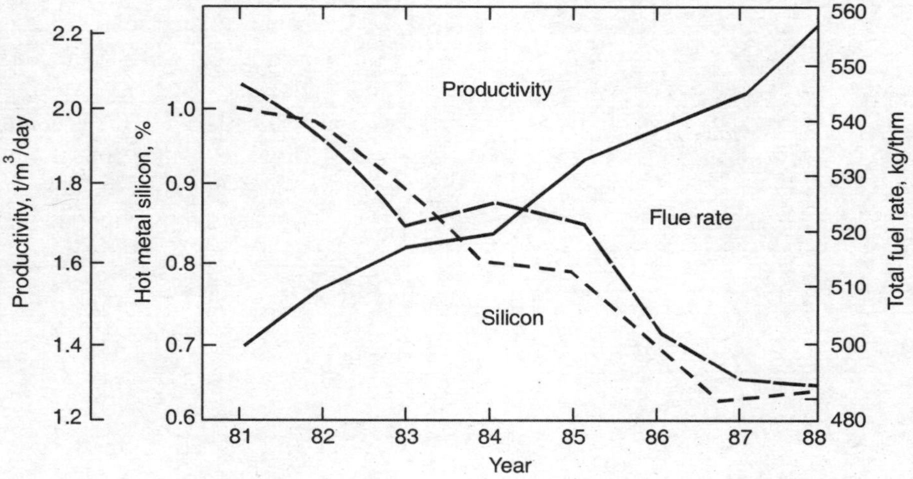

Figure 10.16 Blast furnace performance at British Steel from 1980 to 1988.

REFERENCES

Clixby, G., *Ironmaking and Steelmaking*, Vol. 13 (1986) 169.

Gupta, K.N., in *Blast Furnace Ironmaking* (Eds.) S.S. Gupta and Amit Chatterjee, Ch. 9, Tata Steel, Jamshedpur, 1991.

Hartig, W. et al., Ironmaking Conf. Proc., ISS, Vol. 59 (2000), Pittsburgh, 3–16.

Kumar, A. and T. Mukherjee, in *Blast Furnace Ironmaking* (Eds.) S.S. Gupta and Amit Chatterjee, p. 106, Tata Steel, Jamshedpur, 1991.

McDonald, N.D., *Future of ironmaking in blast furnace*, Special Report, 72, Iron and Steel Inst., London (1962), p. 151.

Nicolle et al., *Proc. 6th Int. Iron & Steel Cong.*, Nagoya (1990), ISIJ, Vol. 2, p. 430.

Oshnock, T.W., Iron & Steelmaker, ISS-AIME, January 1995, p. 45.

Peters, K.H., *Ironmaking Conf. Proc.*, Detroit, Vol. 49 (1990), ISS, pp. 277–278.

Shimitzu et al., *Proc. 6th Int. Iron & Steel Cong.*, Nagoya (1990), ISIJ, Vol. 2, p. 423.

Turkdogan, E.T., Met. Trans B, Vol. 9B (1978), p. 163.

Watanabe, S., in *Agglomeration*, (Ed.) W.A. Kuepper, Interscience Pub, New York (1962), p. 865.

Zhang, S. and X. Bi, Ironmaking and Steelmaking, Vol. 30 (2003), p. 472.

11

Blast Furnace Products and Their Utilisation

11.1 INTRODUCTION

Hot metal of optimal quality, with respect to composition and temperature, is vital for ensuring efficient steelmaking. Attention to hot metal quality is required so that regular production of the desired steel grades at acceptable levels of productivity becomes possible. Consequently, steelmaking today demands hot metal at as high a temperature as possible (minimum 1300°C), with stringent chemical analysis specifications, particularly in terms of the silicon, sulphur and phosphorus contents. This is mandatory not only for the success of BOF steelmaking, but is also demanded by continuous casting, so that the liquid steel made can be cast at relatively high casting speeds to yield cast products (slabs, blooms, billets) of acceptable quality.

The exact stipulation of hot metal quality varies from country to country, and even for different plants in the same country, depending on the type of raw materials used in ironmaking, grades of steel that have to be made, type of the final product, etc. Table 11.1 shows the typical range of hot metal composition stipulated for blast furnaces in Japan, Europe, North America and India. The temperature of hot metal also varies widely—from as low as 1280–1350°C in India to as high as 1500–1550°C in Japan. The temperature of hot metal tapped from blast furnaces depends, to a very large extent, on the actual blast furnace operating conditions, such as RAFT, extent of PCI, slag volume, etc. The temperature of hot metal immediately prior to charging into

Table 11.1 Typical range of hot metal composition (%)

	Japan	Europe	USA	India
Carbon	4.0–4.5	4.0–4.5	4.0–4.5	4.0–4.5
Silicon	0.30–0.45	0.30–0.45	0.40–0.70	0.7–1.3
Manganese	0.20–0.40	0.20–0.65	0.50–0.75	0.04–0.10*
Phosphorus	0.095–0.105	0.060–1.50**	0.040–0.080	0.10–0.30
Sulphur	0.020–0.025	0.020–0.040	0.025–0.065	0.055–0.080

*The manganese content of hot metal made in some blast furnaces is even higher.

**High phosphorus hot metal requires pre-treatment before steelmaking (the details are given in Chapter 16).

BOF vessels is also a function of the time taken to transport hot metal to the BOF shop, type and capacity of the ladles used for transport, extent of hot metal pre-treatment (if any), use of a mixer (if any) in the BOF shop, etc.

11.2 COMPOSITION OF HOT METAL

Since the composition of hot metal produced in blast furnaces depends primarily on the characteristics of the raw materials used, it is necessary to have a close look at the chemistry as well as other features of raw materials.

11.2.1 Overall Input and Output Considerations

To a large extent, silicon, manganese, phosphorus and sulphur contents of hot metal are influenced by the amount of input of these elements into a blast furnace. Some details are given below.

- About 60% of the silica comes from the oxide feed (lump ore, sinter and pellets), and the remainder from the coke ash.
- The total input of manganese varies considerably—around 60% of the manganese can come through BOF slag if it is used as part of the sinter feed, as well as any manganese ore fines that may be used in sintering. The remainder comes from coke ash. In case sinter (or even low manganese lump iron ore) containing small amounts of manganese oxide is used, the relative contribution of coke ash would increase correspondingly. However, in all cases, low manganese hot metal is preferred for steelmaking, since the entire manganese that enters the BOF is lost in the slag.
- Coke is responsible for over 90% of the sulphur input; the remaining 10% or less comes from the oxide feed.
- Around 65–70% of phosphorus input comes from the oxide feed and the remainder from coke. If BOF slag is re-circulated into the blast furnace, or is used as part of the sinter feed, the phosphorus input tends to keep on increasing gradually. As a result, the use of BOF slag has to be suspended periodically, and the system 'purged'.

In terms of the output of these elements from any blast furnace, the following is to be noted.

- Over 85% of the total silica input gets transferred into the slag. The balance is reduced to silicon and reports to hot metal. The operating regime employed in any blast furnace in terms of *RAFT*, *geometry of the cohesive zone*, *drip-zone height, slag volume, blast velocity at the tuyere*, etc. have a decisive role to play.
- Over 90% of sulphur can be removed along with slag if its chemistry and volume are suitably adjusted; the remainder goes into hot metal (and a very small proportion to the exit gas). However, when the objective of the blast furnace operation is to achieve high productivity, which automatically imposes restriction on slag volume, slag basicity, etc. a larger proportion of sulphur (even up to 60%) can report to the hot metal. External desulphurisation prior to steelmaking (discussed in detail in Chapter 16) then becomes mandatory.
- About 90% of the manganese input finds its way into hot metal.
- Almost all of the phosphorus input into a blast furnace ends up in hot metal.

11.2.2 Silicon Control

The major input of silica into a blast furnace is through the coke ash and the gangue present in the oxide feed. In a few blast furnaces in India, the coke ash accounts for as much as 70% of the total input (on account of high ash in coke used in India). Furthermore, since many Indian furnaces are not well equipped with sufficiently high high-top pressure facilities, that favour the production of low-silicon hot metal, Indian blast furnaces generally produce hot metal with higher silicon contents. For an Indian blast furnace operating with a coke rate of 800 kg/thm using 25% ash-bearing coke, almost 80 kg silica is released at the tuyeres compared with only around 20 kg for more efficient furnaces elsewhere, operating typically with a coke rate of 500 kg/thm using coke with 10% ash. This increased release of silica at the tuyere level, coupled with the operating parameters adopted in many Indian blast furnaces owing to raw material considerations, makes the production of very low-silicon hot metal extremely difficult.

11.2.3 Sulphur Control

Since sulphur enters blast furnaces primarily through coke ash, higher coke rates directly result in higher sulphur inputs. At the same time, it needs to be recognised that while coke rates in Indian blast furnaces are often above the international norms (a direct consequence of high ash in coke), the sulphur content in Indian coking coal (around 0.6%) is among the lowest in the world. Consequently, despite Indian blast furnaces operating with relatively low slag basicities, abnormally high-sulphur containing hot metal is often not produced. One of the reasons why Indian blast furnaces are forced to operate with relatively low *tap slag* basicities is that if this basicity becomes high, the corresponding basicity of the *bosh slag* (i.e. before the ash in coke is completely released) becomes so high that its fluidity is drastically impaired. The use of low basicity tap slag automatically results in lower slag–metal sulphur partition coefficients in Indian blast furnaces, thereby resulting in higher sulphur levels in hot metal.

11.2.4 Phosphorus Content of Hot Metal

The phosphorus content of hot metal in India can sometimes be as high as 0.200–0.250%. This is much higher than the phosphorus levels in hot metal in Japan, the USA, etc. but lower than high-phosphorus (around 1.5%) metal often used in BOFs in Europe. Such high phosphorus levels in European hot metal are a direct consequence of the use of high phosphorus iron ores in the blast furnaces in Europe (essentially from Sweden).

The 'intermediate' phosphorus content in Indian hot metal is a consequence of the use of high-phosphorus bearing Indian ores (many with phosphorus contents of 0.080–0.120%) as well as coke (around 0.20%). The phosphorus content of Indian hot metal is thus quite unique. It calls for a new blowing strategy in oxygen steelmaking, since normal single-slag BOF steelmaking practice is applicable to hot metal with less than 0.20% phosphorus. For hot metal containing around 1.5% phosphorus, double-slag practice or concurrent blowing of powdered lime and oxygen through the lance (LD–AC process) has to be resorted to. For the intermediate phosphorus levels in Indian hot metal, an appropriate blowing practice has to be adopted in the BOFs. Chapters 15 and 17 contain the details of the strategy adopted in India, where adequate dephosphorisation has been achieved by:

- Using a larger number of holes (6–8 instead of 3–4) in the oxygen lance, even for relatively small (130–150 t) BOF converters
- Higher lance height
- Concurrent purging of argon/nitrogen through the bottom tuyeres
- Using a higher slag volume.

11.3 HANDLING HOT METAL AND SLAG

In any blast furnace, molten iron and slag gradually accumulate in the hearth. Since the hearth has a limited volume, hot metal and slag are periodically removed.

11.3.1 Tapping of Hot Metal and Slag

Hot metal is removed (operation referred to as tapping) by opening the tap hole which is a peripheral opening in the upper part of the hearth (some large blast furnaces are provided with two/three tap holes). The tap hole(s) (sometimes referred to as *iron notch*) is normally kept in the closed condition by using a suitable fireclay mix to block it. Before tapping hot metal (an operation normally carried out every three to four hours), a hole is pierced through the patched plug using a high-powered, electrically-operated tap hole drilling machine. Once tapping is completed, the hole is again closed by the refractory mix using an electric gun.

The slag (or *cinder* as it is often called) is also removed periodically through a similar tap hole located at a level slightly higher than the iron notch (since lighter slag floats on the hot metal pool in the hearth). Owing to its lower density, the volume of slag is relatively high; and usually two slag taps (i.e. every two hours) for each iron tapping is carried out. Unlike the iron notch, the slag hole is made by fixing a water-cooled copper ring on the furnace shell, which is commonly referred to as the *monkey*. The life of the monkey varies from a few days to a month, after which the copper ring has to be replaced. After each slag tap, the slag hole is closed by using an easily removable slag notch stopper. No large machine is required to open the *slag notch*.

The slag notch and the iron notch are normally positioned at an angle of around 45° to each other, in order to ensure ease of handling of hot liquids and maintenance of the *runner*(*s*), which are refractory coated, trough-shaped channels in the furnace tapping area (known as the *cast house*). The hot liquids flow out of the furnace through the runners as shown in Figure 11.1. In some blast furnaces, hot metal and slag are tapped from the same tap hole, in which case, slag tapping immediately follows hot metal tapping. Once again, for the sake of operational convenience (maintenance of the tap hole and the runners), usually two such tap holes, 136° apart, are provided and used alternately.

Hot metal and slag tapped are collected in separate ladles. Some amount of slag always flows out of the iron notch, even if there is a separate cinder notch. Since it is detrimental to allow slag and hot metal to flow into the same ladle, a system of gates is provided in the slag runner/metal runner to arrest the concurrent flow of slag with metal, to the extent possible.

The partially covered, or sometimes totally uncovered, iron and slag runners, are lined with sand and coke breeze respectively. The trough-shape is made by using a water-based clay that is mixed manually. Any good runner material must possess properties, such as resistance to erosion-corrosion from flowing liquids, thermal stability, shock resistance, etc.

Figure 11.1 Flow of liquid metal in a blast furnace runner.

11.3.2 Transportation of Hot Metal

Hot metal that is tapped is collected in holding vessels, called *ladles*. Earlier, open-top bucket-shaped ladles (60–80 tonnes capacity) were used, but in recent times, large capacity (150–300 tonnes) *torpedo ladles* have come into vogue. These ladles are called torpedoes because they are shaped like a torpedo—conical ends and a cylindrical barrel-shaped central body. Figure 11.2 shows the cross sectional view of a torpedo ladle. These ladles have a central opening at the top through which the hot metal flows into the ladle as it is filled near the blast furnace. Once the torpedo ladle reaches the steelmaking shop, the hot metal is poured out through this opening as the entire ladle is slowly rotated using an electromechanical device. Torpedo ladles are placed on cars that are hauled by locomotives from the blast furnaces to the steel melting shops. Because of the large thermal mass and a small opening at the top, the loss

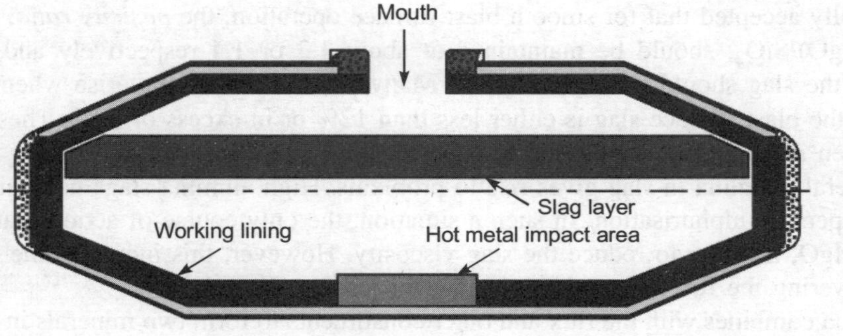

Figure 11.2 Cross sectional view of a torpedo ladle containing hot metal (and some slag).

of heat from such ladles during this transit is fairly small. This is quite different from open-top ladles where excessive heat loss cannot be prevented. This is one of the prime reasons why open-top ladles were gradually discarded.

The slight loss of heat during the transit of torpedo ladles is essentially a result of conduction through their refractory walls. However, at the melt shop when hot metal is poured from these torpedo ladles into the open-top transfer ladles required for subsequent hot metal charging into BOFs, considerable heat loss takes place on account of radiation. For this reason, metal and slag tend to solidify around the mouth of torpedo ladles. Therefore, it becomes necessary to remove the solidified slag/metal from the mouth of the torpedoes periodically. In general, 200 tonne torpedoes can easily transfer 300,000 tonnes of hot metal before relining, while 320 tonne ladles can transport as much as 500,000 tonnes.

11.4 BLAST FURNACE SLAG AND ITS UTILISATION

When iron ore, sinter, pellets, coke and different types of fluxes are smelted in a blast furnace, hot metal is produced and the impurities in the feed get separated as slag. Thus, slag is a product formed by the chemical combination of fluxes with the aluminates, silicates and other gangue constituents in iron oxide and coke ash. A typical analysis (%) of blast furnace slag is given below:

CaO	SiO_2	MgO	Al_2O_3	FeO
40–45	35–40	5–12	12–20	1–2

Obviously, wide variations can exist in slag analyses depending on the chemical analysis of the burden materials. Whatever be its exact composition, molten slag at over 1300° C is cooled, either by air or water/steam, to near room temperature. If cooling of the blast furnace slag is rapid enough, glassy phases are formed. This type of quenched blast furnace slag becomes a valuable material for further processing, particularly as an additive to clinker in cement production. Therefore, all modern blast furnaces are provided with slag quenching facilities, and several commercial systems are available for carrying out this operation, either in the blast furnace area, or sometimes, at a separate location in close proximity.

11.4.1 Slag Characteristics

It is generally accepted that for smooth blast furnace operation, the *basicity ratio*, CaO/SiO_2 or $(CaO + MgO)/SiO_2$, should be maintained at about 1.2 or 1.4 respectively and the alumina content of the slag should not exceed 18%. Many practical problems arise when the alumina content of the blast furnace slag is either less than 12% or in excess of 20%. These difficulties become even more pronounced when low-silicon hot metal has to be produced.

In general, alumina in slag gives rise to problems. High alumina slags have high viscosity, which hampers desulphurisation. In such a situation, the only course of action that is often left is to add MgO, in order to reduce the slag viscosity. However, this increases the slag volume, thereby lowering the furnace productivity and increasing the coke rate.

Alumina combines with the flux and other constituents to form two minerals in blast furnace slag—*gehlinite* ($2CaO \cdot Al_2O_3 \cdot SiO_2$) or *anorthite* ($CaO \cdot Al_2O_3 \cdot 2SiO_2$). Gehlinite is the predominant phase at basicities of around 1.9, while anorthite is formed when the basicity is around 0.5. Although both these minerals are refractory in nature with melting points of about 1550°C, they form a eutectic at 1380°C, containing equal proportions of both these constituents. Thus it is important to operate blast furnaces between these two extremities of basicity so that both gehlinite and anorthite are present.

It needs to be borne in mind that in the normal range of blast furnace slag compositions, magnesia also forms two minerals—*akermanite* ($2CaO \cdot MgO \cdot 2SiO_2$) and *monticellite* ($CaO \cdot MgO \cdot SiO_2$). Akermanite is found in slags containing low amounts of alumina and magnesia. On the other hand, if the alumina or the magnesia content of the slag is high, magnesia combines with lime and silica to form monticellite. A study of the viscosity of blast furnace slags reveals that acceptable viscosities are obtained with either 5% or 10% MgO in the slag, for slags containing up to 20% alumina. However, for slags containing more than 20% alumina, MgO exhibits a pronounced fluxing effect, so much so that the amount of MgO present must be taken into account when estimating the slag basicity (hence the two formulae for slag basicity given right at the beginning of this section).

11.4.2 Usage of Blast Furnace Slag

Depending on its chemical composition and physical characteristics after solidification, blast furnace slag can be put to various uses. *Air-cooled slag* is obtained when the molten blast furnace slag is allowed to flow into a slag bank or a slag pit, where it is cooled by air (forced/natural convection). After cooling, the slag is crushed, screened and then used as a filler between rail-road sleepers, as a constituent of portland cement (only in special cases), mineral wool, glass sand, ceramicware, etc.

If the molten slag is quenched in a pool of water, or cooled rapidly using powerful water jets, it gets pulverised. A fine, granular, and almost fully non-crystalline powdery solid is obtained. This type of material exhibits latent hydraulic properties that make it an important input for the cement industry. After further grinding, *granulated slag* can combine with cement clinker to produce blast furnace slag–cement, which exhibits excellent cementitious properties. The reactivity of ground granulated blast furnace slag is an important parameter for assessing its effectiveness in cement-making, and even 50–55% slag can be used if it has the appropriate properties. Granulated slag can also be used as a soil conditioner, for making building blocks, in ceramicware etc.

Expanded or *lightweight slag* is a 'foamed' product obtained when molten slag is 'expanded' by using controlled quantities of water and air or steam for cooling. The amount of cooling agent used in this case is far less than for granulation. As a result, a relatively dry, cellular, lump product is obtained, which can be used for making floor tiles, bricks, curtain walls, building blocks, etc.

11.5 BLAST FURNACE GAS AND ITS UTILISATION

The gas that exits from the top of any blast furnace along with dust, is valuable since it contains some amount of carbon monoxide. The dust (referred to as *flue dust*) essentially comprises iron oxide and carbon. After cleaning, the exit gas can be gainfully utilised as a fuel in the downstream and upstream facilities of any steel plant for which, sometimes, the blast furnace gas has to be mixed with richer coke oven gas. Blast furnace gas and coke oven gas can also be used for in-plant power generation.

The typical analysis and calorific value of blast furnace gas are compared with coke oven gas, natural gas, etc. in Table 11.2 (Ray 2005).

Table 11.2 Typical analyses and calorific values of some gaseous fuels

Type of gas	Analysis, volume %							Net calorific value, MJ/m^3
	H_2	CO	CH_4	C_2H_6	N_2	CO_2	O_2	
Blast furnace gas	3.7	26.3	0.0	0.0	57.1	12.9	0.0	3.9
Producer gas	15.0	24.7	2.3	0.0	52.2	4.8	0.2	5.8
Coke oven gas	57.0	5.9	29.7	1.1	0.7	1.5	0.0	21.5
Water gas	49.7	39.8	1.3	0.1	5.5	3.4	0.2	11.4
Oil gas	50.0	10.2	27.6	–	5.1	2.6	0.2	19.7
Natural gas	0.0	0.0	94.5	0.5	4.0	0.2	0.3	35.7

11.5.1 Cleaning of Blast Furnace Gas

Ironmaking in a blast furnace produces between 1500 and 1700 Nm^3 of gas per tonne of hot metal. This gas has a calorific value as high as 3500–4000 kJ/Nm^3. It needs to be highlighted that this gas accounts for about one-third of the total energy input into any blast furnace, and, therefore, its maximum utilisation is desirable.

The properties of blast furnace gas depend on the fuel rate in the furnace, extent of oxygen enrichment of the blast, amount of indirect reduction in the furnace shaft, and other operating conditions. However, blast furnace gas always contains solids, amounting to 40–50 kg/thm when it exits from the blast furnace at a temperature of around 150–300°C. Therefore, cleaning of the gas becomes mandatory before it can be used.

Different systems are available for gas cleaning, which can be conveniently classified into two groups: *wet-type* and *dry-type* gas cleaning plants. Traditionally, wet-type gas cleaning plants were more common. The unit processing steps in wet-type gas cleaning plant are illustrated in Figure 11.3. The first stage consists of a *dust catcher*, where heavy and coarse

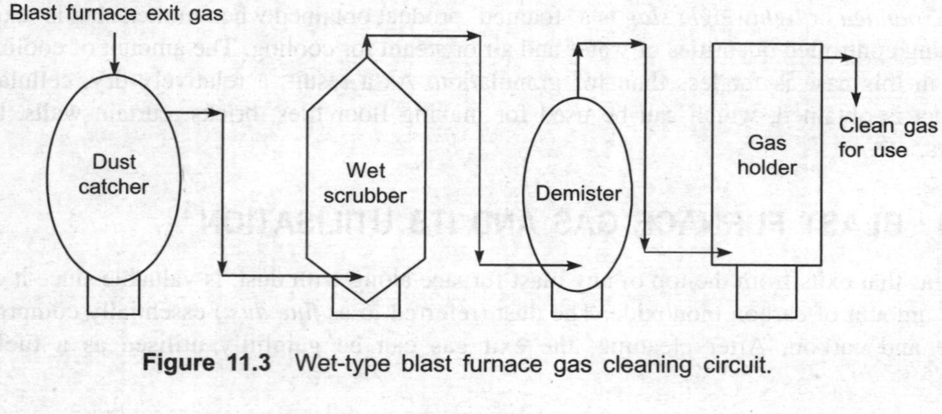

Figure 11.3 Wet-type blast furnace gas cleaning circuit.

particles are mechanically separated by sudden expansion of the gas, accompanied by a change in its direction of flow. Dust catchers are actually common to both wet and dry gas cleaning plants as the first step in removing the dust. Typically, the dust removal efficiency of dust catchers varies between 60 and 70%, i.e. for an inlet dust loading of 20–25 g/Nm^3, dust catchers can reduce the dust content to 4–6 g/Nm^3. The dust collected in the dust catchers is completely dry and is, therefore, ideal for recycling directly to the sinter plant, where its iron content can be utilised. The typical composition(%) of blast furnace dust is: total Fe 30–32, silica 6–7, alumina 2–3, lime 2.5–3, traces of sulphur (and sometimes zinc), and the remainder carbon.

In the second stage of wet-type gas cleaning, generally *venturi scrubbers* are employed to remove the finer dust particles using high pressure water jets. The dust content of the gas gets reduced from 4–6 g/Nm^3 to approximately 5 mg/Nm^3. However, simultaneously, the gas becomes saturated with water, thereby requiring a subsequent treatment in a demister to bring the mist content down to 5 g/Nm^3. Furthermore, though venturi scrubbers offer high-dust cleaning efficiencies, they give rise to substantial pressure drops in the system. This can be particularly disadvantageous if the gas has to be transported for power generation. Further, during wet gas cleaning, the sensible heat of blast furnace gas is lost, and a large amount of waste water is generated. Consequently, additional capital investment is required for water recycling. Problems can also be encountered in recycling the sludge, particularly if the zinc content is high.

An alternative technique that has recently come into vogue is dry gas cleaning. In dry cleaning of blast furnace gas, bag filters or electrostatic precipitators are used. By adopting this method, it is possible to eliminate completely the use of water, simplify the return of the dust that is removed, and facilitate the utilisation of the sensible heat of the gas in downstream facilities like blast furnace stoves and boilers in power plants. Another distinct advantage of the dry system is its lower pressure drop, which allows gas from furnaces operating with high top pressure to be directly coupled with gas turbines. In such a situation, the increased enthalpy of the blast furnace gas as well as its higher pressure enhances power generation by almost 40%.

The choice of the gas cleaning system to be adopted remains an issue of debate among ironmakers today, particularly since both environmental and energy conservation considerations are involved. While most European steel plants favour the wet-type system, in recent times there is a growing popularity of the dry-type system among the Chinese and Japanese steelmakers.

REFERENCE

Ray, H.S. et. al., *Energy in Minerals and Metallurgical Industries*, Allied Publishers, 2005.

12

Blast Furnace Modelling and Control

12.1 INTRODUCTION

Increase in productivity, improvement in product quality and decrease in the cost of production are the objectives that are common to all blast furnaces. While earlier, the skill and experience of the operators were important in fulfilling these goals, in recent years, the art of mathematical modelling has advanced to such an extent that it has also become an effective tool. As a result, mathematical models have been extensively applied for better understanding and improved process control of blast furnaces.

12.2 GENERAL APPROACH

In view of the non-linear, multiple input–multiple output conditions encountered in the blast furnace process, a multi-zone approach is normally required to understand the overall trend of operation of blast furnaces. The distinct regimes that prevail within a blast furnace include: layered structure formation of the burden materials, their descent, the countercurrent gas flow, the heat and mass transfer between the ascending gases and the descending solids, the phase changes, the chemical reactions at high temperatures, the formation of the cohesive zone, the combustion of coke in the raceway, etc. Separate models have to be developed to simulate each of these stages, and then integrated together to form a comprehensive model that can be used for real-time process control. Only in this way can an attempt be made for on-line monitoring of the internal state of any blast furnace.

This requires the on-line recognition of the relationship between the process variables and the operating conditions in any blast furnace. Several probes have to be incorporated within the furnace to gather the data required, as illustrated in Figure 12.1. Figure 12.2 provides a list of various probes that are employed to gather the data. The same figure also gives an idea of the relationship between the measurements that are made by the probes, and the phenomena within the furnace which they help throw light on. Of course, ultimately all the data gathered have to be used to validate the models developed before they can be used for control purposes.

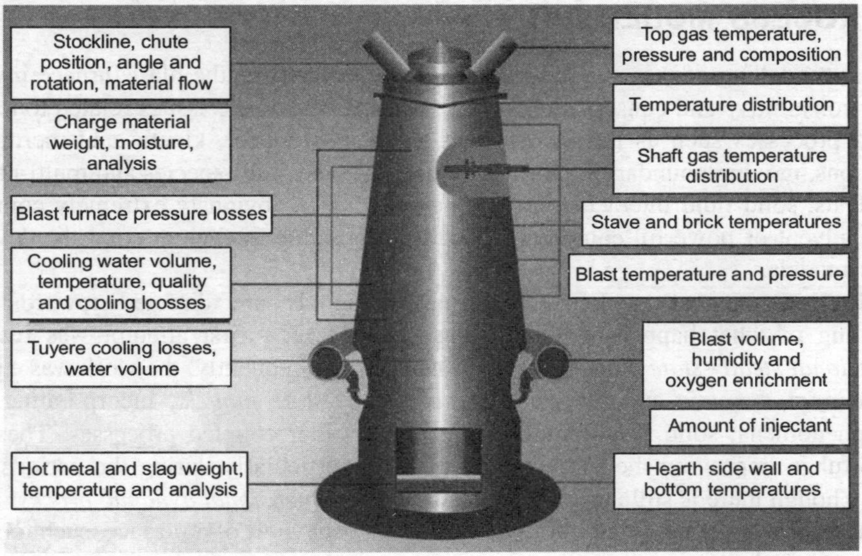

Figure 12.1 Data required for process control of a blast furnace.

Probe	*Measurement/phenomena explored*
Profilometer	Layer thickness across the radius at throat Radial ore by coke ratio Burden descent rate
Top probe	Gas flow distribution
Vertical probe	Location and shape of various isotherms Presence of reserve zones Behaviour of burden—decrepitation, reduction rates
Shaft upper probe	Gas flow pattern Shape of cohesive zone
Shaft middle probe	Gas flow pattern Shape of cohesive zone
Stave thermometer	Scaffold development and dislodging Location of root of cohesive zone
Belly probe	Layer thickness in the cohesive zone Status of burden reduction Gas composition and temperature Early warning of furnace thermal level change
Tuyere coke sampler	Coke condition at tuyere Raceway depth
Core probe	Deadman condition Coal combustion behaviour
Hearth thermometer	Liquid flow phenomena Wear pattern in the hearth

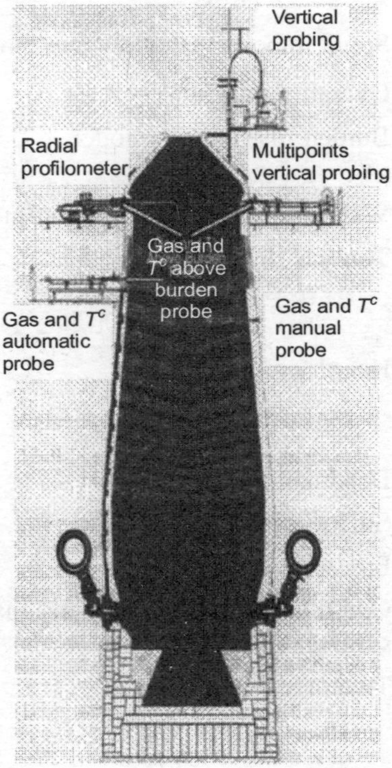

Figure 12.2 Various probes used in a blast furnace (the utility of the measured parameters in understanding the different phenomena occurring within the furnace is also included).

12.3 PROCESS MODELLING

The process modelling of moving bed metallurgical reactors like the blast furnace involves the non-linear constitutive and conservation equations. It has to address issues related to a multitude of coupled processes such as fluid flow, heat and mass transfer, kinetic and thermodynamic considerations, moving boundaries, phase change dynamics, multi-species and multi-phase flow, stress analysis, solid-fluid interactions, etc. The situation is obviously extremely complex, and before the advent of powerful computers, it was not possible to even attempt the development of process models.

All developments of mathematical process models are directed towards a better understanding of what happens within a blast furnace. The first attempt was restricted to *one-dimensional steady-state models* based on kinetics. Subsequently, the work was extended to *one-dimensional dynamic* and *two-dimensional steady-state models*, incorporating rate and transport phenomena, solid flow, phase changes, and other coupled processes. These models proved useful in improving the furnace performance, particularly during the periods of stable operation. Though there is still a need for a global *three-dimensional dynamic process model* for a better understanding of the internal state and process behaviour of a furnace, such models have not been extensively used.

12.3.1 Blast Furnace Models and Their Purpose

Some important models that have been developed for various purposes are listed below.

Overall model	High rates of injection, top gas recycling, etc.
Burden distribution model	Charging programmes of the sequence of charging various solids
Wall temperature distribution model	Detection and visualisation of patterns
Top gas distribution model	First principles model with parameter estimation based on the classified probe readings
Hearth erosion model	Interpretation based on thermocouple readings and understanding of liquid behaviour in the hearth
Deadman model	Motion of the dead-man zone
Silicon prediction models	Prediction of the silicon content of hot metal
Freeze-line model	Detection of accretion formation/melting
One-dimensional/two-dimensional shaft simulation models	Dynamics of the thermal state in the shaft and gas flow in the shaft
Tuyere state model	Flow of gases to and from the tuyere level

12.3.2 Types of Models Available

The mathematical models that are available can be broadly classified into three categories:

- Fundamental or mechanistic models
- Empirical models
- Population-balance models.

Effective process monitoring and simulation using any of these three types of models can at best provide support for short- and long-term decision-making.

For developing a comprehensive blast furnace model, it is necessary to consider the conditions within the furnace as being made-up of a series of flow of packets of steady state solids, gases and liquids. Dynamic models involve the utilisation of mathematical/numerical techniques as well as optimisation and control packages based on *artificial neural networks* (ANN) and *fuzzy logic* based modules. Such models facilitate the mapping of input/output conditions, estimation of the internal state of the furnace, and the prediction of important control variables. The irregularities in the process such as improper burden descent can be predicted using fuzzy logic based heuristic schemes. In addition, it may also comprise open-loop synthesis modules and real-time modules for various raw data based process calculations. These modules can form the knowledge-base required to provide real-time information to various control process variables based on measured data. Finally, it becomes essential to interface the plant *Distributed Control System* (DCS) or *Data Acquisition System* (DAS) with the model(s) using the client-server architecture. A protocol has to be developed for communication between the client and server machines, for handshaking and smooth data transfer.

12.4 STEPS INVOLVED IN MATHEMATICAL MODELLING

12.4.1 General Formulation

Transport and rate phenomena play critical roles in quantifying all the in-furnace phenomena that take place. However, certain limitations exist. The major pitfalls of utilising this approach for prediction include: the insufficiency of information as well as the lack of accurate methodology for estimating the transport and rate parameters involved in the individual steps. The generic forms of the governing transport/conservation equations for mass, energy, momentum and chemical reaction that are applied to simulate the internal state of the furnace are available in standard literature, and hence, are not included here.

12.4.2 Identification of Framework

The internal zones in a blast furnace have been dealt with in Chapter 7. Another way of subdividing a blast furnace into various zones is:

- Pre-heating zone
- Indirect reduction zone
- Direction reduction zone
- Melting and dripping zone (cohesive zone)
- Tuyere or raceway zone
- Hearth/deadman zone.

Figure 12.3 is an illustration of these zones. The figure also lists the probes used to gather the data required in order to undertake process analysis of each of these zones. The process variables that play a role in defining the internal state of a blast furnace in any of these zones include:

- Temperatures of the gaseous and liquid phases
- Molar fractions of CO, CO_2, H_2 and water vapour
- Fractional reactions of the burden materials (iron oxide, limestone and coke)
- Bulk density of the solids
- Gas pressure.

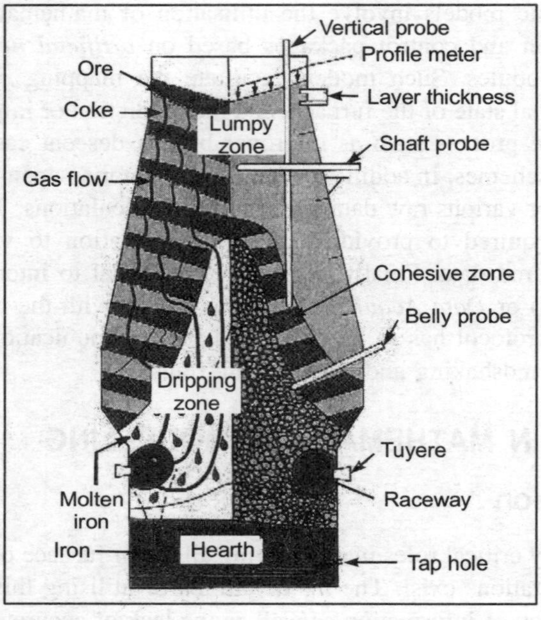

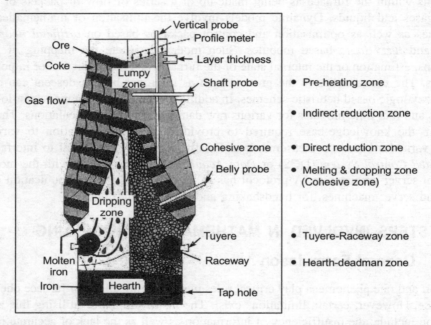

Figure 12.3 Various zones in a blast furnace and the position of the probes.

The first step is to describe the process variables in terms of differential equations. These differential equations can be derived based on conservation principles. The important reactions that are normally modelled include:

- Indirect reduction of iron oxide by CO and H_2
- Solution–loss reaction
- Limestone decomposition
- Direct reduction of molten wustite
- Water gas reaction
- Water gas shift reaction.

A brief description of the various process models that have been developed so far using this approach are presented in the next section.

12.5 IMPORTANT PROCESS MODELS

12.5.1 Burden Distribution Model

The charge in a blast furnace descends through the downcomer before striking the variable throat armour (VTA) or entering the rotating chute, depending on whether the furnace has: (a) a bell-type top, or (b) a bell-less (Paul Wurth) top. After striking the VTA in the case of (a), or leaving the rotating chute in the case of (b), the solids in the charge experience free-fall, until they reach the stockline of the furnace.

The burden distribution model describes the trajectory of these solids as a function of the chute design and the VTA position (the angle at which the throat armour plate is inclined) for furnaces of type (b), and type (a) respectively. For bell-less top, the model predicts the burden profile after a given number of revolutions of the chute at any given angular position. Since the chute rotates around a centreline, it is obvious that the stockline profile is symmetrical about the chute axis, which is the central line of the furnace.

Any solid particle that leaves the VTA or the chute tip as it begins free-fall has a certain velocity, made up of vertical, radial and tangential components. The velocity becomes zero when the particle reaches the stockline. During free-fall, the principal forces acting on each particle are: gravitational, centrifugal, and corriolis forces. The equation of motion of any such particle can be developed and solved with the appropriate initial conditions to generate the trajectories of each particle, till it comes to rest on the stockline. The upper and lower boundaries of the trajectory of the particles during their flight can be computed for any assumed initial stockline profile. This trajectory simulation model then becomes the basis for predicting the new stockline geometry. Based on this new stockline geometry, another set of computations can be carried out to predict the descent of the next set of solid particles. The cycle can be continued till the fall of the entire charge is simulated.

Figure 12.4 (Das, 2006) illustrates the particle size distribution of the burden materials at four different locations in the stockline starting from the central line, for a VTA-equipped furnace. It may be noted that the solids segregate to different extents, depending on their particle

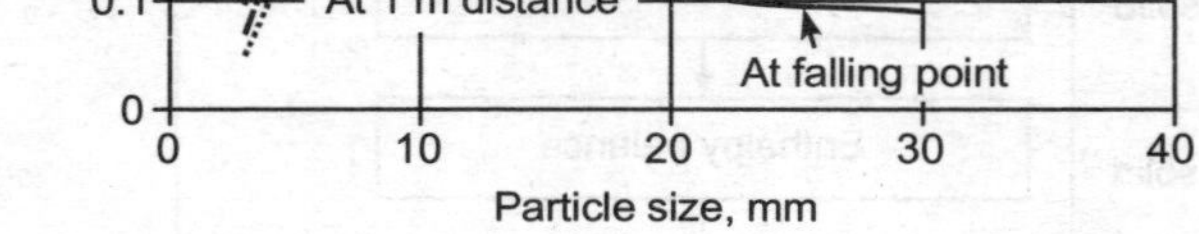

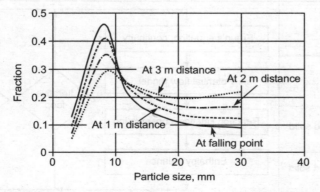

Figure 12.4 Predicted particle size distribution of the burden materials at four different locations in the stockline of a blast furnace with variable throat armour.

size and the distance away from the zone of free-fall. Similarly, Figure 12.5 (Das 2006) plots the inner and outer trajectories of the solids discharged at various chute angles from a rotating chute bell-less top. It also contains the actually measured data that show close agreement between the model prediction and the actual measurements.

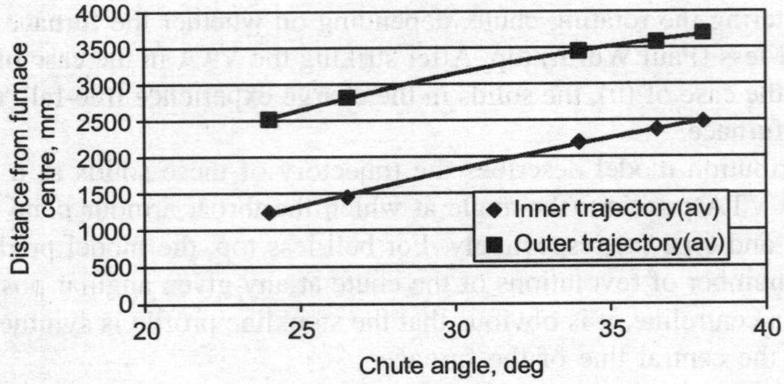

Figure 12.5 Predicted and measured inner and outer trajectories of the solids discharged at various chute angles from a rotating chute.

12.5.2 Thermochemical Model

The structure of a thermochemical model, which can be used to predict the internal state of a furnace, is depicted in Figure 12.6. It involves two-dimensional mapping of the temperature and chemical composition profiles of gases and solids from the stockline to the raceway periphery, including the cohesive zone. Once the detailed inputs of the distribution of gases, solids and other inputs in terms of liquid flow velocity, pressure, volume fraction of coke and ore, voidage

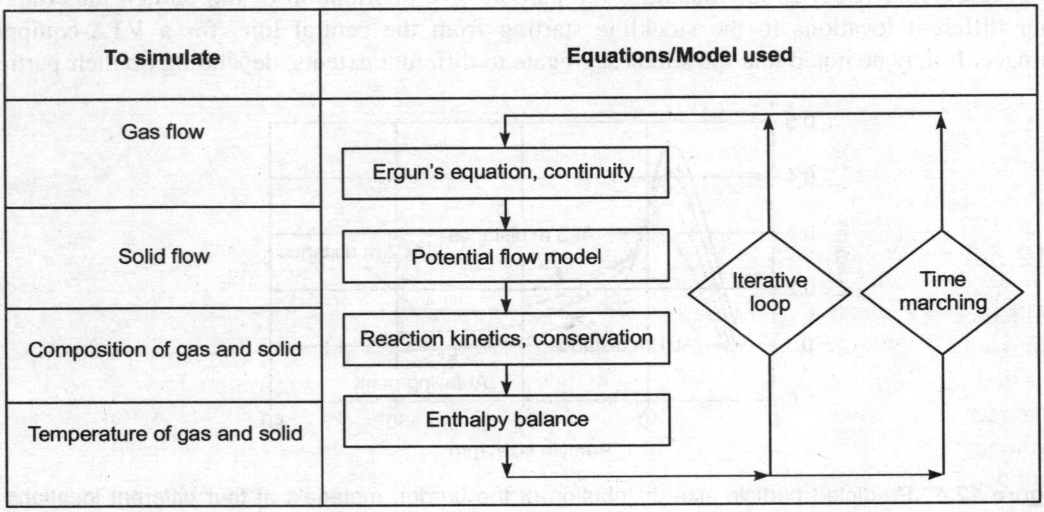

Figure 12.6 Structure of the thermochemical model.

within the stack, as well as particle size distribution, etc. are made available for inclusion in the entire computation domain, the model can simulate the internal state of a blast furnace at any instant of time. In addition, the reduction reactions (from magnetite to wustite and from wustite to iron) as well as carbon gasification reaction can also be modelled. The model can be further augmented by seamless coupling of all the associated phenomena like the flow of solids/gas/liquids, chemical kinetics as well as heat and mass transfer.

Such a model can provide a reasonably representative chemical and thermal picture of the furnace, with regard to the various phases present under a given set of operating conditions. The model can be further refined using plant data and experimental data obtained from softening–melting experiments (see Chapter 9, Section 9.8.5) as inputs. A typical prediction of the steady state temperature profiles that can be obtained once this is done, is shown in Figure 12.7 (Das, 2006). The predicted profiles appear to be reasonable, although the simulation results do not clearly show the existence of a thermal reserve zone.

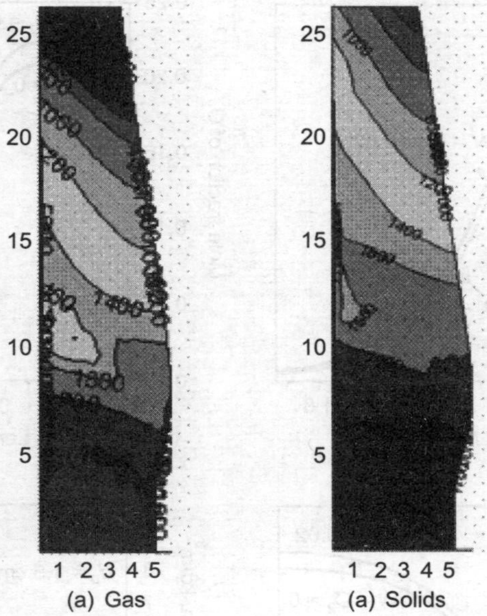

Figure 12.7 Steady state temperature profiles.

12.5.3 Model of the Raceway

The raceway is the zone around the tuyeres of a blast furnace where the combustion of coke and supplementary fuels (like pulverised coal, natural gas, etc.) takes place in the presence of the pre-heated air blast. This generates most of the heat required by the process. Physically speaking, the raceway comprises the zone ahead of the tuyeres where the hot air blast is discharged at high velocity and pressure through each tuyere. Under these conditions, a part of the packed bed of solids (mainly coke) directly in front of each tuyere is displaced/evacuated resulting in 'voids'. These voids are an integral part of the raceway in any blast furnace. The flow of air through the coke bed in front of the tuyeres, the shape of the evacuated area, the shape of the flame front where the combustion takes place in front of the tuyeres, the consumption of coke, etc. have an influence on the reduction of iron oxide and its subsequent melting beyond the raceway zone. Most of the gases in a blast furnace (CO and H_2) are generated in the raceway.

The configuration of the raceway zone and the different physical processes that occur therein can be simulated by a mathematical model. Often, one-dimensional analysis is the first step, before the two-dimensional numerical solution of the conservation equation of mass, momentum and heat for both the carrier phase (air) and the dispersed phase (coke) is taken up. The state-of-the-art models of reaction kinetics of the combustion of coke and the auxiliary fuel are considered when developing the raceway model. Commercial CFD software packages are available to model the flow characteristics in the raceway and solve the associated differential equations.

Based on this approach, a large variety of model predictions are available. Some typical results that have been obtained for the predicted radial distributions of CO_2, O_2, CO and coke are presented in Figure 12.8 (Das 2006).

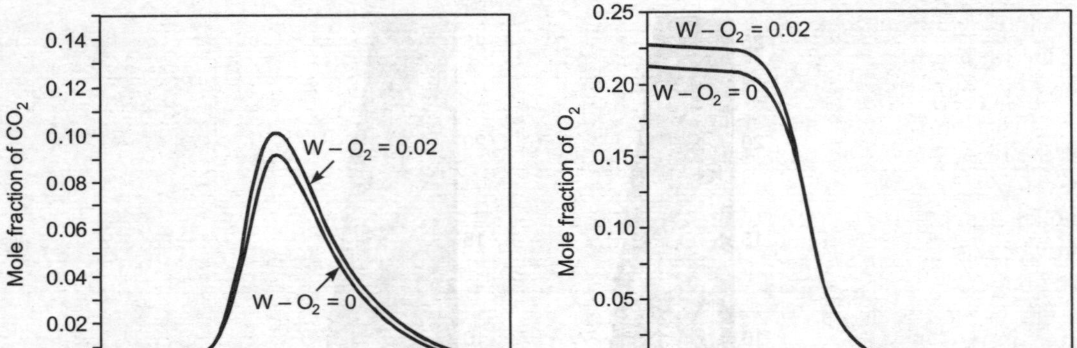

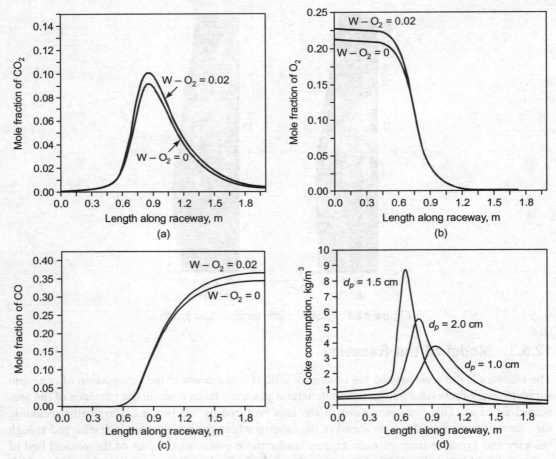

(W – O_2 denotes the extent of oxygen enrichment of the blast; W – O_2 = 0 denotes no enrichment; W – O_2 = 0.02 denotes 2% oxygen enrichment.)

Figure 12.8 Radial distribution of: (a) CO_2, (b) oxygen, (c) CO, and (d) coke.

12.5.4 Freeze-line Model of the Hearth

The hearth of all modern blast furnaces is lined with high-quality carbon having controlled porosity in order to ensure long campaign life (even up to 20 years). To prevent premature blowing-out of a blast furnace for interim repairs during such a long campaign, and also to ensure that the refractories are maintained in a healthy condition till the end of the campaign, it is necessary to exercise certain precautions.

Any damage to the lining in the hearth area of a furnace occurs mainly because of chemical reactions between the penetrating alkalis and the refractories, the thermal shock arising out of the stress changes within the furnace wall, along with repeated flushing of hot metal and slag. These factors are influenced by the temperature distribution as well as the extent of fluctuation of temperature in the hearth walls. Therefore, an understanding of heat transfer to and from the furnace walls is essential in order to identify the conditions under which the walls may get worn out. On this basis, techniques to restrict such wear can be developed.

In principle, this objective can be met by direct measurements of the temperature distribution in the furnace walls. However, in practice, it is difficult to ascertain the exact nature of wear of the blast furnace lining based on a limited set of temperature measurements.

In such a situation, mathematical models can help in quantifying the temperature distribution in the hearth as well as the furnace walls. One of the approaches that is often adopted is to develop an *axisymmetric conductive heat transfer model* using finite element analysis. Such a model can predict the temperature profile and hearth wear in a particular blast furnace and provide some insight into the efficacy of cooling of the side walls and the bottom of the hearth. The output is in the form of thermal contours of the hearth zone, the most important of which is the 1150°C isotherm. This temperature represents the freeze-line for a carbon saturated iron eutectic (hot metal present in the hearth is always saturated with carbon). Figure 12.9 (Das, 2006) shows the prediction of temperature profiles in the hearth of a typical furnace, which includes the freeze-line 1150°C isotherm, obtained by using this approach.

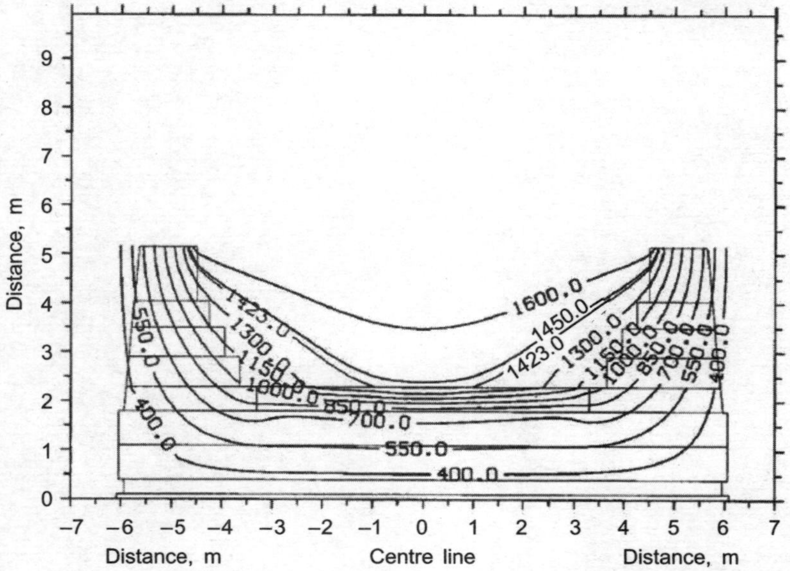

Figure 12.9 Computed temperature profile in the hearth of a blast furnace.

12.6 REAL-TIME PROCESS SIMULATOR

Each of the models referred to in the preceding sections can be used for calculation, prediction and estimation of the variables affecting a blast furnace under any given set of conditions. In order to arrive at the total picture in any given situation, it becomes necessary to integrate the individual models. Only in this way, can a simulator for a blast furnace be developed. The objective of a simulator is to calculate all the different parameters for a specified desired performance. Such a simulation can then be extended to another situation in which a part of the existing specifications can be coupled to some indicators of the desired performance, in order to estimate the profiles of the internal state of the furnace.

The computation would involve one or more of the following:

- Transport phenomena-based or rigorous models
- Compartmental or semi-rigorous models
- Lumped parameter models to arrive at a quick large picture
- Artificial intelligence-based models.

The simulator would also make use of other standard modules like heat and mass balance. Using such a simulator, it is possible to predict parameters like productivity, basicity of the slag, flame temperature, extent of CO-utilisation, percentage of direct reduction, coke rate, sulphur partition coefficient, etc. for any given set of conditions prevailing during the chosen sampling interval.

REFERENCE

Das, S.K., R.P. Goel, S.P. Mehrota and Maruthi Prasad, Steel Tech., Vol. 1, August 2006, pp. 25–33.

Part C

Alternative Ironmaking

- Sponge Ironmaking
- Smelting Reduction

13

Sponge Ironmaking

13.1 INTRODUCTION

Iron units in various forms are required for making steel. Traditionally, blast furnace hot metal and recycled steel in the form of scrap have been the main sources of iron. However, blast furnace hot metal production has decreased over the years owing to problems associated with the availability of high-grade metallurgical coke. With increased efficiencies in steelmaking as well as with the advent of continuous casting, scrap generation has also decreased. All these factors have contributed towards the development of alternative technologies to 'produce' iron units. Today, processes are available to produce solid iron (Fe) in the form of *sponge iron* (also referred to as *Direct Reduced Iron* or *DRI*) as well as to produce hot metal without high-grade coke, i.e. via *Smelting Reduction* (*SR*).

The reactions and physicochemical fundamentals of ironmaking processes (including the alternative methods) have already been discussed in Chapter 5. Hence, these are not repeated in this chapter.

13.2 PROCESSES OF MAKING SPONGE IRON

Direct reduction (DR) includes a family of processes in which iron ore (in the form of fines, lumps or pellets) is reduced to the solid-state either by solid or by gaseous reducing agents. Reformed natural gas or non-coking coal is generally employed as the reductant as well as the primary source of energy. The final product from all DR processes is a solid, which has to be melted during steelmaking in a manner similar to scrap. For gas-based processes, the reactors used are shaft furnaces, fluidised beds, or retorts, while for coal-based DR, rotary kilns, rotary hearth furnaces and multi-hearth furnaces are employed.

A large number of DR processes are available today, which can be grouped as follows:

- Coal-based processes using rotary kilns.
- Coal-based processes using other types of reactors like rotary hearth furnaces, vertical retorts, etc.
- Batch-type gas-based processes using retorts.

- Continuous gas-based processes in shaft furnaces.
- Gas-based processes using fluidised bed reactors.
- Special processes developed for reducing steel plant wastes containing iron oxide(s).

Irrespective of the process adopted, the cost of raw materials typically constitutes approximately 65–75% of the total cost of producing sponge iron. As a result, in order to curtail costs and improve the flexibility of the system used, the trend in all the recently developed DR processes is to shift from lump ore to fine ore, and to use less-expensive energy sources, e.g. coal fines, waste gases, etc.

Some advantages of DR processes over blast furnace ironmaking are:

- Elimination of dependence on coking coal
- Smaller module size
- Lower total capital investment (optimally-sized DR units are less capital intensive than blast furnaces)
- Superior environmental friendliness
- Easier process control and improved process manoeuvrability in most cases.

At the same time, DR processes have certain limitations which include the following:

- Final product is a solid and requires melting
- The individual module size is relatively small as a result of which the benefits of economies of scale of operation become questionable (specific investment ~220–250 US$ per annual tonne of product compared with ~120–150 US$ per tonne for blast furnaces, of course, of higher size)
- Low productivity in terms of unit volume of the reactor(s)
- Low carbon content in the final product (which in some cases can give rise to difficulties during subsequent steelmaking).

13.3 PROPERTIES OF SPONGE IRON

Depending on the raw materials used and the process adopted, the apparent density of the final product varies between 1.5 and 4.0 g/cm^3 while the bulk density varies between 1.5 and 1.9 t/m^3 for DRI. It is higher for the hot briquetted form of DRI, known as *Hot Briquetted Iron* (HBI). The specific surface area of DRI is in the range of 0.5–4.0 m^2/g (usually around 1.0). The carbon content varies over a wide range: 0.10–0.15 for coal-based DRI and up to 2.5% for gas-based DRI. Since sponge iron production does not involve any melting, both the basic geometric shape and the gangue content of the oxide feed are preserved in the final product. However, the removal of oxygen leaves a porous structure (apparent only under a microscope)—hence the name *sponge* iron. As a result, the density of sponge iron is lower, and the specific surface area far higher than that of the oxide feed.

The high porosity and large specific surface area of sponge iron make it prone to reoxidation, which takes place if DRI gets heated in air to its ignition temperature of 200°C. Reoxidation can also take place automatically if DRI comes in contact with moisture, even at normal atmospheric temperatures, since heat gets generated along with the evolution of hydrogen. This phenomenon is often referred to as *in-situ rusting*. Several passivation techniques have been developed to retard oxidation of sponge iron in the presence of air and/or water to prevent/reduce reoxidation during storage and shipment. However, the fact remains that DRI always has a tendency to reoxidise. This plays a role even during subsequent melting under reducing conditions, particularly if the rate of melting is slow. Reoxidation certainly poses problems if sponge iron has to be pre-heated prior to charging into any high-temperature furnace, and, therefore, pre-heated sponge iron is seldom employed in steelmaking.

Sponge iron should have a low gangue content (preferably below 4–5%). Otherwise, subsequent melting would consume extra energy for melting the gangue constituents. Generally speaking, DRI is required to have a uniform chemical composition with a narrow range of variation—both these requirements are easily fulfilled. In gas-based DR processes, the sulphur content is usually very low, provided the sulphur content of the oxide feed is low, whereas, in coal-based processes, the sulphur content is higher because of the unavoidable sulphur pick-up from coal. *Tramp elements* such as copper, zinc, tin, lead, arsenic, etc. are not found in DRI since it is produced from selected raw materials. Uniformity in composition, absence of tramp elements and the low levels of sulphur normally present, make DRI an ideal charge material for replacing scrap in the production of high-quality steel and special grades of cast iron (like SG iron).

Being a bulk material with a controlled size, DRI can be stored in bins, continuously metered when discharged, and then, transported by belt conveyors for continuous charging into any melting unit. These are the major advantages of DRI compared with other solid charge materials like, scrap and pig iron. Handling of the latter materials is difficult, the materials are not amenable to close control during feeding, and continuous charging is often totally ruled out. Unlike scrap/pig iron, DRI always contains FeO. The residual FeO in DRI, as long as it is not very high, can sometimes also be an advantage. Addition of DRI leads to CO formation when the residual oxygen reacts with carbon present in the melt, resulting in stirring of the molten bath.

13.4 USES OF SPONGE IRON

DRI has been successfully used in the following steel melting units:

- Electric arc furnaces, as a substitute for scrap
- Basic oxygen furnaces, as a coolant during the blow, and/or as a substitute for scrap in the initial charge
- Induction furnaces, as a feedstock (particularly applicable to DRI fines below 3 mm)
- Open hearth furnaces, as a charge for melting
- Ladle furnaces, as trimming addition.

Under certain special circumstances (e.g. shortage of hot metal during blast furnace relining, or excess capacity in the steps following ironmaking, etc.), sponge iron can be used in blast furnaces. However, this is seldom practised on a regular/sustained basis. DRI can also substitute cold pig, to a certain degree, in cupolas for the production of cast iron.

13.5 COAL-BASED SPONGE IRON PROCESSES

Depending on the type of reductant employed, DR processes can be broadly classified into two categories, viz. coal-based processes and gas-based processes. The sections that follow give a general idea (by no means exhaustive) of some important DR processes in both these categories using different types of reduction units.

13.5.1 Sponge Iron Production in Rotary Kilns

A simplified flow sheet of sponge iron making in rotary kilns is given in Figure 13.1. In all coal-based DR processes using rotary kilns, sized lump iron ore (or pellets) and a relatively coarse fraction of non-coking coal are fed into the kiln from the inlet end. Coal not only acts as a reducing agent, but it also supplies the heat required for maintaining the temperature profile of the charge within the kiln. A finer fraction of coal is introduced from the discharge end of the kiln to help complete the reduction, since by the time the charge travels to around 70% of the length of the kiln, very little coarse coal is available to complete the last stages of reduction.

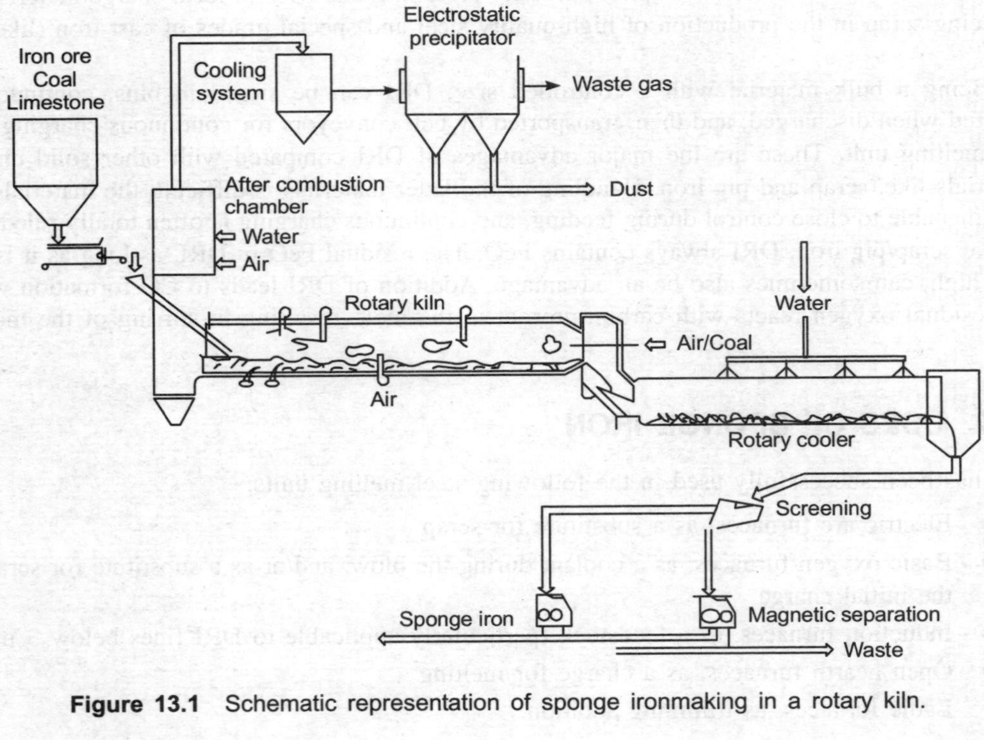

Figure 13.1 Schematic representation of sponge ironmaking in a rotary kiln.

All rotary kiln-based DR processes operate on the countercurrent principle i.e. the gases move in a direction opposite to the flow of solids. Various *unit operations* and *unit processes* like transport, mixing, charge separation by size, heating, gas generation, and reduction occur both in parallel as well as in series. Segregation of the charge materials (ore, coal, flux) on account of size and density differences, as well as because of the slope and rotation of the kiln, has to be prevented to the extent possible, by adopting the appropriate kiln design and through proper operating measures.

Another area of critical importance in rotary kiln operation is the prevention/minimisation of localised areas of high temperature. Unless this is successfully carried out, partial melting of coal ash takes place, leading to the *formation of accretions* (build-ups) on the kiln lining as well as clusters of fused materials (in the shape of spheres/balls) within the bed. The difference between the gas-phase temperature and the charge-bed temperature (normally about 100–150°C) has a major influence on both these phenomena.

To prevent such occurrences, the temperature of the charge bed inside the kiln has to be confined to a maximum of around 950–1050°C so that the ash in coal does not fuse, and the entire charge remains strictly in the solid state. High reactivity of coal encourages reaction of CO_2 in the gas phase with solid carbon in the bed resulting in the formation of CO. Since this is a highly endothermic reaction, high reactivity automatically ensures that the gas temperature does not exceed the solid bed temperature by more than the stipulated limit of 150°C maximum. A flux (like limestone or dolomite) has to be added along with coal so that CaO forms CaS by reaction with sulphur, thereby controlling the sulphur in sponge iron.

The product discharged from the kiln is cooled to room temperature in an indirectly cooled rotary cooler. No water normally comes in direct contact with the reduced product in the cooler and, therefore, there is very little chance of re-oxidation. Since sponge iron is magnetic in nature, it can be easily separated from the non-magnetic portion of the cooler discharge, consisting mainly of coal ash (or char), by using magnetic separators.

The most critical part of rotary kiln reduction is the controlled combustion of coal and its conversion to carbon monoxide, for which the role of the reactivity of coal has already been highlighted. This conversion is also aided by controlled introduction of air from the discharge end of the kiln as well as through blowers mounted on the kiln shell, which rotate with the kiln and supply air to the secondary air pipes protruding up to the centre line of the kiln. The shell-mounted blower and the secondary air pipe assembly, thus provide air at several locations in the space above the charge bed, axially along the kiln length. Radial/submerged injection of air into the charge bed through under-bed nozzles is also often resorted to in the pre-heating zone of a rotary kiln, covering about 30% of the initial length.

A 100,000 tpa (i.e. tonnes per annum) rotary kiln (300–330 tpd), which is a common size can generate around 80,000–85,000 m^3 of gas at 950–1000°C, from which 7.5 MW of power can be generated. For a 500 tpd, 150,000 tpa plant, which is the largest single kiln that is available at present, the corresponding figures are 110,000 m^3 and 10 MW. More than 70% of the power generated becomes surplus after meeting the requirements of the entire DR plant.

Several coal-based rotary kiln processes are available, e.g. SL/RN, Codir, Accar, TDR, DRC, Jindal, etc. all of which are similar in terms of their broad process features. The contribution of all the different coal-based processes towards the global sponge iron production for the year 2005/2006 was only 8.4/10.6 Mt, corresponding to 15/19.7% of the total world production of DRI. Though globally natural gas is the preferred reductant for producing sponge iron, because of the restricted and localised availability of natural gas in India (only off-shore in Bombay High), coal-based rotary kiln processes are more popular in India. They contributed as much as 5.42/7.1 Mt (54/60.2 %) out of 10.1/11.8 Mt to India's production in 2004–05/2005–06. In both the years, India was the highest producer of DRI in the world; a situation that has emerged over the last three years.

13.5.2 Coal-based Processes Using Rotary Hearth Furnaces

In this category, the following processes are worth mentioning, viz.

- INMETCO process developed by International Nickel Company in 1970 which so far, has been restricted to the treatment of steel plant wastes only.
- FASTMET process, developed originally by Midrex Corporation, USA, and since 1990, jointly by Midrex Corporation and Kobe Steel, Japan.
- COMET (SIDCOMET) process, developed originally by CRM Laboratories, Belgium in the 1990s and later by Paul Wurth. However, subsequent commercial trials at Sidmar in Belgium gave rise to some difficulties resulting in the development of the process being suspended at present.

Amongst all these processes, Fastmet has been a commercial success; therefore, it will be presented in some detail.

Fastmet process

The Fastmet process is a solid reductant-based rotary hearth furnace (RHF) process. Successful trials began in 1991 in a 2.5 m diameter pilot rotary hearth furnace to treat fine oxides (particularly wastes). The Fastmet process flow sheet is shown in Figure 13.2.

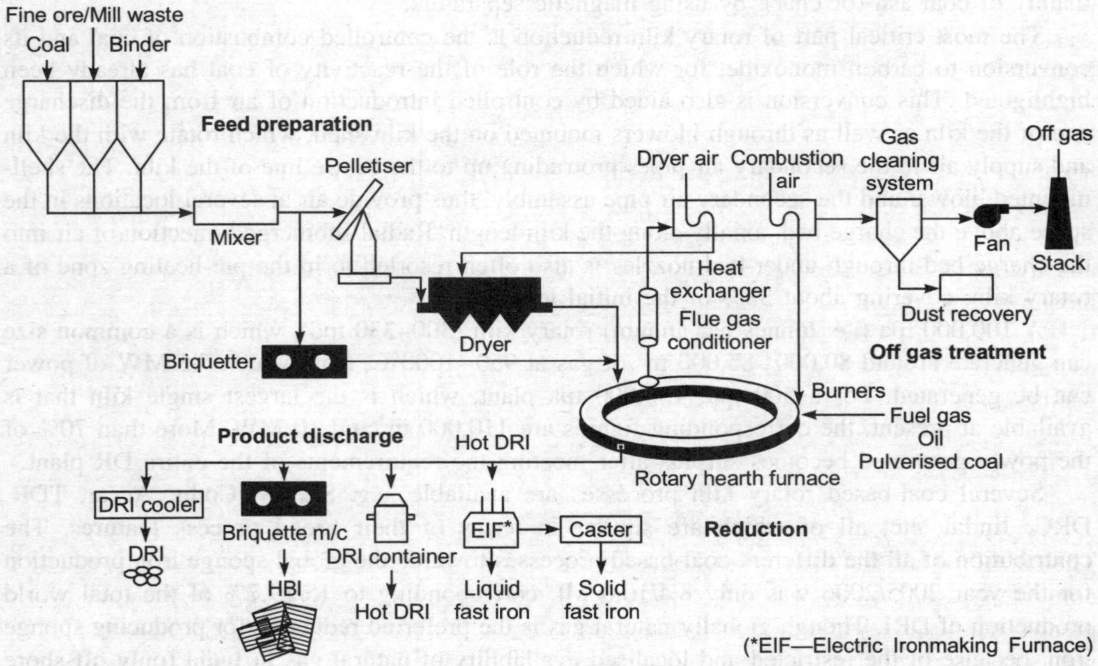

Figure 13.2 Flow sheet of the Fastmet process.

When the primary oxide feedstock is virgin iron ore, the oxide in the form of concentrate fines along with reductant fines are pelletised, dried, and then charged to the RHF in a single layer. In those cases where steel mill wastes are the primary feed material, the feed is often briquetted before charging on the hearth, again in a single layer. As the hearth rotates, the pellets/briquettes are heated to 1250–1400°C by combustion of gas, oil or pulverised coal. The agglomerates containing the reductant get reduced to metallic iron. As explained in Chapter 5, the reduction is accomplished by intimate contact between the carbon contained within the pellets/briquettes and the iron oxide fines, at these relatively high temperatures. Since the reduction is very rapid, the residence time of the charge on the hearth is typically as less as 6 to 12 minutes, during which 90 to 95% of the iron oxide is converted to metallic iron. The DRI produced is continuously discharged at around 1000°C from the furnace, either into refractory lined cans for hot transfer to the melt shop, or into briquetting machines for the production of HBI. The carbon content in the product can be controlled between 1 and as high as 6%, if required. It becomes an ideal material for steelmaking since it is highly metallised and contains sufficient carbon.

In April 1994, Midrex and Kobe Steel constructed a Fastmet demonstration plant at Kobe Steel's Kakogawa Works in Japan, which was designed for a production capacity of 2.2–2.5 tph, using an 8.5 m diameter rotary hearth furnace. The first commercial Fastmet plant was commissioned at the Hirohata Works of Nippon Steel in April 2000 to process around 190,000 tpa of pellets made from steel plants wastes in a 21.5 m diameter RHF. A second commercial plant began operations in May 2001 at Kobe Steel's Kakogawa Works to process 14,000 tpa of wastes like blast furnace flue dust, BOF/EAF dust and mills scale (in the form of pellets rather than briquettes) in an 8.5 m diameter RHF (the same as in the demonstration plant) fuelled by waste oil.

13.6 GAS-BASED PROCESSES

In all gas-based processes, the reductant is *natural gas*. Natural gas consists primarily of carbon and hydrogen compounds in the form of hydrocarbons, which are straight chain compounds having the formula C_nH_{2n+2}. Though the most common hydrocarbon in natural gas is methane (CH_4), it may also contain heavier paraffins such as ethane, propane, etc. and contaminants such as carbon dioxide, nitrogen and sulphur compounds. If natural gas were to be directly used for gas-based DR, the problems encountered would be as follows:

- Very slow reduction as compared to H_2 and CO (especially H_2)
- Carbon soot formation and consequent process problems, such as choking, etc., and unfavourable thermal balance in the reactor owing to endothermic effects.

Therefore, natural gas cannot be employed in its virgin form for direct reduction. It has to be converted (often after desulphurisation) at a temperature above 1000°C into a mixture, predominantly of H_2 and CO, to increase the calorific value and to increase the proportion of reducing gas in relation to the oxidising gases (like CO_2). This step of conversion into CO and H_2 is known as *reforming*. Reforming also automatically takes care of the problem of thermal balance, since reduction with a 75% H_2 + 25% CO mixture has almost zero heat effect on the system (exothermic CO reduction is balanced by endothermic reduction by H_2 at this proportion of the two gases).

13.6.1 Reforming of Natural Gas

When natural gas is reformed using a steam oxygen mixture, the following reactions take place (equations formulated for methane, which is the main component):
Steam reforming (endothermic):

$$CH_4 + H_2O = CO + 3H_2 \tag{13.1}$$

Partial oxidation (exothermic):

$$CH_4 + (3/2)O_2 = CO + 2H_2O \tag{13.2}$$

Water gas shift reaction (slightly exothermic):

$$CO + H_2O = CO_2 + H_2 \tag{13.3}$$

These reactions proceed rapidly in the presence of a suitable catalyst (nickel or any noble metal deposited on a substrate material) at temperatures above 700°C. Under these conditions, the required amount of hydrogen is generated by reaction Eq. (13.1). Thermodynamically, this reaction is favoured by high temperature and low pressure. Hydrogen is also generated by the equilibrium of the so-called shift reaction, Eq. (13.3), which is slightly exothermic.

A proper balance of the above reactions has, therefore, to be maintained to feed the reformed gas into the sponge iron reactor at an optimum temperature of 1000–1100°C. By controlling the temperature conditions in any commercial gas reformer, it is possible to adjust the proportion of CO, H_2 and CO_2, H_2O. Reformed gas should contain around 85–90% CO + H_2 (with equal proportions of both) and around 12–15% CO_2 + H_2O (with around four times more CO_2 than H_2O).

13.6.2 Gas-based Direct Reduction in Fluidised Beds—Finmet Process

The *Fluidised Iron Ore Reduction* (FIOR) process was developed by Esso Research and Engineering Co., USA for the continuous reduction of iron ore fines by reformed natural gas in a train of fluid bed reactors. The first commercial Fior plant was built at Matanzas in Venezuela in 1976 with an annual capacity of 400,000 t. It faced problems with regard to the operation of the fluidised beds and was closed down in the year 2000. At present, there is no Fior plant operating anywhere in the world.

The original Fior process was substantially improved jointly by Fior de Venezuela, and Voest Alpine (VAI) of Austria culminating in the development of the Finmet process. The Finmet process uses a train of four fluid bed reactors (Figure 13.3) in which the gas and solids moving in countercurrent directions come in contact throughout the entire reactor train. The feed concentrate (–12 mm iron ore fines) is charged to the reactor train at the topmost reactor (R4 in Figure 13.3) via a pressurised lock hopper system. The upper lock hopper cycles continuously from ambient to reactor pressure, and the ore is fed continuously to the reactors out of the lower lock hopper, which is always maintained at the reactor pressure of 11–13 bar. In the topmost reactor, the feed is pre-heated to 500–570°C by the reducing gas coming from reactor R3. Pre-heating, dehydration, and reduction of haematite to magnetite and then to FeO take place in stages as the feed is transferred downwards to the subsequent reactors. The gas required for reduction is a mixture of recycled top gas and fresh reformer make-up gas provided by a

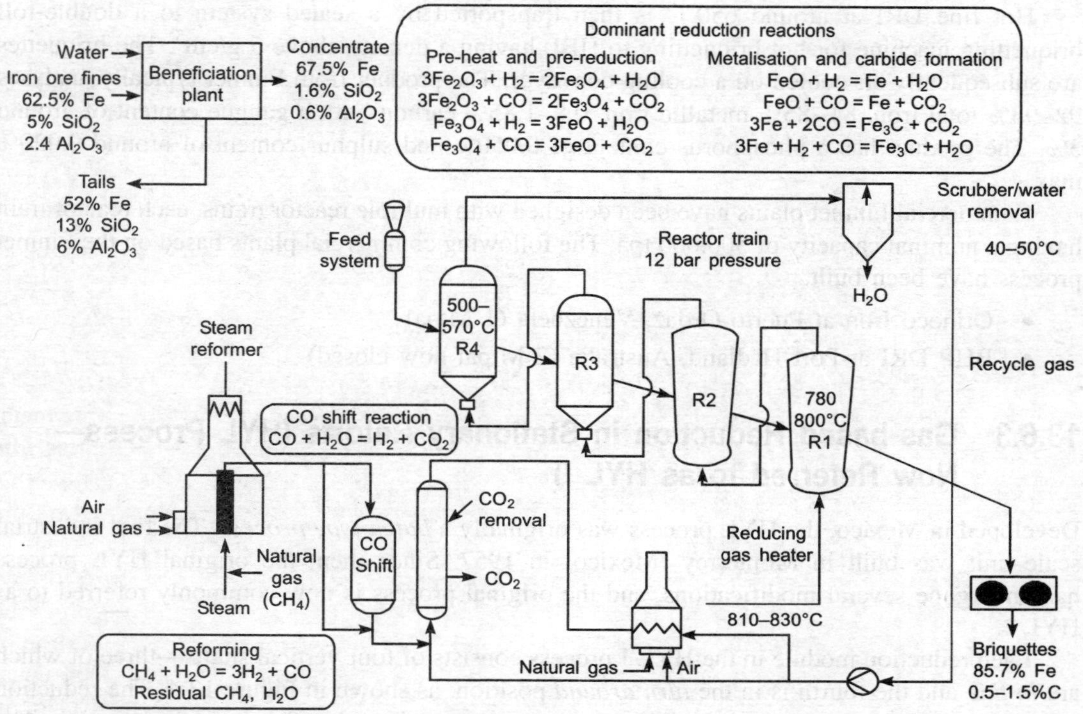

Figure 13.3 Flow sheet of the Finmet process.

standard steam reformer. The composition of the recycle gas entering the last reactor is adjusted in accordance with the desired carbon content of the product. The recycle gas taken from the top gas leaving R4 is first quenched to 40–50°C and then scrubbed in a wet scrubber to remove dust and water produced by the hydrogen reduction reactions. The clear recycle gas is compressed in a centrifugal compressor before a portion is passed through a CO_2 removal system for control of the CO_2 level in the reducing gas. The make-up gas required to balance the gas consumed in the reduction reactions and as a fuel, is supplied from a conventional steam reformer system.

The temperature in reactor R1 is maintained at around 780–800°C so that the final reduction to 93% metallisation takes place. This is accompanied by carburisation of some of the Fe to iron carbide.

Metallisation and carbide formation reactions

$$FeO + H_2 = Fe + H_2O \tag{13.4}$$

$$FeO + CO = Fe + CO_2 \tag{13.5}$$

$$3Fe + 2CO = Fe_3C + CO_2 \tag{13.6}$$

$$3Fe + H_2 + CO = Fe_3C + H_2O \tag{13.7}$$

$$Fe + CO + H_2 = Fe(C\ (free)) + H_2O \tag{13.8}$$

$$3Fe_2O_3 + 5H_2 + 2CH_4 = 2Fe_3C + 9H_2O \tag{13.9}$$

$$Fe_3O_4 + 2H_2 + CH_4 = Fe_3C + 4H_2O \tag{13.10}$$

Hot fine DRI at around 650°C is then transported by a sealed system to a double-roll briquetting machine for hot briquetting to HBI, having a density above 5 g/cm^3. The briquettes are subsequently air cooled on a cooling conveyor. The product from Finmet typically analyses 92–93% total iron, 84–85% metallic iron, 0.8–1.85% carbon with a gangue content of around 3%. The product has a phosphorus content of 0.050% and sulphur content of around 0.020% max.

Commercial Finmet plants have been designed with multiple reactor trains, each reactor train having a nominal capacity of 500,000 tpa. The following commercial plants based on the Finmet process have been built.

- Orinoco Iron at Puerto Ordaz, Venezuela (1 Mtpa)
- BHP DRI at Port Hedland, Australia (2 Mtpa; now closed)

13.6.3 Gas-based Reduction in Stationary Retorts (HYL Process—Now Referred to as HYL I)

Developed in Mexico, the HYL process was originally a *batch type process.* The first industrial scale unit was built in Monterrey (Mexico) in 1957. Since then, the original HYL process has undergone several modifications, and the original process is now commonly referred to as HYL I.

Each reduction module in the HYL I process consists of four vertical shafts—three of which are *in line* and the fourth is in the *turn around* position, as shown in Figure 13.4. The reduction is completed in three stages, each of these stages is approximately of three hours duration. The

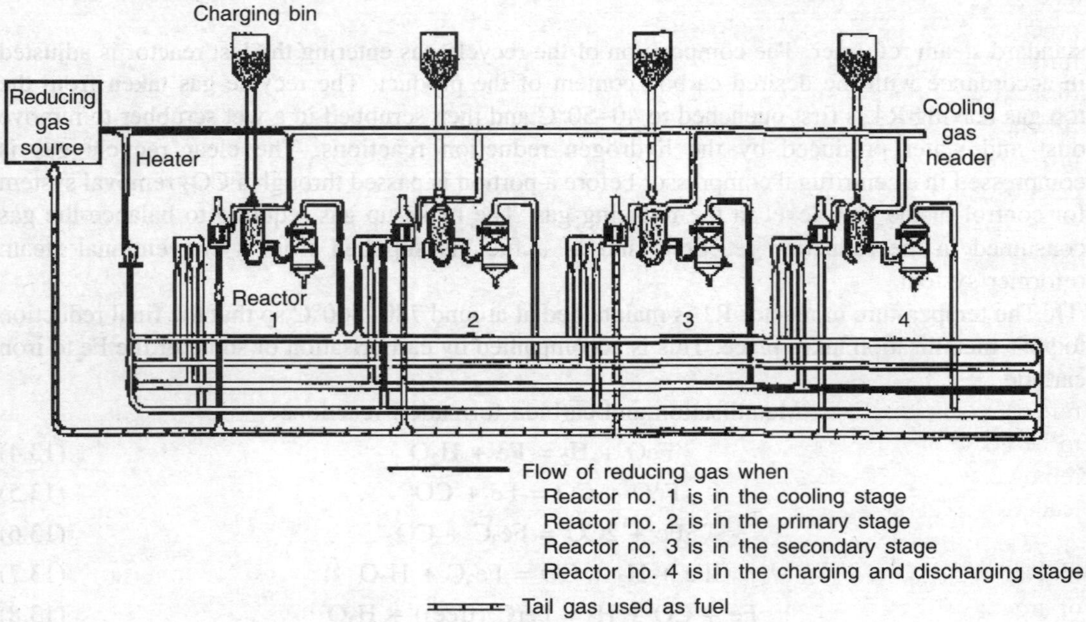

Figure 13.4 HYL I process flow sheet.

first stage consists of heating and preliminary (secondary) reduction of the iron oxide that has just been charged, using gas from the subsequent reactor where the main (primary) reduction takes place. Once the secondary reduction is completed, the first reactor is switched to the second stage of reduction by means of automatic valve manipulation. The bulk of the reduction by reformed and desulphurised natural gas then begins, using gas that is richer in composition.

In the HYL process, natural gas is reformed using excess steam in the presence of a catalyst. The steam is condensed before the reducing gas is brought to a temperature of 870–1030°C. This hot gas first partially reduces the reduced ore and then the fresh ore during the secondary phase of reduction. To obtain the desired temperature in the reactor, part of the reducing gas is burnt with air pre-heated to the same temperature as the reducing gas. When most of the reduction is completed, the reactor is changed to the cooling and carburisation mode, where the final stages of reduction take place along with carbon deposition on the product. The gas used in this stage is fresh gas coming directly from the reforming unit (75% H_2, 14% CO, 7% CO_2 and 4% CH_4).

At present, three HYL I plants (located in Venezuela, Indonesia and Iran) having 9 modules with total plant capacities varying from 1 to 2 Mtpa, are in operation. However, being a batch process the popularity of HYL I has continuously been on the wane. The production from HYL I plants all over the world, which was as high as 3.04 Mt in 1994, has gradually come down to just over 1.0 Mt in 2004. HYL I, which in its heyday in the early eighties, contributed almost 40% to global DRI production, now has less than 1% share.

13.6.4 Gas-based Shaft Furnace Processes

The gas-based shaft furnace processes, which have become by far the most popular for the production of sponge iron, employ a vertical shaft furnace in which, as in the case of a blast furnace, lump ore and pellets are charged at the top using a charging system similar to a blast furnace. Reformed natural gas after pre-heating is introduced in the lower portion of the shaft. As the hot reducing gas flows upwards, reduction takes place continuously. Hence, these processes are often referred to as *continuous countercurrent moving bed processes*. In this category, the Midrex process is dominant, followed by HYL III and HYL IV.

Midrex process

This process was developed by Midland Ross Corporation of Cleveland, USA in 1967. Figure 13.5 shows the basic flow sheet. The reducing gas is, as usual, generated by reforming natural gas. In the Midrex reforming system, a proprietary nickel catalyst is used. A single reformer is utilised instead of a reformer/heater combination and the reformed gas does not need to be cooled before it is used in the process. Hence, there is also no need for a separate CO_2 removal system. These are some of the advantages of this process, which has made it the world leader in direct reduction.

The iron oxide feed to a Midrex shaft can be in the form of pellets or lump ore as shown in Table 13.1 (Amit Chatterjee et al. 2001). However, generally speaking, the charge consists of around 60% pellets and 40% lump ore of a particular type. Pellets are the preferred feedstock owing to their superior physicochemical characteristics compared with lump ores. As a result,

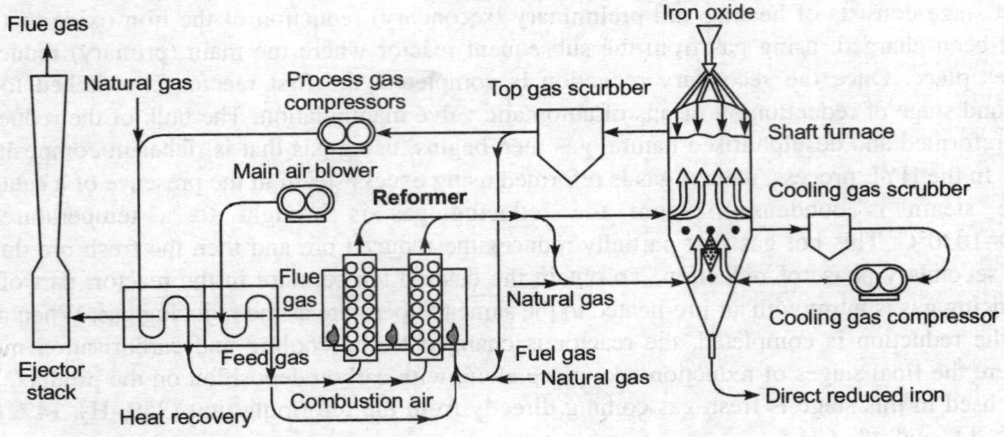

Figure 13.5 Flow sheet of the Midrex process.

Table 13.1 Typical chemical composition of the oxide feed to the Midrex process

Weight %	**Pellets**	**Lump ore**
Fe (total)	67–69	66–68
SiO_2	0.9–1.0	0.5–0.7
Al_2O_3	0.2–0.3	0.3–1.3
CaO	1.1–1.2	0.06 and below
MgO	0.80	0.05
P	0.015	0.030–0.060
S	0.006	0.005–0.008
Moisture	1.5 max.	4.0 max.

in most cases, a minimum amount of pellet usage becomes mandatory. Figure 13.6 shows the movement of solids and gases in the shaft of a Midrex furnace.

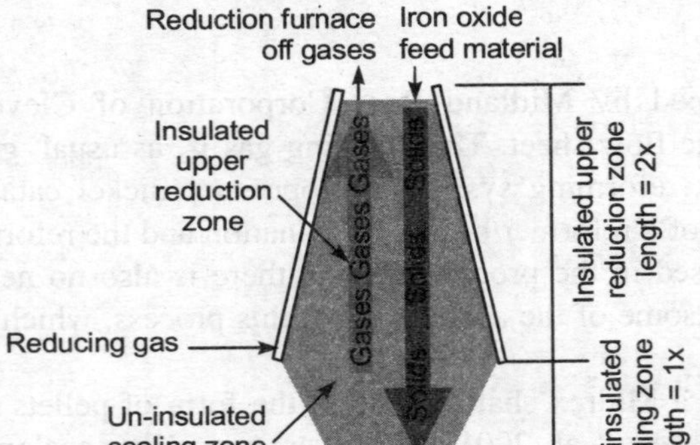

Figure 13.6 Material movement in a Midrex shaft.

The spent reducing gas (or top gas) leaving the shaft furnace at a temperature of 400–450°C is cooled and cleaned in a gas scrubber before approximately 60% of the gas is returned to the reformer; and the rest used as a fuel. The process gas is compressed and pre-heated before entering the reformer at around 900°C, where it is mixed with make-up natural gas. The reformed gas made up mostly of carbon monoxide and hydrogen exits from the reformer at about 850°C. The ratio of H_2 to CO is controlled at about 1.5–1.8, and the *reducing quality of the gas* (CO + H_2 as a proportion of CO_2 + H_2O) is maintained at 11–12 for best operations.

The iron oxide burden is first heated to the process temperature before it is metallised by the upward flowing, countercurrent reducing gas injected at 800–870°C through tuyeres located at the bottom of the cylindrical section of the shaft. The reduced material then passes through a transition zone before reaching the lower conical section of the furnace. Low carbon DRI (less than 1.5% C) is directly cooled using a circulating stream of cooled exhaust gas introduced in the conical section, before cold DRI is discharged. When higher carbon DRI (up to 4.0% C) has to be produced, natural gas is introduced along with cooling gas into the conical section. In this zone, natural gas readily decomposes (cracks) in the presence of highly reactive metallic DRI, thereby generating nascent carbon, which gets absorbed in the product before it is discharged. In both cases, the final product is DRI with 93–94% metallisation, with the desired carbon content.

A large number of Midrex plants are operating successfully all over the world. Without any doubt, Midrex is the most widely used DR process in the world today. The actual production in 2007/2008 was 39.7/39.85 Mt out of 67.2/68.5 Mt DRI produced in the world, i.e. just over 75% in both years. Plant capacities vary from 0.35 Mtpa (minimum) with one module in many plants to five modules in the 3.2 Mtpa at Mobarakeh Steel Plant in Iran, which is the largest Midrex plant in the world. Essar in Hazira, Gujarat has five modules, three with a capacity of 440,000 tpa each and two modules of 0.6 and 1.8 Mtpa capacity. It is the world's largest gas-based merchant HBI plant.

HYL III process

In 1979, after continuous research for many years, HYL announced a new process called HYL III (III signifying the third generation of HYL reactors, though II was not a separate process, but only an improvement of I). The details of the HYL III process are shown schematically in Figure 13.7. The principal change introduced (over HYL I) was the modification of the four fixed-bed reactors by a single moving-bed reactor, utilising the same gas reforming plant, auxiliary equipment and quenching towers.

Though it is claimed that the HYL III process can operate with 100% pellets, 100% lump ore or mixtures thereof, normally 70% pellets and 30% lump ore are charged. In some cases, it is extremely important to add 5% non-sticking ore in the feed, in order to check the sticking tendency of the pellets, and thereby improve the furnace performance in terms of uniform descent of the burden.

In HYL III reactors, characterised by a high operating pressure of 5.5 kg/cm^2 absolute, the feed is charged through a sealing mechanism. An automated system of valves permits the pressurisation and de-pressurisation of the inlet bins to enable charging. As the burden descends through the stack by gravity, its rate of descent is regulated by a rotary valve at the reactor exit.

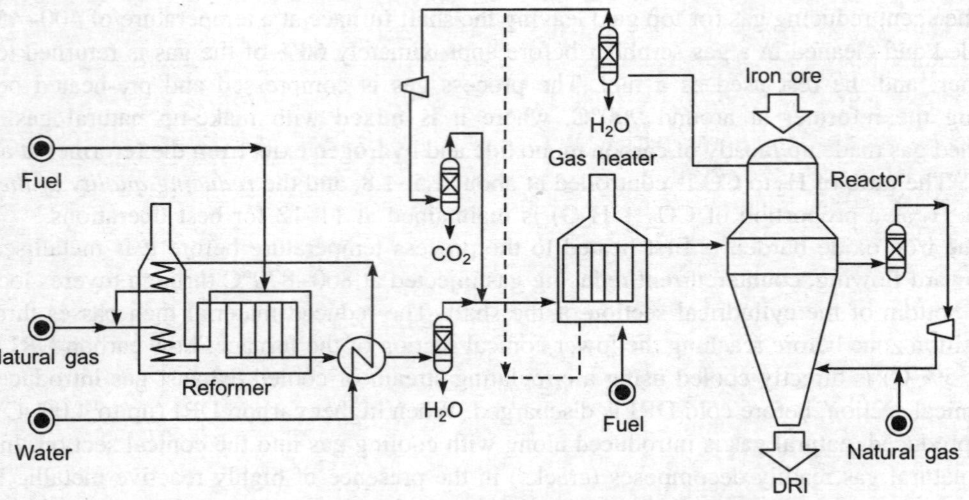

Figure 13.7 Flow sheet of the HYL III process.

The upper zone of the furnace is fed with hot reducing gases from a heater, which receives cooled, scrubbed reducing gas from the top of the reactor, along with fresh make-up reducing gas from the natural gas reformer. The cooling zone in the lower part of the reactor is supplied with cooling gas, which is recycled by means of a gas compressor. Suitable cooling gas is fed as *make-up* in this recycle stream. After cooling, the DRI is discharged through a sealing mechanism, similar to the one at the feed end of the reactor.

Some of the distinctive features of the HYL III process are given below.

- Natural gas reforming is carried out using only steam in the presence of a catalyst.
- To maintain the highest possible temperature for reduction, a combustion chamber is incorporated in the reducing gas inlet to the reactor. Partial combustion of natural gas also improves the carburising efficiency of the gases, and makes it possible to achieve reduction temperatures in excess of 900°C. This also enables HYL III units to produce high carbon containing DRI.
- The reducing zone in the upper part of the shaft furnace is separated from the cooling/carburisation zone in the lower part by an isobaric zone, which prevents the gases from mixing in the cooling and reducing zones. This helps in independent control of metallisation and carbon content of sponge iron. Accordingly, it is possible to produce DRI (or HBI) with different carbon levels to meet the specific demands of steelmakers. This has given rise to the concept of *equivalent metallisation* (actual metallisation + five times the carbon content in DRI), since the carbon content of DRI has a strong influence on its melting behaviour during steelmaking.
- High pressure (4 atmospheres or more) operation allows the equipment size in the gas handling plant to be reduced. It also lowers the energy requirements.
- The reforming section is independent of the reduction section, thus allowing the reformer to operate stably and maintaining the appropriate operating conditions reliably over long periods.

- The process gas is not recycled through the reformer resulting in longer life of the catalyst. As a result, high sulphur inputs can be tolerated, without any deleterious effect on the equipment, or on the quality of DRI, without having to utilise a bypass route.

The energy consumption in the HYL III process varies between 9.0 and 10.0 GJ/tonne of DRI. HYL III plants are available in capacities between 0.25 and 2.0 Mtpa. Eighteen modules, in at least 10–12 plants all over the world, with a total capacity of around 11 Mtpa are now in operation. In 2007/2008, just over 11.3/9.9 Mt of DRI/HBI was produced in these plants. As far as India is concerned, the world's largest HYL III module, with a capacity of 0.9 Mtpa of HBI, was installed at Raigarh in Maharashtra in 1993 by Grasim.

Shaft furnace process with self-reforming—HYL IV M process

Both HYL and Midrex conventionally utilise a reformer to transform natural gas into H_2 and CO. The latest trend is to go in for self-reforming, in which reforming of natural gas occurs within the reduction reactor itself, with the metallic iron in DRI acting as the catalyst. This allows *in situ* reforming of natural gas to proceed in parallel with the reduction of iron oxide and carburisation of DRI. No separate gas reformer is required.

Figure 13.8 is a schematic representation of the self-reforming process. The process starts with the injection of natural gas, which together with recycled gas, enters a humidifier, where the required amount of water is supplied. This gas then enters a heater where its temperature is increased to above 900°C. In the transfer line to the reduction reactor, oxygen is injected for partial combustion of the reducing gas to increase its temperature above 1020°C. This gas, upon introduction at the bottom of the shaft furnace, flows upwards into the reduction zone, countercurrent to the moving bed of solids. In the lower part of the reduction zone, *in situ* reforming reactions occur, when the hot gas comes in contact with metallic DRI. As a result, some of the DRI reacts with the carbon, and is carburised to Fe_3C, leaving some excess free carbon.

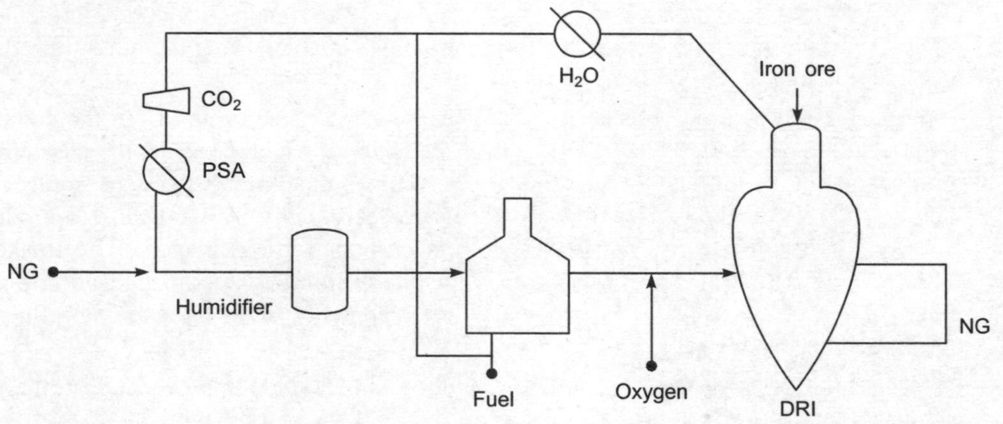

Figure 13.8 Schematic representation of self-reforming.

Both the reducing and the reforming reactions take place inside the reactor. The reacted exit gas leaves the top of the reactor. Steam is condensed and is removed before the gas is compressed and sent for CO_2 removal, after which, it is mixed with natural gas, thereby closing the circuit. Figure 13.8 also shows an optional cooling circuit, if the product has to be cold discharged. In the latter case, the natural gas is split between the reduction and the cooling sections. The cooling circuit consists of a compressor and a quenching system to maintain a closed circuit with make-up natural gas to cool the DRI down to 45°C. The reducing gas entering the reactor contains controlled concentrations of H_2O and CO_2, and when it comes in contact with metallic iron which acts as catalyst, some reforming of methane takes place. The reactions consume oxidants and produce reducing agents, which react with the remaining iron oxides and produce more oxidants.

The HYL IV M process employs a moving-bed shaft furnace (similar to HYL III) to reduce iron ore pellets and lump ore at normal reduction temperatures, but at intermediate reduction pressures. The process can produce cold/hot DRI as well as HBI. The first HYL IV M plant began production in April 1998 in Monterrey, Mexico; hence the suffix M. This IV M plant has a capacity of 675,000 tpa, and consists of only three (rather than four) main units—the reduction system, the DRI handling system and the external cooling system (i.e. no reforming section).

Midrex has also adopted self-reforming in some of their existing plants.

REFERENCE

Chatterjee, Amit, Ramesh Singh and Banshidhar Pandey, *Metallics for Steelmaking—Production and Use*, Allied Publishers, 2001.

14 Smelting Reduction

14.1 INTRODUCTION

Until recently, blast furnaces were the only source of hot metal on a bulk scale. However, with the world witnessing a gradual shift from integrated steel plants using the Blast Furnace–BOF combination to a multiplicity of smaller mini-mills essentially based on electric arc furnaces, alternative means of producing hot metal using *Smelting Reduction* (SR) have come into existence. The *raison d'être* of smelting reduction is to produce liquid hot metal, i.e. a product similar to blast furnace hot metal, by reducing iron oxide feeds (preferably those not acceptable for traditional blast furnace ironmaking, for both physical and chemical reasons) using coal, oxygen and/or electrical energy.

To fulfil these requirements, several SR processes have been suggested. All of them aim to produce hot metal, without using either coke or high-grade iron oxide as the feedstock. However, it needs to be stressed that only a very few of the SR processes that have been conceptualised till date, have reached commercial scale. This has happened despite the fact that these new processes are one-generation ahead of classical blast furnaces, in terms of their intrinsic process versatility as well as superior environmental friendliness. Even in future, it remains to be seen whether many of the SR processes presently under development, can go past the rigours of pilot plant trials before getting commercialised.

14.2 RAW MATERIALS FOR SMELTING REDUCTION

A broad comparison of the raw materials used in conventional blast furnaces and in smelting reduction processes is presented in Table 14.1.

In both blast furnace ironmaking as well as in smelting reduction, the cost of raw materials constitutes around 60% of the total cost of producing hot metal. Consequently, in SR (and even DR discussed in Chapter 13), efforts have been made (and will continue to be made) to reduce the cost of production by using less expensive raw materials. The quality specifications for raw materials used in SR processes are less stringent than those in the case of blast furnaces. Most SR processes, therefore, use low-grade fine ores, iron-bearing plant wastes, etc. as the iron oxide

Table 14.1 Raw materials used in blast furnaces and in smelting reduction

Process	Oxide feed	Reductant	Product
Blast furnace including mini blast furnace	Lump ore, sinter, pellets	Coke plus coal, oil, tar, natural gas	Hot metal essentially for BOF steelmaking
Smelting reduction	Ore fines, lump ore, waste iron oxides	Coal plus oxygen and/or electricity	Hot metal for EAF steelmaking (sometimes, other steelmaking processes as well)

feedstock and non-coking coal, and use carbon-bearing fines as well as other relatively inexpensive carbon/hydrogen containing materials as the reductant(s). Oxygen and electricity are used as required. The ultimate goal is to exclude coke to the maximum possible extent, if not, eliminate it completely.

A forecast of the technologies to be adopted for hot metal production in the foreseeable future is shown in Figure 14.1 (Amit Chatterjee et al. 2001). It may be noted that while it is expected that SR technologies would find increasing applications in future, the traditional blast furnace ironmaking is likely to maintain its dominance even after a century from now.

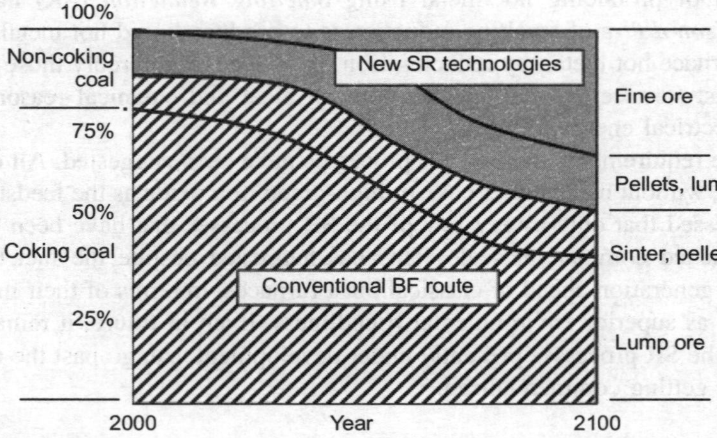

Figure 14.1 Forecast of the technologies to be adopted for hot metal production.

14.3 FUNDAMENTALS OF SMELTING REDUCTION

As the name implies, smelting reduction involves both reduction and smelting, i.e. melting accompanied by chemical reaction(s). The unit operations that take place in any smelting reduction process are summarised in Figure 14.2. In an ideal SR reactor, in the strictest sense, all the reduction reactions should take place together in the liquid state in a single-step. In actual practice, for effective process control, most SR processes utilise two reactors and at least two, if not three, process steps that include: the removal of oxygen from the oxide in the solid-state

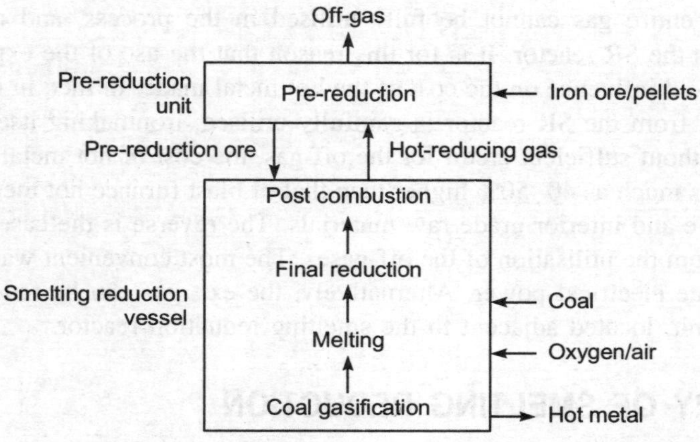

Figure 14.2 Schematic representation of smelting reduction technology.

to varying extents in stage one, followed by the removal of the remaining oxygen via liquid phase reduction reactions in stage two. Sometimes, the latter is completed in two steps rather than one, i.e. SR then becomes a three-stage operation.

The initial reduction of iron oxide begins in the temperature range of 850°C to 1050°C. The basic reactions involved are as follows:

$$3Fe_2O_3 + CO = 2Fe_3O_4 + CO_2 \tag{14.1}$$

$$Fe_3O_4 + CO = 3FeO + CO_2 \tag{14.2}$$

$$FeO + CO = Fe + CO_2 \tag{14.3}$$

The carbon monoxide required for reduction, is generated by the well-known Boudard reaction:

$$C + CO_2 = 2CO \tag{14.4}$$

Up to this stage, SR is similar to solid-state DR. Beyond solid-state reduction of haematite/magnetite to wustite, smelting reduction, essentially involves reduction of molten FeO by CO. This gives rise to far higher transport rates owing to convection, and a remarkable increase in the conversion rate because of enlargement in the specific phase contact area. The latter is a direct consequence of the dispersed nature of the phases. These two major advantages of SR accrue because of the formation of liquid phases, which does not happen in DR.

From studies on the oxidation and reduction behaviour of pure molten iron oxide by CO/CO_2 mixtures at 1500°C, it has been concluded that the rate controlling step for both oxidation and reduction is the inter-diffusion of iron and oxygen atoms within the melt. It has also been found that mass transport plays an important role in the reduction kinetics. The overall reaction rate is proportional to the square root of the gas flow rate. Therefore, all out efforts are made to increase the amount of gas that is available for reduction.

To generate sufficient amount of reducing gas, all SR processes consume fairly large quantities of reductant (normally coal). Having generated the large volume of gas that is required, its effective utilisation becomes extremely important. However, this gives rise to one of the inherent deficiencies of SR, i.e. with most SR reactor configurations given the productivity requirements, the entire gas cannot be fully utilised in the process, and rich gas at a high temperature leaves the SR reactor. It is for this reason that the use of the export gas in any SR process has a marked influence on the cost of the hot metal made. In fact, in many cases, unless the net export gas from the SR reactor is gainfully utilised, ironmaking itself becomes totally uneconomical. Without sufficient credit for the off-gas, the cost of hot metal made by smelting reduction can be as much as 40–50% higher than that of blast furnace hot metal, despite starting with less expensive and inferior grade raw materials. The reverse is the case if adequate credit can be obtained from the utilisation of the off-gases. The most convenient way to utilise the exit gas is to cogenerate electrical power. Alternatively, the exit gas can be fed to a shaft furnace direct reduction unit, located adjacent to the smelting reduction reactor.

14.4 HISTORY OF SMELTING REDUCTION

14.4.1 The Early Stages

SR was first conceived in Sweden in 1938. Martin Wiberg injected a mixture of iron ore and coal into an open-hearth furnace bath. Preliminary findings revealed that liquid phase reduction was taking place. This became the genesis of further investigations on smelting reduction. The first sustained effort to develop a SR process was undertaken by the Engells in Denmark (1938–1939), in which a mixture of iron ore and coal powder was sprinkled on the surface of a moving high carbon iron bath, and the carbon monoxide so generated was burnt above the bath.

14.4.2 The Second Stage

Global interest in the development of SR technology then waned, mainly because direct reduction came to the fore. The initial rate of growth of direct reduction was astronomical. During the period 1930–1950, tunnel kilns, small shaft furnaces and small rotary kilns were employed for producing sponge iron in Sweden and in other countries. The world witnessed the development of near-perfect coal and gas-based DR processes to suit a wide spectrum of conditions. Consequently, sponge iron (DRI) began to be projected as the most preferred material for augmenting the existing source(s) of iron, i.e. scrap and hot metal. Later, DR could not make a real dent on ironmaking despite this early promise, essentially because of some inherent drawbacks like low productivity, high cost of production, tendency for sponge iron to reoxidise, etc.

This forced steelmakers to examine the alternative liquid ironmaking routes once again. There was a re-awakening of interest in SR, as a result of which, it got a second *lease of life*, following a lull period of more than two decades.

14.4.3 Commercialisation of SR

The first SR process that was suggested after this 're-awakening' was INRED (Intensive Reduction). Work on this process began in Sweden in 1972. INRED was a novel concept of producing hot metal of blast furnace quality at a very rapid rate. The process was tried out in a 60,000 tpa demonstration plant set up at Mefos, Lulea, Sweden. In the INRED process, the two-stages of reduction—the first stage reduction of iron oxide to FeO, followed by the second stage comprising final reduction of FeO to Fe—were performed in a single reactor. The ore concentrate (in fine form) was pre-reduced to wustite by flash smelting using coal along with a large amount of oxygen. This step consumed about 90% of the total process energy. Final reduction was carried out in an electrically-heated furnace that formed the lower part of the reactor, in which the balance of the required energy was supplied in the form of electricity.

The products from the INRED furnace were hot metal, slag, and waste gas. The waste gas was relatively small in volume owing to the extensive usage of oxygen. The exit gas was completely burnt to produce steam that was used to drive a steam turbine generator for producing electrical energy required for the oxygen plant, the electric furnace, and other auxiliaries.

Despite considerable global interest in this technology in the early years (Indian raw materials were also tested at Mefos at considerable cost), it was finally not found to be ready for commercial exploitation. The pilot plant work showed that precise control of a rapid process like flash smelting was virtually impossible. Further, development was abandoned in the late 1970s. However, it needs to be emphasised that many of the features of INRED, such as the use of fine ore, non-coking coal, oxygen, quick reaction time, ability to stop and start at short notice, use of the export gas for power generation, etc. became an integral part of all subsequent SR developments.

INRED was followed by ELRED, another Swedish development. The only major difference was that pre-reduction was carried out under pressure in a circulating fluidised bed. The ELRED process was also abandoned later, for more or less the same reasons as INRED.

Many SR processes have since been suggested and tried, but only 3–4 have reached commercial scale. This clearly shows that SR involving high temperature liquid iron oxide reduction by CO gas is not always easy to control, at least in reactors other than the blast furnace. Hind sight clearly shows what a versatile process the blast furnace actually is, although it was developed centuries ago. Usage of high-quality coke and iron oxide are, of course, the major deficiencies of blast furnaces, which triggered the development of SR.

14.5 SR PROCESS CATEGORISATION

It is possible to classify SR processes in several ways as given below.

14.5.1 Classification Based on the Number of Stages Involved

The SR processes can be divided into single-stage or two-stage processes.

Single-stage processes

This group of processes, in which both reduction and smelting take place in the same reactor, is the simplest. A schematic flow sheet of the single-stage process concept is given in Figure 14.3(a). Since the reactor is fed with wet iron ore without any pre-reduction, the energy requirement in these processes is higher. The total energy is supplied by the combustion of coal in the presence of oxygen. It is also necessary to ensure that the degree of *post-combustion* of

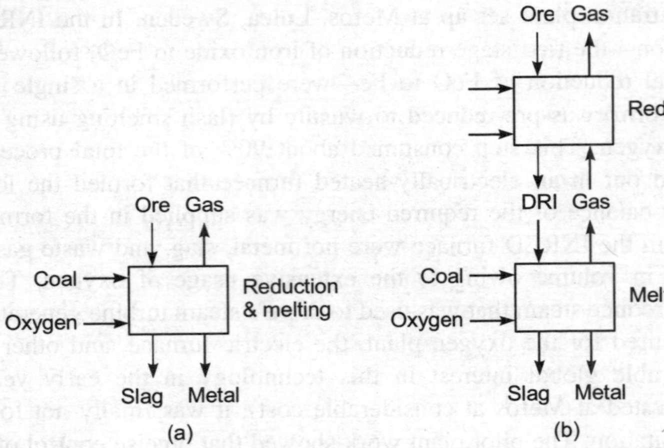

Figure 14.3 (a) Single-stage SR processes, and (b) two-stage SR processes.

the reducing gas leaving the bath is also high (about 70%). Obviously, the oxygen and coal requirements in these processes are high on account of the limited opportunity to utilise the reducing gas. Consequently, single-stage SR processes are often inefficient and economically unattractive, unless adequate credits are obtained from the large amount of high value (high temperature and high reduction potential) off-gases produced. Proper control of the foamy slag produced in the reactor and erosion of the reactor refractories are the two other problems associated with single-stage processes. On the other hand, the main advantages are low capital cost, use of ore and coal without any pre-treatment, and the ability to accept low-grade ore and coal.

The only single-stage SR process on which considerable demonstration scale work has been carried out is Romelt. However, the development work has now been suspended, and thus the future of this process is uncertain.

Two-stage processes

The concept involves two separate reactors—one for *pre-reduction* and a second for *smelting reduction* as depicted in Figure 14.3(b). The off-gases from the smelting stage are utilised for pre-reduction, thereby reducing the energy requirement for final reduction and melting. However, this automatically means that for any two-stage process to work efficiently, it is necessary to ensure a close match between these two independent operations.

Depending upon the degree of pre-reduction and post-combustion, such processes can be further classified into two subgroups. The first group consists of processes showing a high degree of pre-reduction and a very low degree of post-combustion. Processes like Corex belong to this group. In such processes, smelting has to be controlled by partial combustion of coal in such a way that the composition and the amount of the off-gases generated are just sufficient to meet the requirements of producing highly-metallised DRI in the preceding step. Such a stipulation automatically demands careful selection of coal.

The second subgroup contains those two-stage processes that are based on a low degree of pre-reduction and a high degree of post-combustion. They are superior to the first subgroup insofar as making use of the degree of metallisation as a control parameter for guaranteeing balanced operation between the two process stages. The net result is that such processes can operate in a self-balancing manner—as the metallisation decreases, the extent of reduction in the smelter increases, thereby generating more off-gases for pre-reduction.

Processes like Hismelt, Dios, AISI, etc. belong to this category.

The efficiency of two-stage processes can be improved by separating the gas reaction zone from the smelting zone. Heat loss in a normal two-stage process occurs because the melter off-gas has to be cooled from around 1600°C to 800°C (representing an energy loss of 1.8 GJ/thm) before it can be used for reduction. However, if carbon is present in the gas reaction zone, it can help in reducing the temperature of the melter off-gases, without loss of energy because of the following endothermic reactions:

$$C + CO_2 = 2CO \tag{14.5}$$

$$H_2O + C = H_2 + CO \tag{14.6}$$

It is obvious that for these reactions to occur, the gas must contain an oxidised species (like carbon dioxide). The thermodynamics of the carbon–oxygen system is such that below 1000°C, the equilibrium gas mixture in contact with carbon, contains increasing quantities of CO_2 with decreasing temperature; for example, it contains 5% CO_2 at 900°C and 15% CO_2 at 800°C. The incorporation of this step can help in controlling the gas temperature to that required for gaseous direct reduction, thereby resulting in minimum energy losses. This has so far been incorporated in some SR processes and as a result, the energy consumption in SR processes varies compared with that in blast furnaces (Figure 14.4).

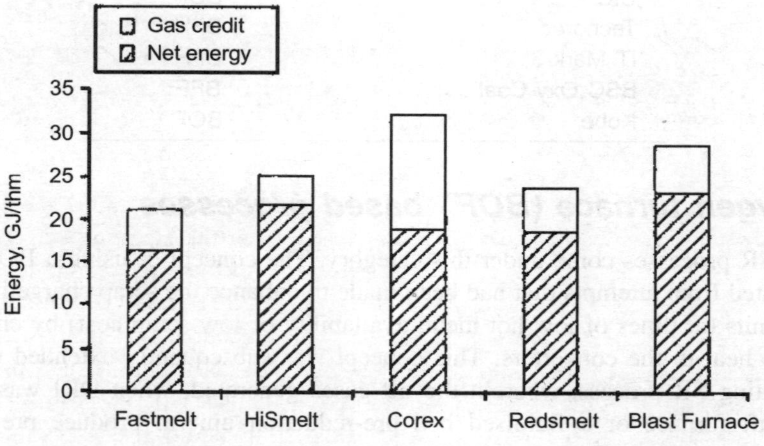

Figure 14.4 Net energy consumption and gas credit in smelting reduction processes vis-à-vis those in blast furnaces.

14.5.2 Classification Based on the Type of Furnace Used for Smelting

Table 14.2 lists the types of smelting furnaces employed by various SR processes, including those that are working and those that have been abandoned.

Table 14.2 Smelting reduction processes classified in terms of the type of furnace utilised

Process	Classification
Corex (earlier KR)	BOF
Finex	BOF
Hismelt	BOF
AISI Direct Steelmaking	BOF
Dios	BOF
Ausmelt	OH
Romelt (earlier FLPR)	OH
Combismelt	BOF
Coin	BOF
Sumitomo SC	BFH
Hoogovens	BOF
BSC Continuous Melter	BOF
Plasmasmelt	BFH
INRED	EAF
ELRED	EAF
Pirogas	BFE
IDI	BOF
Kawasaki SR	BFH
CIG	BOF
Tecnored	BFH
IT Mark 3	BFH
BSC Oxy-Coal	BFE
Kobe	BOF

Basic oxygen furnace (BOF) based processes

Many of the SR processes come under this category. The concept of using a BOF type reactor for SR originated from attempts that had been made to enhance the scrap charge in normal BOF steelmaking units (at times of low hot metal availability or low scrap cost) by charging coal to generate extra heat in the converters. This concept was subsequently extended to a combined reduction–melting SR process, wherein the off-gases generated, when DRI was melted, were used in a shaft furnace or a fluidised bed pre-reduction unit to produce pre-reduced iron. Processes like Hismelt fall in this category.

Processes based on blast furnace type hearth (BFH)

The processes in this group utilise vertically standing vessels with a coke bed as the melting reactor, rather than a liquid iron bath as used in the BOF-based processes. Coal and oxygen are injected into the bed and the heat liberated is used to smelt DRI (or pre-reduced ore) produced in a separate reactor, using the smelter off-gases. The processes in this category, therefore, aim at partially utilising the principles of a blast furnace, while minimising the consumption of coke. For instance, the Sumitomo SC process, which is based on this concept, needs a coke input of about 30–40% of the total fuel requirement. The Kawasaki SR process is similar. The Corex process may also be included in this category, with the difference that it uitilises a very high degree of pre-reduction (above 90%), unlike the other processes mentioned in this group.

Processes based on open-hearth type rectangular furnace (OH)

Some SR processes (e.g. Romelt) utilise long, rectangular furnaces with an extended bath for smelting ore fines and coal, similar to that used in open-hearth steelmaking.

Electric furnace based processes

Processes in this category utilise an electric arc furnace to melt DRI produced in a separate coal-based reduction unit. The off-gases from the reduction stage, together with that from the electric furnace serve as the fuel required for generating electrical power, which is sufficient (and in some cases, more than sufficient) for the arc furnace. All the energy requirements for such an integrated combination can be fully met by coal—INRED and ELRED are examples.

Processes based on blast furnace enhancements (BFE)

Such systems include operational modifications of existing blast furnaces by the adoption of new technologies like oxy-coal combustion and plasma coal injection, so as to reduce the coke consumption to the barest minimum. Some of these developments aim at utilising coal, both as the reductant and the energy source, while in others, coal is employed only as the reducing agent and electricity is the auxiliary energy source. The latter is of interest only in those countries where electricity is available at low cost—examples of processes which adopt this approach are Plasmasmelt.

14.6 SALIENT FEATURES OF IMPORTANT SR PROCESSES

The major SR processes, including those which have some merits but have not been commercialised so far, are listed in Table 14.3. Some of the more important ones will now be discussed.

14.6.1 Corex Process

The first smelting reduction process to go beyond the laboratory/pilot plant scale was Corex. The process was developed in order to produce hot metal from lump ore/pellets using non-coking coal as the reductant. After pilot plant work in Germany, the first 1000 tpd plant was installed in Pretoria, South Africa, which after operating for 3–4 years has now been shut down. Three commercial Corex plants are presently in operation—Saldanha Steel in South Africa with concurrent DRI production using the export gas, Jindal South West (JSW) Steel in India with concurrent power generation, and Posco in South Korea where the export gas is used in the steel

Table 14.3 Details of important smelting reduction processes developed till date

Process	Developer	Type of unit operations	Status
Corex	Korf Stahl, Germany and Voest Alpine, Austria	Pre-reduction in shaft furnace followed by melting in melter-gasifier.	The first SR process to be commercialised. Commercial plants now operating in India, South Africa, South Korea.
Romelt	Moscow Alloy and Steel Institute, Russia	Only example of single reactor, single-stage process.	0.3 Mtpa demonstration plant at Novolipetsk Steel Works operated for many years beginning 1986. Now closed. Commercial plants (1000 tpd) planned in many places (including India) but not constructed.
AISI	American Iron and Steel Institute, USA in collaboration with HYL, Mexico.	Pre-reduction (up to FeO stage) in shaft furnace followed by molten iron bath reactor.	Trials with cold pre-reduced FeO pellets conducted in a 120 tpd pilot plant near Pittsburgh, USA. Now abandoned.
Dios	Japanese national project involving 8 steelmaking companies.	Fluidised bed pre-heating and pre-reduction in converter type vessel.	500 tpd plant was to be installed at Keihin Works of Nippon Steel, Japan but later given up.
Hismelt	Klockner, Germany; CRA, Australia and Midrex, USA were originally involved. Now RTZ, Australia.	Pre-reduction up to FeO stage in circulating fluidised bed followed by melter-gasifier.	0.1 Mtpa demonstration plant operated successfully at Kwinana, Australia led to installation of a commercial plant at the same site (capacity 0.8 Mtpa).
ELRED	Stora Kopperberg and Asea, Sweden.	Fluidised bed pre-reduction and smelting in DC arc furnace.	Pilot plant trials conducted for pre-reduction. No further development.
INRED	Boliden, Sweden	Partial reduction by flash smelting followed by final reduction and melting in EAF.	8 tpd pilot plant trials conducted at Mefos, Sweden with various inputs (including from India). Later abandoned.
Combismelt	Lurgi and Mannesmann Demag, Germany	Pre-reduction in coal fired rotary kiln and then smelting in submerged arc furnace (SAF).	0.3 Mtpa plant operating in New Zealand.
Plasmasmelt	SKF Steel, Sweden	Pre-reduction in fluidised bed or shaft furnace followed by plasma smelting.	50,000 tpa plant installed in 1981 by SKF Steel at Hofors, Sweden.

(*Contd.*)

Table 14.3 Details of important smelting reduction processes developed till date (Contd.)

Process	Developer	Type of unit operations	Status
Kawasaki SR	Kawasaki Steel, Japan	Fluidised bed pre-reduction followed by smelting in a melter-gasifier using coal and oxygen.	10 tpd pilot plant test work conducted at Chiba Works, Japan in 1987–88. Process since abandoned.
Kobe	Kobe Steel, Japan and Midrex Corporation, USA	Shaft furnace for pre-reduction and melting in converter using coal through bottom tuyeres.	Separate pilot scale studies undertaken in converter in Japan and shaft furnace in the USA. No progress thereafter.
Ausmelt (Ausiron)	Ausmelt Limited, Australia	Single converter type vessel in which oxygen and coal fines are blown through top lance(s) onto a liquid metal bath.	1 tph pilot plant at Dandenong in Victoria, Australia operated batchwise for many years. Process not applied to iron/steel so far but used extensively in non-ferrous industry .
Fastmelt	Midrex, USA and Kobe Steel, Japan	Pre-reduction in rotary hearth furnace (RHF) to produce DRI (Fastmet process) followed by DRI melting in electric ironmaking furnace.	Two commercial plants to treat 190,000 and 16,000 tpa of steel plant wastes operating in Japan.
Finex	Posco, Korea, RIST, Korea and VAI, Austria	Pre-reduction in fluidised beds (similar to Finmet DRI process) and melting in a melter-gasifier (similar to Corex).	600,000 tpa plant under construction at Pohang, to start-up in November 2006. Plant engineered after experience with Corex operation in Posco, Korea.
IDI (Redsmelt)	Iron Dynamics, USA, Sumitomo, Japan and Mannesmann Demag.	Pre-reduction in RHF (Inmetco DRI process) and then melting in SAF.	0.5 Mtpa commercial plant at Butler, USA, operated intermittently since 1999.
IT Mark 3	Kobe Steel, Japan and Midrex, USA	Green composite pellets of iron oxide and coal heated to 1350–1500°C in RHF. Partial melting helps in-situ slag separation. Product pure iron nuggets.	0.5 Mtpa commercial plant under construction. Was to be ready by the end of 2006.
Tecnored	CAEMI, Brazil	Coal and oxide containing green pellets melted in a low shaft furnace of special design.	0.3 Mtpa commercial plant operating in Brazil since 2005.
Cleansmelt	CSM (Brazil) and ILP (Italy)	DR based on cyclone converter furnace and then melting in a melter-gasifier.	5 tph hot metal pilot plant operating at Taranto, Italy.

plant. It should be noted that the use of the export gas, accomplished in three totally different ways in the three commercial plants, is part-and-parcel of hot metal production using this process. The reasons for the same have already been elaborated (Section 14.3).

It has also been mentioned in Section 14.1 that SR processes aim to use fine ore and non-coking coal along with oxygen, so that quick reaction rates can be achieved in a reactor(s) that can be stopped and started as and when required. As far as the Corex process is concerned, it fulfils these objectives except that the iron oxide feed is a mixture of pellets (6–20 mm) and closely-sized and carefully-screened lump ore (6–30 mm). Some of the other unique features of this process are as follows:

- The process is designed to operate at a pressure of up to 5 bars.
- The process can accept high alkali containing ores without any build-up inside the reactor.
- The specific melting capacity is very high—at least twice that of blast furnaces so that productivities of the order of 3.0–3.5 $t/m^3/d$ can be achieved.
- As in a blast furnace, almost 100% of the phosphorus input reports to hot metal, thereby restricting the maximum phosphorus content acceptable in the oxide feed.

The flow sheet of the Corex process is given in Figure 14.5. Reduction of iron ore and subsequent melting take place in two separate reactors, viz. (i) the reduction furnace and (ii) the melter-gasifier. The process utilises essentially the same quality of iron-bearing raw materials as a blast furnace. However, as far as the reductant is concerned, coke is largely replaced by coal.

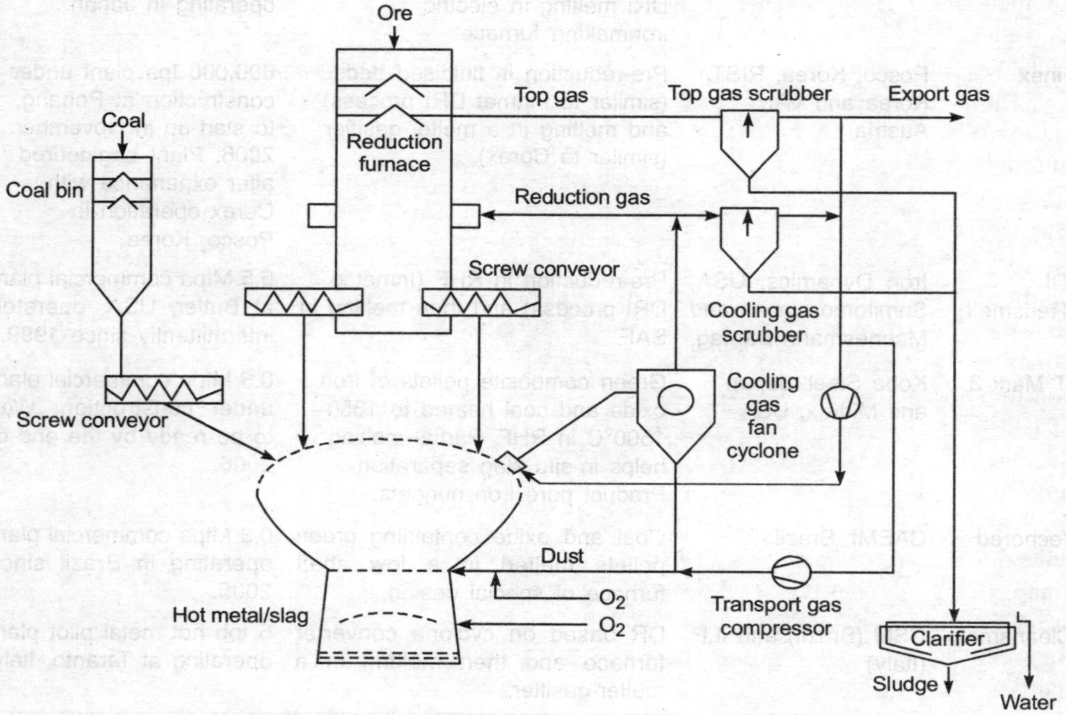

Figure 14.5 Basic flow sheet of the Corex process.

In the reduction shaft, iron oxide is reduced to sponge iron by the countercurrent flow of reducing gas generated in the melter-gasifier. The hot sponge iron produced is directly discharged into the melter-gasifier, for further heating and melting. Liquid iron at a temperature of 1400–1500°C and slag are the final products.

Coal (6–50 mm in size with 50% above 10 mm) is charged into the gasifier section of the melter-gasifier, where it comes in immediate contact with hot reducing gases (at approximately 900 to 1300°C) and gets dried and devolatilised. The Corex process requires 500–700 kg fixed carbon per tonne of hot metal to be supplied through coal, in order to generate the large amount of gas/heat required by the process (reasons for the same have been given in Section 14.3). Around 600 to 800 Nm^3 of oxygen per tonne of hot metal is also required to oxidise the fixed carbon to carbon dioxide and carbon monoxide. The velocity of the gases flowing in the lower part of the gasifier has to be adjusted in such a way that stable fluidised bed conditions are maintained at a temperature of 1500–1800°C.

Under these conditions, optimum transfer of heat plays a crucial role in determining the overall process efficiency. An important parameter is known as the *post combustion ratio* (PCR), which is the volumetric ratio of $(CO_2 + H_2)/(CO_2 + H_2O + CO + H_2)$ in the exit gas from the melter-gasifier. For the process to be energy efficient, it is essential to optimise the partial combustion of CO and H_2 generated in the melter, by the injection of oxygen above the bath, at the rate required to yield the desired *degree of pre-reduction* (PRD). In any Corex unit, the gas from the melter-gasifier predominantly contains CO and H_2, with very little or no post-combustion. Under these conditions, high PRD is possible provided the appropriate conditions are maintained. Use of oxygen in the melter, generates sufficient volume of combustion products as well as heat. This provides the conditions required to melt the DRI produced in the upstream reduction unit, which in turn, calls for high *heat transfer efficiency* (HTE).

The reducing gas exiting from the melter-gasifier in the Corex process contains about 85% carbon monoxide. The gas is cooled to 800–900°C, dedusted in a hot dust cyclone, and then, introduced into the reduction shaft for pre-reducing the oxide feed. Limestone, dolomite, and silica sand are used as additives for adjusting the basicity of the slag, depending on the ore chemistry and the analysis of the coal ash.

Experience has proven that the Corex process can accept various types of oxides, but a minimum amount of pellets is required for efficient operation (60% as per the experience of JSW). Further, JSW has been found that all-coal operation is normally not possible, and at least 10–15% of coke is required as the reductant along with non-coking coal—the typical consumption figures are: 120–150 kg/thm coke plus 800 kg/thm coal. When a minimum quantity of pellets and coke are required in the Corex process, there is all the more reason that unless the export gas (extent of generation: 1650 Nm^3/thm; calorific value: 7500 kJ/Nm^3) is profitably utilised, the cost of hot metal production cannot compare with that of the blast furnace hot metal.

Thus, in order to make operations economical, the installation of a power plant or a direct reduction shaft along with the Corex facilities becomes a must. This makes the total cost of a complete Corex plant plus auxiliaries fairly high. A capacity of 2000–3000 tpd of hot metal is at present the optimum size of any individual Corex unit (a 3000 tpd unit is being installed by Baosteel in China). Considering the necessity of a large oxygen plant, a power plant or a DRI shaft furnace, the total capital cost can, in many cases, become prohibitive. This may have contributed towards JSW Steel's decision to augment hot metal production using blast furnaces, although the two Corex units in JSW have been setting international benchmarks. Essar has recently purchased the Hanbo (Korea) Corex units. The Corex units produced as much as 700,000 to 800,000 tonnes of hot metal in 2004–2005. The increase in hot metal production in JSW Steel since 1999 using the Corex modules in the initial years followed by the installation of two blast furnaces is illustrated in Figure 14.6.

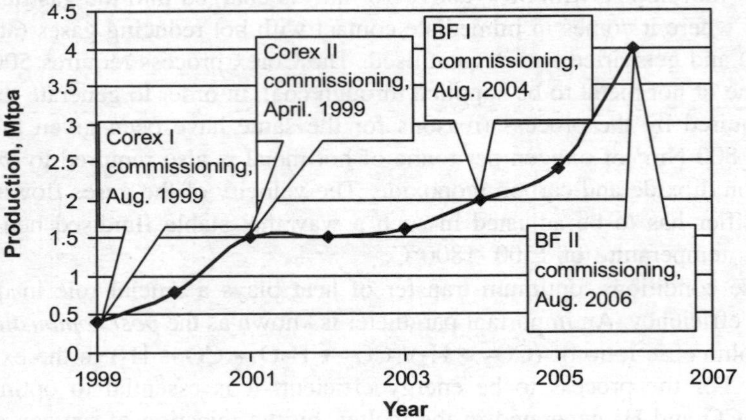

Figure 14.6 Hot metal production in JSW Steel since 1999.

14.6.2 Hismelt Process

Hismelt technology was developed in a large-size (0.1 Mtpa) demonstration plant at Kwinana, Western Australia during trials spanning several years. Based on this work, a commercial plant of 0.8 Mtpa has been constructed at the same site as the original demonstration plant, which began hot metal production in November 2005 (operating at 65% capacity in 2006–07). This has made Hismelt the second SR technology to be commercialised.

Demonstration plant operations had proven that the Hismelt process can use a wide range of coals as well as iron oxide feed of various types, including steel plant wastes. In the Hismelt process (Figure 14.7), iron oxide in the form of fines (–6 mm), (the ore fines can be at room temperature or pre-heated using the process off-gas to increase plant capacity by around 25%), fine non-coking coal (–6 mm) along with fluxes are injected through especially designed water-cooled injection lances into a carbon saturated molten iron bath, where the primary reactions take place. As a result, intensive reduction of iron oxide and quick slag formation are achieved. This creates sufficient turbulence in the bath in order to ensure effective mixing. As a result, the refractories in the vessel get exposed to relatively low FeO containing slags at uniformly low temperatures. This is an important feature of Hismelt, since these had been problem areas in many earlier smelting reduction processes in which attempts were made to use a similar system configuration (including Hismelt itself, in the original trials conducted in a horizontal reactor).

The Hismelt vessel operates at a moderate positive pressure (less than 1 bar), which helps in eliminating the ingress of air and permits an increase in the process intensity. Use of the optimal vessel design and the selection of appropriate material feed rates are important in controlling the entire process. The process has the advantage that when the feed materials are injected directly into the molten iron bath (either at room temperature or after pre-heating to 400–500°C in a fluidised bed pre-heater), they get reduced within the bath by the carbon

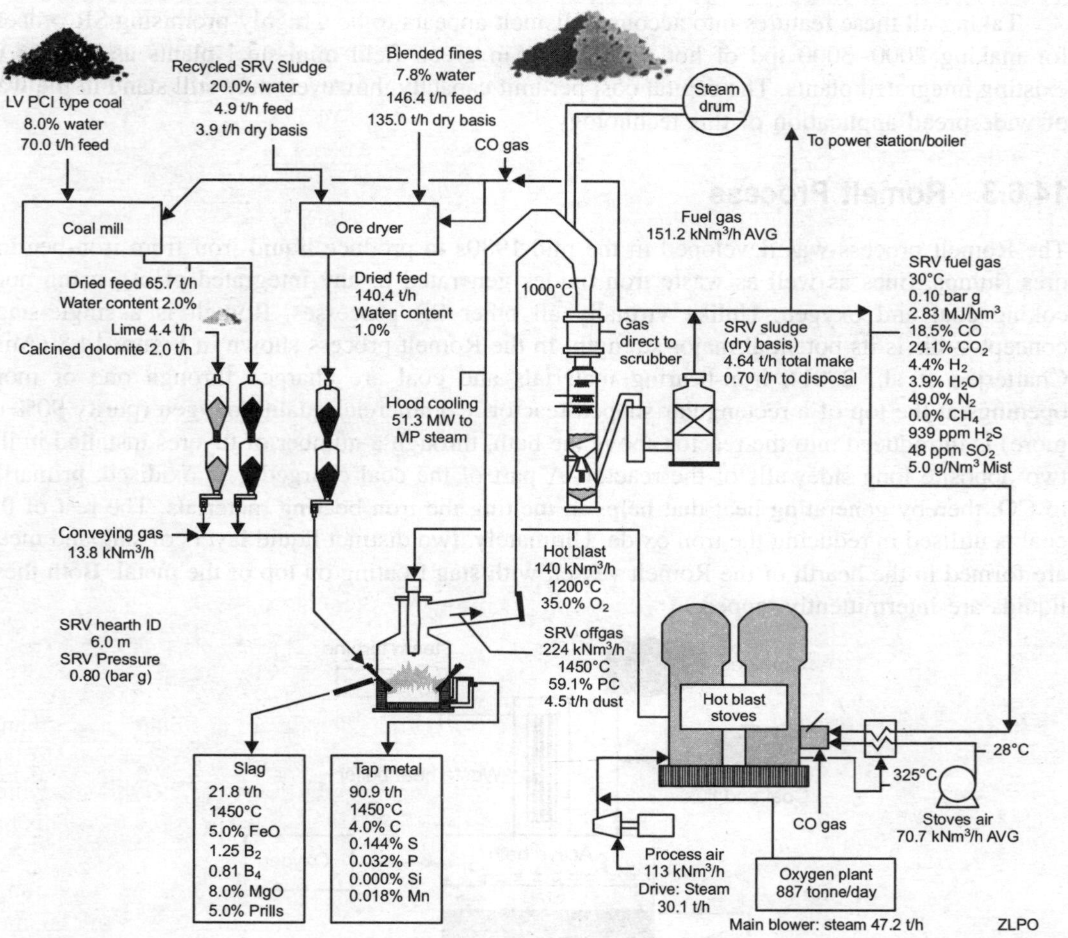

Figure 14.7 Flow sheet of the Hismelt process, along with consumption figures (0.6 Mtpa unit).

dissolved in the bath itself. For this reason, the export gas from Hismelt is not as rich as it is in the Corex process. Whatever gas is generated can, if necessary, be used to pre-heat the feed in a fluidised bed reactor. Furthermore, pure oxygen is not required, and air, or oxygen-enriched air (containing 30% oxygen) is used. Hismelt has also claimed that it is a *green technology* since reduction in emissions of CO_2 by at least 20%, SO_x by 90% and NO_x by 40% over the blast furnace process is possible.

Perhaps the most noteworthy feature of the Hismelt process is that, amongst all the SR processes, it is the most akin, in many ways, to the blast furnace, e.g. in the pre-heating of the blast in hot blast stoves, etc. It has some unique advantages in terms of the composition of hot metal made. Hismelt hot metal contains no silicon whatsoever. Further, partition of 90–95% of the input phosphorus into the slag is possible, thereby allowing low phosphorus metal to be produced even from high phosphorus ore fines. In addition, it uses iron ore fines rather than lump ore/agglomerates, and 100% coal (no coke).

Taking all these features into account, Hismelt appears to be a highly-promising SR process for making 2000–3000 tpd of hot metal, both in green field mini-steel plants as well as in existing integrated plants. The capital cost per unit capacity, however, may still stand in the way of widespread application of this technology.

14.6.3 Romelt Process

The Romelt process was developed in the mid-1980s to produce liquid iron from iron-bearing ores (lumps, fines as well as waste iron oxides generated in any integrated plant), using non-coking coal and oxygen. Unlike virtually all other SR processes, Romelt is a single-stage concept—this is its potential major strength. In the Romelt process shown in Figure 14.8 (Amit Chatterjee et al., 2001), iron-bearing materials and coal are charged through one or more openings at the top of a rectangular-shaped reactor. Commercial quality oxygen (purity 90% or more) is introduced into the reactor above the bath, through a number of tuyeres installed in the two opposite long sidewalls of the reactor. A part of the coal charged gets oxidised, primarily to CO, thereby generating heat that helps in melting the iron bearing materials. The rest of the coal is utilised in reducing the iron oxide. Ultimately, two distinct liquid layers of slag and metal are formed in the hearth of the Romelt vessel, with slag floating on top of the metal. Both these liquids are intermittently tapped.

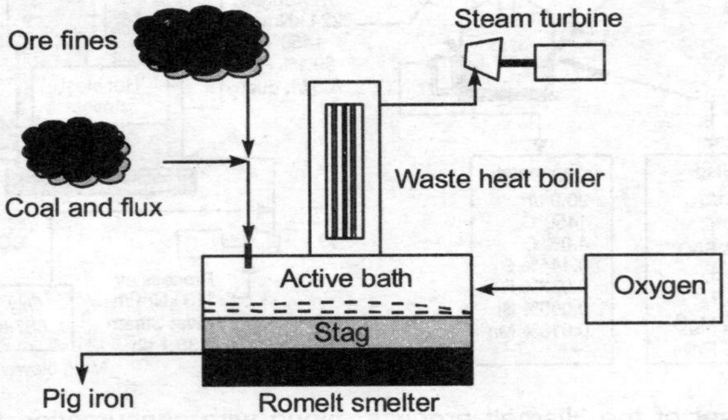

Figure 14.8 Flow sheet of the Romelt process.

The Romelt process is based on a relatively simple concept. It is also likely to be extremely environment-friendly, since it operates under a slight negative pressure (–2 mm water column). However, the process also has a few intrinsic weaknesses because it is a single-stage process—it uses large amounts of coal (1020–1050 kg/thm for coal with 20–25% ash, and as much as 1300 kg/thm for 30% ash coal) as well as oxygen (1060–1080 Nm^3/thm). The process generates very high value, rich exit gas (volume: 2800 Nm^3/thm; calorific value: 7100 kJ/Nm^3) at an exit temperature as high as 1600°C. This large amount of gas, with appreciable sensible and chemical heat content, has to be utilised effectively (e.g. for power generation to meet the demand of the oxygen plant), for hot metal production by this process to be economical.

Though several attempts have been made (including in India), no commercial Romelt plant is operating anywhere in the world today. This may perhaps be a result of the large coal and oxygen consumption, as well as problems in controlling a process in which all the reactions occur simultaneously in a single-stage reactor.

14.6.4 Finex Process

Finex is a process that uses ore fines in a series of fluidised bed reactors for initial pre-reduction (similar to the Finmet process dealt with in Chapter 13, Section 13.6). Posco developed this process with the objective of utilising the fines that were being generated during processing of the feed required by their Corex unit. They found that large amounts of fine ore (–8 mm) and fine coal (–6 mm) remained unutilized, causing difficulties. They were also keen to explore the possibility of utilising the export gas from the Corex melter-gasifier for ironmaking, rather than for auxiliary usage in the steel plant.

All the steps involved in pre-reduction of fine ore in the set of fluidised bed reactors in the Finex process are the same as in the Finmet process (see Chapter 13, Section 13.6.2). In the Finex process (Figure 14.9) fine ore below 8 mm is pre-heated and reduced to DRI in a four-stage fluidised bed system that precedes the melter-gasifier. Reactors R4 and R3 are primarily used to pre-heat the ore fines to the reduction temperature, which can be adjusted by partial combustion of the off-gas from reactor R2. In R2, fine ore is pre-reduced to a degree of reduction (RD) of about 30%. The final reduction to DRI (RD about 90%) takes place in R1, directly coupled to the melter-gasifier off-gas handling line. The operational pressure in R1 to R4 is approximately 4–5 bars.

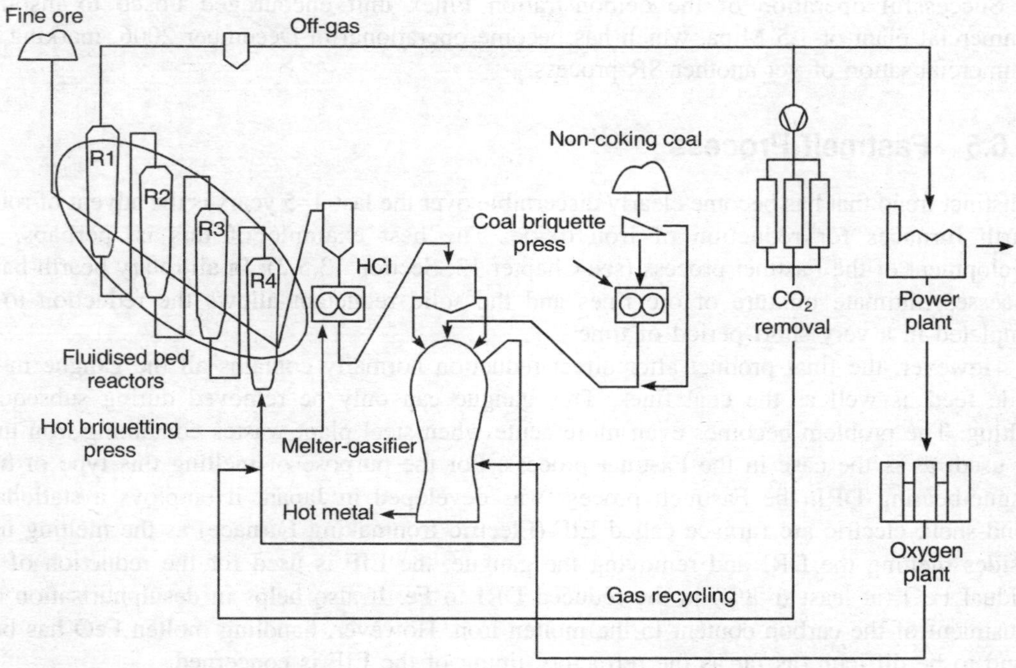

Figure 14.9 Flow sheet of the Finex process.

The discharge from R1 is in the form of fines and before charging to the melter-gasifier of the Finex unit, this material is compacted in a hot briquetting press to make *hot compacted iron (HCI)*. This step of agglomeration is necessary to ensure permeability of the bed in the Corex melter-gasifier. Fine non-coking coal is also briquetted before it is fed to the melter-gasifier of the Finex process where it is gasified with oxygen. This gas is used to reduce the fine ore particles in the reactors preceding the melter-gasifier. The hot compacted iron charged in the melter-gasifier is further reduced to 100% metallic iron, melted, carburised to hot metal, and the impurities removed in the form of slag. By introducing a step of agglomeration of the DRI, one of the limitations of Corex, i.e. inability to accept either ore fines/coal fines is completely circumvented. Further, using the Finex configuration, it is possible to get around another intrinsic limitation in the Corex process, which is that the residence times in the melter-gasifier and the reduction shaft are necessarily closely interdependent.

In order to test the Finex concept, Posco installed a 0.2 Mtpa demonstration plant in 1997. A number of trials were carried out during which the process was debugged. During the trials, the coal consumption, which was initially 1050 kg/thm, was gradually reduced to 890 kg/thm. Very importantly (unlike Corex), no coke was found to be necessary for ensuring the permeability of the bed in the lower regions of the melter-gasifier. The hot metal composition obtained was: C 4.3–4.5%, Si 0.8–0.9% and S 0.017–0.020%.

Successful operation of the demonstration Finex unit encouraged Posco to install a commercial plant of 1.5 Mtpa, which has become operational in December 2006, marking the commercialisation of yet another SR process.

14.6.5 Fastmelt Process

A distinct trend that has become clearly discernible over the last 4–5 years is the advent of rotary hearth furnaces for reduction of iron oxide. The best example of this is, perhaps, the development of the Fastmet process (see Chapter 13, Section 13.5.2). In all rotary hearth-based processes, intimate mixture of ore fines and the solid reductant allows the reduction to be completed in a very short period of time.

However, the final product after direct reduction normally contains all the gangue in the oxide feed as well as the coal fines. This gangue can only be removed during subsequent melting. The problem becomes even more acute when steel plant wastes containing iron units are used, as is the case in the Fastmet process. For the purpose of melting this type of high gangue-bearing DRI, the Fastmelt process was developed in Japan. It employs a stationary, round-shell, electric arc furnace called EIF (Electric Ironmaking Furnace) as the melting unit. Besides melting the DRI and removing the gangue, the EIF is used for the reduction of the residual FeO (at least 6–8%) in the reduced DRI to Fe. It also helps in desulphurisation and adjustment of the carbon content in the molten iron. However, handling molten FeO has been found to be difficult, as far as the refractory lining of the EIF is concerned.

Fastmelt plants can be designed for capacities ranging from 150,000 tpa to more than 1 Mtpa. In the work carried out in Japan, the Fastmelt process has demonstrated the ability to produce hot metal at high productivity rates.

14.6.6 ITmk3

One way of not encountering problems with refractories in any electric ironmaking furnace, used for melting FeO containing pre-reduced material with high gangue contents, is to separate the gangue prior to melting. This is the concept used in ITmk3. Kobe Steel, who developed this process, views ITmk3 as a third generation ironmaking technology: Mark 1, the first generation, being blast furnace ironmaking; gas-based direct reduction being Mark 2.

In this new ironmaking technology, iron of similar quality as blast furnace hot metal is the end product from a reactor charged with iron oxide and a solid reductant, but the iron is in the form of solid nuggets. In the ITmk3 process (flow sheet shown in Figure 14.10) green composite pellets of fine ore and pulverised coal are charged into a rotary hearth furnace (RHF) where they are heated to a temperature ranging between 1350°C and 1500°C. The temperature range is much higher than in other RHF-based processes (like Fastmet). The residence time continues to be very short (like in Fastmet) owing to the fast rate of reduction of the composite ore–coal pellets.

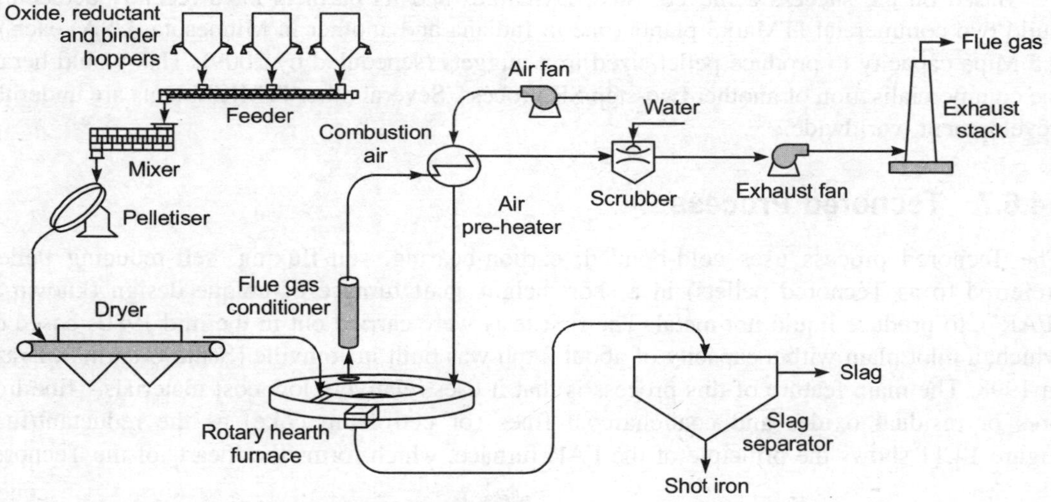

Figure 14.10 Process flow sheet of ITmk3.

Because of the higher temperature, the composite pellets not only get reduced to iron rapidly, but they become partially molten. This enables iron to get cleanly separated from the liquid slag formed within the pellets, which oozes to surface of the nuggets (cluster of pellets). The slag can then be separated to leave behind the ITmk3 iron nuggets containing 96–98% iron, 2.5–4.5% carbon, 0.2% silicon, 0.1% manganese and 0.050–0.060% each of sulphur and phosphorus. These nuggets can be directly fed into an EAF or BOF for steelmaking.

The ingenious method of removing gangue from low-grade ores and the use of composite pellets made from iron ore fines and coal fines are the two distinctive features of the ITmk3 process. Some of the other unique features of ITmk3 are given below.

- The one-step process produces iron nuggets in a very short time—reduction, melting, and slag removal are completed in only about 10 minutes.

- The process is flexible as far as the type of iron ore that can be used. Magnetite, haematite as well as pellets made of taconite (low-grade iron ore found in the USA) have been processed.
- The process emits at least 20% less carbon dioxide than that emitted by blast furnaces. Further, since ITmk3 does not require either coke ovens or sintering plants, there would be less NO_x, SO_x and particulate matter emissions.
- If the ITmk3 facility is located within a steel plant, iron nuggets can be fed in the hot condition, directly into an EAF or BOF, thereby contributing to improved productivity and superior energy efficiency.

Work on this process began in 1986 and a pilot plant scale RHF of 4 metre diameter with a production capacity of 3000 tpa was built at Kobe Steel's Kakogawa Works in Japan. In March 2002, Kobe Steel, along with some partners, began operations of a demonstration plant with an annual capacity of 25,000 tonnes in Silver Bay, USA. The first lot of nuggets from this unit that were melted in the EAF shop of Steel Dyanmics in Butler, USA, produced encouraging results.

Based on the success achieved, Steel Dynamics and its partners have recently decided to build two commercial ITMark3 plants (one in Indiana and another in Minnesota, USA) each of 0.5 Mtpa capacity to produce pellet-sized iron nuggets (scheduled by 2009). This would herald the commercialisation of another two-step SR process. Several other ITMK3 plants are under the development worldwide.

14.6.7 Tecnored Process

The Tecnored process uses cold-bonded, carbon-bearing, self-fluxing, self-reducing pellets (referred to as Tecnored pellets) in a short height shaft furnace of unique design (known as 'FAR'), to produce liquid hot metal. The first tests were carried out in the mid 1980s based on which, a pilot plant with a capacity of about 2 tph was built in Joinville (Santa Catarina), Brazil in 1998. The main feature of this process is that it uses relatively low cost materials—fine iron ores or residual oxides and coal/charcoal fines (or petroleum coke) as the reductant/fuel. Figure 14.11 shows the principle of the FAR furnace, which forms the 'heart' of the Tecnored

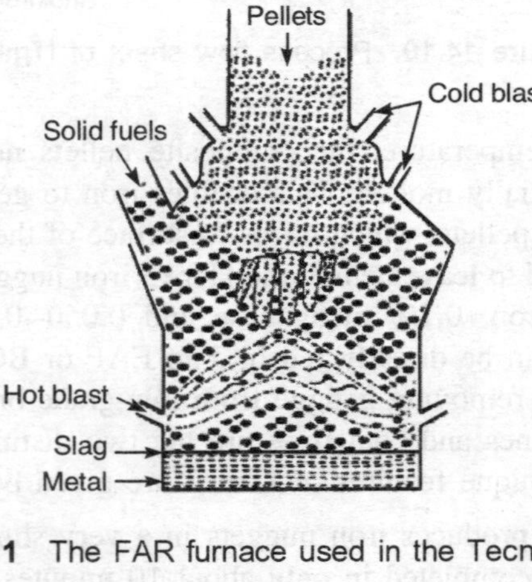

Figure 14.11 The FAR furnace used in the Tecnored process.

The process consists of pelletising iron ore fines (below 140 mesh) and coke fines (below 200 mesh) along with a flux like hydrated lime (below 140 mesh) using cement as the binder. The pellets are cured and dried at 200°C, before they are fed to the top of the FAR furnace, the internal pressure of which is maintained at about 3.5 to 5.2 psig. The total residence time of the charge in the furnace is 30 to 40 minutes, compared with 6 to 8 hours in blast furnaces. This is possible because of the intimate mixing of ore and reductant fines during pellet making. Lump coke (30–60 mm in size, containing upto 30% ash and 25% VM) is fed in the furnace below the hot pellet area, using side feeders. A blast of hot air at about 1150°C is blown through tuyeres located at the periphery of the furnace, to allow the combustion of coke. Cold blast air is also blown in a region higher in the furnace, to promote post combustion of CO in the upper shaft. The specific consumption figures (per tonne of hot metal) are: 250 kg coal and 310 kg coke to produce hot metal containing carbon 3.0–4.5% and silicon 0.2–1.0%, at a temperature of 1380–1430°C.

The Tecnored process appears to be flexible with regard to the type of iron- and carbon-bearing raw-materials that it can process. The ability of the process to smelt either pellets or briquettes, or even mixed charges of both, can provide means of using a wide range of alternative feed materials. Efforts are being made to commercialise the Tecnored process in the proximity of iron ore mine sites in Brazil, and other countries may follow. It has also been claimed that the process is suitable for producing ferro-alloys like ferro-manganese.

14.7 MINI BLAST FURNACE

Development of the compact blast furnace and the mini blast furnace (MBF) has allowed BF technology to cover the size range of final output, for which alternatives like SR were originally developed. Therefore, though MBF technology cannot be strictly classified into smelting reduction, MBFs being small (50–350 m^3) can produce hot metal in the same tonnage range as most SR processes. MBF technology is not only well proven, but prior experience is also readily available. Therefore, there is little or no risk in installing MBFs. It is not surprising, therefore, that MBFs are becoming increasingly popular as an economic and reliable option for ironmaking in foundries as well as for forward integration with steelmaking units in new EAF/EOF (and sometimes even small BOF) based steel plants, i.e in all situations where limited tonnages of hot metal is required.

Hot metal from mini blast furnaces is virtually of the same quality as that from normal blast furnaces. The only apparent drawback of MBFs is that, since the hot blast temperature is somewhat lower (1050°C rather than 1150°C in normal blast furnaces) because the heating system used is less efficient, and the specific heat loss is higher, the coke rate tends to be around 150 kg/thm higher than in a blast furnace. Another limitation of MBFs is that coal injection is normally difficult, and the entire energy requirement has to be met by coke, normally purchased from external sources, since the limited amount of coke required by individual MBFs does not normally justify the installation of independent coke ovens.

To produce hot metal (low silicon metal for steelmaking as well as 2.5% silicon hot metal for foundries), mini blast furnaces have been used extensively in India and in countries like Brazil and China. There are at least around 20 mini blast furnaces varying in size from 175 to 300 m^3 (installed capacity from 75,000 to 300,000 tpa) with a total capacity of around 2.7 Mtpa of pig iron that are already in operation in India, and more are being considered. These MBFs either use metallic blast pre-heaters to heat the blast to 800°C, or small conventional stoves to give hot blast temperatures of 1020–1050°C. The MBFs normally use 100% lump ore (10–40 mm in size) and coke (imported from neighbouring countries) with low ash (12%) to give productivities as high as 2.2 t/m^3/day, with coke rates of 650–725 kg/thm.

In China, around 55 Mtpa of hot metal is at present produced in 250–275 MBFs. Several innovations have been made in the Chinese MBFs, like injection of pulverised anthracite to the extent of 60 kg/thm, to bring down the coke rate by about 40–50 kg/thm to 500–630 kg/thm. Such innovations, along with continuous improvements in refractories to increase the plant availability, have made MBFs a well-accepted, risk-free ironmaking option for small scale production.

The MBF technology today is certainly a competitor to SR processes, in situations where limited tonnages of hot metal are required.

REFERENCE

Amit Chatterjee, Ramesh Singh, and Banshidhar Pandey, *Metallics for Steelmaking—Production and Use*, Allied Publishers, 2001.

Part D

Steelmaking

- Physical Chemistry of Primary Steelmaking
- BOF Plant Practice
- Metallurgical Features of Oxygen Steelmaking
- Process Control for Basic Oxygen Steelmaking
- Basic Open Hearth and Electric Arc Furnace Steelmaking
- Secondary Steelmaking
- Stainless Steelmaking

15

Physical Chemistry of Primary Steelmaking

15.1 INTRODUCTION

Chapter 1 contained a broad overview of ironmaking and steelmaking. Chapter 3 presented an outline of modern steelmaking. From those chapters, the following can be noted.

- A modern steel melting shop has three broad groups of facilities, viz. *primary steelmaking, secondary steelmaking,* and *casting of liquid steel.*
- Primary steelmaking is dominantly carried out in top-blown *Basic Oxygen Furnaces* (BOFs). The process has several variants, as already enumerated in Chapter 3. Another category of oxygen-based steelmaking processes rely on bottom-blowing of oxygen through special tuyeres. All these latter processes can be clubbed together under the generic category of Basic Oxygen Steelmaking (BOS) processes.

Electric Arc Furnace (EAF) steelmaking is in addition to BOF and BOS, i.e. there are three broad methods of making steel. These three groups of processes together account for almost the entire liquid steel production in the world today.

Chapters 16 to 18 will cover various aspects of BOF steelmaking, along with a very brief discussion of BOS processes like OBM, etc. (in Chapter 17) while Chapter 19 will deal with EAF steelmaking. Since the open-hearth process of steelmaking has been phased out and is virtually non-existent today, only a very brief discussion of open-hearth steelmaking is included in Chapter 19.

The present chapter is concerned with some relevant physicochemical aspects of steelmaking, that are applicable to all the primary steelmaking processes. These fundamentals also constitute the basics of secondary steelmaking processes. However, BOF/BOS is the principal focus of this chapter.

Primary steelmaking is a process of oxidation. The principal oxidising agent is gaseous oxygen, along with iron oxide (added as iron ore). The extent of refining in oxygen steelmaking processes is substantial since the principal metallic feed is blast furnace hot metal containing high percentages of carbon, silicon, phosphorus and manganese. In EAF steelmaking, the extent of refining is far less since a large proportion of the metallic feed is in the form of steel scrap containing low levels of impurities.

The oxidation reactions are exothermic and constitute the source of heat in BOF and BOS processes, leading to an increase in the bath temperature to 1600–1650°C at the end of refining, from an initial temperature of 1250–1300°C. On the other hand, in EAF steelmaking the major heat source is electrical power.

Oxidation of Si, Fe, Mn, P (and sometimes small amounts of Ti) leads to the formation of SiO_2, FeO, MnO, P_2O_5 (and TiO_2). These oxides combine with the fluxing agents added (principally lime, sometimes along with fluorspar, ilmenite, dolomite, etc.) to form a basic molten slag, which helps in refining. Carbon is oxidised in the form of gaseous carbon monoxide.

15.2 REACTIONS AND HEAT EFFECTS

Chapter 6, Section 6.1.1 has briefly dealt with the basic procedure of mass and heat balance with specific reference to blast furnace ironmaking. A similar procedure is to be adopted to predict the temperature rise during steelmaking, which will be taken up in Chapter 18. This section will briefly present the *thermochemical aspects of enthalpy changes.*

Chapter 4 has reviewed the fundamentals of thermodynamics for the application of Gibbs free energy (ΔG) criterion for process calculations. As discussed there, only *isothermal* reactions and processes can be handled using this approach. The reactions can be *reversible* or *irreversible;* the only stipulation is that the initial and final temperatures should be the same.

Consider the process:

$$\begin{matrix} \text{State 1 (at temperature } T) & \rightarrow & \text{State 2 (at temperature } T) \\ (G_1, H_1, S_1) & & (G_2, H_2, S_2) \end{matrix} \tag{15.1}$$

$$\begin{aligned} \Delta G &= G_2 - G_1 \\ &= (H_2 - TS_2) - (H_1 - TS_1) \\ &= (H_2 - H_1) - T(S_2 - S_1) \\ &= \Delta H - T\Delta S \end{aligned} \tag{15.2}$$

As mentioned in Chapter 4, Section 4.2.3, the variation of the *standard free energy of formation* of a compound (ΔG_f^0) as a function of temperature is approximately linear. Therefore, for practical purposes, the simplest form of the equation (Eq. (4.22)) viz.

$$\Delta G_f^0 = AT + B$$

is employed in which A and B are empirical constants.

Again, from Eq. (15.2),

$$\Delta G_f^0 = \Delta H_f^0 - T\Delta S_f^0 \tag{15.3}$$

where ΔH_f^0 and ΔS_f^0 are *standard enthalpy* and *entropy of formation* of the compound respectively.

A comparison of Eq. (15.3) and Eq. (4.22) shows that $A = \Delta H_f^0$ and $B = -\Delta S_f^0$, and these have been assumed to be independent of temperature. Table 4.1 has presented the values of A and B for the formation of some oxides. Hence, A is to be taken as ΔH_f^0.

Table 4.2 contained values of the *free energy of mixing* of some elements at 1 wt% standard state in liquid iron ($\bar{G}_i^m$) as a function of temperature as

$$\bar{G}_i^m = C + DT \tag{15.4}$$

Again, from the above analysis, it is possible to take $C = \bar{H}_i^m$ and $D = -\bar{S}_i^m$.

Primary steelmaking is concerned with the oxidation of solutes dissolved in liquid iron. For example, the oxidation of silicon may be written as

$$[\mathrm{Si}]_{\text{dissolved in iron}} + \mathrm{O_2(g)} = \mathrm{SiO_2(s)} \tag{15.5}$$

At 1 wt. % standard state, it may be written as

$$[\mathrm{Si}]_{1\text{ wt\% ss in Fe}} + \mathrm{O_2(g)} = \mathrm{SiO_2(s)};\quad \Delta H_f^0(\text{wt. \%}) \tag{15.6}$$

From Tables 4.1 and 4.2,

$$\mathrm{Si(l)} + \mathrm{O_2(g)} = \mathrm{SiO_2(s)};\ \Delta H_f^0 = -947676\ \mathrm{J\cdot mol^{-1}} \tag{15.7}$$

$$\mathrm{Si(l)} = [\mathrm{Si}]_{1\text{ wt\% std. state}};\ \bar{H}_{\mathrm{Si}}^m = -131500\ \mathrm{J\cdot mol^{-1}} \tag{15.8}$$

Subtracting Eq. (15.8) from Eq. (15.7), Eq. (15.6) is obtained. Hence,

$$\Delta H_f^0(\text{wt\%}) = \Delta H_f^0 - \bar{H}_{\mathrm{Si}}^m = -816176\ \mathrm{J\cdot mol^{-1}} \tag{15.9}$$

On the basis of the above, the ΔH_f^0 (wt. %) values (except for Fe, because it is the solvent) have been listed in Table 15.1. For convenience, these have been reported as ΔH_f^0 in kilojoules per mole with the values rounded-off to 4 digits. The table also includes values of ΔS_f^0 in $\mathrm{J\cdot mol^{-1}\cdot K^{-1}}$.

Table 15.1 Standard enthalpies and entropies of formation of some oxides from elements dissolved in liquid iron

Reaction	ΔH_f^0, kJ · mol^{-1}	ΔS_f^0, J · mol^{-1} · K^{-1}
$\mathrm{Fe(l) + (1/2)\,O_2(g) = FeO(l)}$	−259.6	−62.55
$\mathrm{[C] + (1/2)\,O_2(g) = CO(g)}$	−134.3	129.9
$\mathrm{[C] + O_2(g) = CO_2(g)}$	−416.7	43.1
$\mathrm{[Cr] + (3/4)\,O_2(g) = (1/2)\,Cr_2O_3(s)}$	−585.2	−175.3
$\mathrm{[Mn] + (1/2)\,O_2(g) = MnO(s)}$	−412.2	−126.9
$\mathrm{[P] + (5/4)\,O_2(g) = (1/2)\,P_2O_5(g)}$	−663.0	−260.5
$\mathrm{[Si] + O_2(g) = SiO_2(s)}$	−816.2	−216.0
$\mathrm{[Si] + O_2(g) = SiO_2(l)}$	−804.9	−210.0
$\mathrm{[Ti] + O_2(g) = TiO_2(s)}$	−889.1	−218.8

Note: For Fe, pure iron is the standard state; for others, values correspond to those for 1 wt. % standard state in liquid iron.

All these reactions involving the oxidation of metalloids are *highly exothermic*. Among them in BOF/BOS steelmaking, the major heat producing reactions are oxidation of Si, C, and Fe, since large quantities of these species are present. The *endothermic steps* include heating-up of the inputs and the additions made during the blow to steelmaking temperatures. The principal inputs are: molten hot metal at around 1250–1300°C, and scrap, lime (and other fluxes), iron ore, pig iron all at room temperature. Sometimes, other minor additions are made depending on the practice adopted; however, they can be ignored in this general analysis.

Equation (6.5) of Section 6.1.1, gives the general equations for *sensible heat* ($H_T - H_{298}$) of a substance as a function of temperature. As a simplification, hot metal, pig iron and scrap may all be assumed to be pure iron. Similarly, iron ore may be assumed to be either pure F_2O_3 or pure Fe_3O_4. Table 15.2 (Kelley 1960) lists the ($H_T - H_{298}$) values on this basis. The range of temperature at which they are valid are also shown.

Table 15.2 Sensible heats of some substances as function of temperature

Substance	$H_T - H_{298}$, J · mol^{-1}	Temperature range, K
Fe(l)	$40.9T + 0.837 \times 10^{-3}T^2 - 2805$	1812–3000
CaO(s)	$48.85T + 2.26 \times 10^{-3}T^2 + 6.53 \times 10^5T^{-1} - 16957$	298–2000
$Fe_2O_3(\gamma)$	$132.7T + 36.84 \times 10^{-3}T^2 - 35355$	1050–1800
$Fe_3O_4(\beta)$	$200.9T - 52953$	900–1800

Other thermochemical data required for thermal calculations are enthalpies of dissolution (i.e. *heats of mixing*) in liquid metal and slag. These are smaller quantities in comparison with the exothermic oxidation reactions and sensible heats, and may be ignored for approximate calculations.

As discussed earlier, for liquid iron solution, data have already been provided in Table 4.2. Steelmaking slag may be considered as a mixture of dicalcium ferrite, dicalcium silicate and calcium phosphates, for which the heats of formation data are noted in Table 15.3 ((1) Ward 1962; (2) Bogdandy and Engells, 1971).

Table 15.3 Heats of formation of some double compounds of oxides at steelmaking temperatures (approximate values)

Source	Formation reaction	ΔH^0_f, kJ · mol^{-1}
(1)	$2CaO(s) + SiO_2(s) = 2CaO \cdot SiO_2(s)$	–124
(1)	$3CaO(s) + SiO_2(s) = 3CaO \cdot SiO_2(s)$	–123
(2)	$2CaO(s) + Fe_2O_3 = 2CaO \cdot Fe_2O_3(l)$	–109
(1)	$3CaO(s) + P_2O_5(g) = 3CaO \cdot P_2O_5(s)$	–1697
(1)	$4CaO(s) + P_2O_5(g) = 4CaO \cdot P_2O_5(s)$	–1740

EXAMPLE 15.1

For a BOF heat, the following data are given.

(i) Hot metal contains 1% Si, 0.15% P, 0.25% Mn and 3.5% C.
(ii) Weight of scrap is 10% of hot metal.
(iii) Steel at tap contains 0.2% C.
(iv) Slag has 54% CaO, 18% FeO, 2.5% MgO, 2.5% MnO, and CaO/SiO_2 ratio = 3.2.

Calculate the following per tonne (i.e. 1000 kg) of steel.

(a) Weight of hot metal charge
(b) Weight of slag produced
(c) Quantity of lime required.

Solution: The procedure is to be iterative.

Si–balance: Si in hot metal = Si as SiO_2 in slag (Ex.15.1)

Assuming weight of hot metal (W_{HM}) as 1 tonne as first approximation, and noting that wt. % SiO_2 in slag = 54/3.2 = 16.9%,

$$1000 \times 0.01 = W_{slag} \times 0.169 \times 28/60, \text{ giving } W_{slag} = 127 \text{ kg as first approximation.}$$

Fe–balance: Fe in HM + Fe in scrap = Fe in steel + Fe in slag (Ex.15.2)

Assuming scrap as pure iron, and noting that wt. % Fe in HM = 94.10%, wt. % Fe in slag $= 18 \times \dfrac{56}{72} = 14\%$, scrap wt. is 10% of W_{HM}, and steel has 99.8% Fe,

Fe–balance: $W_{HM}(0.9410 + 0.1) = 0.998 + 0.127 \times \dfrac{14}{100}$, giving $W_{HM} = 975$ kg

Using this value of W_{HM} in Si–balance, the revised value of slag weight is 130 kg.

CaO–balance: CaO to be added = CaO in slag = $W_{slag} \times \dfrac{54}{100} = 70.2$ kg

EXAMPLE 15.2

For the heat in Example 15.1, calculate the quantity of oxygen required per tonne of steel. Assume that the exit gas of the converter contains 10% CO_2 and 90% CO as average of the entire heat.

Solution: Noting atomic masses of C, O, Si, P, Mn, Fe as 12, 16, 28, 31, 55 and 56 respectively,

Oxygen required = Oxygen to form ($CO + CO_2 + SiO_2 + FeO + MnO + P_2O_5$)

$$= \frac{W_{\text{steel}}}{100} \times \left[\text{wt.\% C oxidised} \times \left(0.9 \times \frac{16}{12} + 0.1 \times \frac{32}{12}\right) \right.$$

$$+ W_{\text{HM}} \times \left(\text{wt. \% Si} \times \frac{32}{28} + \text{wt. \% Mn} \times \frac{16}{55} + \text{wt. \% P} \times \frac{80}{62}\right)$$

$$\left. + W \text{ slag} \times \text{wt. \% FeO in slag} \times \frac{16}{72} \right] \qquad \text{(Ex. 15.3)}$$

Noting that W_{steel} = 1000 kg, wt. % C oxidised = (W_{HM} × 3.5 – W_{steel} × 0.2)/W_{steel} = 3.205, W_{HM} = 975 kg, wt. % Si = 1, wt. % Mn = 0.25, wt. % P = 0.15, W_{slag} = 130 kg, and wt. % FeO in slag = 18.

Calculations yield quantity of oxygen required = 59.5 kg = 59.5 × 22.4/32 = 41.7 Nm^3.

15.3 PRIMARY STEELMAKING SLAGS

Chapter 4, Section 4.4.2–4.4.4 has briefly presented the fundamentals of structure, physicochemical properties, activities, basicity and capacity concepts of molten slags, as well as some slag models. In Chapter 5, Section 5.4.1 the salient features and data of blast furnace slags have been covered.

As mentioned, control of carbon, phosphorus and titanium are not possible in blast furnace ironmaking and these impurities have to be removed, to the extent desired, during steelmaking. Out of these impurities, phosphorus removal has received principal attention in primary steelmaking; the details will be discussed later in this chapter. For the time being it will suffice to mention that the removal of phosphorus requires low temperature and a highly basic and oxidising slag containing CaO and FeO as the two major constituents.

For producing carbon and low alloy steels, the composition of slags in primary steelmaking processes varies within the following range, depending on the final carbon content of steel tapped:

40–60% CaO, 10–28% SiO_2, 5–35% FeO (total), 1–3% P_2O_5, 2–8% MgO, 1–8% MnO, 1–2% Al_2O_3, 0–2% CaF_2, 0.1–0.2% sulphur, and minor amounts of other slag constituents.

The composition of turndown BOF slag at Tata Steel, for example, is as follows:

CaO 50–55%, SiO_2 14–17%, Fe_{total} 14–21%, P_2O_5 2.8–3.5%, S 0.06–0.2%, MgO 0.7–1.4%, MnO 0.4–0.8%, Al_2O_3 0.6–1.3%, TiO_2 0.7–1.0%, Cr_2O_3 0.25–0.45%.

15.3.1 Phase Diagram and Activity-Composition Diagram

In Chapter 4, Section 4.2.3 the thermodynamics of oxidation–reduction reactions has been discussed. It has been shown that for equilibrium pure M-pure M_xO_y–O_2:

$$\Delta G_f^0 = RT \ln (p_{O_2})_{\text{eq}} = [\mu_{O_2}] \text{ at equilibrium} \qquad (4.24)$$

where μ_{O_2} is the *chemical potential of oxygen*.

Figure 4.1 has presented the variation in ΔG_f^0 as a function of temperature for some oxides. It may be seen that the chemical potentials of oxygen follow the following order at steelmaking temperatures: μ_{O_2} (Fe–FeO) > μ_{O_2} (Si–SiO_2) > μ_{O_2} (Ca–CaO).

Since Fe–FeO has highest μ_{O_2}, its concentration determines the chemical potential of O_2 in slag. Again, Fe is present as Fe^{2+} and Fe^{3+} ions in slag. Actually, μ_{O_2} in the slag is governed by the equilibrium of the reaction:

$$4\,(FeO) + O_2(g) = 2(Fe_2O_3) \tag{15.10}$$

The Fe^{3+}/Fe^{2+} ratio varies to a very major extent during steelmaking. It is also not measured for all heats on a regular basis because of difficulties in taking representative samples. Therefore, the standard practice is to determine the metallic Fe concentration in the slag and report it as FeO. This is represented as either FeO (total) or 'FeO'.

The ternary CaO–SiO_2–FeO (or Fe_2O_3) constitutes the basic phase diagram in primary steelmaking. Figure 15.1 (Muan and Osborn, 1965) shows the isothermal sections at 1600°C, in contact with metallic iron, as well as in contact with air. The liquid fields are shown along with the solid compounds at equilibrium with various liquid field boundaries. The solid circle corresponds to the nominal turndown slag composition (assuming CaO + SiO_2 + FeO (or Fe_2O_3) = 100%). Of course, the actual compositions lie over a range around this region. It may be noted that the solids, which are likely to coexist with the primary steelmaking slag are $2CaO \cdot SiO_2$, $3CaO \cdot SiO_2$ and CaO.

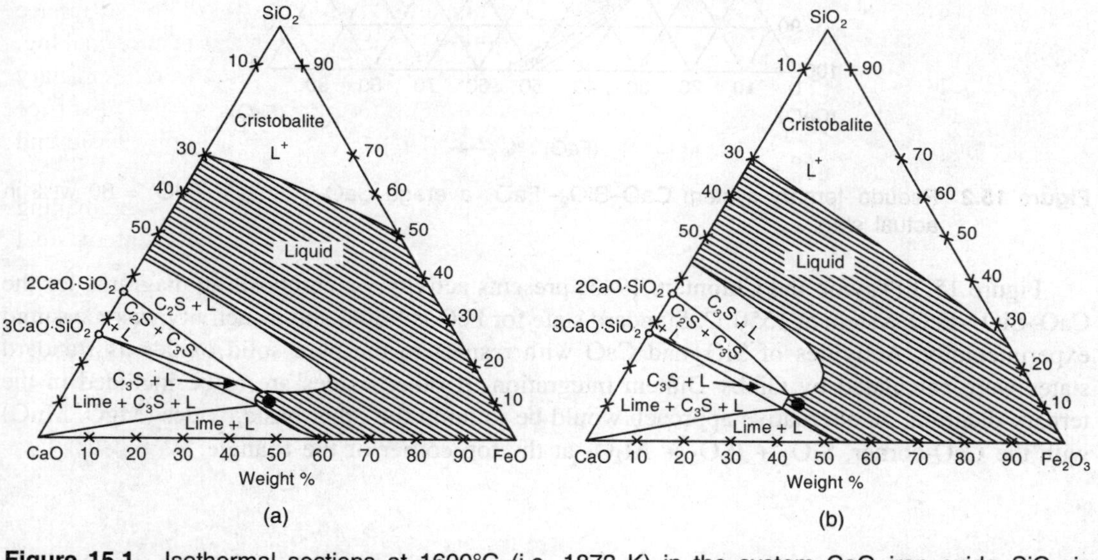

Figure 15.1 Isothermal sections at 1600°C (i.e. 1873 K) in the system CaO–iron oxide–SiO_2, in contact with (left) metallic iron, (right) air.

However, it has been demonstrated that the effects of other slag components cannot be completely ignored. For this reason, a wider liquid region exists in commercial slags at 1600°C, than what can be inferred from the ternary diagram for pure compounds. The total concentration of CaO, SiO_2 and FeO(t) is in the range of 80–90%, and if the sum of CaO + SiO_2 + FeO(t) is taken as 100% and the phase diagram recalculated, it does not make a major difference. Of course, such recalculations lead to some errors (Walker and Anderson, 1972). Figure 15.2 (Bardenheuer et al. 1968) shows such a diagram.

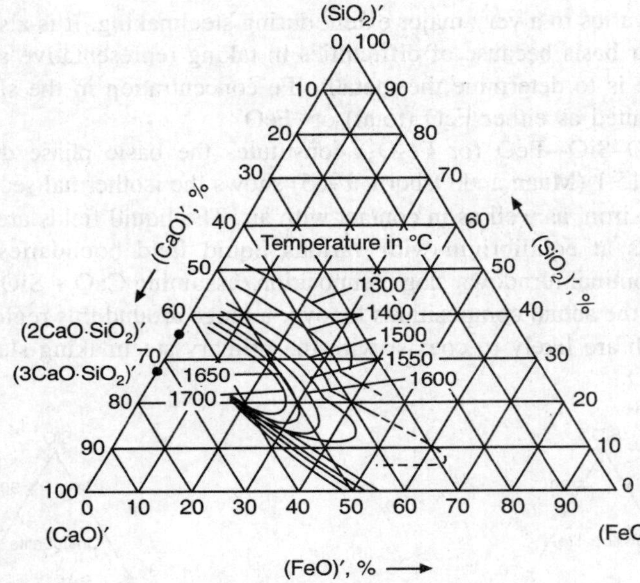

Figure 15.2 Pseudo–ternary system CaO–SiO_2–'FeO'; average CaO + SiO_2 + 'FeO' = 80 wt% in actual slag.

Figure 15.3 (Taylor and Chipman, 1943) presents activity vs. composition diagrams for the CaO–SiO_2–FeO system at 1550°C. Standard state for FeO is liquid and its activity was measured experimentally. Activities of SiO_2 and CaO with respect to the pure solid oxides as standard states were calculated by Gibbs–Duhem integration. If other oxides are to be included in the ternary diagram, an alternative approach would be to lump the other basic oxides (MgO, MnO) with the CaO-corner, SiO_2 + P_2O_5 + Al_2O_3 at the top corner of the triangle.

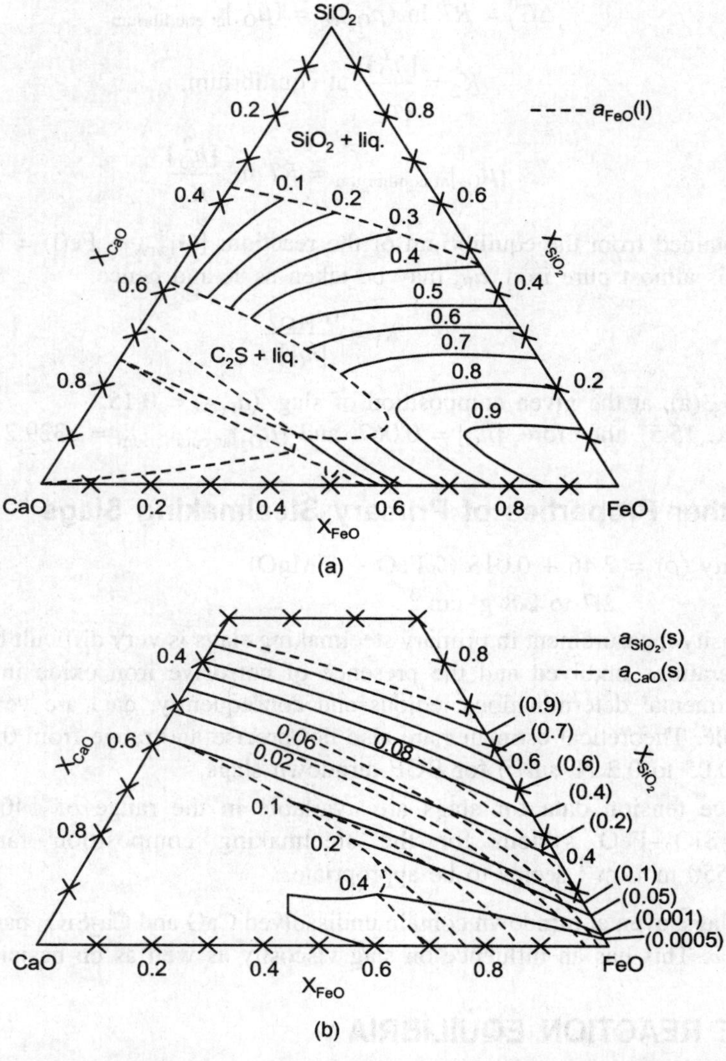

Figure 15.3 Activities of FeO, CaO, SiO_2 in CaO–FeO–SiO_2 melts in equilibrium with liquid iron at 1550°C (i.e. 1823 K).

EXAMPLE 15.3

Calculate the oxygen potential of liquid steel at equilibrium with a molten slag at 1600°C. Given:

(i) Slag contains CaO, SiO_2 and FeO with 0.45, 0.4 and 0.15 mole fractions respectively,

(ii) $[O]_{wt\%}$ + Fe(l) = FeO (l); K_1 = 4.78 at 1600°C from Eq. (15.13),

(iii) $O_2(g) = 2[O]_{wt\%}$; $K_2 = 6.89 \times 10^6$ at 1600°C.

Solution:

$$\Delta G_f^0 = RT \ln (p_{O_2})_{eq} = [\mu_{O_2}]_{\text{at equilibrium}} \tag{4.24}$$

Since,

$$K_2 = \frac{[h_O^2]}{p_{O_2}} \text{ at equilibrium,}$$

$$[\mu_{O_2}]_{\text{at equilibrium}} = RT \ln \frac{[h_O^2]}{K_2} \tag{Ex. 15.4}$$

h_O can be obtained from the equilibrium of the reaction: $[O]_{wt\%} + Fe(l) = FeO\ (l)$

As steel is almost pure iron, a_{Fe} may be taken as 1, and hence,

$$K_1 = \frac{(a_{FeO})}{[h_O]} \tag{Ex. 15.5}$$

From Fig. 15.3(a), at the given composition of slag, $(a_{FeO}) = 0.15$.
From Eq. (Ex. 15.5), therefore, $[h_O] = 0.067$, and $[\mu_{O_2}]_{\text{at equilibrium}} = -329.2$ kJ/mol O_2.

15.3.2 Other Properties of Primary Steelmaking Slags

1. Density $(\rho) = 2.46 + 0.018\ (\%FeO + \%MnO)$
   $= 2.7$ to $2.8\ g \cdot cm^{-3}$
2. Viscosity measurement in primary steelmaking slags is very difficult because of the high temperatures involved and the presence of corrosive iron oxide in slag. This makes experimental determinations tedious and consequently, data are very limited and not reliable. Theoretical estimates are also not precise and range from 0.5 poise to 2 poise (i.e. 0.05 to 0.2 $N \cdot sm^{-2}$) for BOF turndown slags.
3. Surface tension data for slags are available in the range of 1400–1450°C. In the $CaO–SiO_2–FeO$ system for the steelmaking composition range, a value of 450–550 $mN \cdot m^{-1}$ seems to be appropriate.

Molten slags, even at turndown contain undissolved CaO and Ca_2SiO_4 particles to the extent of 5–10 wt. %. This has an influence on slag viscosity as well as on basicity and capacities.

15.4 THE REACTION EQUILIBRIA

15.4.1 Introduction

1. SiO_2, TiO_2 are very stable compounds (see Figure 4.1). Therefore, Si and Ti in hot metal are removed as oxides in the early part of steelmaking, and are of no concern thereafter.
2. Desulphurisation of hot metal occurs to some extent within the blast furnace and subsequently, during hot metal pretreatment. As discussed in Chapter 5, Section 5.4.3, sulphur can be transferred efficiently from metal to slag, only under reducing conditions. Since primary steelmaking slags are highly oxidising in nature, very little sulphur transfer to slag can be achieved in primary steelmaking. Low levels of sulphur required in most steel today and ultra-low sulphur levels in some special steel grades can only be attained through further refining in secondary steelmaking processes. Hence, it is not discussed here.

3. Reaction of chromium is dealt with in Chapter 21 (stainless steelmaking). Oxidation of iron, carbon, phosphorus and manganese takes place throughout the blow and precise control is required to obtain the required steel quality.

Since gaseous oxygen reacts with liquid iron very rapidly, for all practical purposes, only reaction with oxygen dissolved in the liquid metal bath rather than gaseous oxygen needs to be considered. This is what is done in the following section.

15.4.2 Oxidation of Iron

For the slag–metal reaction:

$$[\mathrm{Fe}] + [\mathrm{O}]_{\mathrm{wt\%}} = (\mathrm{FeO}) \tag{15.11}$$

the equilibrium constant is given as:

$$K_{\mathrm{Fe}} = \left\{ \frac{(a_{\mathrm{FeO}})}{[a_{\mathrm{Fe}}][h_{\mathrm{O}}]} \right\}_{\mathrm{eq.}} \tag{15.12}$$

$$\log K_{\mathrm{Fe}} = \frac{6150}{T} - 2.604 \tag{15.13}$$

Since Fe in steel is almost pure, $a_{\mathrm{Fe}} \sim 1 \cdot h_{\mathrm{O}} = f_{\mathrm{O}} \cdot w_{\mathrm{O}}$, where w_{O} is wt. % oxygen in liquid steel. Also, $\log f_{\mathrm{O}} = -0.17[w_{\mathrm{O}}]$ for Fe–O binary. For pure FeO, calculations yield equilibrium (i.e. saturation) concentration of oxygen in liquid iron as 0.18 wt. %, 0.227 wt. % and 0.252 wt. % respectively at 1550°C, 1600°C and 1650°C. From Figures 15.1 and 15.3, a_{FeO} for BOF type slags may be taken as 0.5 approximately. Accordingly, saturation concentrations would be about half of the above values. It may be mentioned here that the turndown oxygen level ranges from 600 to 1000 ppm (0.06 to 0.1%), which is lower than the saturation value at normal BOF steelmaking temperature of 1600–1650°C.

15.4.3 Reactions of Carbon

For the reaction

$$[\mathrm{C}] + [\mathrm{O}] = \mathrm{CO(g)} \tag{15.14}$$

the equilibrium constant is given as

$$K_{\mathrm{CO}} = \left\{ \frac{p_{\mathrm{CO}}}{[h_{\mathrm{C}}][h_{\mathrm{O}}]} \right\}_{\mathrm{eq.}} \tag{15.15}$$

$$\log K_{\mathrm{CO}} = \frac{1160}{T} + 2.003 \tag{15.16}$$

As a first approximation, it may be noted that $h_{\mathrm{C}} = w_{\mathrm{C}}$ and $h_{\mathrm{O}} = w_{\mathrm{O}}$. It has been shown that the error is small if these assumptions are made.

Figure 15.4 (T. Saeki et al. 1978) shows the relationship between dissolved carbon and dissolved oxygen in a molten iron bath in a 100 kVA induction furnace at 1600°C. The line corresponds to equilibrium with $p_{\mathrm{CO}} = 1$ atm. The dissolved oxygen contents were measured by a solid electrolyte oxygen sensor with two types of reference electrode.

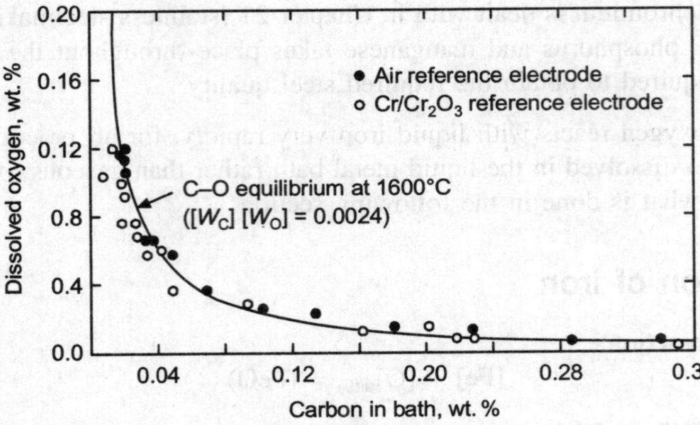

Figure 15.4 Dissolved oxygen content of liquid iron as a function of bath carbon at 1600°C (1873 K) in a 100 kVA induction furnace.

Carbon also reacts with FeO and MnO in slag. The reaction with FeO is

$$(FeO) + [C] = [Fe] + CO(g) \tag{15.17}$$

for which the equilibrium constant is

$$K_{FC} = \left\{\frac{[a_{Fe}]\cdot p_{CO}}{[h_C](a_{FeO})}\right\}_{eq.} \cong \left\{\frac{p_{CO}}{[w_C](a_{FeO})}\right\}_{eq.} \tag{15.18}$$

Combining Eqs. (15.13) and (15.16),

$$\log K_{FC} = -\frac{4990}{T} + 4.607 \tag{15.19}$$

Turkdogan (1996) has proposed several simplified correlations for reactions in steelmaking for the convenience of users. He assumed a slag basicity of 3.2 and the average pressure of CO in BOF vessels as 1.5 atm. Noting that γ_{FeO} = 1.3 at this basicity, at 1600°C his equilibrium correlation turns out to be

$$(w_{FeO})[w_C] \cong 1.0 \tag{15.20}$$

Similarly, for the reaction:

$$(MnO) + [C] = [Mn] + CO(g) \tag{15.21}$$

$$K_{MC} = \left\{\frac{[w_{Mn}]\cdot p_{CO}}{[w_C](a_{MnO})}\right\}_{eq.} \tag{15.22}$$

and

$$\log K_{MC} = -\frac{13182}{T} + 8.574 \tag{15.23}$$

Again simplification, assuming γ_{MnO} in slag = 2.05, leads to the equilibrium correlation:

$$\frac{[w_{Mn}]}{(w_{MnO})} = 0.4\,[w_C] \text{ at } 1600°C \tag{15.24}$$

15.4.4 Oxidation of Silicon

The reaction is

$$[\text{Si}] + 2[\text{O}] = (\text{SiO}_2) \tag{15.25}$$

for which the equilibrium constant is

$$K_{\text{Si}} = \left\{\frac{(a_{\text{SiO}_2})}{[h_{\text{Si}}][h_{\text{O}}]^2}\right\}_{\text{eq.}} \cong \left\{\frac{(a_{\text{SiO}_2})}{[w_{\text{Si}}][w_{\text{O}}]^2}\right\}_{\text{eq.}} \tag{15.26}$$

and,

$$\log K_{\text{Si}} = \frac{30110}{T} - 11.4 \tag{15.27}$$

From Figures (15.1) and (15.3), for a typical BOF slag, a_{SiO_2} may be taken as 5×10^{-4}. Calculations at 1600°C yield

$$\{[w_{\text{Si}}][w_{\text{O}}]^2\}_{\text{eq.}} = \frac{5 \times 10^{-4}}{4.74 \times 10^4} \cong 10^{-8} \tag{15.28}$$

Assuming $w_{\text{O}} = 0.08$ wt. % at turndown, wt. % Si at equilibrium becomes 1.6×10^{-6}, which is extremely low. Hence, this equilibrium is not of any importance and it only confirms that all the silicon present should get oxidised in primary steelmaking.

15.4.5 Reaction of Phosphorus

As mentioned earlier, the removal of phosphorus from liquid steel is of major interest. It can be effectively carried out only in primary steelmaking operations to achieve phosphorus contents of around 0.025–0.030 wt. % in steel. With increasing demand for ultra-low phosphorus steel (wt. % P < 0.005) for some special grades (like steel used in automobiles), removal of phosphorus has become of even greater significance. Therefore, there have been extensive investigations on slag–metal phosphorus reaction for over 60 years, the salient features of which will now be presented briefly.

The earliest systematic documentation was done by Ward (1962). At steelmaking temperatures, the stable state of phosphorus is gaseous P_2. P_2O_5 is also a gas. Phosphorus has a very high solubility in liquid iron as well. Tables 4.1, 4.2 and 15.1 contain free energy, enthalpy and entropy data. Hence, they will not be repeated here.

From Table 4.1, for

$$2\text{P}_2(\text{g}) + 5\text{O}_2(\text{g}) = \text{P}_4\text{O}_{10}(\text{g}) \tag{15.29}$$

$$\Delta G^0_{29} = -3140929 + 964.83T \quad \text{J} \cdot \text{mol}^{-1} \tag{15.30}$$

From Table 4.2,

$$\frac{1}{2}\text{O}_2(\text{g}) = [\text{O}]_{1\ \text{wt\%}} \tag{15.31}$$

$$\Delta G^0_{31} = -117150 - 2.89T \quad \text{J} \cdot \text{mol}^{-1} \tag{15.32}$$

and

$$\frac{1}{2}\text{P}_2(\text{g}) = [\text{P}]_{1\ \text{wt\%}} \tag{15.33}$$

$$\Delta G^0_{33} = -122170 - 19.25T \quad \text{J} \cdot \text{mol}^{-1} \tag{15.34}$$

From Eqs. (15.30), (15.32), (15.34), for

$$2[P] + 5[O] = P_2O_5(g) \tag{15.35}$$

$$\Delta G^0_{35} = \frac{1}{2}\Delta G^0_{29} - 5\Delta G^0_{31} - 2\Delta G^0_{33}$$

$$= -740375 + 535.365T \quad J \cdot mol^{-1} \tag{15.36}$$

for reaction (15.35),

$$K_p = \left\{ \frac{(a_{P_2O_5})}{[h_P]^2 [h_O]^5} \right\}_{eq.} \tag{15.37}$$

$$\log K_P = -\frac{\Delta G^0_{35}}{2.303\, RT} = \frac{38668}{T} - 27.96 \tag{15.38}$$

Assuming $h_P = w_P$ and $h_O = w_O$, at 1600°C (i.e. 1873 K), and at equilibrium

$$\frac{(a_{P_2O_5})}{[w_P]^2 [w_O]^5} = 4.0 \times 10^{-8} \tag{15.39}$$

Assuming wt. % P and wt. % O in steel at turndown to be 0.01 and 0.08% respectively, $a_{P_2O_5}$ in slag at equilibrium (with respect to gaseous P_2O_5 as standard state) is 1.57×10^{-17}. If wt. % P_2O_5 = 2, then mole fraction of P_2O_5 in slag ($X_{P_2O_5}$) is about 0.01. Since, $a_{P_2O_5} = X_{P_2O_5} \cdot \gamma_{P_2O_5}$, $\gamma_{P_2O_5}$ (i.e. activity coefficient of P_2O_5) in slag at equilibrium should be 1.31×10^{-15}.

This is indeed a very low value. Such a low $\gamma_{P_2O_5}$ is possible only in a highly basic slag since P_2O_5 is an acidic oxide. Correlations based on experimental data have been proposed. One of the earliest by Turkdogan and Pearson (1953) is reproduced below:

$$\log \gamma_{P_2O_5} = -1.12[22X_{CaO} + 15X_{MgO} + 13X_{MnO} + 12X_{FeO} - 2X_{SiO_2}] - \frac{42000}{T} + 23.58 \tag{15.40}$$

where X is mole fraction in slag.

Figure 15.5 (Turkdogan and Pearson, 1953) presents this relationship. It may be noted from Eq. (15.40) that CaO is the most powerful dephosphoriser. Of course, Na_2O, BaO are more powerful than CaO, but they cannot be used in steelmaking owing to their tendency to attack the lining of the furnace. The approximate dephosphorisation power ratio for some cations in slag has been estimated as (Ward 1962):

Ca^{2+}		Mg^{2+}		Mn^{2+}		Fe^{2+}
30,000	:	1000	:	3	:	1

Coming back to the issue of $\gamma_{P_2O_5}$, from Eq. (15.40) at X_{CaO} = 0.6 and T = 1873 K, $\gamma_{P_2O_5} = 2.36 \times 10^{-14}$. Ward proposed a temperature correction for Eq. (15.40), which was $-44600/T + 23.80$. Accepting this suggestion, $\gamma_{P_2O_5} = 1.6 \times 10^{-15}$. This shows that for highly basic, limey slags it is possible to obtain sufficiently low $\gamma_{P_2O_5}$ for effective dephosphorisation.

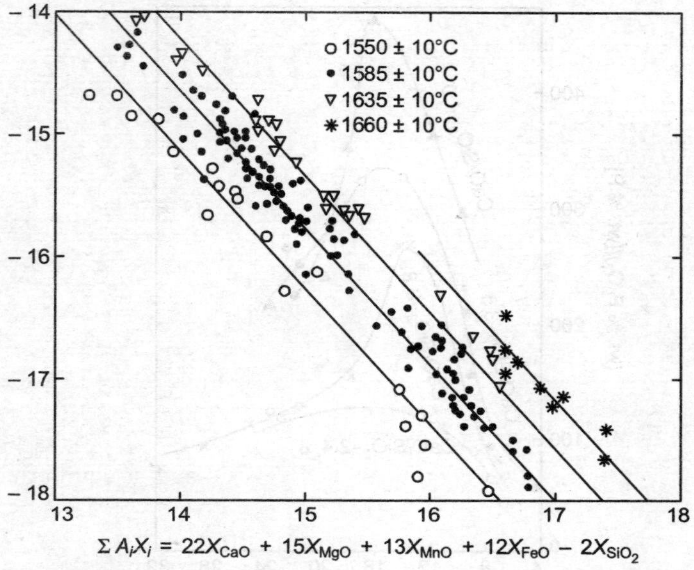

Figure 15.5 Log $\gamma_{P_2O_5}$ versus ΣX_{MO} in slag at different temperatures.

Again, the dissolved oxygen content of steel is approximately proportional to a_{FeO} in slag. Therefore, an alternative way of writing the phosphorus reaction is

$$2[P] + 5(FeO) = (P_2O_5) + 5[Fe] \tag{15.41}$$

Hence, removal of phosphorus also requires a high concentration of FeO in the slag, besides high CaO. However, higher is the wt. % FeO, lower will be the wt. % CaO, and this will adversely affect the dephosphorsing ability of the slag. Balajiva et al. (1946), in their pioneering study found that extensive dephosphorisation requires an optimum FeO content in steelmaking slags as shown in Figure 15.6.

This leads to the concept of phosphate capacity of slags (Eq. (4.54), Chapter 4). It was first employed by Healy (1970). Turkdogan (1996) has recently critically analysed and assessed the phosphorus reaction. He expressed the reaction as:

$$[P] + \frac{5}{2}[O] + \frac{3}{2}(O^{2-}) = (PO_4^{3-}) \tag{15.42}$$

and the *phosphate capacity of slag* as:

$$K_{PO} = \frac{(w_P)}{[w_P]}[w_O]^{-2.5}$$
$$= L_{P,e}\,[w_O]^{-2.5} \tag{15.43}$$

where $L_{P,e}$ is the *slag–metal phosphorus partition ratio at equilibrium.*

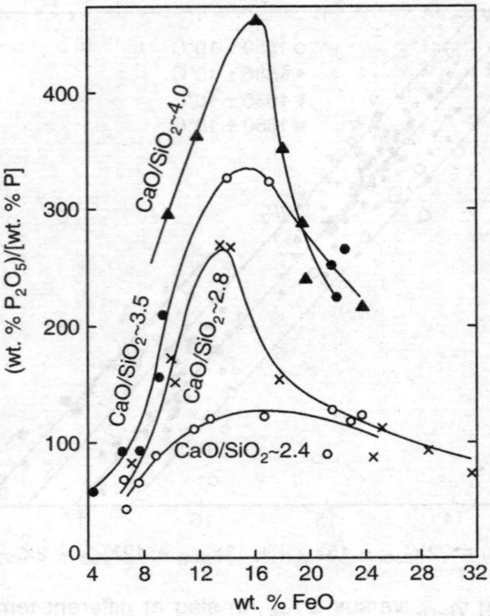

Figure 15.6 Dependence of the ratio, (wt. % P_2O_5)/[wt. % P], on the iron oxide content of slags at different CaO/SiO_2 ratios in laboratory experiments at 1685°C.

Figure 15.7 (Turkdogan 1996) shows the dependence of K_{PO} on slag composition for BOF type slags. The correlation is based on data for widely differing slag compositions. The master correlation including temperature variation can be written as

$$\log L_{P,e} = \frac{21740}{T} - 9.87 + 0.071BO + 2.5 \log [w_O] \tag{15.44}$$

The relationship of $[w_O]$ with wt. % FeO in slag was estimated as:

$$\frac{[w_O]}{(w_{FeO})} = (0.1T - 155.3) \times 10^{-4} \tag{15.45}$$

In a recent study (Choudhary et al. 2005), the important correlations proposed in literature were critically examined, and the semi-empirical correlation of Turkdogan (Eq. (15.44)) was accepted as the most reliable. However, not all the lime added dissolves in slag; some of it remains undissolved as free CaO particles or free calcium disilicate in slag. These particles do not, by and large, absorb P_2O_5 owing to the slow kinetics. Therefore, they should be subtracted, and the overall slag composition should be corrected for the calculation of equilibrium $L_{P,e}$. Since free lime is not determined during routine slag analysis, it poses some uncertainty. Choudhary et al. assumed 0% and 10% free lime in their calculations.

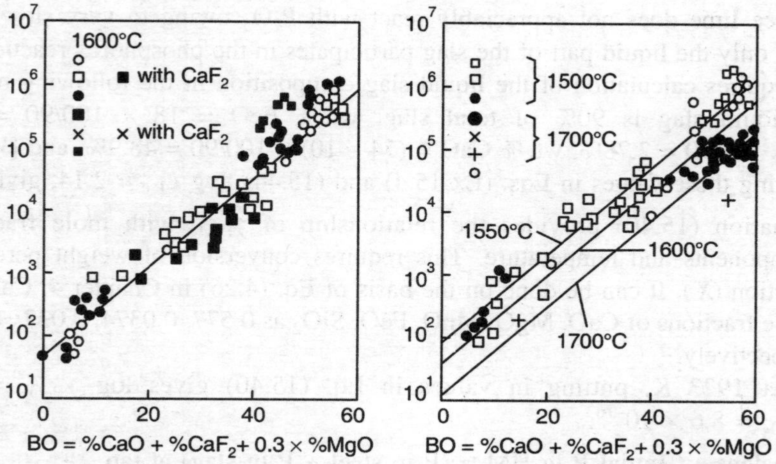

Figure 15.7 Equilibrium data from several investigations showing the decisive effects of CaO, CaF_2 and MgO on phosphate capacities of simple and complex slags.

The best conditions for phosphorus removal from liquid steel from a thermodynamic viewpoint can be summarised as:

- A highly basic, lime-rich slag
- A satisfactorily high level of oxidation of iron
- The lowest possible temperature
- The lowest possible amount of undissolved free lime in slag.

EXAMPLE 15.4

For the BOF heat, as in Examples 15.1 and 15.2,

(a) Calculate the equilibrium slag–metal phosphorus partition coefficient ($L_{P,e}$) at 1650°C. Assume 0% and 10% free lime in slag.

(b) Calculate the activity coefficient of P_2O_5 (i.e. $\gamma_{P_2O_5}$) in slag at 0% free lime.

(c) Calculate the wt. % P in metal and slag at slag–metal equilibrium as well as for $R_P = 0.4$. R_P is the ratio of actual L_P and equilibrium L_P (see Eq. (17.4)).

Solution: (a) $L_{P,e}$ can be calculated by using Eqs. (15.44) and (15.45).
From Figure 15.7,

$$BO = \text{wt. \% CaO} + \text{wt. \% } CaF_2 + 0.3 \text{ wt. \% MgO, in slag} \qquad \text{(Ex. 15.6)}$$

$$= 54 + 0 + 0.3 \times 2.5 = 54.75$$

From Eq. (15.45), $[W_O] = 0.0666\%$.

Noting that wt. % FeO in slag = 18 wt. % and $T = 1923$ K,

From Eq. (15.44), Log $L_{P,e} = 2.385$, giving $L_{P,e} = 242.7$ at 0% free lime.

Since, free lime does not appreciably react with P_2O_5 owing to very slow kinetics, it is assumed that only the liquid part of the slag participates in the phosphorus reaction at 10% free lime. This requires calculation of the liquid slag composition in the following manner.

Since, liquid slag is 90% of total slag, wt. % FeO = 18 × 100/90 = 20%, wt. % MgO = 2.5 × 100/90 = 2.78%, wt. % CaO = (54 – 10) × 100/90 = 48.9%, and $[W_O]$ = 0.074%.

Substituting these values in Eqs. (Ex 15.4) and (15.44), log $L_{P,e}$ = 2.14, giving $L_{P,e}$ = 138.

(b) Equation (15.40) provides the relationship of $\gamma_{P_2O_5}$ with mole fractions of slag components and temperature. This requires conversion of weight percent into mole fraction (X). It can be done on the basis of Eq. (4.26) in Chapter 4. Calculation gives mole fractions of CaO, MgO, MnO, FeO, SiO_2 as 0.577, 0.0374, 0.022 , 0.15 and 0.169 respectively.

At 1923 K, putting in values in Eq. (15.40) gives log $\gamma_{P_2O_5}$ = –15.06, i.e. $\gamma_{P_2O_5} = 8.6 \times 10^{-16}$.

(c) P–balance: Initial P in HM = (P in steel + P in slag) at tap (Ex. 15.7)

i.e.
$$\frac{W_{HM} \times \text{wt. \% P in HM}}{100} = \frac{1}{100} \times [W_P] \times (W_{steel} + W_{slag} \times L_{P,e})$$

where $[W_P]$ is wt. % P in steel at tapping.

i.e.
$$973 \times \frac{0.15}{100} = [W_P] \times (1000 + 242.7 \times 130) \times \frac{1}{100}$$

This gives $[W_P]$ = 0.00448%.

$$(W_P) = L_{P,e} \times [W_P] = 242.7 \times 0.00448 = 1.088\%$$

If R_P = 0.4, then L_P = 0.4 × 242.7 = 97.08.

Calculations in a similar manner give $[W_P]$ = 0.0107%, and (W_P) = 1.040%.

15.5 MASS TRANSFER AND KINETICS IN STEELMAKING

In Chapter 4, Section 4.5 some fundamental features of kinetics, mixing and mass transfer were briefly presented. These will be used in connection with process description, kinetics and process control in the later chapters, as and when required. Here, only some data on density (ρ), viscosity (η), kinematic viscosity ($\nu = \eta/\rho$), surface/interface tension (σ) and diffusion coefficient (D) of molten steel and slag are presented in Table 15.4 (*Slag Atlas*, 1981; Elliott, Gleiser and Ramakrishna, 1963).

Table 15.4(a) Viscosity (η), density (ρ), kinematic viscosity (ν) and interfacial tension (σ) of some steel and slag melts

Liquid (Composition, wt. %)	Temperature, K	η, $N \cdot m^{-2} \cdot s^{-1} \times 10^3$	ρ, $kg \cdot m^{-3} \times 10^{-3}$	ν, $m^2 \cdot s^{-1} \times 10^6$
Iron	1809	5.51	7.1	0.78
	1900	4.76	7.1	0.67
	2000	4.12	7.1	0.58
Iron, 4% Carbon	1800	5.0	6.4	0.78
$CaO–Al_2O_3$	1873	110	2.75	40.0
(45% CaO)	1973	75	2.75	27.3
$CaO–Al_2O_3–CaF_2$ (55% CaO, 35% Al_2O_3)	1873	75	2.7	27.8
$CaO–Al_2O_3–SiO_2$ (60% CaO, 35% Al_2O_3)	1773	3500	2.5	1400
$CaO–Al_2O_3–CaF_2–SiO_2$ (49% CaO, 41% Al_2O_3, 2.5% CaF_2, 7.5% SiO_2) (assumed)	1873	110	2.5	44.0

Interfacial tensions of some slags with liquid iron at 1850 to 1950 K (approximate)—from *Slage Atlas*, 1981

Slag	σ, $Nm^{-1} \times 10^3$
CaO-45%, Al_2O_3-55%	1300
CaO-55%, Al_2O_3-35%, CaF_2-10%	1400
CaO-60%, Al_2O_3-35%, SiO_2-5%	1000–1100

Table 15.4(b) Some diffusion coefficient values in liquid iron and iron alloys

Medium (composition in wt. %)	Diffusing species	Temperature, K	D, $m^2 \cdot s^{-1} \times 10^9$
Iron	C	1863	7.2
	H	1873	90.0–140.0
	Mn	1953	63.0
	N	1873	3.8
	O	1833	2.3
	P	1823	4.7
	S	1873	4.8
	Si	1833	10.8
Fe, 3.5% C	C	1823	6.7
Fe, 2.5% Mn (C-saturated)	Mn	1773	3.7
Fe, 2.2% Si (C-saturated)	S	1658	3.0
Fe, 2.2% Si (C-saturated)	S	1843	3.8
Fe, 1.5% Si (C-saturated)	Si	1773	2.3

REFERENCES

Balajiva, K., A.G. Quarrell and P. Vajragupta, J. Iron Steel Inst., Vol. 153 (1946), p. 115.

Bardenheuer, F. et al., Arch Eisenh, Vol. 39 (1968), p. 571.

Bogdandy, L. Von. and H.J. Engells, *The Reduction of Iron Ores*, Springer Verlag, Berlin, 1971.

Choudhary, S.K., S.N. Lenka and A. Ghosh, Tata Search, 2005, pp. 117–124.

Elliott, J.F., M. Gleiser and V. Ramakrishna, *Thermochemistry for Steelmaking*, Vo1. 2, Addison-Wesley, Reading, Mass., USA, 1963.

Healy, G.W., J. Iron and Steel Inst., Vol. 208 (1970), pp. 664–668.

Kelley, K.K., *Contributions to the Data on Theoretical Metallurgy*, Bulletin 584, Bureau of Mines, Washington D.C., USA, 1960.

Muan, A. and E.F. Osborn, *Phase Equilibria Among Oxides in Steelmaking*, Addison–Wesley, Reading, Mass., USA, 1965.

Saeki, T. et al., Trans ISIJ, Vol. 18 (1978), p. 501.

Slag Atlas, Committee for Fundamental Metallurgy, Verlag Stahleisen, Dusseldorf, 1981.

Taylor, C.R. and J. Chipman, Trans AIME, Vol. 159 (1943), p. 228.

Timucin, M. and A.E. Morris, Met. Trans., Vol. 1 (1970), p. 3193.

Turkdogan, E.T. and J. Pearson, J. Iron Steel Inst., Vol. 175 (1953), p. 398.

Turkdogan, E.T., *Fundamentals of Steelmaking*, Institute of Materials, London (1996), p. 188.

Walker, R.D. and D. Anderson, Reaction Mechanisms in Basic Oxygen Steelmaking, Part I, *Iron and Steel*, June 1972, pp. 271–276.

Ward, R.G., *An Introduction to the Physical Chemistry of Iron & SteelMaking*, Edwin Arnold, London, 1962; Appendix.

16

BOF Plant Practice

16.1 INTRODUCTION

The modern, high-performance BOF converter is the outcome of continuous developments over the past fifty years. Ever since Voest-Alpine commissioned the first LD converter in 1952 in Linz, Austria (Chapter 3), several improvements have been made to make the process more versatile. The physicochemical principles governing the chemical reactions in BOF and other processes of primary steelmaking have been introduced in Chapter 15. The metallurgical features of BOF steelmaking will be covered in greater detail in Chapter 17. This chapter will discuss some practical aspects of BOF steelmaking, including pre-treatment of hot metal.

16.2 BOF OPERATION

In steelmaking, hot metal containing carbon ranging from 4.0% to 4.5%, 0.4% to 1.5% silicon, manganese varying from 0.15% to 1.5% (sometimes even more), 0.045% to 2.5% phosphorus (normally between 0.060% and 0.250%), and sulphur 0.150% maximum (normally 0.050–0.080%) is refined. In the BOF process, all these impurities are removed virtually to zero levels so that steel of the desired composition can be produced.

The tap-to-tap time of each BOF heat, which is typically around 30–40 minutes in operations today, is sequentially made up of the following:

- Charging of scrap (for which a charging pad is normally provided) and hot metal into the converter using a charging crane with the vessel inclined towards the charging side (5–8 minutes)
- Making the vessel upright, lowering the lance and then beginning oxygen blowing at the desired rate (Mach number 1.8–2.5; flow rate 550–600 Nm^3/min. for a 160–180 t converter) for around 15–20 minutes
- Stopping the blow, raising the lance, and then inclining the vessel again towards the charging side to take a metal sample (if necessary, also a slag sample) to check the bath composition and temperature (6–10 minutes)

- Tapping the vessel by rotating it to the opposite side so that steel flows through the tap hole in the nose portion of the vessel into a ladle kept below the converter floor (4–8 minutes).

During tapping of steel, simultaneous outflow of slag is prevented to the maximum possible extent, by using a pneumatic slag stopper arrangement at the tap hole, or by introducing suitable slag arresting devices into the converter like refractory darts, that are heavier than slag but lighter than steel. Once steel is tapped, the vessel is turned further (almost to 180° from the upright position) so that most of the slag within the converter flows into a slag ladle that is subsequently sent by rail road for cooling. Some slag is often retained for slag splashing (details given later in Section 16.3.1). BOF slags containing 18–22% iron and with high basicity (sometimes, even free lime) are used in sintermaking, or as a soil conditioner for acidic soil.

The exit gas generated during blowing [120–130 Nm^3/tonne liquid steel (tls)], which is rich in CO for up to 90% of the duration of the blow, and contains dust to the extent of 20 kg/tonne liquid steel, is sent to the gas-cleaning plant before it is stored.

16.3 BOF SHOP LAYOUT AND INDIVIDUAL CONVERTER COMPONENTS

Any BOF vessel is equipped with:

- Mechanical rotating device that allows proper positioning of the vessel
- Lance carriage to keep the water-cooled lance in the vertical position
- Nose cone section through which the gases exit
- Tap hole for draining metal/slag
- Overhead bins for adding iron ore, fluxes, slag-forming agents, etc. as required during the blow, into the converter kept in the vertical position.

Figure 16.1 presents a typical layout of a two-converter BOF shop in which at least one converter is always in operation and the other, is either operating or is under relining. The heart of the shop is obviously the converter, which is a cylindrical vessel made of welded steel plates, with refractory lining inside. The entire vessel is supported by a suspension system which transmits the load to the trunnion ring as shown in Figure 16.2. The trunnion ring, in turn, is supported by a trunnion shaft so that the total load of the vessel, including the refractories and molten metal, is transferred to the foundation.

16.3.1 BOF Vessel Design and Refractory Lining

The refractory lining within the converter shell consists of a safety layer and a working layer. It is the working lining that wears out after each campaign that can normally last anywhere between 3000 and 10,000 heats. Sometimes, campaigns can be even longer, particularly when sophisticated refractories like magnesite carbon are used instead of the normal pitch-bonded dolomite or pitch impregnated fired magnesite. At the end of each campaign, the worn-out lining is mechanically dislodged before beginning work on relining *in situ*. Once relining is completed and the refractories are thoroughly dried, the converter is ready for use. This entire relining procedure normally takes 4–5 days.

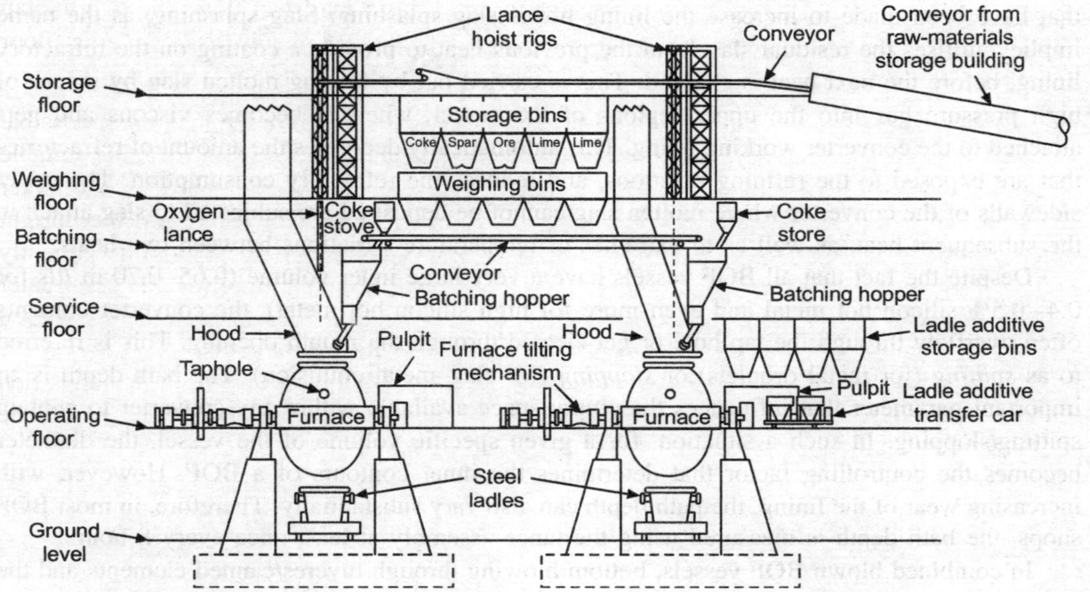

Figure 16.1 Layout of a typical two-converter BOF shop.

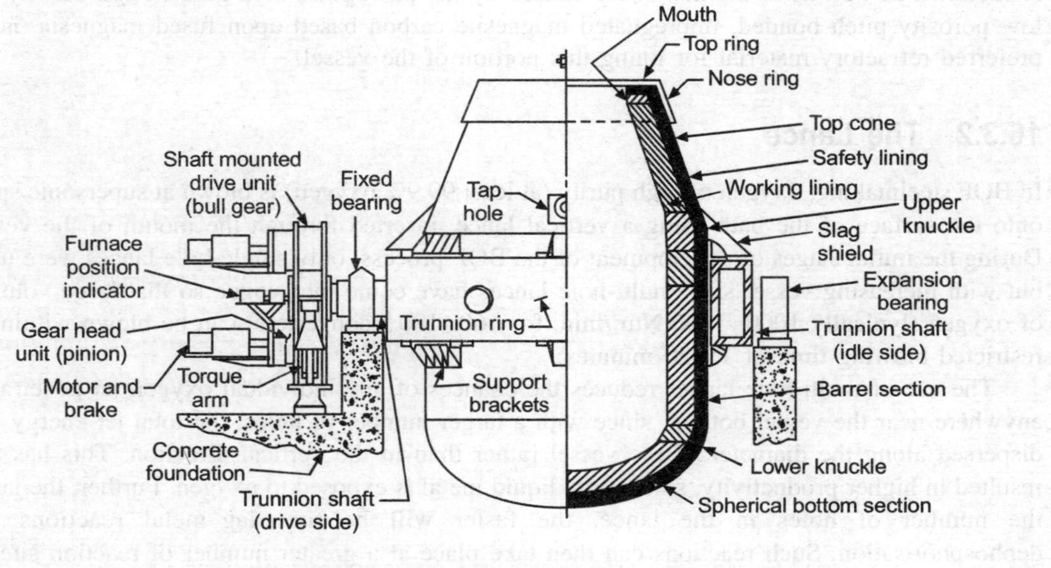

Figure 16.2 Typical components of a BOF vessel.

Since the early 1980s, dramatic improvements have taken place in the length of converter campaigns because of process developments as well as developments in refractory lining technology. This has not only resulted in considerable reduction in the refractory cost per tonne of steel, but has also reduced the downtime. One of the most innovative process improvements that have been made to increase the lining life is slag splashing. Slag splashing, as the name implies, utilises the residual slag from the previous heat to provide a coating on the refractory lining, before the next heat is charged. This is carried out by forcing molten slag by means of high pressure gas into the upper regions of the vessel, where it becomes viscous and gets attached to the converter working lining. This automatically decreases the amount of refractories that are exposed to the refining reactions, and reduces the refractory consumption. The upper sidewalls of the converter where molten slag cannot be deposited are subjected to slag attack in the subsequent heat, as well as to extremes of temperature variations between two heats.

Despite the fact that all BOF vessels have a very large inner volume (0.65–0.70 m^3/tls for 0.4–0.5% silicon hot metal and even more for high silicon hot metal), the converter contents often overflow through the tap hole or get ejected through the mouth opening. This is referred to as *spitting* (for metal droplets) or *slopping* (for slag–metal emulsion). The bath depth is an important parameter that influences the empty space available within any converter to contain spitting/slopping. In such a situation, for a given specific volume of the vessel, the diameter becomes the controlling factor that determines the inner contours of a BOF. However, with increasing wear of the lining, the bath depth can also vary substantially. Therefore, in most BOF shops, the bath depth is measured using the lance assembly at least once every 8 hours.

In combined blown BOF vessels, bottom blowing through tuyeres/canned elements and the resultant bath agitation, contribute to localised wear of the refractory components at the converter bottom. The wear is attributable to turbulent flow of molten metal giving rise to erosion of the refractories as well as to thermal stress caused by the passage of cold gases. High density and low porosity pitch bonded, impregnated magnesite carbon based upon fused magnesia, is the preferred refractory material for lining this portion of the vessel.

16.3.2 The Lance

In BOF steelmaking, oxygen of high purity (at least 99.9% oxygen) is blown at supersonic speed onto the surface of the bath using a vertical lance, inserted through the mouth of the vessel. During the initial stages of development of the BOF process, only single-hole lances were used, but with increasing vessel size, multi-hole lances have come into vogue so that large volumes of oxygen (typically 1000–1200 Nm^3/min. for 160–180 t converters) can be blown within the restricted blowing time of 15–20 minutes.

The use of multi-hole lances reduces the chances of any individual oxygen jet penetrating anywhere near the vessel bottom, since with a larger number of holes, the total jet energy gets dispersed along the diameter of the vessel rather than in the vertical direction. This has also resulted in higher productivity, since more liquid metal is exposed to oxygen. Further, the larger the number of holes in the lance, the faster will be the slag–metal reactions like dephosphorisation. Such reactions can then take place at a greater number of reaction sites.

16.3.3 Gas Cleaning System

Irrespective of the converter size, on an average, 50–60 Nm^3 of oxygen is blown through the lance per tonne of liquid steel. The gas exiting through converter mouth at the rate of 120–130 Nm^3/tls, essentially contains carbon monoxide and carbon dioxide. The gas leaves the

BOF at temperatures close to 1600°C and contains dust particles comprising iron oxides and lime, mainly below 200 mesh size. This gas has to be cooled before it can be cleaned in the gas cleaning plant. The load on the gas cleaning plant is the highest when iron ore is added as a coolant during the blow since the exit gas flow automatically increases owing to the extra oxygen. At such times, the generation of dust also increases, varying between 20 and 30 kg/tls. However, when scrap alone is the coolant, the amount of dust is restricted to 10–25 kg/tls. In some cases, hazardous pollutants like cadmium, chromium, lead, manganese, and nickel may also be present. Zinc compounds are present in BOF fume in varying amounts, if process scrap containing zinc is charged.

Carbon monoxide in the gas is partly burnt to CO_2 at the converter mouth. The remainder of the combustible gases is extracted at a largely constant air ratio, by using a hood pressure control device. Positive gas routing to avoid explosions then becomes a basic requirement for any gas-cleaning equipment. If the proper system is chosen and operated efficiently, it is possible to recover about 9600 kJ of energy per tonne of liquid steel from the waste gas. Through heat recovery in the waste gas cooling system, 210–215 kJ of additional energy per tonne of liquid steel can be recovered, i.e. 90% of the total energy content in the waste gas is recoverable.

The equipment used for gas cleaning and dust collection include: a quencher for cooling, venturi-type washer and cooling tower in series for dust extraction, and a clarifier or thickening basin for handling water containing dust that settles as sludge. Clean water leaving the clarifier contains less than 0.25 g solids per litre of water, and the clean gas stored in the gas holder contains a maximum of 1.6 g of solids per cubic metre.

16.3.4 Engineering Features of BOF Shops

The success of any BOF shop operation is heavily dependent on proper utilisation of the space available, so that efficient and economical flow of materials to/from/in the shop can be ensured. This calls for careful plant engineering, taking factors like logistics, complexity, time required for each operation, etc. into consideration.

All the inputs used in BOFs, viz. molten iron, steel scrap, and fluxes enter from one end of the shop. The fluxes are handled by conveyors and stored in bins above the converters. Molten iron arrives in torpedo ladle cars and is then poured into transfer ladles (sent for desulphurisation and slag removal when necessary) before charging into the converter, using the charging-side overhead crane. Steel scrap (normally 10–15% of the total charge), collected either in-house or purchased from external sources, is filled in scrap boxes and charged first into the BOF using the same overhead charging crane. In some cases, hot metal coming from the blast furnaces is stored in a mixer (a barrel-shaped, cylindrical, refractory-lined vessel of 1000–1500 tonnes capacity) located at the entry-end of the BOF shop. The mixer serves dual purposes, viz. as a storage vessel as well as means for mixing successive lots of hot metal coming from blast furnaces. In this way, the chemical composition of the hot metal charged can be made more uniform. Although hot metal mixers were earlier always an integral part of any steel melting shop, with the advent of large capacity torpedo ladles, they are now seldom utilised since torpedo ladles serve as 'mini' mixers.

16.4 REFINING

In Chapters 17 and 18, the details of the metallurgical features and process control in basic oxygen steelmaking will be presented. Hence in this section, only a brief outline is given.

During refining, controlled oxidation of the impurities in hot metal (with the exception of sulphur) takes place once oxygen is blown at supersonic speeds (Appendix II contains more details of supersonic jets and their relevance to BOF steelmaking) onto the liquid bath. The interaction of the oxygen jet(s) with the bath produces crater(s) on the surface, from the outer lip(s) of which, a large number of tiny metal droplets get splashed. These droplets reside for a short time in the slag above the bath. Therefore, the existence of a metal–slag–gas emulsion within the vessel, virtually during the entire blowing/refining period is an integral part of BOF steelmaking. This is the reason why the slag–metal reactions like dephosphorisation and gas–metal reactions like decarburisation proceed so rapidly in the BOF process (earlier, it was erroneously believed that the existence of a high temperature, 2500–2600°C, zone on the bath surface was responsible for the high rates of reactions). The droplets ultimately return to the metal bath. The extent of emulsification varies at different stages of the blowing period, as depicted schematically in Figure 16.3.

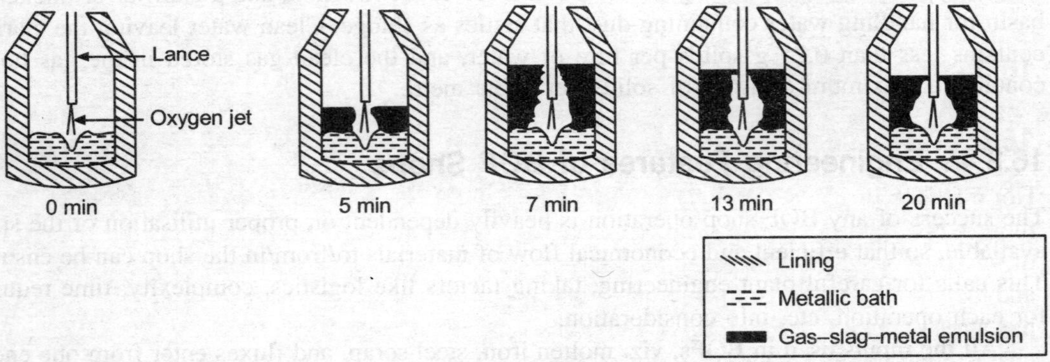

Figure 16.3 Schematic representation of the bath conditions within a BOF at various stages of the blow.

A minimum amount of slag, with the desired characteristics, is necessary for ensuring that the emulsion is stable, i.e. the slag should not be too viscous, or too 'watery'. Only in this way can the kinetics of the removal of the impurities be enhanced. For encouraging quick formation of the appropriate type of slag, lime/dolomite/other fluxing agents with adequate *reactivity* are added right from the beginning of the blow. The reactivity of the fluxing agents, primarily lime (consumption 60–100 kg/tls), determines how quickly slag is formed (typically within 4–5 minutes after the commencement of the blow). The rate at which oxygen is blown through the lance, the number of openings (holes) on the lance tip, the distance between the lance tip and the bath surface (lance height), the characteristics of the oxygen jets as they impinge on the bath surface, the volume, basicity and fluidity of the slag, the temperature conditions in the bath, and many other operational variables influence the rate of refining. In most cases, to encourage slag formation a high lance height (1.5–2.0 m) is used at the beginning of the blow, and then the lance is lowered (0.8–1.2 m) for decarburisation.

The basic design of the converter, the extent of combustion of waste gases, the total blowing time, characteristics of the slag during the entire blowing period, post-blow operations (if any), etc. have a profound influence on the composition and the temperature of the bath at the end of refining. If the desired end-point, in terms of composition and/or temperature, is not reached (i.e. the *hit rate* is suboptimal), oxygen has to be blown again—this is referred as *reblowing*. Hit rates of 88–92% can be achieved if adequate process control measures are adopted.

In order to withdraw a sample to check the bath composition/temperature, the blow has to be temporarily suspended, the lance withdrawn, and then a spoon inserted after inclining the converter in such a way that the bath becomes horizontal. Once the sample is taken, the vessel is made upright before resuming blowing. This is a time-taking procedure. To avoid such delays, most modern BOF shops are equipped with a *sublance*. The sublance is an inclined lance positioned next to the oxygen lance, which can be mechanically lowered into the bath to collect metal/slag sample and measure the bath temperature, keeping the converter in the vertical position. Solid probes attached to the sublance tip are used for this purpose. They have to be renewed after each dip, and can add to costs since they are quite expensive.

16.5 MAJOR INPUTS FOR BOF STEELMAKING

16.5.1 Hot Metal

Hot metal quality is clearly of prime importance in BOF steelmaking. The importance becomes more when high *hot metal ratios* (the proportion of hot metal in the total charge) of the order of 95–99% are used. The reverse is true when scrap (or other coolants) is abundantly available and the hot metal ratio is intentionally lowered to 70–75%. The subject of hot metal composition has already been discussed in Chapter 11 and will not be elaborated further. However, another characteristic of hot metal, viz. its temperature is also of significance in BOF steelmaking. The hot metal temperature has to be high enough to permit easy transfer from the torpedo ladles to the transfer ladle, efficient pre-treatment without giving rise to problems like skull formation on the injection lance, smooth charging into the BOF, etc.

16.5.2 Coolants

In determining the amount of solid charge used in a BOF at any point of time, the primary factors are cost/availability of hot metal, cost/availability of scrap or iron oxide (both are coolants) and the amount of fluxes required. The physical condition of all these solids is also important, since it influences their melting rate during the progress of the blow.

The quality and the composition of scrap are of particular significance in achieving the final composition of the steel tapped. If the scrap charged contains elements like copper, tin and nickel, these elements do not get removed as oxides, and the metals report to steel, resulting even in off-grade products. Another area of concern is the degree of oxidation of the scrap, which may have a significant influence on the *charge balance* (proportion of liquid to solid charge), since

Fe_2O_3 contents as high as 15% may be introduced in this way. A virgin alternative iron source is direct reduced iron (DRI) and with increasing availability of DRI, its usage in the appropriate size (3–15 mm) in BOF steelmaking is also increasing. When calculating the amount of the coolant required, it is important to note that DRI cools 10% more efficiently than scrap for the same weight; whereas, the *cooling factor* of iron ore is 3.0–3.5 times greater. Usage of large amounts of iron ore is often precluded by extensive slopping from the vessel mouth, since the iron ore added is not immediately 'in equilibrium' with the bath. Slopping can be reduced by decreasing the rate of iron ore addition and/or altering the blowing strategy so that the emulsion collapses.

16.5.3 Flux Materials

The quality of fluxes to be used for slag making is an important issue. The flux materials must have sufficient strength to withstand handling during transport to the bins above the converter. Reactivity is another factor that determines the quality of the flux. Insufficient physical strength gives rise to extensive dust generation and carry-over of the flux (as lime powder) into the exit gas, resulting in erroneous basicity of the slag as well as an increase in the p_H level of water in the gas-cleaning plant. This causes deposition of lime in the water treatment section, which has to be avoided to the maximum extent.

16.5.4 Oxygen

This is an important input material whose quality is often not adequately highlighted. The minimum purity of oxygen to allow the production of the full range of carbon steel products should be 99.9%. The final turndown nitrogen and hydrogen contents of steel are dependent not only on the amounts of these elements present in hot metal/fluxes, but also on oxygen.

During the early stages of the oxygen blow, when the rate of carbon monoxide evolution is high, the nitrogen content of the bath decreases, i.e. de-nitrogenisation occurs. However, when the decarburisation rate begins to fall (after 12–15 minutes) the nitrogen content can increase substantially if oxygen of adequate purity is not used.

16.6 PRE-TREATMENT OF HOT METAL PRIOR TO STEELMAKING

Owing to the stringent demands placed in recent years by steel consumers as far as the properties of steel products in terms of their strength, toughness, drawability under extreme forming conditions, etc. are concerned, it has become mandatory to reduce the impurity levels in steel drastically; in some cases, even to a few parts per million (ppm).

Silicon, carbon, sulphur and phosphorus are the elements present in hot metal that have to be removed. At the end of the oxygen blowing period, the carbon level in the bath is normally between 0.03% and 0.04%. For lower carbon levels, vacuum treatment is normally resorted to. As far as silicon is concerned, it gets removed almost completely during steelmaking since this is a thermodynamic precondition for the oxidation of carbon. However, the removal of sulphur and phosphorus are not as straightforward. These elements continue to remain in liquid steel, to various extents, at the end of the blow.

To produce internal crack-free products with acceptable surface quality, it is necessary to lower the levels of sulphur and phosphorus to less than 0.010 percent each (sometimes, even less than 0.005%). To achieve such low values, it is often desirable to charge hot metal containing low amounts of sulphur and phosphorus into the BOF. Otherwise, under the oxidising conditions prevailing during steelmaking, it becomes almost impossible to reduce both sulphur and phosphorus economically. At the same time, owing to factors like decreasing availability of low sulphur coke and the use of high phosphorus-bearing iron ores, it is not always possible to produce low sulphur, low phosphorus hot metal in blast furnaces. Hence, pre-treatment of hot metal to remove sulphur/phosphorus prior to BOF steelmaking has gained worldwide acceptance as an intermediate operation. For this purpose, an extra step (in some cases, more than one step) has to be introduced between the blast furnace and the BOF shop.

The details of the reactions involved in the removal of these elements from liquid iron have been covered in other chapters. Chapter 4 has dealt with the general physicochemical fundamentals, including slag basicity and their capacities to absorb of sulphur/phosphorus. Chapter 5 has discussed the theory of reactions of sulphur, and silicon. Chapter 15 provides an insight into the physical chemistry of steelmaking reactions for silicon, carbon, phosphorus, etc. Hence, these are not being repeated here.

16.6.1 Objectives of Pre-treatment

Hot metal pre-treatment envisages removal of sulphur, and sometimes even silicon plus phosphorus, by the addition of suitable reagents. To increase the surface area so that the reactions occur rapidly, these reagents are normally injected into hot metal in the form of fine powder. While desulphurisation of hot metal has now become standard practice in virtually all plants, in some cases, desiliconisation also becomes necessary, particularly since it is a pre-requisite for the removal of phosphorus. However, desiliconisation automatically decreases the amount of scrap that can be concurrently used in the BOF charge (the extent of heat generation becomes restricted), which is not always desirable from an economical point of view. This is particularly detrimental if the objective is to decrease the hot metal ratio from 92–95% (common in the last few years in countries like Japan owing to excess hot metal capacity) to 82–85% (at times when scrap is relatively inexpensive).

Over and above the ability to produce steel with very low levels of sulphur and phosphorus, there are some additional advantages that accrue from hot metal pre-treatment. These include:

- increased opportunity to recycle steelmaking slags (low in phosphorus) to the blast furnace for recovering iron and manganese units
- possibility of 'slagless' or 'limeless' steelmaking from hot metal low in silicon, sulphur and phosphorus. The advantage of 'slagless' refining is less flux consumption, decreased slopping, increased productivity, and improved hit rates at the end of the blow. The ultimate goal is to use BOFs for decarburisation alone (many Japanese plants have already been successful in achieving this goal).

16.6.2 Removal of Silicon

Silicon in hot metal can be removed by injecting an oxidising agent like mill scale (accompanied by lime to help produce a neutral slag), or by taking recourse to a separate step of oxygen blowing in another converter to produce highly siliceous slag (in the presence of lime) before the desiliconised hot metal is transferred to a second converter, for the other reactions to proceed. This type of two-slag BOF operation gives rise to the following advantages:

- Improved dephosphorisation during steelmaking since highly basic slags can be formed early in the blow
- Reduction in the converter slag volume accompanied by an increase in the iron yield (less iron loss in the slag), longer converter campaigns (less attack on the lining from siliceous compounds in the primary slag), etc.
- Lower consumption of ferro alloys because of higher recovery arising on account of the lower levels of dissolved oxygen in liquid steel
- Easier dynamic control of the process to arrive at the desired end point.

Despite these advantages, desiliconisation is not normally practiced essentially because of problems in handling the highly siliceous slag that is produced. Such slags have high temperature and are extremely fluid, thereby causing aggressive attack on most refractories. Instead, efforts have been made to produce low silicon (0.3–0.6%) hot metal directly in blast furnaces to the maximum possible extent, as discussed in Chapter 11.

16.6.3 Desulphurisation

Desulphurisation is better at the hot metal stage rather than at the steel stage because of the reasons given in Table 16.1 (Gupta and Chatterjee, 1995). Desulphurisation of hot metal in blast furnace ladles en route to the steel melting shop has become a standard practice because:

- The productivity of blast furnaces can be improved by 6–8% when sulphur control within the blast furnace is not required, and a leaner slag chemistry as well as lower slag volume can be chosen
- The consumption of coke as well as fluxes decreases, thereby reducing the total energy consumption per tonne of hot metal
- Build-up of alkalis in the blast furnace gets restricted, and
- The production of low silicon hot metal becomes easier.

Table 16.1 Comparison of desulphurisation of hot metal vis-à-vis steel

Parameter	Hot metal desulphurisation	Steel desulphurisation
Oxygen potential	Low (slag FeO = 0.25%)	High (slag FeO = 18–20%)
Temperature	1300–1550°C	Greater than 1600°C
Activity coefficient	4.5–6	1.5
Cost of desulphurisation	Low	High
Desulphurisation efficiency	High	Low
Temperature drop	Can be manipulated	Cannot be manipulated

16.6.4 Dephosphorisation

Theoretically speaking, dephosphorisation of hot metal allows:

- Increased recycling of BOF slag to the blast furnace, thereby reducing the cost of hot metal
- Steel for continuous casting to be tapped at higher temperature without the risk of rephosphorisation
- Control on the extent of segregation of phosphorus during continuous casting
- Lower final sulphur and phosphorus contents in steel, particularly high alloy steel.

However, dephosphorisation is normally not carried out during the production of bulk steels, since from free energy considerations, it can only be done under oxidising conditions, and in the presence of a highly basic slag. This is possible only after the total removal of silicon (dictated by thermodynamics). At the same time, while phosphorus is best removed at low temperature, desiliconisation automatically increases the temperature (the reaction of oxygen with silicon is highly exothermic). The dichotomy of the situation is evident. Therefore, alternative strategies for controlling the phosphorus content of hot metal by choosing appropriate raw materials, or by adopting a modified BOF process (e.g. concurrent injection of lime and oxygen in the converter) to process high phosphorus (1–2%) hot metal, have found favour. However, some Japanese steel plants, which produce very low silicon hot metal (less than 0.3%) in their blast furnaces, have been able to practice simultaneous desulphurisation and dephosphorisation of hot metal.

16.7 REAGENTS USED FOR PRE-TREATMENT

16.7.1 Soda-ash

When soda-ash (sodium carbonate) is added to hot metal, dense fumes are generated, which can create environmental problems. Disposal of soda-bearing slags gives rise to ground water contamination. This is the primary reason why the use of soda-ash has been restricted in recent times, though it is an effective reagent for both desiliconisation and desulphurisation.

Sodium carbonate is comparatively stable up to 1200°C, above which it decomposes:

$$Na_2CO_3(l) = Na_2O(l) + CO_2(g) \tag{16.1}$$

A portion of the Na_2O produced dissolves in liquid Na_2CO_3 (m.p. = 851°C) while the remainder decomposes:

$$Na_2O(l) = 2Na(g) + \tfrac{1}{2}O_2(g) \tag{16.2}$$

In hot metal containing carbon and silicon, the following reactions take place:

$$Na_2CO_3(l) + 2[C] = 2Na(g) + 3CO(g) \tag{16.3}$$

$$Na_2CO_3(l) + [Si] = Na_2O.SiO_2 + [C] \tag{16.4}$$

$$Na_2CO_3(l) + 2[C] + [S] = Na_2S + 3CO(g) \tag{16.5}$$

Since the reactions related to the decomposition of Na_2O and Na_2CO_3 to Na (g) proceed rapidly at high temperature, lower temperatures are preferable for desulphurisation (reaction 16.5). Soda-ash is a very effective reagent for desulphurisation and dephosphorisation in the case of low silicon hot metal.

16.7.2 Mixture of Soda-ash and Sodium Sulphate

The use of sodium carbonate and sodium sulphate together for pre-treatment of hot metal has also been investigated. The incorporation of sodium sulphate helps in dephosphorisation in the following manner:

$$Na_2SO_4(l) + (4/5)P = (2/3)Na_2O(l) = (2/5)P_2O_5(l) + (1/3)Na_2S(l) + (2/3)SO_2 \quad (16.6)$$

A mixture of soda ash and sodium sulphate is advantageous in pre-treating hot metal because of the low melting points of the constituents: Na_2CO_3 (m.p. = 851°C) and Na_2SO_4 (m.p. = 884°C). A mixture of the two in the weight ratio of 2 soda-ash and 1sodium sulphate is considered to be the optimum.

16.7.3 Mill Scale, Sintor Fines, etc.

Desiliconisation can be carried out by using primary reagents like gaseous oxygen, mill scale, sinter fines, iron ore/manganese ore fines, etc. Along with the primary reagent, an auxiliary agent containing CaO, (CaO + CaF_2), (CaO + CaF_2 + Na_2CO_3) is also added. In several cases, BOF slag is used.

16.7.4 Calcium Carbide and Magnesium Granules

The desired level of sulphur in steel for efficient continuous casting is a maximum of around 0.020%. In the case of special steel plates, the sulphur content has to be restricted to around 0.010% normally. However, there is demand for sulphur levels as low as 10 ppm (0.001%), in the case of steel used in pipe lines (commonly referred to as line pipe steel) that have to be guaranteed against hydrogen induced cracking when sour gas is conveyed. To cater to all such requirements, the sulphur content in hot metal has to be brought down to at least 0.010–0.025%. This is normally achieved by injecting suitable powders like calcium carbide. In actual practice, calcium carbide containing limestone, lime and carbon is used as a mixture as in Table 16.2 (Dutta et al. 1996).

Table 16.2 Typical calcium carbide mixtures used for desulphurisation

Grade	Reagent composition, %			
	CaC_2	$CaCO_3$	CaO	C
CAD 60	48	31	17	4
CAD 70	56	22	19	3
CAD 80	64	14	20	2
CAD 85	68	9	22	1

Lime contributes towards enhancement of the basicity of the micro-slags that are formed, while dissociation of limestone provides carbon dioxide that is beneficial for agitation. On the other hand, carbon in the mixture helps in maintaining the necessary atmosphere at the reaction sites. These mixtures are injected using nitrogen (in some special cases argon) as the carrier gas. Co-injection of carbide and magnesium metal granules (in the ratio of 2.5–7.0 : 1) at injection rates of typically 20–25 kg/min. and 10–12 kg/min. is also resorted to when extremely low levels of sulphur in hot metal (circa 0.010%) are required. The use of magnesium granules helps to reduce the injection time as well as the slag volume. Addition of lime/soda ash during injection is also practised, when it is necessary to bring down the slag raking time or to reduce the metal loss in the slag. External desulphurisation with such mixtures produces very dry slags, in which substantial amount of metal as granules (below 3 mm) tend to get entrapped.

16.7.5 Injection of Desulphurising Agents

A schematic representation of the entire equipment system employed for the injection of powders into melts is given in Figure 16.4 while Figure 16.5 provides a pictorial view of the same. The powder injector (Figure 16.6) is the most important component of the system.

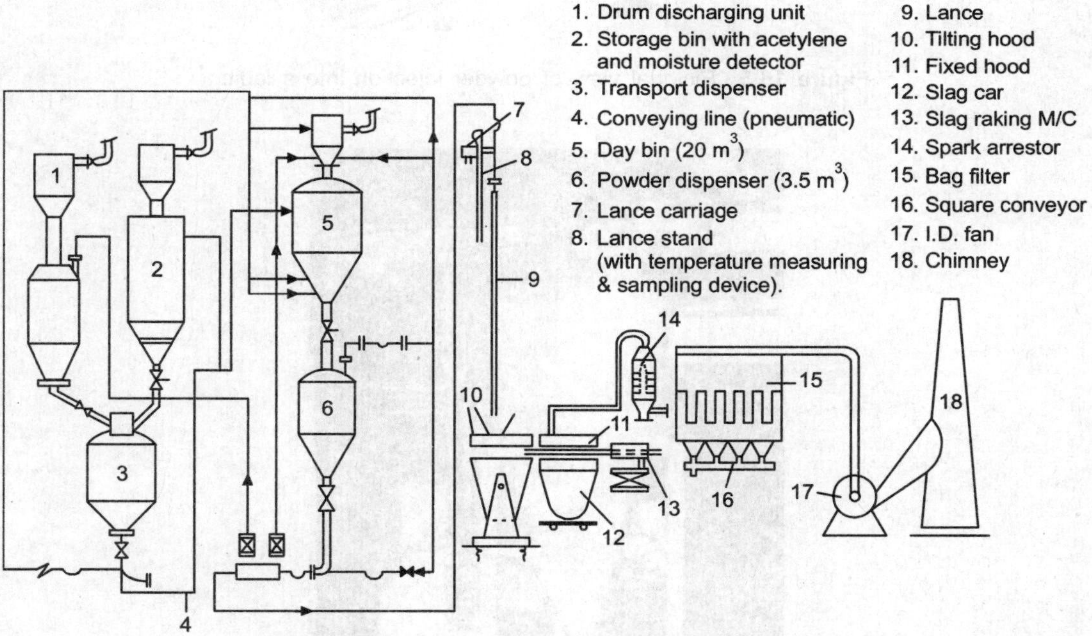

Figure 16.4 Schematic representation of the entire powder injection system.

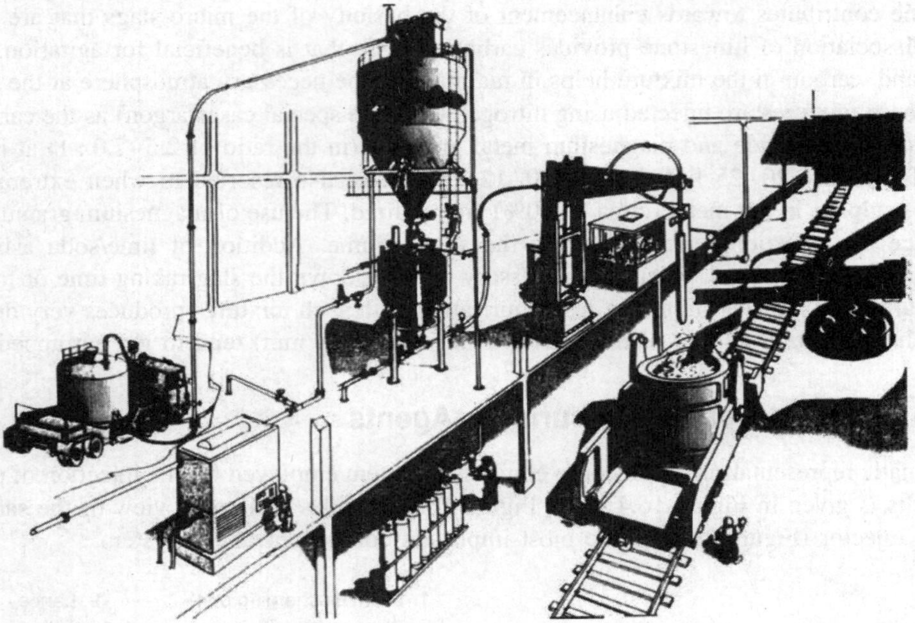

Figure 16.5 Pictorial view of powder injection into a ladle.

Figure 16.6 Close-up of a typical powder dispenser.

When a powder like calcium carbide is injected, using a carrier gas (nitrogen/argon), the gas and calcium particles penetrate into the liquid hot metal as a gas particle jet until their momentum is dissipated, which has been confirmed by water model studies. At the bottom of the jet, a *plume* (photograph taken in room temperature model studies shown in Figure 16.7) is created, where the gas forms spherical-cap bubbles, 20 to 100 mm in diameter. The physical and chemical phenomena in the plume are shown schematically in Figure 16.8.

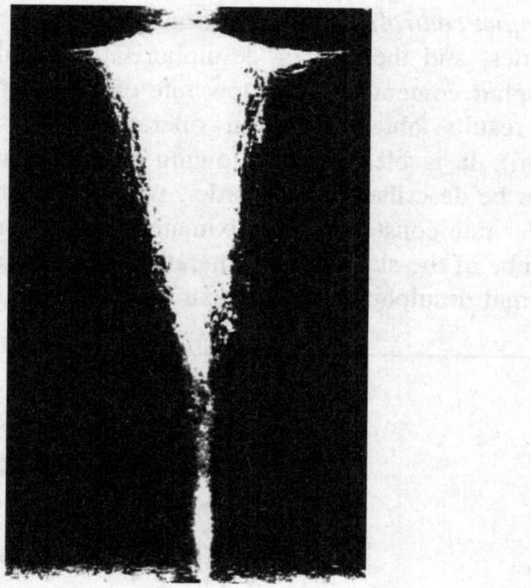

Figure 16.7 Photograph of the plume (air-water room temperature model).

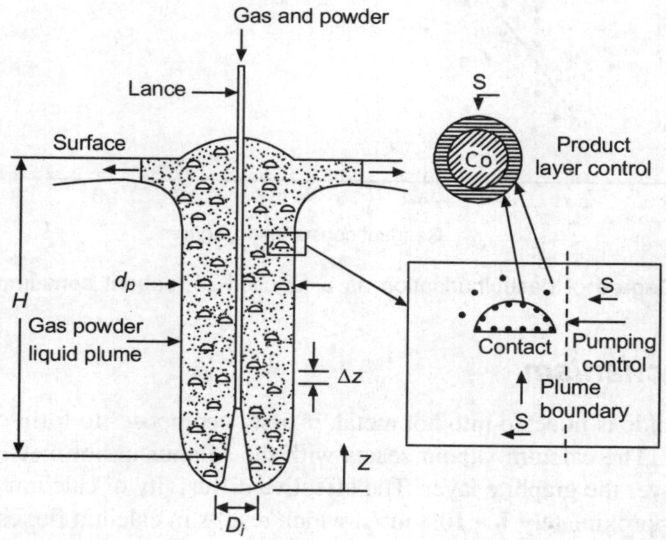

Figure 16.8 Physical representation of bubble formation and powder dispersion following injection.

Owing to buoyancy the gas rapidly accelerates and the drag force between the gas and the liquid causes the liquid to be accelerated as well. The carbide particles which are also buoyant then start to rise—a fraction of the particles rise on the bubble interfaces, while the remainder rises, dispersed in the melt. The particles and gas are heated as they rise, and the particles react, resulting in the removal of sulphur. The rate of mass transfer is governed by the rate at which sulphur-rich liquid is pumped into the plume by entrainment (normally termed *pumping control*) as well as the rate at which sulphur diffuses through the boundary layers to the particles (normally called *contact control*). The rate of desulphurisation with respect to time follows first order reaction kinetics, and the rate of desulphurisation in the plume is determined by the reduction of the sulphur content and the flow rate of liquid at the top of the plume.

Some typical results obtained in an operating unit are presented in Figure 16.9 (Pandey et al. 1996). It is clear that following calcium carbide injection, the kinetics of desulphurisation can be described as first order, with respect to the sulphur content in the hot metal. The first order rate constant is approximately proportional to the square root of the gas flow rate, and the cube of the slag weight. Therefore, removal of slag to the maximum possible extent prior to external desulphurisation, is extremely important.

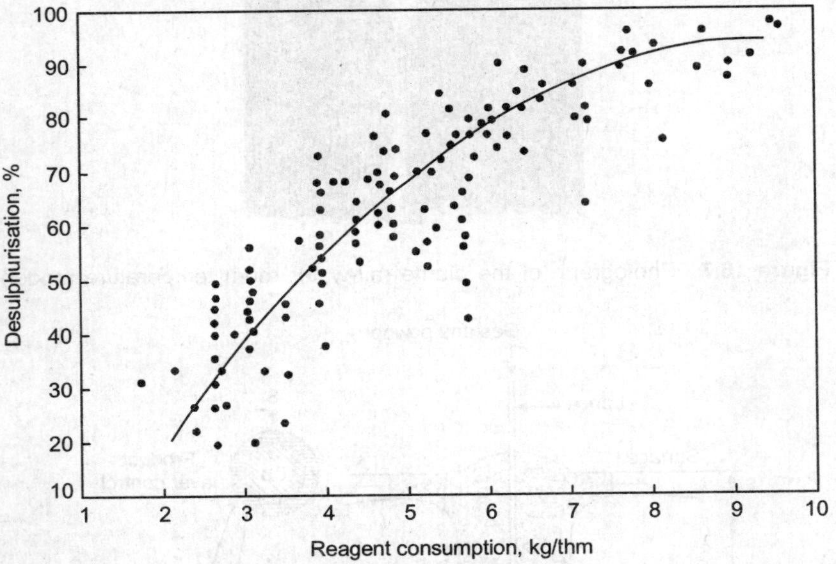

Figure 16.9 Degree of desuplhurisation as a function of reagent consumption (CAD 80).

Reaction mechanism

When calcium carbide is injected into hot metal, it first decomposes to form calcium vapour and a layer of graphite. The calcium vapour reacts with the sulphur in hot metal to form a layer of calcium sulphide over the graphite layer. The effective diffusivity of calcium vapour through the product layers is approximately 7×10^{-7} m^2/s, which results in calcium fluxes much greater than fluxes of sulphur through the boundary layers, around each particle. Therefore, the step of calcium diffusion through the product layers does not contribute any significant resistance to the overall rate of desulphurisation. The layers of graphite and calcium sulphide progressively thicken so that the calcium vapour has to diffuse through them. These two layers are formed topo-chemically on the surface of the particles, and the mass transfer resistance offered by the chemical reaction rate is negligible. As a result, the rate of desulphurisation is relatively fast.

16.8 HOT METAL PRE-TREATMENT STATION(S)

16.8.1 Desiliconisation

The blast furnace runner, transfer ladle or torpedo car can be used as the place for desiliconisation as shown in Figure 16.10. The desiliconisation agent is added using one of the following methods:

- Top charging with nitrogen bubbling
- Blasting
- Injection.

Method	In blast furnace runner		In torpedo car and ladle	
	Top addition (1)	Top addition (2)	Top addition	Injection
Schematic diagram		(Slag separation by skimmer)		

	• Additional process not required		• Selective treatment possible	
Merits		• Easy separation of desiliconisation slag		• High desiliconisation efficiency ([Si] 0.10% attainable)
Demerits	• Slag foaming in torpedo car	• Low desiliconisation efficiency • Restriction due to cast house layout	• Low desiliconisation efficiency	• Complicated equipment
Remarks	• Blasting method is tested		• O_2 blowing practice can be used jointly	

*Both blasting (very high rate of addition) or normal feeding can be applied

Figure 16.10 Desiliconisation processes used industrially.

In Japan, desiliconisation of hot metal is carried out in the blast furnace runner because of advantages, such as adequate mixing of the reagents owing to the energy of the flowing molten iron stream, saving in time, and increased ladle availability compared with separate

…nisation in a ladle. Figure 16.11 shows a typical set-up that is often used for runner …conisation, along with the results obtained (Gupta and Chatterjee, 1995). It needs to be …sed that hot metal from blast furnace has to be separated from slag using a slag skimmer in the main runner before desiliconising agents such as mill scale and calcined lime are added

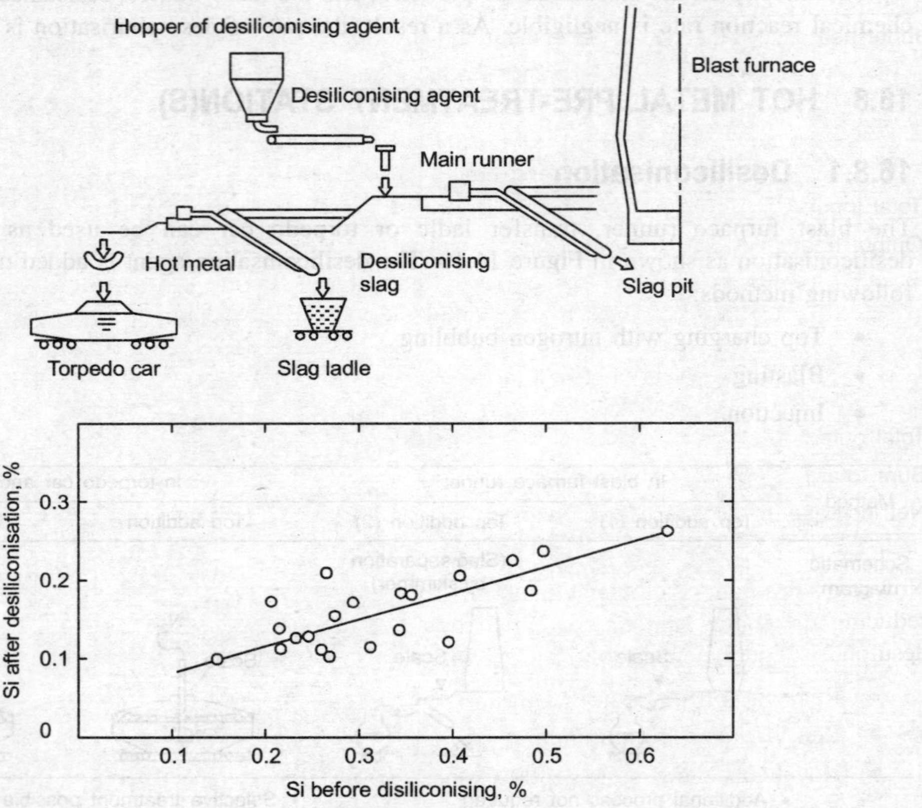

Figure 16.11 Schematic diagram of desiliconisation treatment in a blast furnace runner.

continuously. Only in this way can the reagent efficiency be increased. Normally, about 20 kg mill scale per tonne of metal is needed to reduce the silicon level from 0.5% to less than 0.2%. On the other hand, for reducing silicon from 1.5% to 0.6%, 35–40 kg/thm is required. The heat balance for runner desiliconisation, given in Table 16.3, indicates that there is no temperature drop during this treatment even though it is carried out in an open runner (Gupta and Chatterjee, 1995). This is because of the heat generated by the oxidation of silicon to silica.

16.8.2 Desulphurisation

Previously, desulphurisation used to be carried out by injecting the desulphurising agent in powder form into blast furnace ladles, en route from blast furnaces to steelmelting shops.

Table 16.3 Typical heat balance for runner desiliconisation treatment

Heat source		Desiliconising with mill scale (mixed with 20% lime) kcal/t	Quantity
Input heat	(1) $Si + O_2 \rightarrow SiO_2$ + 7460 kcal/kg-Si	14920	Si = 0.20%
	(2) Mn + (1/2)O_2, >MnO + 1680 kcal/kg-Mn	840	Mn = 0.05%
	(3) $Ti + O_2 \rightarrow TiO_2$ + 2830 kcal/kg-Ti	570	Ti = 0.02%
	(4) C + (1/2)$O_2 \rightarrow$ CO + 2200 kcal/kg-C	220	C = 0.01%
	(5) Average slagmaking heat 140 kcal/kg-slag	1260	Amount of slag: 9 kg/t
Total Input		17810	
Output heat	(1) FeO $\rightarrow$ Fe + (1/2)O_2 – 900 kcal/kg-FeO	9040	FeO in mill scale: 77%
	(2) $Fe_2O_3 \rightarrow$ 2Fe + (3/2)O_2 – 1230 kcal/kg-Fe_2O_3	2570	Fe_2O_3 in mill scale: 16%
	(3) Sensible heat of slag formed 0.217 kcal/kg-slag. °C	2940	Amount of slag: 9 kg/t
	(4) Sensible heat of iron reduced 0.170 kcal/kg Fe °C	2300	Amount of iron reduced: 9 kg/t
Total output		16850	
Sum total		960	
Net increase in hot metal temperature		+5.6°C	

Nowadays desulphurisation stations normally form a part of the BOF shop. In a typical case of reducing the initial sulphur content of hot metal from 0.070% to a level of 0.020%, i.e. a desulphurisation efficiency of 70–75%, the operating parameters would be:

- Reagent consumption: 5 kg/thm
- Reagent rate: 45 kg/minute
- Hot metal temperature: 1300°C and more.

It is possible to complete the treatment in around 15–20 minutes in most cases by adjusting the reagent addition rate. For this purpose, sometimes even two lances are used as shown in Figure 16.12 (Frithjof et al. 1980).

16.9 SIMULTANEOUS REMOVAL OF SULPHUR AND PHOSPHORUS

Based on Japanese research, the optimum conditions for simultaneous removal of sulphur and phosphorus have been identified as follows:

- Slag basicity, CaO/SiO_2 > 2
- Hot metal temperature < 1400°C
- Hot metal silicon < 0.25%

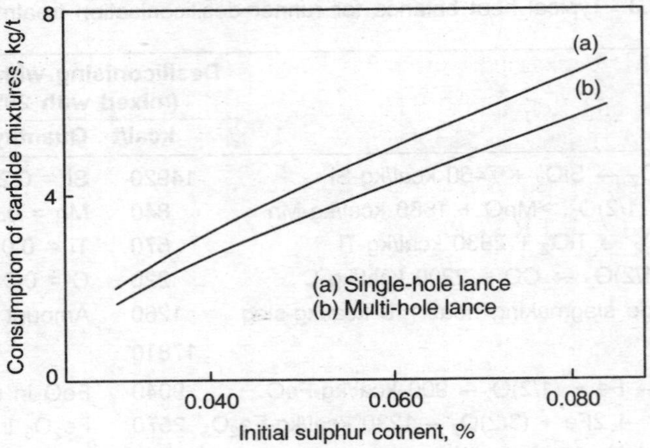

Figure 16.12 Consumption of calcium carbide as a function of the initial sulphur content in hot metal using single-hole and multi-hole injection lances (final sulphur 0.015 %).

The pre-treatment procedure is carried out in two-stages—first, desiliconisation, and second, simultaneous removal of sulphur and phosphorus using either lime-based or soda-based reagents. Since the silicon content of Indian hot metal is far higher than that in Japan, the first-step becomes even more important.

In any case, it is not advisable to attempt the reduction of silicon, sulphur and phosphorus simultaneously because of the following reasons:

- High reagent consumption coupled with abnormal drop in temperature, which would pose problems in steelmaking
- Severe slag handling problems
- Unfavourable techno-economics.

16.10 GENERAL COMMENTS ON PRE-TREATMENT

In recent years, injection metallurgy has been developed to such an extent that it is now widely used to pre-treat hot metal before charging into BOF vessels, thereby virtually restricting steelmaking to decarburisation alone. Desulphurisation has now become an integral part of most integrated steel plants. Reagents like soda ash were directly added into open ladles earlier, but owing to ecological considerations (aggressive fumes, ground water contamination by the post-treatment slag, etc.), injection of calcium carbide based reagents is now widely employed. Efficient removal of the slag after pre-treatment, utilisation of the optimum lance(s) design and geometry as well as the development of suitable refractories for the ladle in which pre-treatment is carried out, are areas in which work is still continuing.

Nonetheless, it can be concluded that with ever-increasing demand for lower levels of impurities in steel (particularly sulphur and phosphorus), pre-treatment of hot metal will be adopted even more widely in the years to come.

REFERENCES

Dutta, M., A. Ramu, M. Venkatraghavan and S. Roy, Tata Search, 1996, pp. 43–46.

Frithjof, T., Eichinger, and Reinhold. K. Grosz, Scanjet II, 2nd International Conference on Injection Metallurgy, Lulea, Sweden, Preprints, Jernkontoret, June, 1980.

Gupta, S.S. and Amit Chatterjee, *Blast Furnace Ironmaking*, SBA Publication, 1995.

Pandey, B.D., U.S. Yadav and R.V. Ramna, Tata Search, 1996, pp. 36–42.

17

Metallurgical Features of Oxygen Steelmaking

17.1 INTRODUCTION

Chapter 3 contained an outline of modern steelmaking processes as an introduction. Chapter 15 presented some important physicochemical aspects of primary steelmaking processes including basic oxygen steelmaking (BOS). The description of BOF plant practices has been given in Chapter 16. This chapter will deal with the metallurgical features of oxygen steelmaking processes only. For the sake of logical presentation of this chapter, some important points from the earlier chapters are reproduced below.

1. In the 1950s, the size of the LD converters was a maximum of 50 tonnes of liquid steel and oxygen was top blown through a single-hole lance. With the passage of time, the vessel size kept on increasing. Converters above 150 tonnes are very common now, and many above 250 tonnes in capacity are in operation. This has necessitated increasing the number of holes in the lance for better distribution of the total oxygen required for refining. 5–6 hole lances are common nowadays and even 8 hole lances are in use.
2. Through extensive investigations in the 1960s, it was found that the molten metal bath was not homogeneous with respect to temperature and composition during oxygen blowing in BOFs, despite stirring by the top jet as well as vigorous evolution of CO gas owing to the reaction of carbon in the bath with oxygen. It was also found that this inhomogeneity was resulting in serious process control problems. Interestingly, it was also found that simultaneous bottom gas injection, even at a very low flow rate, was capable of homogenising the bath.
3. In continental Europe (France, Germany, Luxembourg, etc.), a significant fraction of hot metal contains high phosphorus (1.5–2 wt. %). The classical BOF process was not found suitable. Instead, variants of the original LD process (like, LD–AC) were innovated to refine high phosphorus hot metal by simultaneous blowing of lime powder and oxygen. This resulted in engineering/environmental problems connected with lime fines and was

not an acceptable long-term solution. The problem was resolved in late 1970s by the introduction of specially designed bottom tuyeres through which oxygen could be introduced directly into the bath. To take care of the heat generated in the tuyere area, the inner oxygen tube had to be protected by shielding it with hydrocarbons. This innovation gave rise to the OBM process in Germany, LWS in France and Q-BOP in the USA.

In the decade of 1970s, several commercial processes were patented where oxygen was blown through a top lance, but mixing in the bath was simultaneously enhanced by blowing inert gas at a low flow rate through several bottom tuyeres. These processes, under the generic name of combined blown processes/bath agitated processes, are the most widely used oxygen steelmaking processes in the world today.

In this chapter, the metallurgical features of all oxygen steelmaking processes—exclusive top blowing, combined blowing and bottom blowing will be taken up.

17.2 INTERACTION OF THE OXYGEN JET WITH THE SURROUNDINGS AND THE BATH

17.2.1 Mechanical Interactions

Figure 17.1 schematically shows the nature of jet-bath interaction. The *Mach Number* can be as high as 2.5, when the *Supersonic Jet* emerges from the nozzle. In the potential core (length three to seven times nozzle diameter), the velocity is constant. Then the jet starts entraining the surrounding fluid (in this case, the gaseous converter atmosphere). This *Jet Entrainment* causes lateral expansion of the jet and decreases the jet velocity to make it finally *subsonic*. Beyond a distance about 25–30 nozzle diameters, the supersonic jet becomes fully subsonic.

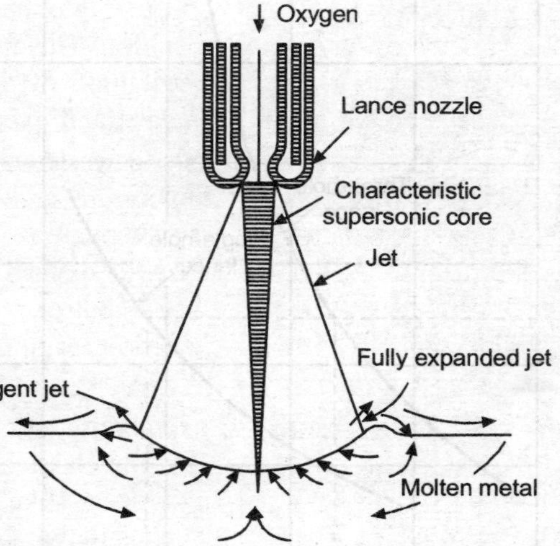

Figure 17.1 Mechanical interaction of oxygen jet with the molten metal bath causing circulation in the bath outwards on the surface and upwards along the axis (schematic).

The jet ultimately impinges on the liquid metal bath surface to form a cavity. The impingement of the jet and the dissipation of the jet momentum causes circulation of the liquid bath in the upward direction at the vessel central axis. The intensity of jet-bath interaction is expressed in terms of the *Jet Force Number* (JFN) defined as:

$$\text{JFN} = \frac{\text{Gas pressure } (P_d) \times \text{Nozzle diameter } (d_n)}{\text{Lance height } (L)} \tag{17.1}$$

where L, the height of the lance tip above the bath surface, is a key operating variable in the BOF process. With changing JFN (say, by changing L), the following behaviour of the liquid bath at the impact zone has been observed.

- *At low JFN*, dimpling with a slight surface depression (as in Figure 17.1)
- *At medium to high JFN*, splashing with a shallow depression
- *At high JFN*, penetrating mode of cavity with reduction in splashing.

Only the last two types of behaviour are usually encountered in BOF steelmaking. Metal droplets are formed on the lip of the cavity and get ejected (i.e. splashed) above the bath in both modes. Several empirical relations have been proposed co-relating the depth of jet penetration into the bath with the variables P_d, d_n, L, etc. They give somewhat different predictions and more importantly, since they are generally for single-hole lance, and nowadays multi-hole lances are employed, these relations cannot be directly applied to current oxygen steelmaking.

As stated earlier, for the larger size BOFs in use today, in order to distribute the oxygen over a larger surface of the bath, multi-hole lances are employed. The axes of each of the nozzles in a multi-hole lance are typically inclined at around 10° with respect to the lance axis. Figure 17.2 shows schematically the increase in jet impact area on the bath by switching over from a single-hole to a three-hole lance.

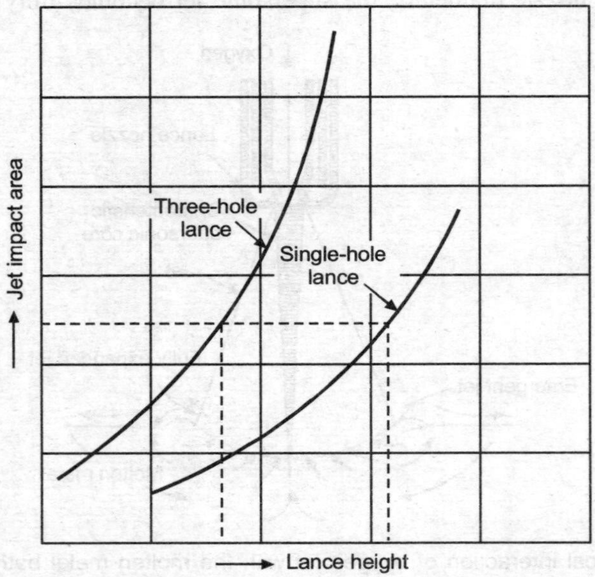

Figure 17.2 Comparison of jet impact areas for single-hole and three-hole lance.

An important phenomenon in oxygen steelmaking is splashing, i.e. ejection of liquid metal droplets from the bath surface because of the impact of the jet on the bath. Investigations on this were carried out primarily in water models with gas blown from a single-hole top lance. It seems that there is a critical minimum depth of the impact cavity for the onset of splashing and splashing is an integral part of BOFs under the blowing conditions employed. The ejected droplets exhibit a size distribution ranging from about 0.2 mm to 10 mm.

17.2.2 Chemical Interactions between Jet and Bath

When a molecule of oxygen strikes the surface of the liquid impure iron, it may interact in any of the following ways.

- Reaction with dissolved carbon, etc. directly
- Reaction with Fe first to form FeO, which subsequently reacts with dissolved solutes
- Dissolution of gaseous oxygen into liquid iron as atomic oxygen.

From a kinetic point of view, the probability of the occurrence of the first is very low, and that of the second is high. Taking note of the fact that a total quantity of oxygen corresponding to about 3% of the mass of iron has to be absorbed in about 15 minutes blowing time, and that the solubility of oxygen in liquid iron is about 0.25 wt. %, the probability of the third mechanism is also low. Hence, the second mechanism, viz. gaseous oxygen first forming FeO, which subsequently reacts with the dissolved solutes is accepted as the major method of the transfer of oxygen.

Oxidation of iron is exothermic. The heat released in the impact zone takes time to dissipate. This causes a large increase of temperature around the impact zone. It has been known as the *hot spot*, whose temperature is above 2000°C, as inferred from experimental measurements in the laboratory.

Since the oxidation of molten iron to FeO is a simple reaction, it can be assumed to be very fast at such high temperatures. This was originally considered to be the reason why refining was possible within a very short time. Later, it was found that the ejection of a very large number of metal droplets from the impact zone (s), and the large specific surface area (i.e. surface area/volume ratio) of the droplets, makes the gas–metal interfacial area for the refining reactions (decarburisation in particular) extremely large. Hence, from a kinetic viewpoint, this reaction is more or less instantaneous. Therefore, it is the rate of supply of oxygen, rather than the rate of oxidation of iron, that is now accepted as the rate limiting step in the process. As a result, blowing velocities and the total supply of oxygen within the shortest possible time have received increasing attention in BOF steelmaking.

17.2.3 Chemical–Thermal Interactions of the Jet with the Surroundings

The oxygen jet also interacts with the surrounding gaseous atmosphere, both chemically and thermally. Also, there is no doubt that it interacts with the slag–metal–gas emulsion formed above the bath surface, but this is being ignored owing to the complexity. Of special importance, is the reaction of the oxygen jet(s) with the CO gas evolved because of the reaction of carbon dissolved in metal with oxygen. This leads to the formation of some CO_2, particularly in regions well above the bath. The exit gas from the BOF contains about 20 volume percent CO_2 initially, and about 5% towards the end of the blow.

This is known as *post-combustion* inside the converter. It is beneficial since oxidation of CO to CO_2 is also exothermic and supplies heat for the endothermic steps (see Chapter 15, Section 15.2 for details). The jet also physically entrains the gases from the surrounding atmosphere. As a result, by the time the oxygen jet reaches the impact zone, it contains some amount of CO and CO_2 and its temperature becomes higher.

17.3 COMPOSITION AND TEMPERATURE CHANGES DURING THE BLOW

In Chapter 15, the thermochemical and thermodynamic aspects of reactions in primary steelmaking with specific reference to basic oxygen processes were discussed and hence, these will not be repeated.

The composition and temperature of the bath changes during the progress of the blow for the reasons enumerated already. The exact magnitude of the changes is illustrated in Figure 17.3 (Deo and Boom, 1993) based on data from the 300 tonne combined blown BOF converter at Hoogovens IJmuiden, Netherlands (now Corus). This converter is equipped with facilities for

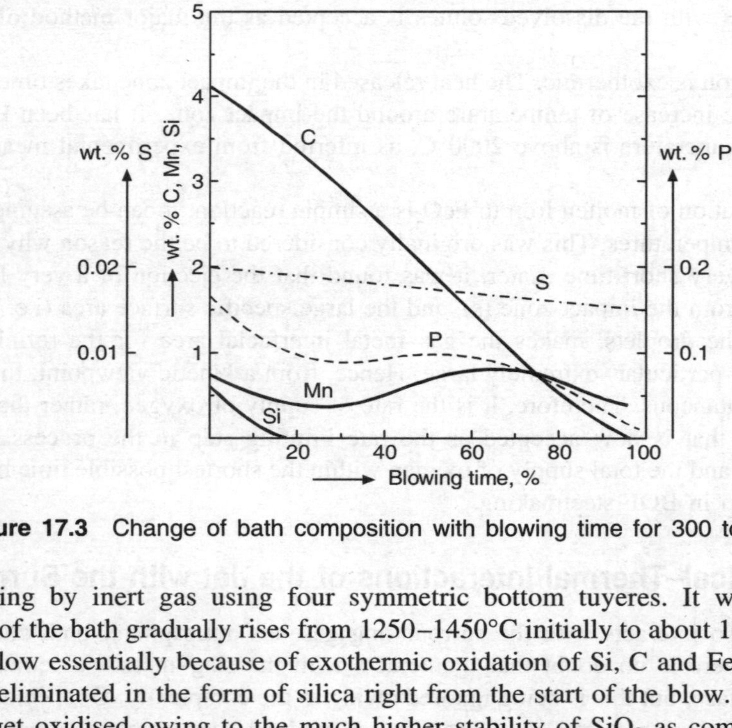

Figure 17.3 Change of bath composition with blowing time for 300 tonne BOF.

bottom stirring by inert gas using four symmetric bottom tuyeres. It was found that the temperature of the bath gradually rises from 1250–1450°C initially to about 1600–1680°C at the end of the blow essentially because of exothermic oxidation of Si, C and Fe. Silicon dissolved in iron gets eliminated in the form of silica right from the start of the blow. Silicon is the first element to get oxidised owing to the much higher stability of SiO_2 as compared to the other oxides. To make sure that this silica is assimilated in the slag as soon as it is formed (otherwise, it would attack the basic vessel lining), lime addition is also begun right from the start of the blow. Once silicon is removed, oxidation of carbon dissolved in the bath to CO starts and continues almost throughout the blow. Significant removal of phosphorus occurs primarily towards the end of the blow.

Figure 17.4 (Deo and Boom, 1993) shows the change in slag composition during the blow for the same converter. The temperature of the slag is always slightly higher than that of the metal—in the initial stages, the difference can be as high as 100°C, but as the blow progresses,

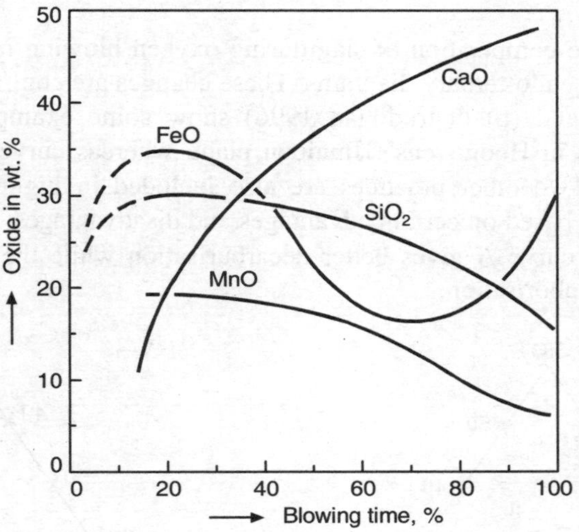

Figure 17.4 Change of slag composition with blowing time (for the same converter as in Figure 17.3).

the difference decreases, till at the end of the blow, the slag temperature is around 30–50°C higher. Often at the end of the oxygen blowing period in combined blown converters (like in Hoogovens), about two minutes of argon stirring is carried out to bring down the temperature difference. Post-blow stirring not only helps in temperature/composition homogenisation, but can contribute significantly towards dephosphorisation since the slag at this stage is rich in FeO and has high basicity. Figure 17.4 also depicts how the concentration of CaO in the slag increases continuously during the blow because of progressive dissolution of lime. The FeO concentration in the slag is initially high when the slag volume is limited, but as the blow progresses and more and more slag is formed, the FeO concentration goes down. Towards the end of the blow, the C–O reaction subsides and oxygen begins to react with iron in the bath (rather than carbon) leading once again to higher concentration of FeO in the slag.

It is to be understood that the quantity of slag, which is nil at the beginning, keeps increasing during the blow as lime dissolution continues. The total amount of lime used depends primarily on the silicon content in hot metal so that a CaO/SiO_2 ratio of at least 3.0 is maintained in the final slag to ensure adequate refining of the metalloids. The extent of lime added can be 60–70 kg/tls for 0.5–0.7% silicon hot metal and as high as 100 kg/tls for hot metal with around 1.2% silicon.

17.3.1 Slag Path and Lime Dissolution in Slag

As noted in Chapter 15, Section 15.3.1, Fe is present in slag as Fe^{2+} and Fe^{3+} ions (i.e. as FeO and Fe_2O_3). The Fe^{3+}/Fe^{2+} ratio varies, to a very large extent, during the blowing period, but it is not determined on a routine basis. Therefore, the standard practice is to assume that the total iron present in slag is in the form of FeO. The ternary phase equilibrium diagram at 1600°C for the $CaO–SiO_2–FeO$ (or Fe_2O_3) system has been presented in Figure 15.1, while Figure 15.2 depicted the change in composition for a commercial slag containing other minor constituents as well.

Such changes in the composition of slag during oxygen blowing in various practices have been reported in such pseudo-ternary diagrams. These changes are commonly referred to as *Slag Path.* Figures 17.5(a) and (b) (Turkdogan 1996) show some examples. In Figure 17.5(a), curve I is that reported in Hoogovens' IJmuiden plant, whereas curve II is for Mannesman's practice in Germany. Two other practices are also included in Figure 17.5(b). The practice adopted in each plant is based on certain advantages and disadvantages; for example, it has been claimed that following curve A gives better decarburisation while the path given by curve B results in better dephosphorisation.

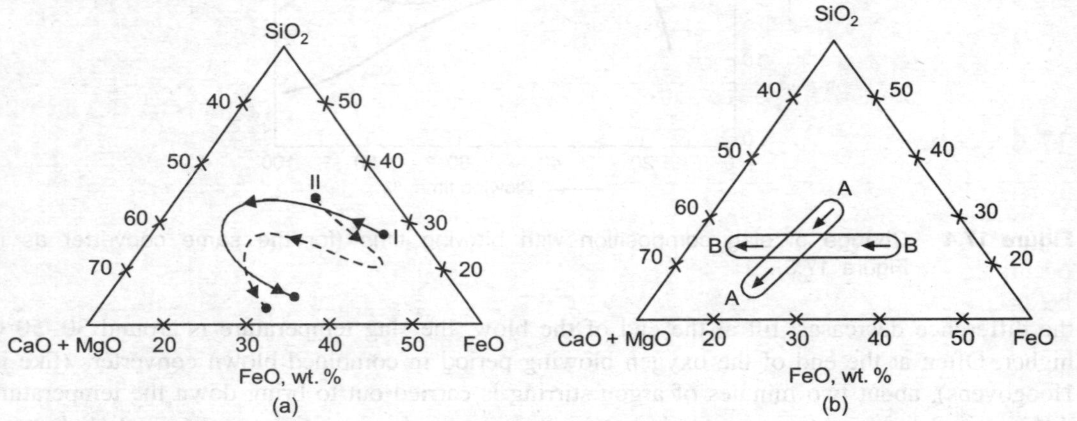

Figure 17.5 Changes in composition of slag during oxygen blowing for various BOF steelmaking practices.

17.3.2 Kinetics of Lime Dissolution

Evolution of slag composition during the BOF blow depends primarily on the rate of dissolution of the solid lime particles into the slag. Besides some plant investigations in BOF converters, several studies on the rate and mechanism of lime dissolution have been carried out in the laboratory. The salient findings are summarised below.

- The rate of dissolution is controlled by mass transfer in the slag.
- Smaller lime particles dissolve faster because of the larger specific surface area. In industrial practice, the particles would have a range of sizes.

- Lime particles having a larger volume fraction of pores are more reactive, and dissolve faster than less porous lime, since the slag is able to penetrate into the pores with consequent increase in the surface area for reaction, and the particles tend to disintegrate into smaller sizes owing to such penetration as well as the lower strength of porous lime. If $CaCO_3$ is calcined at a lower temperature for a longer time it is more porous. However, too low a temperature and/or too short a time of calcining results in a lime containing unacceptable percentage of undissociated $CaCO_3$.
- The commonly accepted test for lime reactivity is the standard slaking test in which water is added at room temperature and the rise in temperature is measured.
- During dissolution of lime, a solid impervious high melting outer coating of dicalcium silicate tends to form (see Figure 15.1). It is important to break this layer by fluxing agents. FeO is a powerful agent. It reacts with dicalcium silicate and forms a low melting CaO-FeO-SiO_2 liquid. MnO has a similar effect.
- Higher temperatures are expected to increase rate of dissolution as a general rule of kinetics. However, it has been reported that lime sinters rapidly at 1600°C and above, making it dense and thus slowing down the rate.
- The final BOF slags have been found to contain some undissolved CaO particles, both free as well as with a coating of dicalcium silicate. The content of free CaO can range between 5% and 10% of the slag weight, in some cases.

17.4 KINETICS OF CARBON–OXYGEN REACTION IN BOF; SLAG-METAL–GAS INTERACTION

Elimination of carbon from liquid iron is quantitywise the most major reaction in the BOF and occurs throughout the blow. Important kinetic features of the carbon–oxygen reaction will now be discussed based on experimental investigations in the original BOFs with only a top lance (i.e. LD converter) and in modern BOFs with concurrent inert gas injection through bottom tuyeres, as well as in laboratories.

1. The specific decarburisation rate is expressed as $(-d[W_C]/dt)$, where $[W_C]$ is the weight per cent carbon in the bath at any instant of time t after the oxygen blowing starts. $-dW_C/dt$ is a function of blowing time and exhibits three stages, as shown in Figure 17.6. Initially, oxidation of silicon dominates. The decarburisation rate increases as the silicon content goes down. The middle stage corresponds to the maximum decarburisation rate and is ideally characterised by a steady value. The last stage is characterised by decreasing $-dW_C/dt$, since the carbon concentration is low and the emulsion subsides.
2. The steady value of $-dW_C/dt$ is proportional to the oxygen blowing rate as shown in Figure 17.7 (Meyer, 1969). This indicates that the decarburisation reaction is very fast and is essentially limited by the rate of supply of oxygen.
3. At the peak decarburisation period, vigorous evolution of CO causes the formation of a *slag–metal–gas emulsion*, which fills-up a considerable portion of the inner volume of the converter. The emulsion subsides in the last stage of decarburisation (Figure 17.6).

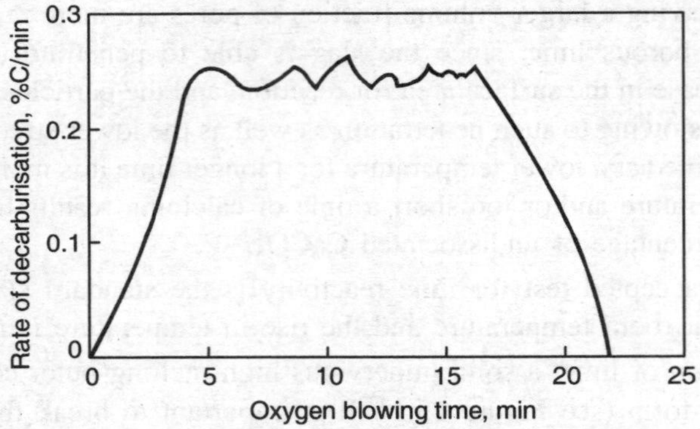

Figure 17.6 Change of decarburisation rate during oxygen blowing in BOF steelmaking (schematic).

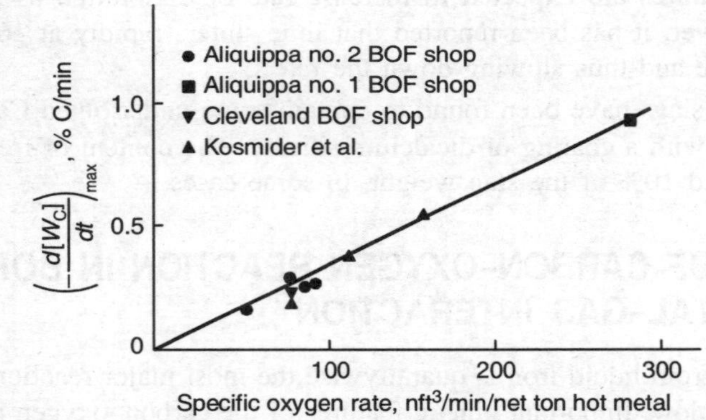

Figure 17.7 Peak (steady state) decarburisation rate as a function of specific oxygen blowing rate.

17.4.1 Foams and Emulsions in Basic Oxygen Steelmaking

An emulsion is a heterogeneous system consisting of at least one immiscible liquid or gas intimately dispersed in a second liquid in the form of droplets or bubbles. A foam is an overgrown gas–liquid emulsion in which the gas bubbles occupy a proportionately larger volume of the system. A typical foam contains 80%, or more, of gas by volume. By this definition, the emulsion in BOFs may be called foam as well, since here the gas volume is 80 to 90%.

The entire slag is assumed to be present in the emulsion and constitutes the continuous liquid phase. Foaming of steelmaking slags was observed in earlier primary steelmaking processes as well. *The slag foam is transient* in nature and is sustained by vigorous CO evolution. The more the viscosity of the slag, the greater is the foam height. In this context, it may be mentioned that the undissolved lime particles suspended in the slag increase the *effective viscosity* of the slag, and thus contribute to more foaming.

The emulsion in basic oxygen converters also contains a significant proportion of liquid metal droplets. The impingement of the jet on to the bath surface causes splashing of metal droplets as already mentioned in Section 17.2.1. It is further enhanced by the ejection of droplets following vigorous evolution of CO. Though estimates vary over a wide range, it is generally agreed that the slag–metal–gas emulsion may contain as much as 80 weight per cent metal. Therefore, in reality, the oxygen jet in BOFs is surrounded by the emulsion during a major part of the blow. This is schematically shown in Figure 17.8.

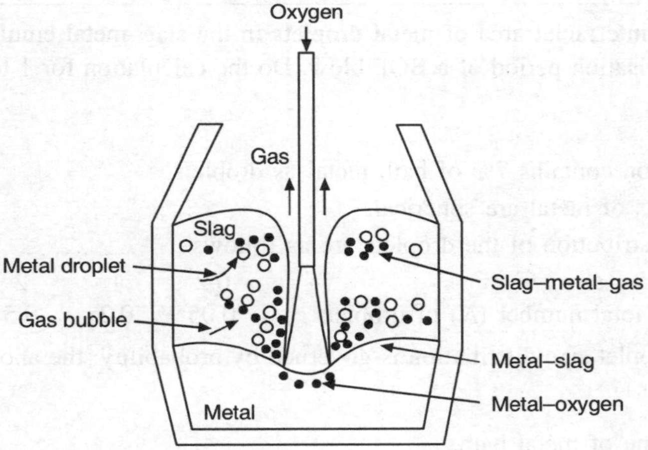

Figure 17.8 Representation of regions in top-blown oxygen steelmaking (schematic).

17.4.2 Mechanism of Carbon–Oxygen Reaction

Samples of the emulsion collected from converter ejections revealed that the metal droplets are hollow (Meyer 1969). This was attributed to the generation of CO gas inside the droplets. Laboratory experiments confirmed this phenomenon. Reaction of carbon in metal droplets with FeO in the surrounding molten slag is responsible. The excessive pressure of the generated CO even leads to the disintegration of the droplets.

Experimental observations by several investigators indicate a wide range of droplet sizes in the emulsion, varying from 0.1 mm to 25 mm. Estimates of droplet–slag interfacial area range from 8 to 250 m^2 per tonne of metal. For a 150 t converter, therefore, it may range from 1200 m^2 to 37500 m^2. It has also been found that the metal droplets are purer than the bulk metal in the bath.

In view of the above, Meyer et al. concluded that the very high rate of peak decarburisation is a result of such a high slag–metal interfacial area in the emulsion. The reacted droplets settle down into the bath and fresh droplets get ejected, leading to continuous refining in the emulsion. Though some investigators differed with this conclusion in the beginning, at present it has been generally accepted that the carbon–oxygen reaction occurs in different parts of the converter—in the impact zone primarily, in the emulsion, and lesser in other locations in the bath.

As Figure 17.6 shows, towards the end of the blow, the decarburisation rate decreases continuously and becomes almost zero. The emulsion collapses. It has been concluded that it happens below a *critical carbon concentration* in the bath (may be taken as 0.3 wt. % as an average), and mass transfer of carbon in the bath becomes rate controlling. Since, $-d[W_C]/dt$ is proportional to $[W_C]$ in such a situation, the rate becomes almost zero at very low carbon levels.

EXAMPLE 17.1

Calculate the total interfacial area of metal droplets in the slag–metal emulsion at steady state (i.e. peak) decarburisation period of a BOF blow. Do the calculation for 1 tonne of liquid steel in the bath.

Assume:

(i) The emulsion contains 7% of bath metal as droplets.
(ii) The droplets of metal are spherical.
(iii) The size distribution of the droplets are as follows.

Diameter (*d*), mm	0.2	1	2	5	10
Fraction of total number (*N*) of droplets	0.05	0.2	0.5	0.2	0.05

(*Note:* Actually droplet size distribution is governed by probability; the above distribution data is for simplification.)

Solution: Per tonne of metal bath,

$$\text{Total mass of droplets} = 1000 \times 0.07 = 70 \text{ kg}$$

$$= \rho_{steel} \times N \times \left(\frac{\pi}{6}\right) \times [0.05 \times 0.2^3 + 0.2 \times 1^3 + 0.5 \times 2^3 + 0.2 \times 5^3 + 0.05 \times 10^3] \times 10^{-9}$$

$$= 6.73 \times 10^3 \times N \times 41.5 \times 10^{-9} \text{ kg, since 1 mm} = 10^{-3} \text{ m.}$$

Calculations give $N = 2.5 \times 10^5$.

17.5 METALLURGICAL FEATURES OF BATH AGITATED PROCESSES

17.5.1 General

As mentioned in the Introduction (see Section 17.1), in the BOF process, the molten bath is not homogeneous with respect to composition and temperature owing to inadequate mixing, and it was found that simultaneous gas injection through the bottom tuyeres even at a low flow rate was capable of satisfactory bath homogenisation. It was also mentioned there that several commercial basic oxygen processes were developed by various steel companies around the world in the decade of 1970, all of which had provisions for some gas blowing through tuyeres/canned elements/porous plugs fitted at the bottom of the BOF vessels.

Better mixing and homogeneity in the bath offer the following advantages:

1. More reliable temperature measurement and sampling of metal and slag, and thus better process control
2. Less slopping, since non-homogeneity causes formation of regions with high supersaturation and consequent violent reactions and ejections
3. Faster dissolution of the scrap added into the metal bath
4. Better mixing and mass transfer in the metal bath with closer approach to equilibrium for [C]–[O]–CO reaction, and consequently, lower bath oxygen content at the same carbon content
5. Better slag–metal mixing and mass transfer and consequently, closer approach to slag–metal equilibrium, leading to:
   - lower FeO in slag and hence higher Fe yield
   - transfer of more phosphorus from the metal to the slag (i.e. better bath dephosphorisation)
   - transfer of more Mn from the slag to the metal, and thus better Mn recovery
   - lower nitrogen and hydrogen contents of the bath.

Items (4) and (5) above assume greater importance for end-point control of composition and temperature, since the emulsion collapses and bath stirring by CO evolution becomes less towards the end of the blow. Then, stirring from the bottom makes significant contribution towards enhancing the rates of reactions. In modern steelmaking practice, after the oxygen blow is stopped, the vessel is tilted for temperature measurement and sampling (this is known as *turndown* or *first turndown*). Then the vessel is made vertical again for about two minutes with only argon flow through the bottom tuyeres. This assists in further homogenisation and closer attainment of equilibria.

Chapter 4, Section 4.5 has briefly reviewed the relevant concepts of kinetics, mass transfer, mixing and *mixing time* (t_{mix}). From there it may be noted that:

more stirring → more bath turbulence → faster mixing and mass transfer → lower t_{mix}.

In general,

$$t_{mix} = BP^{-m}f\text{ (geometry, vessel size)} \tag{4.63}$$

where P is specific stirring power. B and m are empirical constants. For a given vessel, therefore,

$$t_{mix} \propto P^{-m} \tag{17.2}$$

Since P is proportional to the bottom gas flow rate Q,

$$t_{mix} \propto Q^{-m} \tag{17.3}$$

where m has been found to range between 1/3 and 1/2.

Figure 17.9 (Baker et al. 1980) shows the variation of t_{mix} with bottom gas flow rate per tonne of metal for several bath agitated processes. The results are in conformity with the variation expected from Eq. (17.3).

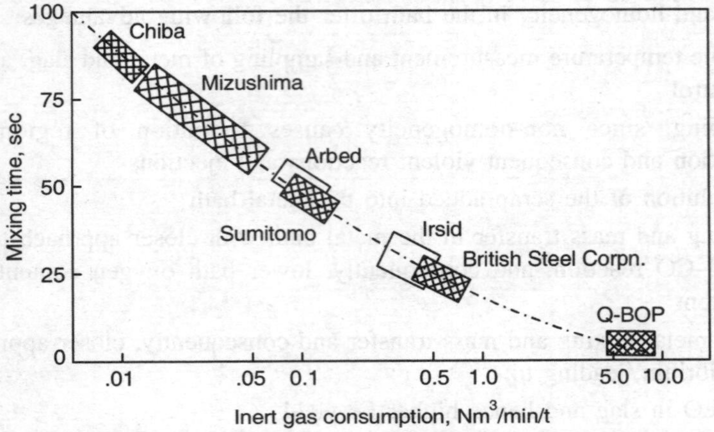

Figure 17.9 Mixing time as function of the bottom gas flow rate for some bath agitated processes.

17.5.2 Some Process Details

Baker et al. (1980), Tupkary and Tupkary (1998), Turkdogan (1996) as well as some others have reviewed the details of bath agitated processes. Here only a brief outline will be presented.

Table 17.1 (Turkdogan, 1996) lists the salient features of some of these processes. They differ in details of bottom blowing arrangements such as:

- Nature of the inert gas blown (N_2, Ar)
- Any other gases blown (O_2, air, CO_2 and CO) along with inert gas
- Gas flow rate, number, and arrangement of the tuyeres
- Design of the tuyeres
- Programme of bottom gas injection during the oxygen blow period.

Table 17.1 Major bath agitated processes

Process	Developed by	Bottom gases injected	Flow rate, $Nm^3\ min^{-1}\ t^{-1}$
LBE	ARBED-IRSID (France)	N_2, Ar	0.01–0.10
LD-CB	Nippon Steel Corp. (Japan)	CO, N_2, Ar	0.02–0.06
LD-KGC	Kawasaki Steel Corp. (Japan)	CO, N_2, Ar	0.01–0.20
LD-OTB	Kobe Steel Corp. (Japan)	CO, N_2, Ar	0.01–0.1
NK-CB	Nippon Kokan K.K (Japan)	CO_2, N_2, Ar	0.02–0.1

The most common choice are processes where only inert gas (N_2, Ar) are employed at volumetric flow rates equal to 2–4% of the oxygen flow rate through the top lance. Indian steel plants have also opted for such processes of combined blowing. The bottom gas is introduced through the bottom tuyeres, ranging in number from 6 to 16, depending on converter size, and are generally arranged symmetrically around the central axis of the converter. Figure 17.10 shows some designs of the tuyere arrangements. In these processes, the operational features are similar to classical LD steelmaking as detailed in Chapter 16. The additional features include:

- Bottom gas flow schedule during oxygen blow
- Post stirring by argon after turndown.

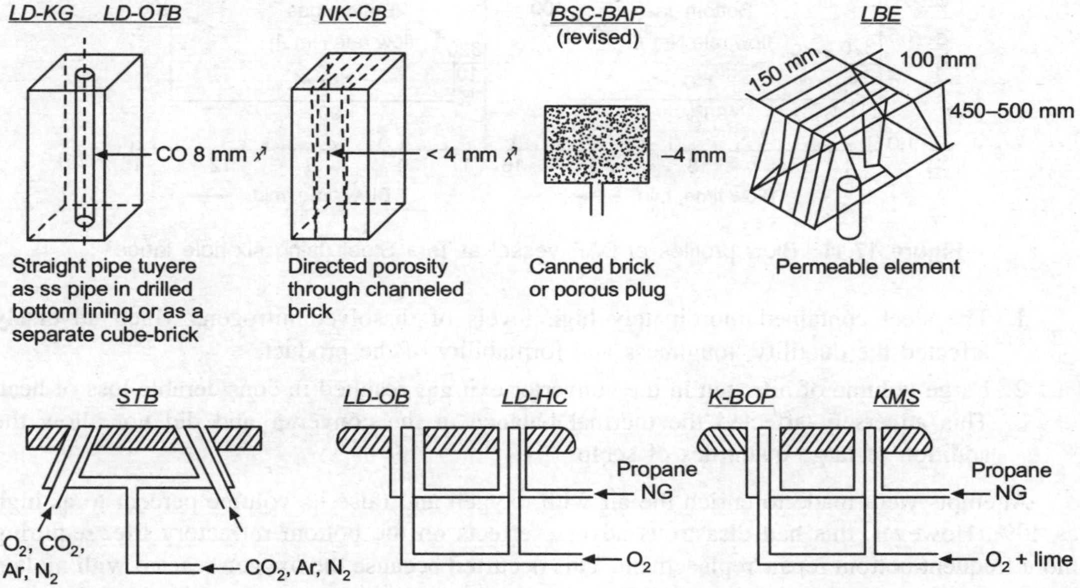

Figure 17.10 Some designs of tuyere channels for bath agitated steelmaking processes (schematic).

Since argon is relatively expensive, nitrogen is used as much as possible. However, the use of nitrogen tends to increase the nitrogen content of steel, and this may adversely affect the eventual steel quality. During the initial stages, large-scale generation and evolution of CO has a flushing action because of which not much nitrogen is absorbed by the metal bath. However, towards the end of the blow, the flushing action is less. It is at this stage that argon has to be employed in the case of low nitrogen steels. Figure 17.11 (Tupkary and Tupkary, 1998) shows the blow profiles for the combined blown BOF vessel at Tata Steel for hot metal silicon below 0.8% and above 0.8%.

17.6 OXYGEN BOTTOM BLOWN PROCESSES

It has been already mentioned in Section 17.1 that in continental Europe, the bottom blown Thomas converters continued to be in use to refine high phosphorus hot metal even after the LD process was commercialised. Since air (containing over 80% nitrogen) was blown through the bottom tuyeres, the following major problems were encountered.

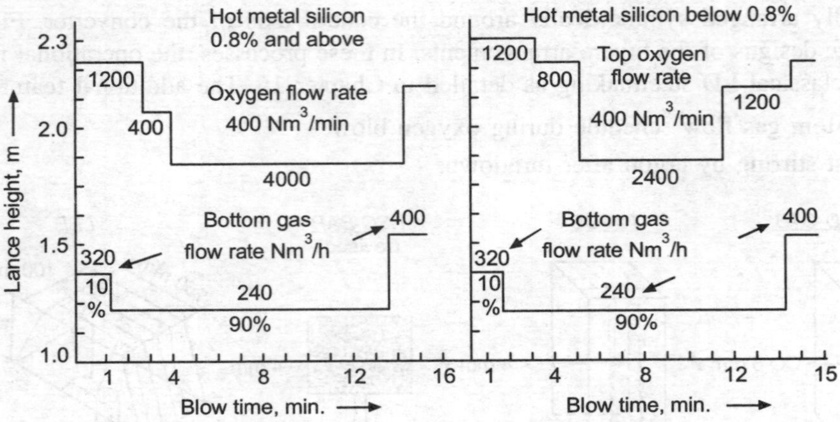

Figure 17.11 Blow profiles of BAP vessel at Tata Steel using six-hole lance.

1. The steel contained inordinately high levels of dissolved nitrogen, which adversely affected the ductility, toughness and formability of the product.
2. Large volume of nitrogen in the converter exit gas resulted in considerable loss of heat. This adversely affected the thermal balance in the converter and did not allow the addition of large quantities of scrap.

Attempts were made to enrich the air with oxygen and raise its volume percent to as high as 40%. However, this had disastrous adverse effects on the bottom refractory life, requiring more frequent bottom repair/replacement. This occurred because the oxygen reacted with molten iron at the tuyere tip forming liquid FeO, which raised the local temperature. Liquid FeO is also very corrosive towards the refractory lining since it encourages the formation of low melting compounds. Both these factors contributed to bottom failure.

Finally, through collaborative R&D efforts essentially in Germany, a novel design of tuyeres was invented. It consisted of two co-axial stainless steel pipes, embedded in the magnesite bottom. Oxygen was blown through the central pipe and some hydrocarbon gas (such as propane) through the annular space between the inner and the outer pipe. The hydrocarbons decomposed into carbon and hydrogen as soon as they came in contact with molten metal. Since the process is endothermic, it cooled the region around the oxygen plume at the tuyere mouth, thus providing protection to the tuyeres and the refractory bottom. This is known as *thermal shielding*. Some local reduction of FeO by carbon and hydrogen provided additional protection resulting in decreased lining wear by corrosion/erosion phenomena. This is *chemical shielding*.

The process was first commissioned at the *Maximillianshutte* Iron and Steel Co., Germany in 1967, and hence, became known as the *OBM process* [Oxygen Bodenblasen (bottom blown) Maximillianshutte]. In France, the LWS process was invented in 1969 where liquid hydrocarbon was employed. Figure 17.12 shows the original OBM converter design along with its tuyere arrangements. Asymmetric layout of the bottom turyeres as well as the converter conical top

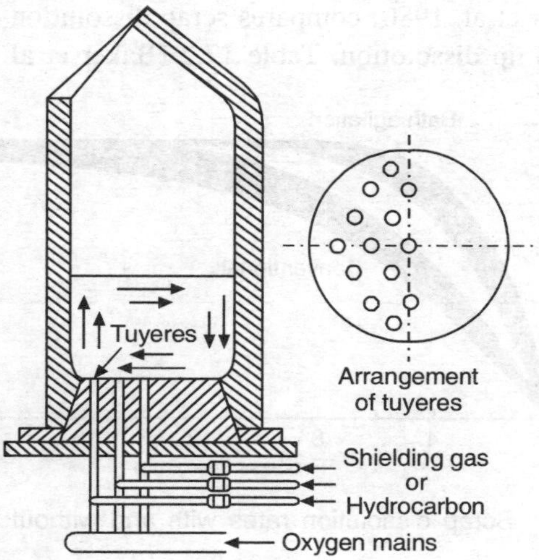

Figure 17.12 Original OBM converter and its tuyere arrangements, bath circulation indicated (schematic).

section made charging and tapping convenient, when the converter is tilted. The operation is similar to that of any normal LD, except that at end of the blow, nitrogen is bubbled through the tuyeres for a few minutes for final bath homogenisation and better approach to reaction equilibria.

As noted in Section 17.5.1, bottom blowing gives several advantages that were confirmed when data from the OBM process were obtained. Therefore, this process generated worldwide interest even for refining low phosphorus hot metal. US Steel Corporation and some other companies installed OBM converters in their modernisation and expansion programmes. The traditional Thomas converter shops in Europe also switched over to OBM or LWS.

Although hydrocarbon shielding considerably improved the bottom life, it was still unsatisfactory compared with the LD process, where the life was much higher. Bottom maintainance with so many pipes was also problematic. On the other hand, the commercial hybrid refining processes developed in the decade of 1970s retained all the advantages of the LD process and brought in significant improvements in terms of better bath mixing. Hence, from the late 1970s/early 1980s, steel plants did not install any more bottom blown units and went for the bath agitated refining processes.

17.7 COMPARISON OF VARIOUS BASIC OXYGEN PROCESSES IN TERMS OF COMPOSITION CONTROL

The superiority of process control of bath agitated and oxygen bottom blown processes over straight LD is well-established. A large number of publications over the last 30 years provide evidence for the same. Here, performance of these processes with respect to control of steel composition will be very briefly demonstrated with the help of some examples.

Figure 17.13 (R. Baker et al. 1980) compares scrap dissolution rates with and without bath agitation. Agitation speeds up dissolution. Table 17.2 (Baker et al. 1980) compares some key

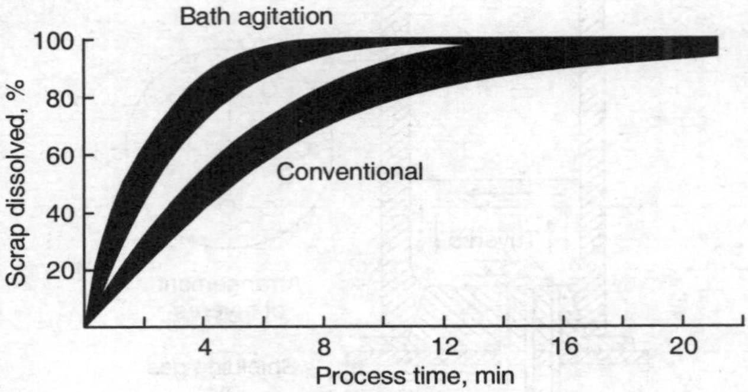

Figure 17.13 Scrap dissolution rates with and without bath agitation.

Table 17.2 Metallurgical parameters of some basic oxygen steelmaking processes (approximate values)

Parameter	**LD**	**LBE**	**LD-OB**	**K-BOP**	**OBM**
Bottom gas flow rate, $Nm^3\ min^{-1}\ t^{-1}$	nil	0.01–0.1	0.1–0.5	1–1.5	up to 5.5
At 0.05% C turndown $\%Fe_t$ in slag	20	18	14–15	13	10
% [O] in metal	0.06	0.05	0.04	0.04	0.03
% [Mn] in metal	0.14	0.18	0.21	0.22	0.3
(P)/[P]	70	80	80–90	110	120
Slopping	yes	minor	nil	nil	nil
Gain of yield of steel as % over LD	nil	+0.3	+0.4	+0.5	+0.7
Mixing time, seconds	100	50–75	30–35	10–30	10

metallurgical performance indices of LD, LBE and OBM processes. Figures 17.14(a), (b) and (c) also show this comparison regarding variation of Fe (total) in slag, pct. [O] and pct. [Mn] in bath as function of pct. [C] in bath.

It may be noted from Table 17.2 that out of the above, performance of the OBM is best, followed by LBE. Superior performance of LBE over LD is due to bottom gas stirring. So far as comparison of OBM with LBE is concerned, the explanation is more complex, since OBM differs from LBE in two major respects, given below.

- In OBM, bottom gas flow rate is much higher than that in LBE
- LBE uses Ar/N_2 as bottom gas, whereas OBM employs oxygen + hydrocarbon during blow, and then N_2 in post-blow.

Experiments at Hoogovens IJmuiden (Mink et al. 1993) have demonstrated beneficial effects of increasing bottom inert gas flow rate on metallurgical performance. These are demonstrated in Figure 17.15 (Mink et al. 1993) for Fe (total) in slag, Mn and P in metal. The figure shows percent changes of values over the practice with only top oxygen blow.

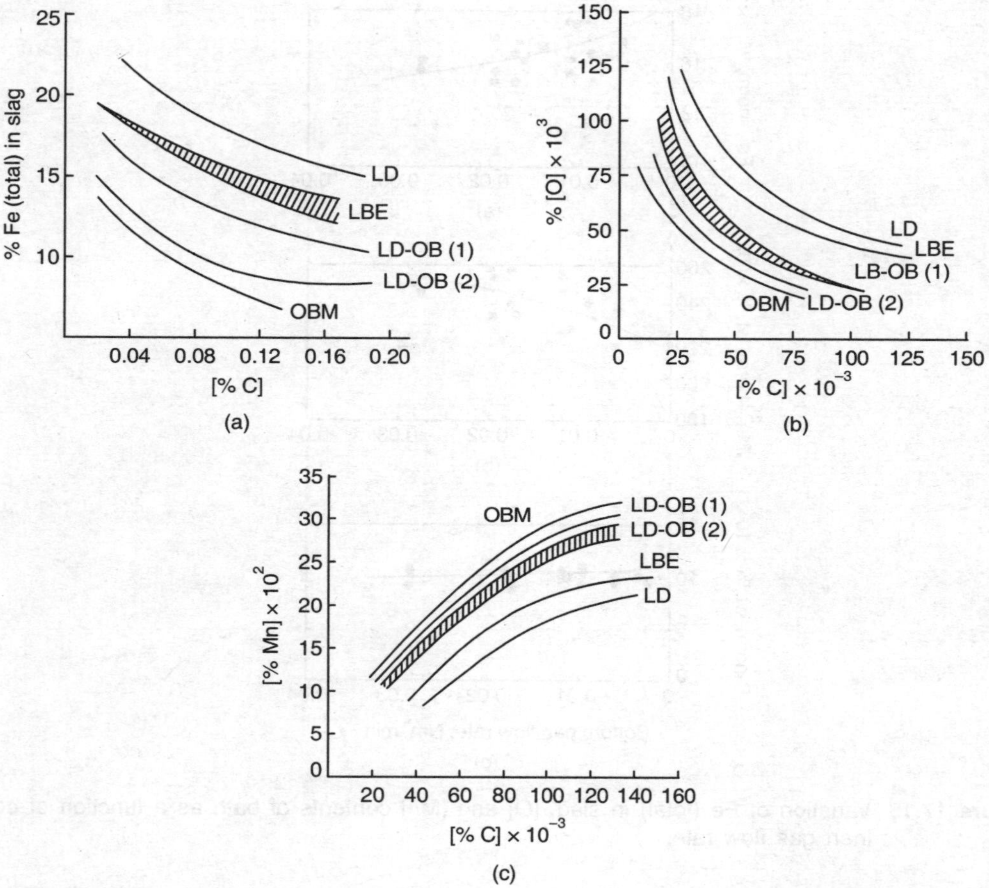

Figure 17.14 Variation of Fe (total) in slag, [O] and [Mn] content of bath as function of bath carbon at turndown for some basic oxygen steelmaking processes.

Mink et al. obtained the following [C]–[O] relationship in molten steel before tapping from the furnace:

- Without bottom stirring, $[W_C] \times [W_O] = 35 \times 10^4$
- With efficient bottom stirring, $[W_C] \times [W_O] = 20.5 \times 10^{-4}$

At the LD-1 shop of Tata Steel, bottom stirring in converters was initiated in early 1980s by four symmetric tuyeres and later by six symmetric tuyeres. In the decade of 1990s, when LD-2 shop was commissioned, both LD-1 and LD-2 shops got fitted with eight symmetric tuyeres. Water model studies found decrease in mixing time with each of these changes. Thus eight bottom tuyeres had more efficient mixing than six tuyeres, and six tuyeres arrangement had more efficient mixing than four tuyeres.

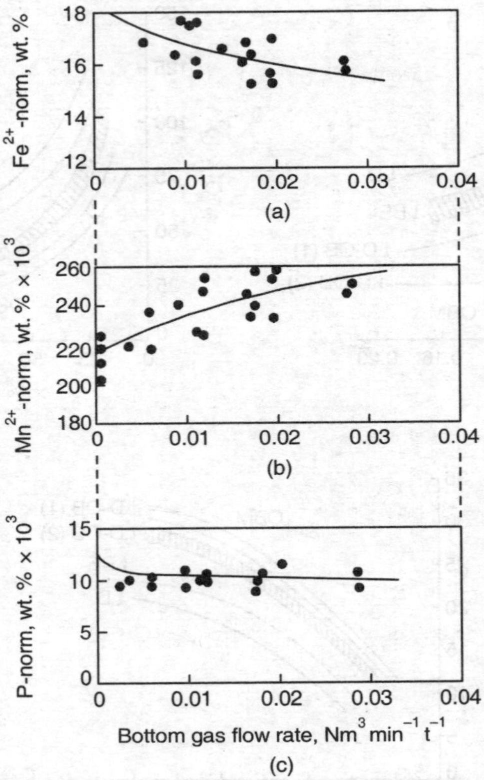

Figure 17.15 Variation of Fe (total) in slag, [O] and [Mn] contents of bath as a function of bottom inert gas flow rate.

Choudhary et al. (2005) evaluated phosphorus partition (L_P) between slag and metal at converter turndown for large number of heats at Tata Steel for each tuyere arrangement. The ratio R_P, as defined below, was employed for assessment.

$$R_P = \frac{L_P}{L_P \text{ (at equilibrium)}} \tag{17.4}$$

It may be noted that R_P is a kinetic parameter.

At slag–metal phosphorus equilibrium, $L_P = L_P$ (at equilibrium), and $R_P = 1$. If kinetic limitations do not allow attainment of equilibrium, then R_P is lower than 1.

Figures 17.16 and 17.17 (Choudhary et al. 2005) show R_P as function of turndown temperature for various tuyere arrangements. Since the turndown slag contains some undissolved lime particles and this is not determined in routine slag analysis data, two values of free lime, viz. 0% and 10%, were assumed. Figures 17.16 and 17.17 show that with better mixing by change of tuyere arrangements, R_P values increased, i.e. dephosphorisation was more efficient. These findings also are in conformity with evidences cited earlier.

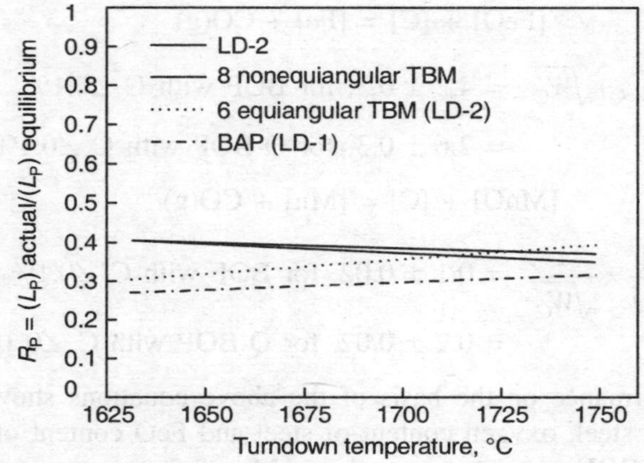

Figure 17.16 Comparison of dephosphorisation characteristics in BOF steelmaking at Tata Steel with different bottom stirring arrangements, assuming 0% free lime in the slag (best fit lines).

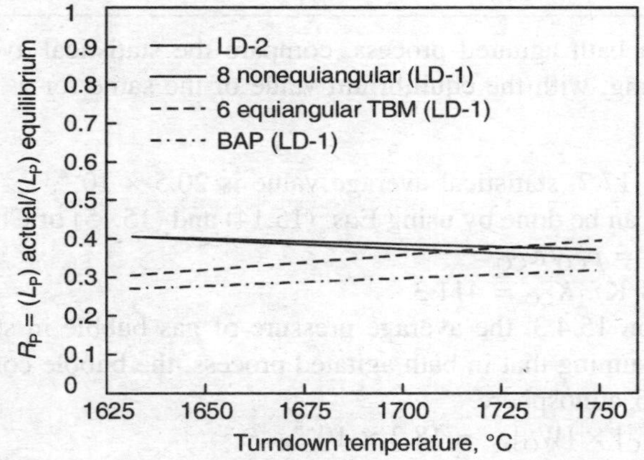

Figure 17.17 Comparison of dephosphorisation as in Figure 17.16 except that 10% free lime in slag assumed.

Turkdogan (1996) has attempted to find out some relationships for various reactions at converter turndown both for the bath agitated processes and OBM converters at US Steel Corporation. *These are respectively known as BOF and Q-BOP at US Steel Corp.* These are empirical relations and are related to some of the reactions discussed in Chapter 15, Section 15.4. Some of them are noted below as useful guides for quantitative estimates.

1. For reaction: $[C] + [O] = CO(g)$ (15.14)

$$[\text{ppm O}]\sqrt{W_C} = 135 \pm 5, \text{ for BOF at C } \angle 0.05\% \quad (17.5)$$

$$= 80 \pm 5, \text{ for Q-BOP at C } \angle 0.08\%$$

2. For reaction: $$[FeO] + [C] = [Fe] + CO(g) \tag{15.17}$$

$$(W_{FeO})\sqrt{W_C} = 4.2 \pm 0.3, \text{ for BOF with C } \angle 0.1\% \tag{17.6}$$

$$= 2.6 \pm 0.3, \text{ for Q-BOP with C } \angle 0.1\%$$

3. For reaction: $$[MnO] + [C] = [Mn] + CO(g) \tag{15.21}$$

$$\frac{[W_{Mn}]}{(W_{MnO})} \times \frac{1}{\sqrt{W_C}} = 0.1 \pm 0.02, \text{ for BOF with C } \angle 0.1\% \tag{17.7}$$

$$= 0.2 \pm 0.02, \text{ for Q-BOP with C } \angle 0.1\%$$

Comparison of performance on the basis of the above equations shows that at the same carbon content of molten steel, oxygen content of steel and FeO content of slag are lower for Q-BOP than those for the BOF at converter turndown. Manganese recovery into the metal is also higher in Q-BOP. These quantitatively demonstrate superiority of Q-BOP over BOF on the above parameters.

EXAMPLE 17.2

For refining of steel in a bath agitated process, compare the statistical average plant data of $[W_C] \times [W_O]$ before tapping, with the equilibrium value of the same for a tapping temperature of 1625°C.

Solution: From Section 17.7, statistical average value is 20.5×10^{-4}. Equilibrium calculations can be done by using Eqs. (15.14) and (15.15) of Chapter 15, according to which: $[W_C] \times [W_O]_{eq.} = p_{CO}/K_{CO}$.

At 1625°C (i.e. 1898 K), $K_{CO} = 411.3$.

In Chapter 15, Section 15.4.3, the average pressure of gas bubble in steel bath was taken to be 1.5 atmosphere. Assuming that in bath agitated process, the bubble contains 50% CO and rest Ar or N_2, $p_{CO} = 0.75$ atmosphere.

Putting in values, $[W_C] \times [W_O]_{eq.} = 18.2 \times 10^{-4}$.

REFERENCES

Baker, R. et al., Ironmaking and Steelmaking, Vol. 7 (1980), p. 227.

Choudhary, S.K., S.N. Lenka and A. Ghosh, Tata Search, 2005, pp. 117–124.

Deo, B. and R. Boom, *Fundamentals of Steelmaking Metallurgy*, Prentice-Hall International (1993), p. 162.

Meyer, H.W., J. Iron & Steel Inst., June 1969, pp. 781–789.

Mink, P. et al., *Proc. European Oxygen Steelmaking Congress*, VDEH, Dusseldorf (1993), p. 65.

Tupkary, R.H. and V.R. Tupkary, *An Introduction to Modern Steelmaking*, 6th ed., Khanna Publishers, New Delhi (1998), p. 336.

Turkdogan, E.T., *Fundamentals of Steelmaking*, The Institute of Materials, London (1996), p. 218.

18

Process Control for Basic Oxygen Steelmaking

18.1 INTRODUCTION

Steel is made in the BOF process at a very fast rate and a key concern is, therefore, the exact determination of the blowing endpoint. Rapid changes in the temperature and chemical composition of the steel bath during oxygen blowing complicate predictions, and direct continuous measurements that are reliable are not possible in many cases even today. In conventional BOF steelmaking, the steel temperature and composition are measured at the end of the heat on the basis of steel samples withdrawn from the bath. This involves an interruption in the steel production process and a corrective oxygen re-blow is usually required leading to a loss in production and disruption in production scheduling. Today, process optimisation systems (Level 2) are available and can be applied to supervise and control BOF operations, starting from the ordering of hot metal and scrap to the alloying during tapping. Process tracking modules and the generations of set points are based on predefined production practices, and on the results from different process models that are activated according to the ongoing treatment phase. The required material quantities and compositions, the time when they are to be charged into the converter, as well as the exact volume of oxygen to be blown are calculated to produce a heat in accordance with the production plan, and which satisfies the specific steel grade requirements.

18.1.1 Chronology of Developments

At the initial stages of BOF process development, the operator had to decide, before the start of the blow, how the oxygen blow would progress, what/when fluxes would be added during the blow, etc. to arrive at the desired endpoint in terms of temperature and composition. The entire 'judgment' was guided by previous experience, and hence involved a large amount of trial and error. After the blow was completed in the predetermined time, the oxygen lance would be withdrawn, the vessel tilted, and the final sampling and temperature measurements carried out before tapping. During the blow, the vessel would have to be similarly tilted to check the actual progress of the blow, in terms of the prevailing bath temperature and composition at that instant of time. Corrections in temperature would be carried out by either making additions of iron ore or scrap to cool the bath, or heat it by further re-blowing, which would also be the method of adjusting the bath composition. The latter was more time consuming since chemical analysis of the samples by spectroscopy in a separate laboratory meant the loss of several minutes. Re-blows to adjust temperature/composition thus caused loss of production and had other adverse effects like lower lining life. Despite intermediate sampling/temperature check (s), often the temperature and/or the composition of the steel at the end of the blow would finish outside the desirable tolerance limits. This resulted in *off-grade heats*.

Following the advent of digital computers, it became possible to carry out fast quantitative calculations before/during the blow for a given set of endpoint conditions. Mathematical models were developed for calculating the initial charge mix, quantities of flux additions during the blow and the total oxygen that had to be blown. Such attempts were initially based exclusively on mass and heat balances. Later, further refinement became possible by incorporating statistically fitted process parameters, as well as slag–metal equilibrium relationships. A large variety of such mathematical models is in use in steel plants and is known as *Static Models*.

In such an approach, the aim is to make all the predictions before the commencement of the blow. How well it is followed during the progress of the blow is left to the operator and his judgement. This type of control is known as *Static Control;* the specific objective of which is to control the *endpoint* (*i.e. at blow-end*) temperature and carbon content of the bath. If it is carried out correctly, there is no need for further re-blowing or for any additions. Although other elements such as phosphorus, nitrogen, etc. are important, quantitywise they are very small, particularly in proportion to carbon. Therefore, elimination of carbon essentially determines the process time.

Static control by using computers improved the hit-rate of endpoint temperature and carbon significantly. As a result, static models have become an integral part of all basic oxygen steelmaking shops. How accurate an estimate such models can provide of the conditions of the bath at the end of the oxygen blow depends on the following factors:

- Accuracy of the model
- Accuracy of inputs to the computer system
- Consistency of steelmaking practices and quality of materials used
- Reliability of the sensors/measuring devices.

It needs to be emphasised that there are many variables which influence the rates of reactions in BOFs and some of these variables are difficult to control. Consequently, two heats with apparently identical inputs and blowing conditions may not finish with the same carbon and temperature. In scientific terminology, therefore, BOF steelmaking is a *Stochastic Process*. Some important sources of irreproducibility from heat-to-heat are:

(a) Errors in weighing the charge and assessing the oxygen flow rate; for example, for a 300 tonne converter, it has been estimated that a small error in hot metal weighing can affect the final output appreciably:

Error in hot metal weighing	T, °C	C, %	Slag Fe, %
		Output errors	
– 1 t	+ 2	– 0.003	+ 0.68
+ 1 t	– 0.9	+ 0.003	– 0.61

(b) Difference in the dissolution of lime owing to its reactivity, particle size, etc.
(c) Dissolution of scrap on account of its size
(d) Height and nature (including its structure) of the emulsion formed
(e) Profile of the converter lining
(f) Extent of mixing induced in the bath.

Out of the above, item (f), i.e. incomplete mixing, has been, by and large, eliminated by concurrent top and bottom gas blowing in BOFs. Mixing is not an issue in pure bottom-blown converters. However, the other sources of irreproducibility continue to exist to various extents, as a result of which, static control alone is not adequate. This has been demonstrated by data from many operating plants. Marked improvements in operation have been brought about by the utilisation of:

- Sub-lance
- Immersion-type carbon sensors
- Immersion-type oxygen sensors.

The sub-lance is an auxiliary lance adjoining the main oxygen lance assembly. No oxygen is blown through the sub-lance, but it is used to house various measurement probes—thermocouple, immersion carbon probe and oxygen probe—that are immersed into the bath from the top of the converter, while the vessel is still in a vertical position. Hence, the converter does not have to be tilted for making any measurements. The same set-up is used to withdraw samples from the bath for chemical analysis. The sub-lance is normally immersed 2 to 3 minutes before the predicted end of the blow. The data collected by the sub-lance probes are automatically fed into a computer, which compares the actual bath conditions with the model predictions to suggest further action to be taken by the operator. This is known as *Semi-Dynamic Control*. While static models by their very nature are not able to predict how to vary the blowing parameters (oxygen flow rate and lance height) with time and when to make additions during the blow, *Dynamic models* (which should not be confused with dynamic control) incorporate dynamic and kinetic features. As a result, the blowing parameters, additions, etc. are taken care of, resulting in better control of the endpoint conditions. Many modern BOF shops, therefore, have incorporated this facility.

The most sophisticated control system, known as *Dynamic Control* involves continuous waste gas analysis and flow rate measurement in order to determine the rate of decarburisation on a continuous basis during the entire blowing period. The information is fed back into a computer leading to continuous predictions and automatic oxygen blowing rate control, along with control of the bottom gas flow rate. This feature is in addition to sub-lance-based control.

Besides marked changes in the composition of the waste gas during the blow, there are variations in the noise level, extension of the outer lance pipe relative to the inner oxygen carrying pipe, lance vibrations during the blow, etc. The intensity of these variations is influenced by the volume of the emulsion formed, the rate of decarburisation, slopping tendency, etc. Many modern converter shops use the trend in these variations as a means of controlling the entire blow; for example, sonic meters are used to gauge the extent and height of the slag–metal emulsion during the blow to get an idea of the rate of decarburisation and the amount of residual carbon in the bath along with the slag characteristics. The other methods can also provide similar information.

These are general features of the strategy and practice used for BOF process control, some specific details of which are given later. For general review, the book by Williams (1983) may be consulted.

18.2 MATHEMATICAL MODELS

18.2.1 Static Models

As stated in Section 18.1.1, static models are principally based on mass and heat balance of the process, taking only the initial and the final state of the system into consideration. Chapter 6, Sections 6.1 and 6.2 have outlined the basic procedure and equations for mass and heat balance exercises in connection with ironmaking in the blast furnace. Chapter 15, Section 15.2 has briefly covered the additional thermochemical features in connection with steelmaking reactions and their heat effects. Standard enthalpies of formation of some oxides along with the sensible heats of some materials have also been presented in a tabular form. These constitute the basis for formulating mass and heat balances in steelmaking processes and hence are not repeated.

Mass balances for Fe, O, C, CaO, MgO, etc. and heat balance yield several simultaneous linear equations, the solution of which requires a basis to be first selected. One metric ton (i.e. tonne) of steel is often taken as the basis. Inputs to the model have to be provided in the form of data and assumptions, such as:

1. Data: End-blow carbon and temperature, nominal heat size in tonnes, hot metal composition, quantity of scrap per tonne of steel, desired CaO/SiO_2 ratio in the slag, heat effects of the reactions, sensible heats as a function of temperature, etc.
2. Typical assumptions (not a complete list)
   - (i) % CO and CO_2 in the exit gas
   - (ii) exit gas temperature
   - (iii) temperature of slag and metal being the same at turndown
   - (iv) FeO and Fe_2O_3 of the slag represented as total FeO
   - (v) constant heat loss rates
   - (vi) slag FeO and MgO contents, as a function of CaO/SiO_2 ratio, for good refining.

Turkdogan (1996) has provided some examples of calculations assuming that the sum of the four primary oxides CaO + MgO + FeO + SiO_2 is in the range of 88 to 92% of the slag weight (the rest being minor oxides). An empirical relationship between the CaO/SiO_2 ratio and the FeO, MgO contents of slag has also been assumed by Turkdogan.

On this basis it is possible to predict:

- Initial quantities of hot metal and scrap charges
- Flux and iron ore additions required during the blow
- Total quantity of oxygen to be blown.

Such predictions have been found to have some uncertainty owing to the simplifying assumptions made. In order to make the predictions more reliable, some terms are adjusted by statistical fitting of the model using a large number of actual data from previous heats. It has been claimed that, if the statistical analysis is properly adjusted along with additional inputs from the operators' know-how, i.e. by application of so-called *Expert Systems*, the accuracy of the predictions improve.

From physical chemistry principles it is possible to calculate the contents of phosphorus, sulphur, carbon, manganese and oxygen in the metal, which are in equilibrium with a given type of slag. Chapters 15 and 17 have presented some details of the various reactions and their application in the BOF. Using this approach, it is possible to predict the composition of the slag that would be present in the converter at turndown. This is necessary in order to arrive at the solute contents in the steel bath at the aimed turndown temperature. Modern versions of static models have also incorporated these in the computation programmes.

EXAMPLE 18.1

Using the data and calculations of the BOF heat in Examples 15.1 and 15.2 of Chapter 15, carry out heat balance calculations to determine the temperature of liquid steel at the end of the blow. Make further assumptions as follows:

(i) Basis of calculation: 1 tonne of steel as in Examples 15.1 and 15.2

(ii) Reference temperature = 298 K

(iii) Hot metal temperature = 1275°C = 1548 K; scrap, lime and oxygen inputs are at 298 K

(iv) Final temperatures of liquid steel and slag are equal; also slag contains 2 wt% P_2O_5

(v) Heat loss by radiation, conduction and exit gas is 10% of the heat input.

Solution: Process heat balance calculations are long. They require extensive data and can be properly solved only by computer-oriented numerical method and iterative procedure. Therefore, many simplifying assumptions need to be made. Some have been listed already and the rest will be mentioned as they come.

From material balance calculations of Examples 15.1 and 15.2, it can be noted that per tonne of steel:

$$W_{HM} = 975 \text{ kg},\ W_{scrap} = 97.5 \text{ kg},\ W_{slag} = 130 \text{ kg},\ O_2 \text{ required} = 41.7 \text{ Nm}^3$$

Heat Balance: Heat Input = Heat Output + Heat Loss (Ex. 18.1)

Sensible heat input by (HM + scrap + CaO + O_2) + Heats of oxidation of (C + Si + Mn + Fe + P) – Endothermic heats of melting of scrap and CaO = Sensible heats of liquid steel and slag at final temperature T + Heat loss. (Ex. 18.2)

Since heat loss is 10% of heat input, Eq. (Ex. 18.1) may be rewritten as:

$$0.9 \times \text{heat input} = \text{heat output} \qquad \text{(Ex. 18.3)}$$

Since, scrap, CaO and O_2 inputs are at 298 K, sensible heat input is only through hot metal. Table 15.2 gives some sensible heat data. Assuming that the sensible heat of HM is the same as liquid Fe,

$$\text{Sensible heat of HM} = 975 \times (1/56) \times 10^3 \times [40.95T + 0.837 \times 10^{-3} T^2 - 2805] \text{ joules}$$
$$= 109 \times 10^7 \text{ J} = 109 \times 10^4 \text{ kJ}$$

$$\text{Sensible heat of liquid steel and slag} = (1/56) \times 10^3 \times [1000(40.95T + 0.837 \times 10^{-3} T^2 - 2805) + 130 (48.85T + 2.26 \times 10^{-3} T^2 + 6.73 \times 10^5 T^{-1} - 16957)]$$
$$= 843.8T + 20.2 \times 10^{-3} T^2 + 15.1 \times 10^5 T^{-1} - 8.945 \times 10^4 \text{ kJ} \qquad \text{(Ex. 18.4)}$$

[*Note:* Sensible heat of slag has been assumed to be equal to that of CaO in the above equation]

Endothermic heats of melting = (1/56) $\{W_{scrap} \times 13807 + W_{CaO} \times 79534\}$ = 12.37×10^4 kJ, where the values of heats of melting are in J/mol.

Exothermic heats of oxidation of elements

On the basis of Example 15.2, it is possible to calculate the number of kg · moles of elements oxidized (n_i). Values of standard heats of formation of these oxides(ΔH_f^0) are available in Table 15.1.

For C → CO reaction, $n = (1000 \times 0.033 \times 0.9)/12 = 2.475$ kg · mol.

Calculations for other reactions with similar procedure give 0.275, 0.348, 0.325, 0.044, 0.034 kg · mol for C → CO_2, Si → SiO_2, Fe → FeO, Mn → MnO, P → 1/2 P_2O_5.

$$\text{Total heat evolved} = \Sigma n_i \times (\Delta H_f^0)_i = 85.68 \times 10^4 \text{ kJ} \qquad \text{(Ex. 18.5)}$$

Estimation of final temperature (T) of steel and slag

$$0.9[109 + 85.68 - 12.37] \times 10^4 = 843.8T + 20.2 \times 10^{-3}T^2 + 15.1 \times 10^5 T^{-1} - 8.945 \times 10^4$$

As first approximation, ignore the T^2 and T^{-1} terms. Then, from the above equation, $T = 2046$ K.

In the next approximation, including the T^2 term too, the trial and error solution gives $T = 1960$ K = 1687°C.

18.2.2 Dynamic Models

Static models can be used to calculate the optimum charge mix, requirement of additions during the blow, total oxygen required, time of blow, etc. They can be utilised for static control as well as semi-dynamic control taking the help of sub-lance measurements. However, by their very nature, static models are not able to predict variations in the blowing parameters (oxygen flow rate and lance height) as a function of time, as discussed earlier. For making such estimates, dynamic models are required.

Dynamic models contain all the features of static models; and in addition have terms for reaction kinetics and process dynamics. The possible approaches include the following.

(i) Instantaneous equilibria amongst the reacting phases may be assumed, i.e. the process is treated as being thermodynamically reversible. However, this is not very commonly followed, since the BOF reactions are far away from equilibrium, except at the end of the blow.

(ii) Reactions are assumed to be mass transfer controlled. Having made this assumption, it is possible to adopt different levels of sophistication. This has been attempted in the past, but it has been found that in view of the complexity of the BOF process, it is not worthwhile to go in for a very high degree of sophistication. Instead, it is preferable to treat the reactions as first order, and adjust the coefficients obtained by statistical fitting of plant data.

(iii) After silicon is oxidised, the major oxidation reactions are those of carbon and iron. In the case of fully dynamic control, the rate of decarburisation as well as the amount of oxygen consumed by carbon is continuously determined from the exit gas data. This allows computation of the rate of iron oxidation as well.

18.3 SEMI-DYNAMIC CONTROL

As stated in Section 18.1, in semi-dynamic control, some measuring probes—thermocouple, carbon sensor, and oxygen sensor—are immersed into the bath with the help of the sub-lance, generally 2 to 3 minutes before the estimated blow end, in order to obtain the actual temperature, dissolved carbon and oxygen contents of the bath. Using the sub-lance it is also possible to withdraw metal/slag samples from the bath for chemical analysis without tilting the converter. Oxygen blowing is normally stopped or the flow rate decreased during the immersion of the sub-lance, the total operation taking less than 30 seconds.

The data thus obtained are fed into the control computer, which compares the actual temperature and carbon in the bath with those predicted by the static model. The computer then provides advice for corrective additions and modifications in the blow, as required. For doing this, the computer uses another programme based on either a static model or a dynamic model.

18.3.1 The Sub-lance

Different designs of the sub-lance are available depending on the manufacturer, but in all cases the sub-lance has to be sturdy enough to withstand repeated usage in the converter atmosphere. Figure 18.1 shows the sub-lance employed by Voest-Alpine AG, Linz, Austria. (Kostersitz et al. 1986). Like the main oxygen lance, the sub-lance is also water-cooled. It is driven by a winch, which uses a computer-controlled variable DC drive along with a counterweight. The probe manipulator is hydraulically-controlled. Before immersion, the probe magazines (cartridges) are electrically-heated. They are then immersed in the bath for 3–5 seconds and the entire measurement operation completed in around 90 seconds.

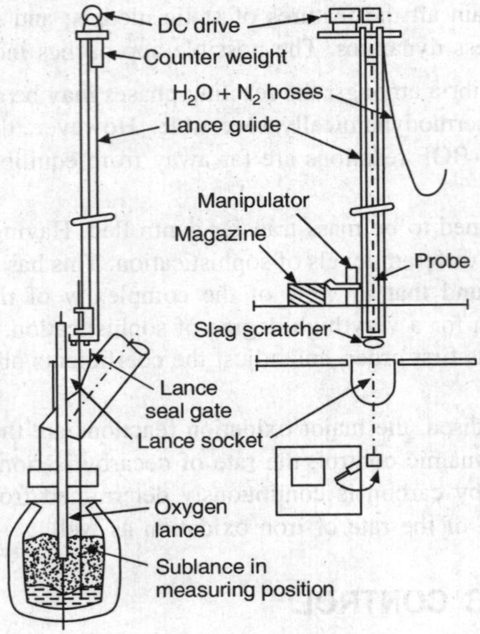

Figure 18.1 Typical sub-lance used for process control.

18.3.2 Immersion Carbon Sensor

The carbon sensor is used for virtually instant *in situ* determination of bath carbon. The probe measures the *Liquidus Temperature* of the steel sample collected from the bath by the standard *Thermal Arrest* technique. The liquidus temperature of iron is lowered by the presence of impurities—for example, 1 wt. % carbon, lowers the temperature by 90°C. In the case of manganese, the lowering is to the tune of 1.7°C, silicon: 6.2°C, sulphur: 40°C, phosphorus: 28°C. Therefore, it is evident that carbon has the most predominating effect and some minor corrections are good enough to determine the carbon content on the basis of liquidus temperature measurements.

Different designs of the sensors are available; one design is shown in Figure 18.2 (Bosworth 1971). It combines the measurement of both temperature and carbon. The carbon sensor is of the disposable type, i.e. one sensor can be used only once since the aluminium cap in the sensor melts when it is immersed. The bottom thermocouple in the sensor measures the bath temperature as soon as liquid metal rushes into the evacuated chamber containing another thermocouple. Once the sub-lance is withdrawn, the metal freezes in less than 30 seconds. The inner thermocouple records the liquidus temperature, from which the carbon content is immediately known with an accuracy of around ±0.01% carbon.

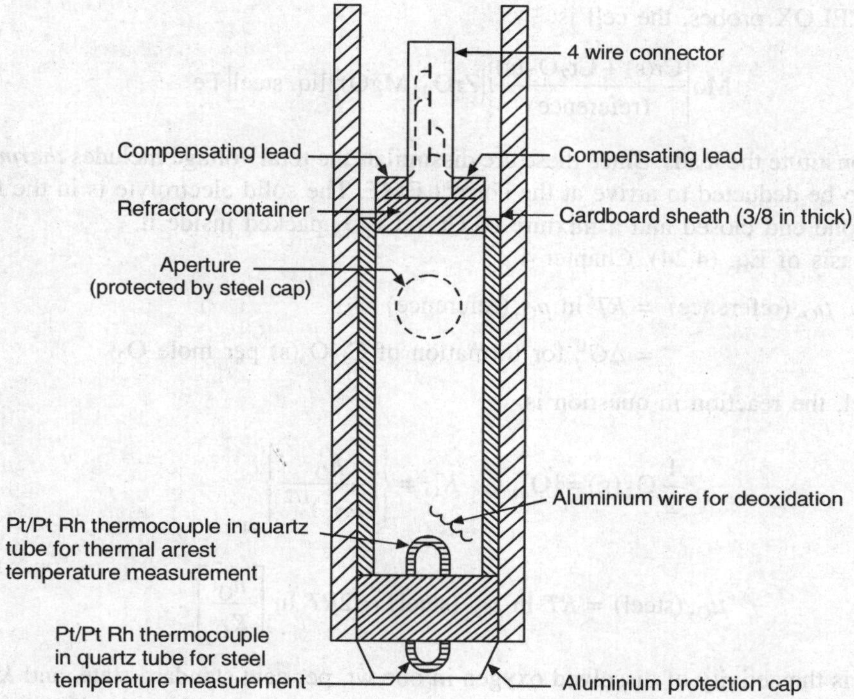

Figure 18.2 Sectional view of an immersion-type carbon and temperature sensor.

18.3.3 Immersion Oxygen Sensor

This is also a combined sensor used to measure both the temperature as well as the dissolved oxygen content of the bath, within 5 seconds of immersion. The most popular version is the CELOX probe, marketed by Electro-Nite of Belgium. The objective of *in situ* measurement of bath oxygen is primarily to help in quick estimation of the bath carbon. It has already been pointed out in Chapter 17, Section 17.7 that carbon and oxygen in the bath before tapping are inter-related, and some statistically averaged empirical relationships are in use. Therefore, the oxygen sensor is an effective tool used in many modern BOF shops before tapping molten steel from the converter.

The oxygen sensor is a tiny EMF cell of the disposable type, which can be used only once. The electrolyte is a solid ceramic material, which is ZrO_2 doped with either CaO, or MgO or Y_2O_3. It has vacancies in the O^{2-} lattice sites through which oxygen ions can move freely, thereby allowing it to be used as an *oxygen concentration cell*, whose EMF (E) is related only to the difference of chemical potentials of oxygen at the two electrodes.

$$\mu_{O_2} \text{ (liquid steel)} - \mu_{O_2} \text{ (reference)} = -ZFE \qquad (18.1)$$

where Z is valency of O_2 = 4, and F is the Faraday constant.

In standard CELOX probes, the cell is:

$$\text{Mo}\left|\frac{\text{Cr(s)} + \text{Cr}_2\text{O}_3\text{(s)}}{\text{(reference)}}\right|\left|\text{ZrO}_2\text{(MgO)}\right|\left|\text{liq. steel}\right|\text{Fe} \tag{18.2}$$

Mo and Fe constitute the leads. Since these are dissimilar, the total voltage includes *thermo-emfs,* which have to be deducted to arrive at the correct EMF. The solid electrolyte is in the form of a tube, with one end closed and a mixture of Cr + Cr_2O_3 packed inside it.

On the basis of Eq. (4.24), Chapter 4,

$$\mu_{O_2}\text{(reference)} = RT \ln p_{O_2}\text{(reference)} \tag{18.3}$$

$$= \Delta G_f^0 \text{ for formation of } Cr_2O_3\text{(s) per mole } O_2$$

In liquid steel, the reaction in question is

$$\frac{1}{2}O_2(g) = [O]_{wt\%};\ K_O = \left\{\frac{h_O}{(p_{O_2})^{1/2}}\right\}_{eq.} \tag{18.4}$$

So,
$$\mu_{O_2}\text{(steel)} = RT \ln p_{O_2}\text{(steel)} = 2RT \ln \left[\frac{h_O}{K_O}\right] \tag{18.5}$$

Here, h_O is the activity of dissolved oxygen in one wt. per cent standard state, and K_O is the equilibrium constant. Since μ_{O_2} (reference), and K_O are known as a function of temperature, from measurements of T and EMF, μ_{O_2} (steel) and h_O are determined. From h_O, the wt. % O is determined.

Cook et al. (1993), have presented a comprehensive coverage of the semi-dynamic control of the BOF adopted at Armco Steel Corporation, USA.

EXAMPLE 18.2

(a) Upon immersion of a CELOX oxygen sensor into a bath of molten steel at 1600°C, the EMF (after correction of thermo-EMF) was −0.10 volt. Calculate wt. % dissolved oxygen in the melt.

(b) Assuming [Al]–[O]–Al_2O_3 equilibrium, calculate wt. % dissolved aluminium in the bath.

Ignore all interactions.

Solution: From Eq. (18.1), μ_{O_2}(liquid steel) – μ_{O_2}(reference) = –ZFE = –4FE

In Chapter 4, Table 4.1 gives the value of ΔG_f^0 for formation of Cr_2O_3(s). Noting that ΔG_f^0 per mole of O_2 is 2/3 of that, and at 1873 K, from Eq. (18.3),

$$\mu_{O_2}\text{(ref)} = -434.13 \times 10^3 \text{ joules per mole of } O_2.$$

For reaction 18.4, Table 4.2 gives the value of ΔG^0 = −117150 – 2.89T J/mol.

At 1873 K, this gives the value of K_O of Eq. (18.5) as 2619.

$$-ZFE = -4 \times 96500 \times (-0.1) = 38.6 \times 10^3 \text{ joules}$$

Ignoring interactions, $[h_O] = [W_O]$. Therefore, from Eq. (18.5),

$$\mu_{O_2}(\text{Steel}) = 2 \times 8.314 \times 1873 \ln (W_O/2619).$$

(a) Inserting the above values in Eq. (18.1), and solving, it is possible to get $[W_O] = 0.008$ wt. %, $[W_{AL}] = 2.2 \times 10^{-4}$ wt %.

(b) From Chapter 20, Table 20.2, different values at 1873 K can be obtained.

For the reaction, $2[Al]_{wt.\,\%} + 3[O]_{wt.\,\%} = Al_2O_3(s)$, $K_{Al} = \{[W_{Al}]^2 . [W_O]^3\}_{eq.} = 2.51 \times 10^{-14}$. This gives the wt. % dissolved Al in liquid steel as 8.94×10^{-4} wt. % (i.e. 8.94 ppm).

18.4 DYNAMIC CONTROL

As stated earlier, dynamic control based on a dynamic model is the most sophisticated type of control. It has all the features of semi-dynamic control and in addition, it also has features like the following:

(i) Chemical analysis, flow rate and temperature measurements in the exit gas
(ii) Continuous in-blow data, e.g. accoustic noise intensity measurement by using a sonic meter.

The data gathered during the course of blowing are fed back to a control computer, which automatically adjusts the lance height, oxygen flow rate, etc.

18.4.1 Measurements on Exit Gas

The exit gas from a BOF consists primarily of CO and CO_2, the volume fractions of which can be determined by a sophisticated gas analyser (mostly mass spectrometer). Gas flow rate measurements are more difficult. In one technique that is commonly used, argon is used as a tracer and is introduced as a pulse-input into the exit gas stream. Its concentration at the exit end allows the calculation of the volumetric flow rate.

The wt. % carbon in the bath at any time during the blow (W_C) is given as:

$$W_C = \text{Initial wt. \% carbon in bath } (W_{C,i}) - \frac{\text{total carbon loss through exit gas } (\Delta m_C)}{\text{mass of metal } (m_{\text{steel}})} \times 100 \quad (18.6)$$

Gas flow rate (Q), temperature of exit gas (T) and mole fractions (X) of CO and CO_2 are related to the carbon loss rate (r_C) in the following manner:

$$r_C = Q\frac{273}{T}(X_{CO} + X_{CO_2})\frac{12}{22.4} \quad (18.7)$$

where r_C is in $kg \cdot s^{-1}$, Q is in $m^3 \cdot s^{-1}$ and T is in kelvin.

$$\Delta m_C = \int_0^t r_C \, dt; \quad \Delta W_C = \frac{\Delta m_C}{m_{steel}} \times 100 \qquad (18.8)$$

where t is the time from the start of the blow. In a similar way, the oxygen going out with carbon can be computed.

It needs to be recognised that precise determination of Δm_C and Δm_O pose several difficulties owing to the following reasons:

- Dust laden and hot gas
- Non-uniformity in gas composition and temperature across the duct
- Leakages to and from the surrounding atmosphere.

Suppose, $W_{C,i}$ = 3.2%, ΔW_C = 3.0%. Then, W_C = 0.2% from Eq. (18.6). If the measurement has 5% error in ΔW_C, which is 0.15%, then actual $W_C = 0.2 \pm 0.15\%$, which is a significant error band. That is the reason why sub-lance based measurements towards the blow-end are a must. Tani et al. (1993) have discussed the dynamic control of BOF at the Kashima Steel Works, Japan.

18.4.2 Application of Sonic Meter

The intensity of acoustic noise emanating from the converter during the blow depends on the slag volume and the nature of the slag (i.e. the emulsion volume during the peak decarburisation period). The greater the slag volume (i.e. slag height), the higher is the noise level. A sonic meter measures the sound intensity continuously during the blow, and this information is fed back into a control computer, which on the basis of this data, adjusts the lance height, oxygen flow rate and bottom gas flow rate automatically to control the emulsion height. By doing this, excessive foaming and slopping can be prevented along with better refining.

Dynamic slag control in the BOF is practised in many plants, for example, ILVA/PIOMBINO Steel Works (Beneini et al. 1993). Figure 18.3 presents a typical situation where slopping was prevented by automatic control of the lance height, etc. by employing a dynamic slag control model. A reduction of 50% in slopping events, improvement in refining control and consequent improvement in converter life have been claimed.

18.5 CONCLUDING REMARKS

The fundamental objective of computer control of basic oxygen steelmaking in the early stages was to achieve endpoint carbon and temperature control, without the need of taking recourse to re-blowing. Even in modern BOF shops, the basic aim remains the same; however, several other objectives have also been incorporated such as the following:

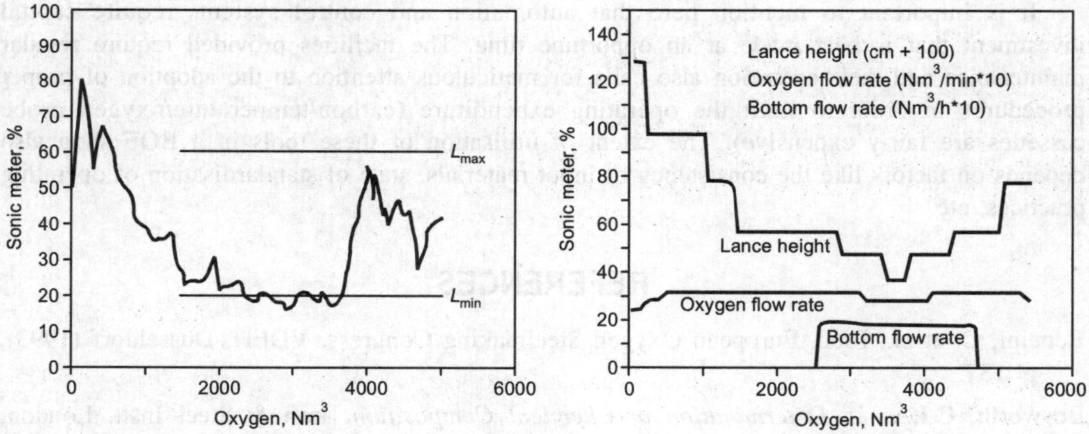

Figure 18.3 Model action based on sonic meter to prevent slopping.

- Longer lining life
- Better overall yield of Fe
- Better control of P, Mn and nitrogen
- Lower bath oxidation levels at tap leading to lower consumption of deoxidisers
- Ease in process control by the operating personnel
- Less slopping
- Standardisation of the operating practice
- Data acquisition for further evaluation.

A large volume of literature on this subject is available (some important references have already been cited). Most of the efforts have been directed towards end-point carbon and temperature control. Both semi-dynamic and dynamic controls have brought about significant improvements in endpoint control, particularly after the advent of sub-lance-based measurements. Additional use of continuous in-blow data, for example through sonic meters has led to better control techniques.

The parameters that are employed to evaluate the efficacy of endpoint carbon and temperature control are as follows:

(i) **Hit rate**: reported as the percentage of heats where the endpoint carbon and temperature are within the specified tolerance bands (100% is the maximum value).

(ii) **Standard deviations** from the aimed values of carbon and temperature (lower the value, the better is the control).

(iii) **Percentage of re-blows** required to arrive at the aimed endpoint (no re-blow is ideal).

With modern semi-dynamic and dynamic control systems, it is possible to achieve hit rates of 90–95% for temperature tolerance of ±10°C and carbon tolerance of 0.015–0.02%; standard deviations of 6–10°C and 0.01% carbon; percent re-blows of 5–10%.

It is important to mention here that automation and control systems require capital investment that is best made at an opportune time. The facilities provided require regular maintenance and their operation also calls for meticulous attention to the adoption of proper procedures in order to limit the operating expenditure (carbon/temperature/oxygen probe cassettes are fairly expensive). The extent of utilisation of these tools in a BOF shop also depends on factors like the consistency of input materials, state of standardisation of operating practices, etc.

REFERENCES

Beneini, C. et al., Proc. European Oxygen Steelmaking Congress, VDEH, Dusseldorf (1993), p. 137.

Bosworth, C.J.A., in *Determination of Chemical Composition*, Iron & Steel Inst., London, Special Report 131 (1971), p. 81.

Cook, S.R., J. Mori and R. Savson, Proc. European Oxygen Steelmaking Congress, VDEH, Dusseldorf (1993), p. 80.

Kostersitz, F. et al., Steelmaking Conference Proceedings, Iron and Steel Soc., Washington D.C. (1986), pp. 579–586.

Tani, J.I. et al., Proc. European Oxygen Steelmaking Congress, VDEH, Dusseldorf (1993), p. 89.

Turkdogan, E.T., *Fundamentals of Steelmaking,* The Institute of Materials, London (1996).

Williams, R.V., *Control and Analysis in Iron and Steelmaking*, Butterworths Publishers, London (1983), Chapter 7.

19

Basic Open Hearth and Electric Arc Furnace Steelmaking

19.1 BASIC OPEN HEARTH STEELMAKING

As stated in Chapter 1, Section 1.3.2, the open hearth process of steelmaking was invented in 1861. Initially, acid open hearth furnaces were used, but they were soon overtaken by *basic open hearth* (BOH) steelmaking. BOH was the primary method of steelmaking for about 100 years till the advent of the basic oxygen process. With the gradual evolution of basic oxygen steelmaking, the number of open hearth furnaces decreased steadily. By the mid 1990s, all recently installed steel plants as well as older plants that had been modernised did not have any BOH furnaces. Though quality steel could be made in open hearth steelmaking, the prolonged heat cycle (stretching over several hours) and the need for external fuel (fired into the rectangular furnaces through burners positioned at either end) were the major drawbacks. At present, only a very small number of steel plants around the world, principally in Russia, continues to employ this process. For any detailed description of open hearth steelmaking, readers may consult Tupkary et al. (1998) and Trubin and Oiks (1974).

Despite its obsolescence, a very brief description of open hearth steelmaking is being included here because of the following reasons.

1. The knowledge of steelmaking has certainly been broadened by an understanding of the advantages of open hearth steelmaking as far as the production of high-quality steels is concerned. Similarly, an appreciation of why the process became gradually obsolete helped in formulating the processes that later came into vogue.
2. The fact that it was possible to observe the interior of an open hearth furnace periodically after each campaign, and also study the progress of steel refining by collecting a large number of metal and slag samples during each heat, contributed to a fundamental understanding of the principles involved in primary steelmaking.

19.1.1 The Open Hearth Furnace

The first open hearth furnace with a capacity of 2.2 t per heat and a hearth area of 3 m^2 was built in France in 1864. Although the operational practices adopted in BOH steelmaking changed considerably over the period of 100 years during which the process was in use, later day BOH furnaces broadly retained the original features of furnace design. Of course, the furnace size increased steadily—from 2.2 tonnes per heat in the very early stages to furnace capacities as high as 200–300 tonnes (and some even as large as 600 tonnes) by 1955, when the process had reached its maturity.

Scrap, cold pig, iron ore, manganese ore, and hot metal are used as charge in open hearth furnaces. The proportion of the solid charge consisting especially of scrap (in various forms) is seldom less than 70%, and a lot of time (at least 3–4 hours) is consumed in the process of charging and melting these solids. In fact, in any open hearth shop, extensive stock yard facilities have to be provided for scrap storage in large heaps. The scrap is then loaded into relatively small charging boxes which can be inserted into the furnaces through the front doors by using especially designed charging cars that operate on the furnace floor.

Figure 19.1 shows a sketch of the longitudinal vertical section of one-half of a BOH furnace. One end wall and burner can be seen. The furnace has another burner located at the opposite end-wall. The furnace itself, which is rectangular in shape, can either be built on a permanent foundation (in the case of stationary furnaces), or so arranged that a part comprising the hearth

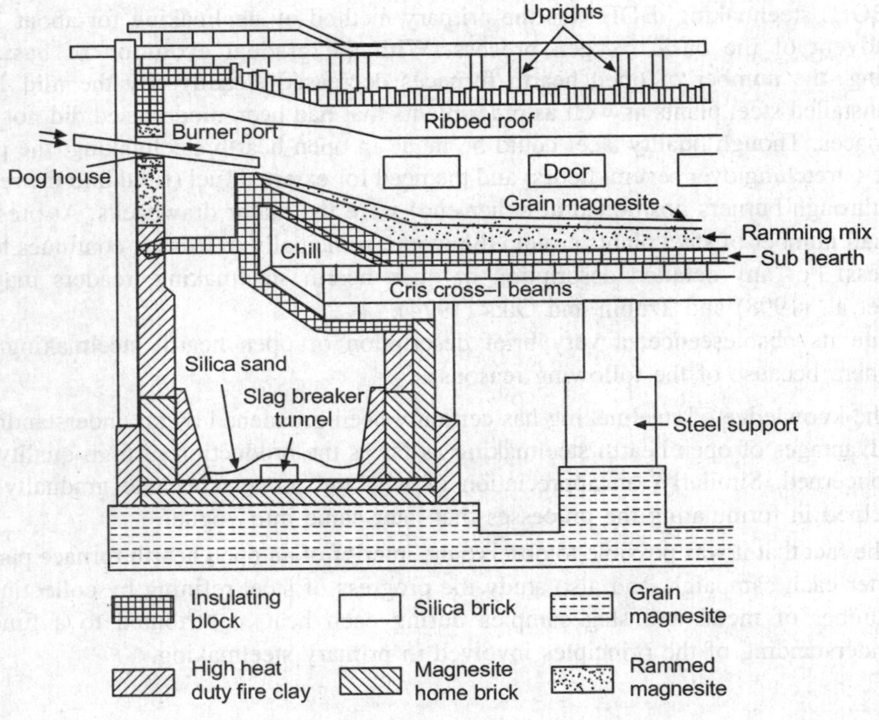

Figure 19.1 Longitudinal vertical section of an open hearth furnace.

may be tilted (for tilting the furnace during tapping of liquid steel). The hearth of the furnace is made of steel plates (typically 25 mm thick). Different layers of refractories are laid on the steel shell to form the hearth bottom—first fireclay bricks, then magnesite bricks, and finally a layer of fritted burnt magnesite (10–30 mm). The main roof of BOH furnaces is made of basic bricks like chrome-magnesite or magnesite-chromite, while in acid furnaces, silica bricks are used.

Charging, observations of the bath during heat making as well as sampling are carried out through the doors provided on the front wall of the furnace, which can be opened or closed by lifting vertically, whenever required. These front doors, located over the entire length of the furnace are also used for fettling the hearth (adding fresh granules of refractory materials like magnesite) at the end of each heat as well as for furnace maintenance. Tapping of molten steel is done through a tap hole located on the back wall of the furnace (opposite side of the doors). The back wall also contains one or two holes that can be used for flushing out the slag during the course of heat making. This facility is particularly useful in large capacity furnaces so that slags can be tailor-made, as per refining requirements (for example, dephosphorisation). This is a unique advantage of open hearth steelmaking—time consuming, but essential for producing high-quality steels even from inferior inputs.

The furnace operating temperature is around 1650–1700°C, which cannot be obtained by combusting the fuel with cold air. Therefore, pre-heated air is normally used in the burners for the combustion of the fuel (fuel oil/coke oven gas/blast furnace gas/producer gas). Preheating of air to about 1000°C is carried out in *regenerators* containing a *checker work* (mesh) of firebricks. The regenerator consists of fire bricks arranged in such a way that the bricks fill about 75% of the total volume and gas flows through the empty regenerator space around the bricks. The brick lattice, i.e. the checkerwork, absorbs heat from the outgoing gases, and this heat is used to pre-heat cold air to 1200–1300°C. Figure 19.2 shows the regenerator arrangement. In the first cycle, air and fuel flow through the right-hand side. The hot products of combustion at about 1600°C pass through the regenerators on the left-hand side, thus heating up the refractory checkerwork. The direction of flow is reversed in the second cycle; each cycle lasting about 30 minutes.

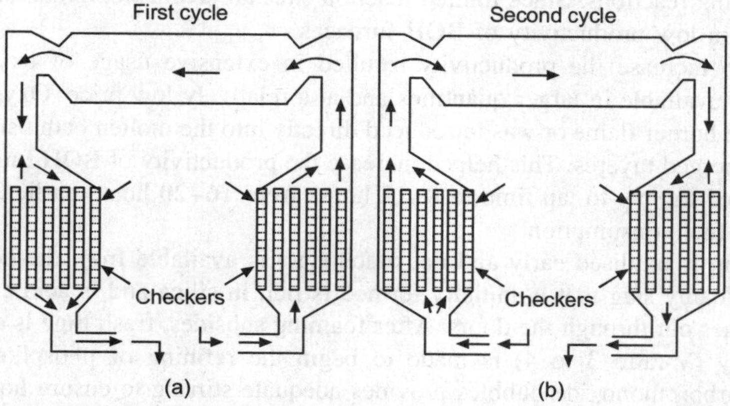

Figure 19.2 Heat regeneration system in an open hearth furnace: *First cycle*: checkers on left being heated by hot flue gas; checkers on right giving heat to incoming air, *Second cycle*: reverse of first cycle.

It may be noted that an open hearth shop is a fairly huge engineering structure equipped with many furnaces, regenerators, waste heat boilers (to recover heat from the exit gases) and instrument panels essentially for thermal control.

19.1.2 Steelmaking in Basic Open Hearth Furnaces

Heat making in BOH steelmaking involves different unit operations.

- Fettling, i.e. inspection and repair of the lining after the previous heat is tapped
- Charging of solids
- Heating the charge
- Charging of hot metal
- Melting and homogenisation of the entire charge
- Refining and finishing including flushing of slag
- Tapping liquid steel.

The charging sequence of solids is: iron ore at the bottom, then limestone, and finally scrap on top of limestone. Once heating begins and scrap reaches the point of melting, molten hot metal is poured. Because considerable oxidation of the scrap takes place during heating, the impurities in the hot metal, especially silicon and carbon, vigorously react with iron oxide. Limestone also dissociates releasing CO_2, which reacts with carbon and silicon in hot metal to form CO and SiO_2 respectively. Evolution of CO results in foaming of the slag, which continues throughout the melting period.

As the impurities get oxidised, the amount of slag on the top of the horizontal bath keeps on increasing and the chemical composition of the metal bath changes continuously. Slag and metal samples are withdrawn throughout the refining period (lasting 90–120 minutes) to monitor the oxidation of carbon, manganese and phosphorus. The SiO_2, MnO and FeO contents in the slag samples provide an idea of the extent of oxidation of the respective impurities. Iron ore added along with the charge as well as during the refining period is the major source of oxygen for these oxidising reactions. Since limited reaction sites are available, oxidation is intrinsically slow, resulting in low productivity of BOH furnaces.

Attempts to increase the productivity resulted in extensive usage of oxygen, once pure oxygen became available in larger quantities and at a relatively low price. Oxygen was used to either enrich the burner flame or was introduced directly into the molten bath using water-cooled top lances/submerged tuyeres. This helped increase the productivity of BOH furnaces by around 20% and reduced the tap-to-tap time to 8–12 hours from 16–20 hours earlier. It also resulted in reduction in fuel consumption.

Since silicon is oxidised early and not much CaO is available from the decomposition of limestone, the foamy slag that is initially formed is rich in silica and is acidic in nature. Most of this slag comes out through the doors. After foaming subsides, fresh lime is added and a slag of high basicity (V-ratio 3 to 4) is made to begin the refining of phosphorus and carbon. Evolution of carbon monoxide bubbles provides adequate stirring to ensure homogenisation of the bath as well as helping in heat transfer. When the bath samples taken indicate that carbon in the metal bath has reached the specified level, the heat is ready for tapping. However, before tapping, some deoxidisers are added into the bath in order to lower the bath oxygen content as well as for minor alloying. Tapping is carried out by physically opening the tap hole at the centre of the back wall of the furnace by oxygen lancing.

19.1.3 Transfer of Oxygen and Heat in Open Hearth Furnaces

Figure 19.3 schematically shows the mechanism of oxygen transfer from the gaseous atmosphere to the liquid metal bath in the hearth via the slag phase. Heat transfer also occurs from the hot gaseous combustion products to the bath via the slag. Radiation is the principal mechanism of heat transfer from gas to slag, for enhancing which the gas should be luminous. Luminosity of the gas is provided by unburnt carbon particles.

The oxygen potential is the highest in the gas (p_{O_2} about 10^{-4} to 10^{-5} atmosphere) and the lowest in the metal phase (p_{O_2} about 10^{-8} to 10^{-9} atmosphere). The concentration of dissolved oxygen in the metal bath depends mainly on its carbon content—the higher the bath carbon, the lower is the oxygen concentration. As shown in Figure 19.3, the transfer of oxygen to the slag occurs by oxidation of Fe^{2+} ions to Fe^{3+} ions at the gas–slag interface. The reverse process transfers oxygen from the slag to the metal.

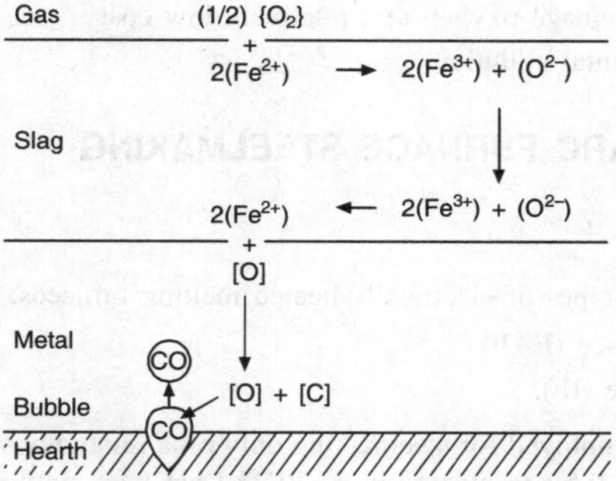

Figure 19.3 Mechanism of oxygen transfer from the gaseous atmosphere to the liquid metal bath in open hearth furnaces.

Dissolved carbon in the metal bath reacts with dissolved oxygen to generate carbon monoxide bubbles. The passage of these bubbles through the bath provides the stirring necessary for enhancing heat and mass transfer rates required for speeding-up all the reactions, as well as for guaranteeing adequate mixing/homogenisation. The formation of bubbles requires *nucleation* and *growth*. While growth does not require much supersaturation, theoretical calculations indicate that a pressure of CO as high as 10^4 atmospheres is required for *homogeneous* nucleation of the gas bubbles. Since such high thermodynamic super saturation simply does not exist in the bath of open hearth furnaces, at first there was considerable debate with regard to the reaction mechanism. The puzzle was resolved when it was demonstrated that the tiny crevices/pores in the hearth refractory lining serve as growth sites, which allows the nucleation stage to be bypassed completely. This phenomenon also restricts the depth of the metal bath in BOH furnaces, both from the point of view of rapid heat transfer and acceptable rates of reactions.

19.1.4 Concluding Remarks

When the open hearth process was invented, *Acid Bessemer Converter Steelmaking* was the existing process for large-scale steel production. The open hearth process succeeded because of the following advantages that it offered.

- Ability to melt scrap which was hitherto lying unutilised
- Inherent flexibility and close control, since it was a relatively slow process that could be monitored by sampling, additions, etc. through the doors.

Later, open hearth furnaces were completely replaced by basic oxygen converters because of the following reasons:

- Slow rates of reactions and restricted productivity in BOHs
- Large consumption of extraneous fuels in BOHs
- Availability of tonnage oxygen at a relatively low cost
- Acute environmental pollution.

19.2 ELECTRIC ARC FURNACE STEELMAKING

19.2.1 General

There are basically two types of electrically-heated melting furnaces:

- Electric arc furnace (EAF)
- Induction furnace (IF).

Induction furnaces are employed for steelmaking only on a relatively very small scale since the furnace size varies from 0.5 t to maximum of 20/25 t per heat, with most furnaces below 5 t. Hence, IFs are used to a limited extent. On the other hand, arc furnace steelmaking is widely used and about 35% of world's steel is produced by EAFs at present (the rest by basic oxygen steelmaking), which is expected to become 50% in the next 10–15 years. The history of EAF steelmaking is marked by continuous improvements in efficiency and productivity. A method that was started in a small way about 100 years back principally for the production of alloy steels, later found widespread application in the production of all types of steels. While earlier EAFs were mostly between 10 t and 50 t, today 200–250 t EAFs are common and 400–500 t EAFs are available.

The advantages of EAFs for alloy steelmaking include:

- Relatively small size
- Cleaner environment
- Flexibility to produce a variety of grades
- Precise control.

Initially, for the bulk production of plain carbon steels, open hearth furnaces were less expensive because of their large size as well as the higher cost of electricity. All these started to change from around 1970, because of the following.

(i) While the cost of liquid fuels started increasing, electricity generation costs became lower and electricity became comparatively cheaper.
(ii) Larger and higher power EAFs could be installed because of the progress in electrical engineering and control systems.
(iii) EAF steelmaking is intrinsically cleaner than open hearth steelmaking.
(iv) Since EAF steelmaking is predominantly scrap based, smaller plants with lower capital investment and faster attainment of rated capacity could be set up, even compared to BF-BOF based plants.

Therefore, EAFs started gradually replacing BOHs for producing plain carbon steels as well. With EAFs ranging in size from 100 t to 250 t (and even 500 t), there are some plants around the world which are producing 1.5 to 2 Mtpa of steel from 2–3 large electric arc furnaces. This type of growth in EAF steelmaking has resulted in scrap shortage. This has been taken care of by partial substitution of scrap by sponge iron (DRI/HBI) and, in some plants with additional charging of cold pig and hot metal.

This chapter will cover the production of plain carbon steel in EAFs. Chapter 21 will separately deal with the production of stainless steel. Many books are available on EAF steelmaking: Electric Furnace Steelmaking, ISS; Making Shaping and Treating Steel, 11th ed., Vol. 2; book by Tupkary et al.

19.2.2 The Furnace and the Auxiliaries

EAF is a *direct arc* furnace, where the arc is struck between the graphite electrodes and the metallic charge/metal bath. The arc temperature is above 4000°C and is used to heat the bath by radiative heat transfer. The traditional power supply is three-phase AC, requiring three electrodes; the modern trend is to go for DC arc.

Figure 19.4 shows the cross section of a conventional EAF. Basic-type electric arc furnaces are employed for steelmaking; hence, the inner lining of the hearth in such furnaces is burnt magnesite. Charging is done from the top, and during charging, the electrodes are lifted up to allow the roof to be swung horizontally to one side, thus providing open access from the furnace top.

Figure 19.5 contains a sketch of a typical EAF shop layout. EAFs can be tilted to one side for metal tapping; slag tapping is carried out through the opposite side slag door, for which the furnace is tilted the other way. The electrodes get worn out and consumed during arcing and before the length of an electrode becomes too small for operation, another electrode is joined to it at the top. In order to do this, each electrode has internal threading at the ends and the threaded ends of the two electrodes are connected by a threaded graphite nipple.

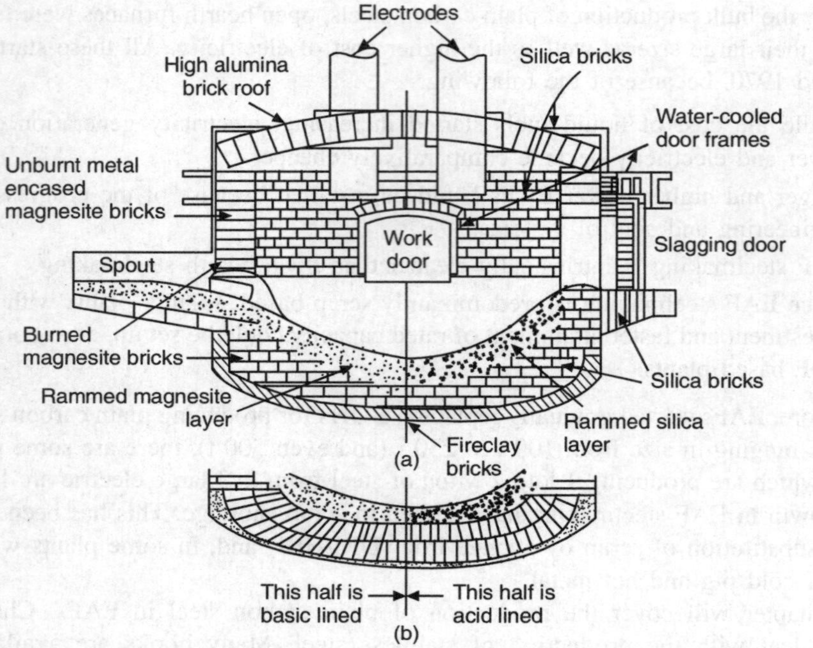

Figure 19.4 Cross section of an electric arc furnace (both acid and basic lining shown for illustration).

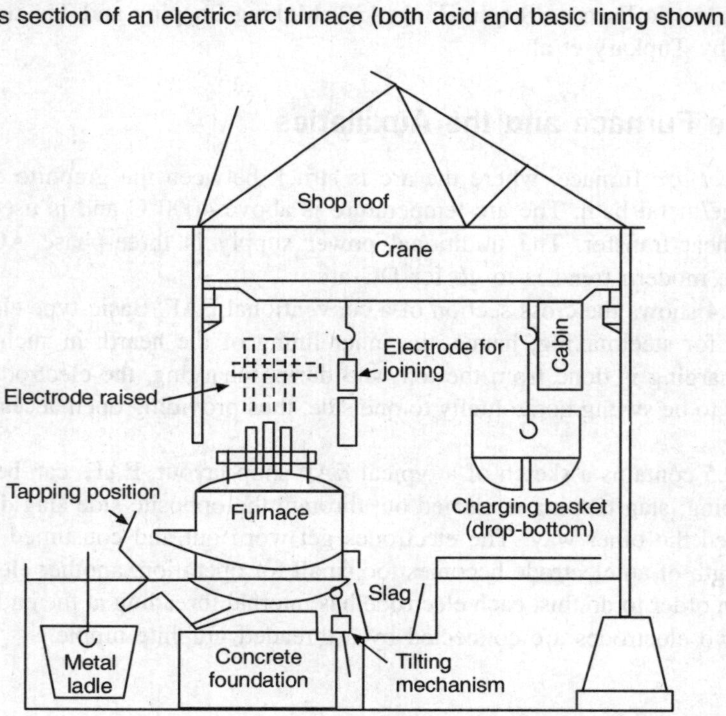

Figure 19.5 Vertical section of an electric arc furnace shop.

The furnace unit itself includes the following parts:

(i) Furnace body consisting of the shell, the hearth, the walls, the spout, doors, etc.
(ii) Gears for furnace body movement
(iii) Arrangements for moving the roof
(iv) Electrodes with their holders and supports
(v) Electrode lifting and lowering mechanism
(vi) Electrical equipment—i.e. transformer, cables, electrode control arrangements, etc.

The furnace shell is made by welding or rivetting steel plates. Its side wall is cylindrical in shape and the bottom is shallow and bowl-shaped. To give an idea, the shell diameter is about 6 to 6.5 m for a 100 t capacity furnace and 5 to 5.5 m for a 50 t furnace.

Large transformers are required for supplying power to any EAF. The primary voltage may be 33 KV or more, and the secondary voltage anywhere from 200 V to 1000 V depending on the furnace size and power supply. The electrical characteristics of the circuit are schematically shown in Figure 19.6. Since the voltage as well as the power factor decrease as the current is increased, the maximum power is obtained at an optimum current.

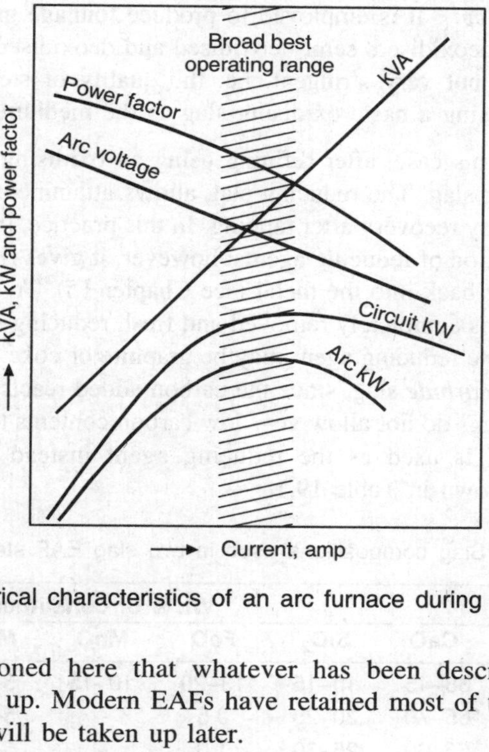

Figure 19.6 Electrical characteristics of an arc furnace during operation (schematic).

It should be mentioned here that whatever has been described above pertains to a conventional furnace set up. Modern EAFs have retained most of the basic design with some additional features that will be taken up later.

19.2.3 Conventional EAF Steelmaking Practice

As mentioned already the process of electric arc furnace steelmaking is about 100 years old.

Through decades of efforts till about 1970, electric furnace steelmaking practices got significantly standardised. This is what is denoted by the term *conventional*—it is practised even now in smaller and relatively older units.

Section 19.1.2 has described the stages in heat making in basic open hearth furnaces. EAF steelmaking involves most of those stages, with the exception of the following:

- Hot metal is not used in conventional practice
- The refining and finishing practices differ widely.

The basic purpose of refining in EAFs is two-fold:

- Removal of undesirable impurities (C, Si, P, S, N, H, etc.)
- Finishing the bath so as to ensure maximum alloy recovery.

Chapter 15 has discussed the reactions in primary steelmaking and their physicochemical aspects. Chapter 5 focused on the reactions of silicon and sulphur, and hence need not be repeated. EAFs produce a wide variety of steels. Therefore, depending on the type of the solid metallic charge and the grade of steel to be produced, the refining practice differs considerably. The type of refining employed may be broadly classified into the following.

Oxidising single slag practice: It is employed to produce tonnage grades of carbon and low alloy steels, as well as non-deoxidised, semi-deoxidised and deoxidised steel. The physical and chemical specifications are not very stringent, i.e. the quality of steel is similar to what is attainable in open hearths using a basic oxidising slag as the medium of refining.

Double slag practice: In this case, after refining using an oxidising slag, further refining is carried out under a reducing slag. The reducing slag allows attainment of lower sulphur levels and also assists in higher alloy recovery after tapping. In this practice, the original oxidising slag can be modified by the addition of reducing agents; however, it gives rise to danger of reversion of phosphorus from the slag back into the metal (see Chapter 15). To preclude this possibility, generally the oxidising slag is completely removed and fresh reducing slag is made by charging lime, fluorspar and silica. The reducing agent may be graphite or coke breeze. This type of slag is commonly referred to as *carbide* slag, since the carbon added reacts with CaO to form some amount of CaC_2. Carbide slags do not allow very low carbon contents to be attained in the bath; in such cases, ferrosilicon is used as the reducing agent instead of carbon. The typical compositions of slag are shown in Table 19.1.

Table 19.1 Slag compositions used in two slag EAF steelmaking

Type of slag	Wt. % of constituents						
	CaO	SiO_2	FeO	MnO	MgO	CaC_2	V-ratio
Oxidising	38–45	10–15	13–20	10–15	5–10	–	1.7–3
Reducing—carbide	65–70	20–25	0.5	–	5–10	1–2	3–3.5
Reducing—non-carbide	55–60	25–30	1.0	–	5–10	–	2–2.5

At this stage, it is worth noting some salient differences in the metallurgical features of basic open hearth and EAF steelmaking. These are noted below.

1. Since EAF steelmaking is primarily scrap/DRI based and both these materials have relatively low levels of residual impurities, the extent of refining is much less than in BOH steelmaking.
2. As a process, EAF is far more versatile than BOH and can make a wide range of steel grades.
3. Sorting out of scrap and choosing the proper scrap grade are important for EAF steelmaking, since the extent of refining has to be managed accordingly. For this purpose, scrap may be classified into the following categories:
   (a) scrap containing clements that cannot be removed by oxidation during refining, such as Cu, Ni, Sn, Mo, W, etc.
   (b) scrap containing partially oxidisable elements, such as P, Mn , Cr, etc.
   (c) scrap containing completely oxidisable elements, such as Al, Si, Ti, V, Zr, etc.
   (d) scrap containing volatile elements, such as Zn, Cd, Pb, etc.

   Scrap of type (b) and (c) can be tackled easily during refining. Type (d) scrap would require some special attention. However, type (a) scrap gives rise to problems like *undesirable residuals* in the final steel. This is where DRI scores over scrap—it is totally free from all the above undesirable elements.
4. In BOH steelmaking, refining begins with the bath containing about 1% excess carbon (often referred to as the opening carbon) in order that evolution of CO following the oxidation of carbon provides the necessary agitation for homogenisation of the bath as well as for enhancing the reaction rates. In EAF steelmaking also, the initial bath carbon is maintained at about 0.3% above the final carbon specification during oxidising refining. However, stirring is absent during refining under a reducing slag, and some other stirring technique (use of mechanical stirrers called rabbles) is required.

19.2.4 Modern Developments in EAF Steelmaking

Introductory comments

Recent developments in EAF steelmaking have taken place primarily in the context of large-scale production of plain carbon and low alloy steels. Of course, some of these developments have also been implemented in smaller scale of operation as well as for the production of high alloy steels, such as stainless steels. Besides a distinct trend towards increase in furnace size, the important developments may be summarised as follows.

- Ultra high power supply (UHP)
- DC arc furnace
- Oxygen lancing (in some cases along with carbon/coke breeze)
- Use of water-cooled elements in the furnace shell, water-cooled electrodes, etc.
- Foamy slag practice
- Bath stirring by argon
- Auxilliary secondary steelmaking facility
- Use of sponge iron (DRI/HBI) to substitute scrap

- Hot metal or cold pig iron as scrap substitute
- Pre-heating of scrap and DRI
- Eccentric bottom tapping
- Emission and noise control
- Process automation and control.

What has already been discussed in Chapters 15, 17 and 20 and is of relevance here is not being repeated. Towards the end of this chapter, a short discussion has been included on the quality of plain carbon and low alloy steels made through the electric furnace route. Hence, the accent here will be on the impact of modern developments on improvements in process efficiency through enhancement in productivity, superior energy utilisation efficiency, cost savings and environmental pollution control. In summary, it can be stated that modern strategy is directed towards employing the EAF primarily for *melting followed by some refining using an oxidising slag. The metal is then tapped from the furnace into a ladle and the rest of the refining, adjustment of composition as well as temperature are carried out during secondary steelmaking.*

Specific developments

For the sake of concise presentation, the modern developments in specific areas are being divided into the following groups.

(a) GROUP 1—First six items of Section 19.2.4, i.e. UHP to foamy slag and argon stirring
(b) GROUP 2—The next three items covering alternative charge materials.
(c) GROUP 3—Other items like charge pre-heating, eccentric bottom tapping, emission control and automation.

(a) GROUP 1

1. Transformers supplying power to electric arc furnaces have been classified as given below.

	Capacity in kVA per tonne steel
(i) Regular power, i.e. for old furnaces	100–400
(ii) High power	400–700
(iii) Ultra high power (UHP)	above 700

Use of UHP enables faster melting of the solid charge, thereby decreasing the tap-to-tap time with consequent increase in the production of steel. An EAF of 100 tonne capacity will require a transformer capacity of above 70 MVA for UHP operations. It has been possible to achieve such figures owing to major advances in electrical engineering in the last few decades.

Another important development is the *use of DC* (*direct current*) in the furnaces. This requires conversion of three-phase AC into single-phase AC supply, and after the step-down transformer conversion of AC into DC. A DC arc has one electrode and the circuit is completed through the conducting electrodes embedded in the furnace bottom. It offers certain distinct advantages over three-phase AC arc, such as smoother arc operation, less noise, etc.

2. *Oxygen lancing* through a top lance gives certain advantages that include: oxidation of carbon and some iron from the bath releasing chemical energy with consequent saving of electrical energy as shown in Figure 19.7 (Kohle 2000); faster removal of carbon and other impurities following faster slag formation and the generation of a foamy slag.

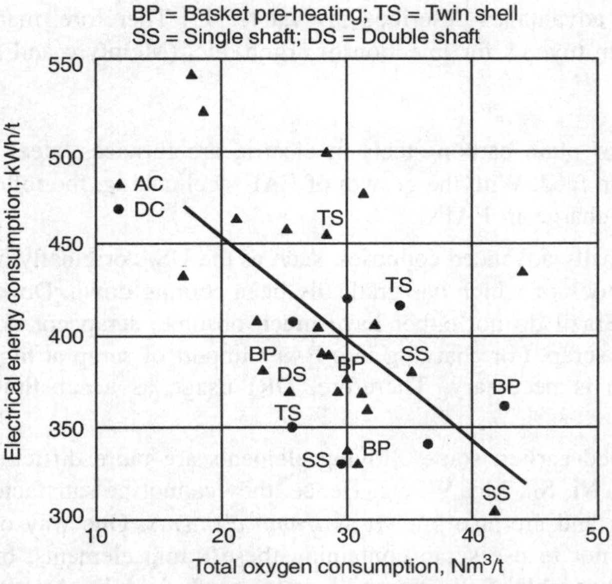

Figure 19.7 Electrical energy consumption versus total oxygen consumption.

In large EAFs the top lance is supersonic, as in BOFs. For greater saving of electrical energy, coke or carbon breeze is also injected along with oxygen in some plants. *Coherent jet* lance design makes these injections more efficient and has been adopted in some EAF shops.

3. Ultra high power input and oxygen/oxy fuel injection, with consequent higher temperature in the arc zone, causes more heat losses. This tends to heat up the furnace shell, the graphite electrodes as well as the connecting electrical cables, etc. thereby causing damage to these parts. The concurrent use of a *foamy slag* helps in insulating some areas thereby lowering the heat loss and providing protection to the electrodes and other parts of the furnace.

Use of *water-cooled* shell panels and water cooling of electrodes, cables, etc. decrease the consumption of refractories/electrodes.

Chapter 17, Section 17.4 introduced the concept of foams and emulsions in the context of BOF steelmaking. These are applicable to the foaming of slags in EAFs as well. To summarise, a slag foam is *transient* and is basically sustained by vigorous evolution of CO following the reaction of bath carbon with oxygen. A foamy slag is actually an emulsion of metal droplets and gas bubbles in slag. Higher slag viscosity and the presence of undissolved solid particles assist foaming, which speeds-up slag–metal reactions, such as dephosphorisation. All modern EAF shops have adopted foamy slag practice.

The subject of mixing and homogenisation of the bath in BOFs has been elaborately discussed in Chapter 17. To help bath mixing, concurrent top and bottom blowing has been adopted by all modern BOF shops. In large EAFs also the problem of mixing exists, to some extent. Oxygen lancing and flow of current through the metal bath in DC arc furnaces induce some amount of bath motion, which is sometimes insufficient. Better mixing in the bath is desirable for all the advantages described in Chapter 17. Therefore, many modern EAFs are equipped with bottom tuyeres for injection of argon, etc. (McIntyre and Landry, 1993).

(b) GROUP 2

For the production of plain carbon steels in electric arc furnaces, steel scrap constitutes the principal metallic iron feed. With the growth of EAF steelmaking, the following problems were faced with all scrap charge in EAFs.

(i) Technologically advanced countries, such as the USA originally had plenty of obsolete scrap, the stock of which has gradually been coming down. Developing countries like India and Brazil do not either have much obsolete scrap nor do they generate large amounts of scrap. For charging into EAFs import of scrap at high cost to supplement home scrap is necessary. Therefore, DRI usage as a substitute for scrap became popular.

(ii) As mentioned earlier, some alloying elements are more difficult to oxidise than Fe, such as Cu, Ni, Sn, Mo, W, etc. Hence, they cannot be satisfactorily removed during steelmaking and are also known as *tramp elements*. One way of getting around this problem is not to use scrap containing these tramp elements, but this is not always economically viable. Substitution of scrap, partly or fully, by alternative iron sources (AIS) is a solution, since these inputs do not contain tramp elements.

Many publications deal with the use of AIS, for example, Jones (2000) and Millman (1999). Besides DRI, the other alternative iron sources are:

- *Hot briquetted iron* (HBI), which is a dense, compacted form of DRI
- Solid pig iron
- Hot metal (i.e. molten pig iron).

Use of AIS is gaining popularity in EAF steelmaking. DRI/HBI is now the principal feed stock next to scrap. In 2005, the worldwide DRI/HBI production was just over 56 million tonnes, which was slightly more than 15% of the scrap consumption.

Solid pig iron and hot metal are also important AIS, constituting about 5–8% of the total feed. In the case of EAF shops located inside an integrated steel plant, blast furnace hot metal is available. Otherwise, hot metal can be produced either in a mini blast furnace or in a smelting reduction unit. Both these have been used in EAF steelmaking, since hot metal charging

- is advantageous from a thermal point of view being already molten and the oxidation of its impurities provides chemical energy; 1 kg hot metal charge per tonne of steel saves electricity by about 0.5 kWh/t
- promotes foaming by the evolution of CO and gives all the advantages of a foamy slag.

However, excess hot metal usage can prolong the refining time and give rise to uncontrolled foaming. Therefore, it is recommended that hot metal charge is restricted to a maximum of 40–45% of the total charge and the best method of usage is to charge it continuously through a side launder.

DRI/HBI has very low impurity content (i.e. P, Si, S, and, of course, the tramp elements) [see Chapter 13, Sections 13.3 and 13.4] and hence does not require any additional refining time. However, it is a porous material that tends to get severely oxidised in contact with moist air at high temperature. Up to about 30% DRI (of the total charge) can be charged along with scrap in buckets, if bucket charging is practised. First a layer of scrap, then DRI and then another layer of scrap are used in each bucket. If continuous charging facilities for charging DRI throughout the heat in small amounts are available, the proportion can be increased to 50–60% and sometimes, even more. In all cases, HBI is preferred since it is dense and does not get oxidised very readily.

With the use of DRI/HBI, melting and refining can proceed simultaneously. In some EAF shop even up to 100% DRI is used by adopting what is known as the *hot heel* practice. Here, molten steel from a previous heat is not tapped out completely and is allowed to remain in the EAF to provide a liquid metal bath for DRI charging right from the beginning of the next heat. Figure 19.8 shows the typical change of weight of metal in the furnace as a function of time during an EAF heat for hot heel practice.

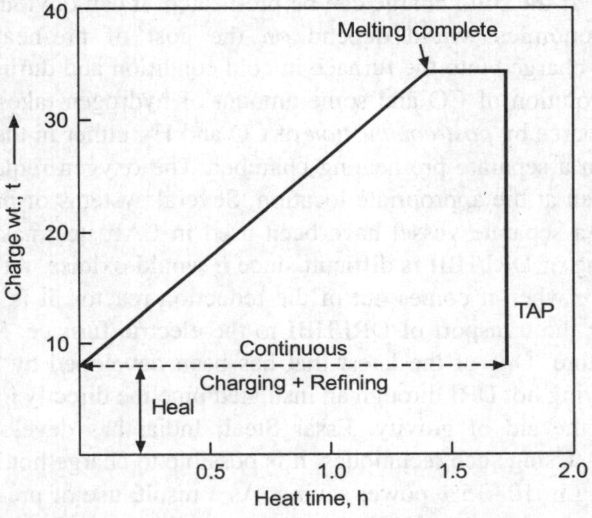

Figure 19.8 Arc furnace operation with high percentage of DRI in the charge using hot heel practice.

The quality of DRI is judged by its following characteristics:

- Gangue content
- Percentage metallisation
- Carbon content
- Levels of other impurities.

The gangue in DRI consists principally of silica and alumina associated with the iron oxide feedstock. For optimum usage in steelmaking, the gangue content should be as low as possible; otherwise, large slag volumes and hence more lime addition are required. This has an adverse effect on the consumption of energy. The *percentage metallisation* (i.e. the percentage of metallic iron in the DRI as a percentage of total iron—the remaining iron is present as wustite) should also be high to keep the energy consumption low. Typically, steelmakers prefer metallisations between 92% and 96% (too high metallisation lowers the turbulence that is induced in the bath when FeO in DRI reacts with the bath carbon).

During the production of DRI (particularly gas-based DRI) carbon in the form of iron carbide gets absorbed in the final product. The carbon percentage in DRI depends on the process of sponge ironmaking—in coal-based processes it is about 0.10–0.15%, while in gaseous reduction processes it can be varied anywhere from 1.5 to 4% depending on the customer demand. Carbon in DRI lowers its melting point and when it reacts readily with any unreduced iron oxide, CO is evolved, which contributes towards the formation of a foamy slag. This is required for efficient steelmaking and hence, steelmakers prefer higher carbon containing DRI, say above 1%. In case this amount of carbon is not available in DRI, additional carbon input by injection of coke breeze along with oxygen becomes necessary. The addition of hot metal can also provide a source of carbon.

(c) GROUP 3

Charge pre-heating: If the solid charge can be pre-heated, it can obviously reduce electricity consumption. The economics would depend on the cost of pre-heating. Under normal circumstances, scrap is charged into the furnace in cold condition and during the progress of the EAF heat, vigorous evolution of CO and some amount of hydrogen takes place. This gas can be an additional heat source by *post-combustion* of CO and H_2, either in the furnace atmosphere or above the furnace in a separate pre-heating chamber. The oxygen required can be supplied by injecting pure oxygen at the appropriate location. Several systems of pre-heating within the furnace chamber or in a separate vessel have been used in EAF steelmaking.

Separate pre-heating of DRI/HBI is difficult since it would oxidise. At the same time, since it is at high temperature when it comes out of the reduction reactor, it is a matter of retaining this temperature during the transport of DRI/HBI to the electric furnace. Several systems have been reported in literature. One of the latest that has been developed by Midrex Corporation, USA consists of conveying hot DRI through an insulated pipeline directly into the EAF shop and then charging it with the aid of gravity. Essar Steel, India, has developed refractory lined containers for transport. Using such techniques, it is possible to charge hot DRI at a temperature of 600–700°C, resulting in 10–15% power saving. As a result, use of pre-heated DRI/HBI has become a standard practice in many EAF plants.

Eccentric bottom tapping: The primary steelmaking slag has iron oxide as well as P_2O_5. This slag is undesirable for subsequent secondary steelmaking. In the case of basic oxygen furnaces, most of the slag is retained in the vessel and not allowed to flow into the ladle during tapping by the use of slag arresting devices (see Chapter 20). In modern EAFs, the bottom has been made eccentric to achieve the same result. The eccentric part of the bottom is suitably covered and insulated. During tapping, when the furnace is tilted, liquid steel primarily flows out it with very little slag and this metal can be tapped through a nozzle at the bottom of the eccentric portion. Some liquid steel is retained in the furnace (hot heel practice). Therefore; the top slag gets very little chance to escape into the ladle during tapping.

Noise control and emission: Day-by-day stricter norms are being formulated for noise control. EAF steelmaking is prone to noise—the arc struck between the electrode and the solid charge right at the beginning of each heat is the principal source of noise. Through improved circuit design, arc control and use of DC arc, noise levels have been brought down significantly.

As far as emissions are concerned, the objectionable emissions from EAFs are:

- Poisonous CO gas
- Toxic NO_x gas
- Dust.

Post combustion of CO into CO_2 is the solution as far as carbon monoxide is concerned. NO_x denotes a group of air pollutants that include: nitric oxide (NO), nitrogen dioxide (NO_2) and nitrous oxide (N_2O). The principal component is NO, typically comprising 90% of the total NO_x emission. NO_x gases are formed primarily by the reaction of atmospheric nitrogen with oxygen at the high temperatures prevailing in the arc zone of EAFs. The most effective means of control is to reduce the formation of NO_x gases by preventing the ingress of air near the arc zone. This can be achieved by using the foamy slag as a shield. The other options are to seal the furnace as much as possible by keeping the doors etc. closed, and maintaining a slightly positive pressure inside the furnace.

Huber et al. (2000) have elaborately discussed dust formation in EAFs. EAFs generate 15 to 25 kg of dust per tonne of steel. The dust comprises mostly spinel-type metal oxide (Fe, Zn, Mn) $O.Fe_2O_3$, some vitreous phases (Fe_xO + SiO_2 + CaO glass) and ZnO. It is, therefore, composed of elements/compounds coming from the steel bath as well as from the slag layer and from volatiles. Zinc, for example, comes from scrap containing galvanised steel. Moreover, the dust also contains small quantities of elements like lead, chromium and cadmium, which are volatile as well as toxic. Although earlier steelmaking dust used to be considered as a process waste, in recent times the higher cost of waste disposal and stricter environmental regulations are leading steelmakers to switch to a co-product recycling strategy.

The mechanism of dust formation in EAFs is shown in Figure 19.9 (Huber et al. 2000). It consists of:

- Localised volatilisation in the arc zone (1) and oxygen zone (1′)
- Ejection of large droplets by CO bubbles and oxygen jet in the arc zone (2) and jet zone (2′)
- Ejection of fine droplets by bursting of CO bubbles (3)
- Fast decarburisation of fine particles in zone (4)
- Direct fly-off of solid particles from the charge (5).

Literature has dealt comprehensively with the subject of emission control in EAF shops. The emissions during the progress of any heat are known as *primary emissions*, which are the most important. These emissions are taken out through a duct attached to an opening in the furnace roof as shown in Figure 19.9. The dust-laden gases are cooled by mixing with cold air before

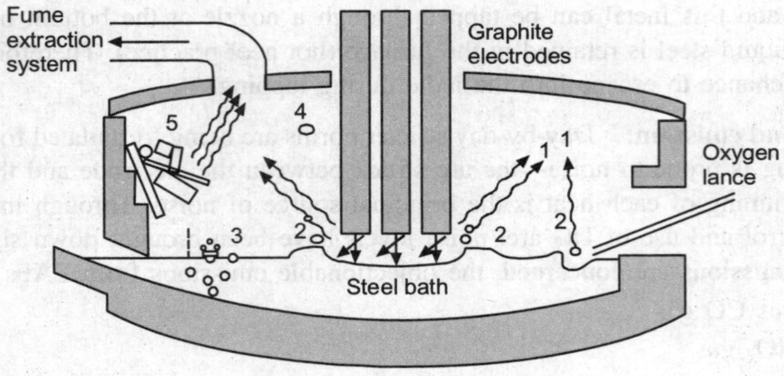

Figure 19.9 Mechanism of dust formation in EAFs.

being passed through dust catchers, scrubbers, and electrostatic precipitators for the removal of dust before the gas is let off into the atmosphere. The dust is collected in a pond as sludge, then separated and used as a by-product for various purposes in a similar way as is done in blast furnaces and BOF shops.

Secondary emissions are defined as those that are emitted during activities other than melting or refining—i.e. during the periods of charging, tapping and slagging, and a result of leakages through the furnace doors, etc. In order to handle these emissions, two systems are available:

- installation of large *canopy hoods* above the furnace where these emissions can be collected by suction
- sealing the entire building and sucking the emissions out through the roof.

Process automation and control: In Chapter 18, various features of process control in basic oxygen furnaces were presented. Elaborate control measures are used including systems such as sub-lance, exit gas monitoring, sonic meter, dynamic and semi-dynamic control with feedback, sensors like carbon sensor, oxygen, sensor, etc. The principal objective of process control in BOFs is to attain the correct end-point, in terms of both carbon and temperature. The additional objectives are to reduce phosphorus, oxygen and nitrogen in molten steel and iron oxide in the slag to as low levels as possible. These objectives have to be achieved in the minimum possible time and without the need for additional steps like reblowing, which has an adverse effect on the final yield and converter lining life.

The same objectives are applicable to electric arc furnaces as well. However, the situation is different, to some extent, as noted below.

(i) The EAF bath is accessible through the doors; hence, gadgets like sub-lance, etc. are not required.

(ii) The extent of refining in EAF is relatively less in comparison to BOF because the former is primarily a melting unit.

(iii) EAF steelmaking is not as fast as BOF.

Therefore, the metallurgical process control features in EAFs are far less elaborate. Automation and control in EAFs are primarily restricted to:

- Power supply and arc management
- Mechanical systems such as charging devices, hydraulic systems, injection devices, etc.
- Charge balances
- Heat balances, thermal efficiency and productivity improvements.

19.3 PERFORMANCE ASSESSMENT OF EAF STEELMAKING

19.3.1 Key Process Performance Indices

Broadly speaking, prior to the 1990s, the tap-to-tap time in EAFs was 4–5 hours, electricity consumption was 650–800 kWh/tonne of liquid steel, electrode consumption around 4 kg/tls and refractory consumption 7–8 kg/tls. S. Kohle (1999) has summarised the data of some modern EAFs, in Japan and in other countries like Europe. Based on the data collected for 35 EAFs, statistical methods were employed to provide values of medians, which categorise the furnace performance into two separate groups, one lying below and the other above the median. Table 19.2 contains some salient data, in which DC arc furnaces are not included. The data for

Table 19.2 Comparison of performance of AC EAFs between 1990 and 1999 (values are medians)

Parameter		1990 Average	1999 Average	Japan	Other
Furnace tap weight	t	86	110	110	112
Transformer power	MVA	60	80	60	93
Specific power	kVA/t	590	758	581	863
Voltage	V	680	900	750	950
Current	kA	50	50	42	54
Total oxygen used	Nm^3/t	24	30	31	28
Tap temperature	°C	1660	1635	1603	1639
Tap-to-tap time	min	105	70	63	78
Electrical energy consumed	kWh/t	450	392	367	416
Electrode consumption	kg/t	2.9	1.9	1.8	2.0
Refractory consumption	kg/t	6.9	3.1	3.4	2.9
Productivity	t/h	61	94	111	82

1990 were taken from a report prepared by the International Iron and Steel Institute, and the corresponding 1999 data collected from several sources. Significant improvements may be noted in all the key performance indices between 1990 and 1999. The data reveal that in this period:

- Tap-to-tap time decreased from 105 to 70 min
- Electrical energy consumption decreased from 450 to 392 kWh per tonne of steel
- Graphite electrode consumption decreased from 2.9 to 1.9 kg per tonne of steel
- Refractory consumption decreased from 6.9 to 3.1 kg per tonne of steel
- Productivity increased from 61 to 94 t/h.

19.3.2 Operating Costs

The relative operating costs are approximately as follows.

	Percentage of total cost
Charge scrap + DRI + other metallics	65
Other charge materials	5
Electric power	10
Electrodes + refractories + other consumables	10
Labour + miscellaneous	10

19.3.3 Steel Quality Control in EAF

Some features of refining in EAFs has been presented in Sections 19.2.3 and 19.2.4 under the heading GROUP 4. It has been noted that the extent of refining is less. The EAF is primarily a melting unit, and final refining including composition and temperature adjustment are carried out during secondary steelmaking. Under these circumstances, it is worth noting that for effective control on the quality of steel:

- Scrap should be low in tramp elements
- DRI/HBI should have low levels of phosphorus and sulphur.

Millman (1999) has reviewed the issue of steel quality in EAF steelmaking. Of all the residual elements, nitrogen is the most difficult to control in EAFs, and is a major limitation in the production of high-quality steels using the arc furnace route. Some nitrogen comes through the scrap, but the major amount absorbed by the molten steel bath comes from nitrogen in the furnace atmosphere. This situation is aggravated by the very high temperature in the arc zone which prompts dissociation of N_2 molecules.

The principal method for the prevention of nitrogen absorption is to maintain a foamy slag right through the heat, thereby shielding the metal bath from the arc zone. Nitrogen is also removed from the bath by the flushing action of the rising CO bubbles. Therefore, all steps that promote these two factors will tend to lower nitrogen in steel. Features like continuous charging of high percentages of DRI, extensive bottom argon injection, etc. are beneficial. However, even after incorporating them, the minimum nitrogen in EAF steel is about 40 ppm.

Hydrogen dissolved in steel also gets flushed out by the rising CO bubbles and typical tap hydrogen contents vary from 2 to 7 ppm. To arrive at lower hydrogen levels in the final product, it is necessary to take recourse to vacuum degassing during secondary steelmaking.

It is not difficult to bring down phosphorus in steel to below 0.015% in EAFs, which is acceptable for most steel grades. However, sulphur cannot be reduced to very low levels directly in EAF steelmaking without sacrificing productivity and incurring high cost. Therefore, desulphurisation is often carried out during subsequent secondary steelmaking.

REFERENCES

Huber, J.C. et al., 58th Elec. Furnace Conf. Proc., ISS (2000), p. 172.

Jones, J.A.T., 58th Electric Furnace Conf. Proc., ISS (2000), pp. 691–718.

Kohle, S., 58th Elec. Furnace Conf. Proc., ISS, Pittsburgh (2000), p. 5.

McIntyre, E.H. and E.R. Landry, Iron and Steelmaker, Vol. 20, May 1993, pp. 61–66.

Millman, S., 57th Electric Furnace Conf. Proc. (1999), pp. 15–25.

Trubin, K.G. and K.N. Oiks, *Steelmaking Open Hearth and Combined Process*, MIR Publishers, 1974.

Tupkary, R.H. and V.R. Tupkary, *An Introduction to Modern Ironmaking*, 3rd ed., Khanna Publishers, Delhi, 1998.

20

Secondary Steelmaking

20.1 INTRODUCTION

Primary steelmaking is aimed at fast scrap melting and rapid refining. It is capable of refining at a macro level to arrive at broad steel specifications, but is not designed to meet the stringent demands on steel quality, and consistency of composition and temperature that is required for various grades of steel. In order to achieve such requirements, liquid steel from primary steelmaking units has to be further refined in the ladle after tapping. This is known as *Secondary Steelmaking*.

Secondary steelmaking has become an integral feature of virtually all modern steel plants. The advent of the continuous casting process, which requires stringent quality control is one of the main reasons for the growth of secondary steelmaking.

The harmful impurities in steel include: sulphur, phosphorus, oxygen, nitrogen and hydrogen. The latter three elements occupy interstitial sites in the iron lattice and hence, are known as *interstitials*. The principal effect of these impurities in steel is loss of ductility, lower impact strength and poorer corrosion resistance.

Oxygen and sulphur are also constituents of non-metallic particles in steel, known as *inclusions*. These particles are also harmful for steel properties and should be removed to as low levels as possible. Carbon is also present as an interstitial in the iron lattice as well as in the form of *Cementite* (Fe_3C). Unlike the other interstitials, some carbon is always required in steel and hence, the content of carbon forms a part of steel specifications. However, in recent times, in some special sophisticated grades like *Interstitial Free* (IF) *steels*, carbon is considered as an impurity and has to be removed to very low levels (*Ultra-low Carbon steels*).

Normally the temperature drop of molten steel during tapping from the primary steelmaking furnace is around 20–40°C. An additional temperature drop of about 30–50°C occurs during secondary steelmaking. Continuous casting involving pouring into a tundish causes additional drop of 10–15°C in liquid steel temperature. Therefore, provisions for heating and temperature adjustment are very desirable, which has led to the development of liquid steel treatment in ladles in special units, such as *Ladle Furnace* (LF), *Vacuum Arc Degasser* (VAD), *CAS-OB unit*, etc.

Table 20.1 presents a list of various secondary steelmaking units and their capabilities (Ghosh Ahindra 2001). Degassing refers to the removal of nitrogen and hydrogen from liquid steel. In common terminology, the abbreviations used and their full forms are:

- VD—vacuum degassing
- VOD—vacuum-oxygen decarburisation
- IGP—inert gas purging in a ladle through bottom porous and slit plugs; or, by lance immersed from the top, i.e. *Overhead Lance Purging* (OLP)
- IM—injection metallurgy, where some solid agents are injected into liquid steel in a ladle; or, nowadays also by wire feeding.

Table 20.1 Various secondary steelmaking processes and their capabilities

Item	Processes						
	VD	VOD	IGP	IM	VAD	LF	ASEA-SKF
Desulphurisation	minor	minor	minor	yes	yes	yes	yes
Deoxidation	yes	yes	yes	yes	yes	yes	yes
Decarburisation	minor	yes	no	no	no	no	yes
Heating	no/yes	yes*	no	no	yes	yes	yes
Alloying	minor	yes	minor	minor	yes	yes	yes
Degassing	yes	yes	no	no	yes	no	yes
Homogenisation	yes	yes	yes	yes	yes	yes	yes
Achieving more cleanliness (i.e. less inclusions)	yes	yes	yes	yes	yes	yes	yes
Inclusion modification	no	no	minor	yes	yes	yes	yes

* Chemical heating only

With the passage of time, customers are demanding higher quality steels, which requires:

- Lower impurity contents
- Better cleanliness (i.e. lower inclusion contents)
- Stringent quality control (i.e. less variation from heat-to-heat)
- Microalloying to impart superior properties
- Better surface quality and homogeneity in the cast product.

Figure 20.1 shows the trends in residuals attained so far as well as those projected for future in Japanese steel plants (Adachi 1990).

This chapter will present a brief outline of secondary steelmaking. For detailed treatment of the subject, the readers may refer to (Ghosh Ahindra 2001).

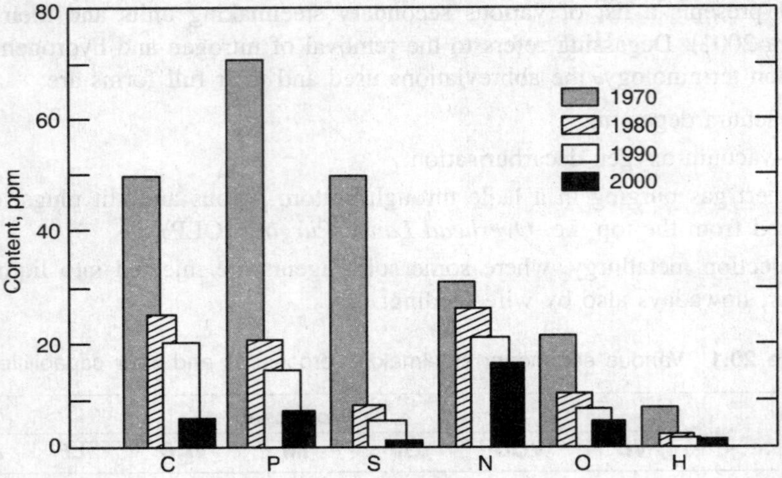

Figure 20.1 Minimum residual levels in steel in Japan.

20.2 INERT GAS PURGING (IGP)

This consists of purging molten steel by argon introduced from the bottom through porous bricks or slit plugs, fitted at the ladle bottom. Purging by argon through a top lance,which is immersed into the melt in an open ladle, is also practised. The primary objective is to stir the bath resulting in homogenisation of temperature and composition of the melt. It offers additional advantages of faster deoxidation and floatation of inclusions (i.e. superior cleanliness). All secondary steelmaking ladles, nowadays, have provision for gas purging.

Some typical designs of refractory purging plugs are shown in Figure 20.2. Over the last three decades, a large number of investigations have been carried out on fluid flow, mixing and mass transfer during gas purging. Fundamental studies have been conducted in *Water Models* at room temperature, in which the vessel used is a transparent perspex model. Water is used to simulate liquid metal. Figure 20.3 presents a sketch of typical water model. The rising gas bubbles create a central two-phase gas-liquid region, known as the *Plume*. The upward motion in the plume causes *recirculatory flow* in the rest of the liquid.

Chapter 4, Section 4.5.4 has very briefly touched on the mixing and the approximate relationship between mixing time and *specific stirring power,* which has been dealt with further in Chapter 17, Section 17.5. For bottom gas flow

$$t_{mix} \propto Q^{-m} \propto P^{-m} \tag{20.1}$$

where m is a fraction, Q is the specific bottom gas flow rate (say, in $Nm^3 \cdot s^{-1}$ per tonne of liquid steel) and P is the specific stirring power (say, in watts/tonne of steel). The mixing time (t_{mix}) is normally taken for a *degree of mixing* of 0.95, i.e. 95% of perfect mixing.

P is related to Q by the equation:

$$P = \frac{340QT}{M} \ln\left(1 + \frac{0.707H}{P_0}\right) \tag{20.2}$$

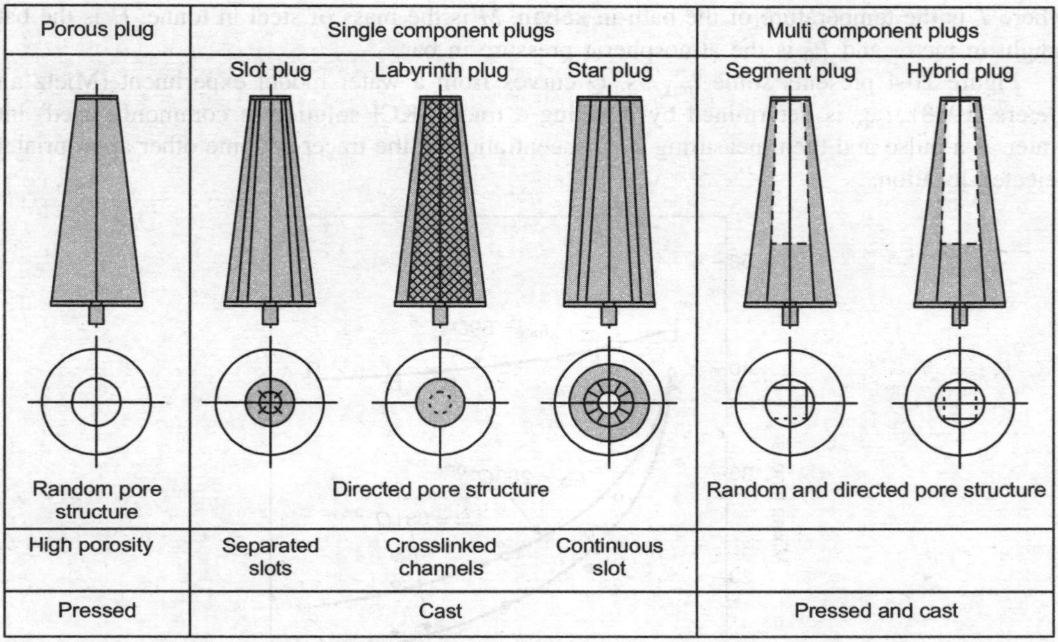

Porous plug
Single component plugs
Multi component plugs
Slot plug
Labyrinth plug
Star plug
Segment plug
Hybrid plug
Random pore structure
Directed pore structure
Random and directed pore structure
High porosity
Separated slots
Crosslinked channels
Continuous slot
Pressed
Cast
Pressed and cast

Figure 20.2 Different types of purging plugs.

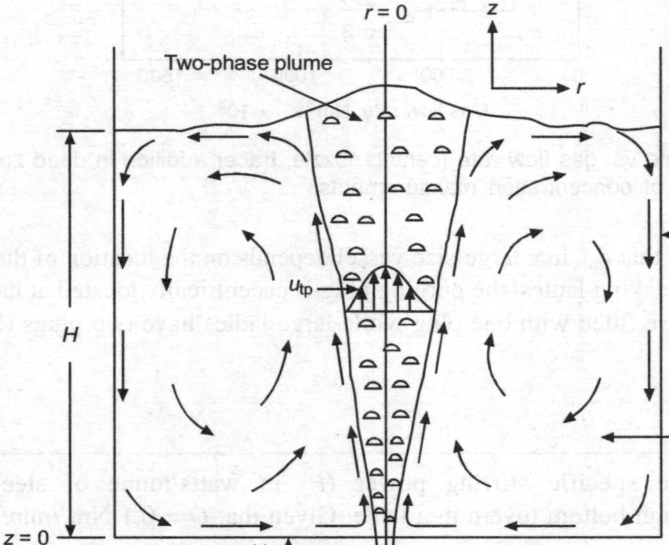

Figure 20.3 Schematic representation of the situation in a gas-stirred ladle.

where T is the temperature of the bath in kelvin, M is the mass of steel in tonne, H is the bath height in metre and P_0 is the atmospheric pressure in bar.

Figure 20.4 presents some t_{mix} vs. Q curves from a water model experiment (Mietz and Oeters, 1988). t_{mix} is determined by injecting a tracer (KCI solution is commonly used) into water as a pulse and then measuring the concentration of the tracer at some other appropriately selected location.

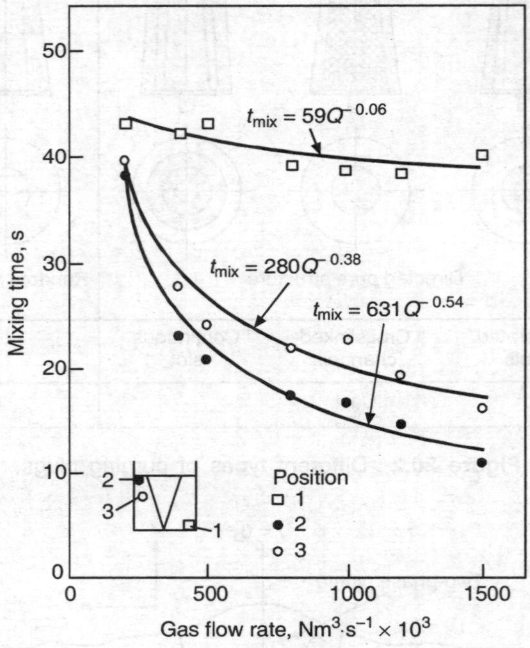

Figure 20.4 Mixing time vs. gas flow rate (centric nozzle, tracer addition in dead zone); 1, 2, 3 are locations of concentration measurements.

Figure 20.4 shows that t_{mix} in a large-size vessel depends on the location of the concentration measurement. In steelmaking ladles, the purging plug is eccentrically located at half radius at the bottom. Small ladles are fitted with one plug while large ladles have two plugs (Mazumdar and Guthrie, 1995).

EXAMPLE 20.1

(a) Calculate the specific stirring power (P) in watts/tonne of steel due to gas purging through bottom tuyere in a ladle. Given that $Q = 0.1$ Nm^3/min/t, $T = 1900$ K, $H = 1$ m.

(b) If the mixing time for the above condition is 60 s, what would be its value if Q is doubled? Assume $m = 1/2$.

Solution:

(a) From Eq. (20.2), $$P = \frac{340QT}{M} \ln\left(1 + \frac{0.707H}{P_0}\right)$$

Here, $\frac{Q}{M} = 0.1 \times \frac{1}{60}$, T = 1900 K, H = 1 m, P_0 = 1 bar (assumed).

Inserting these values in Eq. (20.2), P = 576 watts/tonne of steel.

(b) $t_{mix} \propto P^{-m} \propto Q^{-m}$. Noting that $m = \frac{1}{2}$, $\frac{(t_{mix}) \text{ at } 0.2\ \text{Nm}^3}{(t_{mix}) \text{ at } 0.1\ \text{Nm}^3} = 2^{-1/2}$.

Hence, t_{mix} at 0.2 Nm^3/min/t = 60 × $2^{-1/2}$ = 42.4 s.

20.3 DEOXIDATION OF LIQUID STEEL

In Chapter 15, Sections 15.4.1–15.4.4 the reaction of oxygen dissolved in the bath with Fe, Mn, C and Si has been discussed. Equilibrium relations were presented. Solubility of oxygen in molten iron in equilibrium with FeO also has been indicated there. It was mentioned that the turndown oxygen level in BOF steelmaking typically ranges between 600 and 1000 ppm, and is much higher than even for Fe–[O]–(FeO) equilibrium. In Chapter17, Section 17.7, some empirical correlations have been presented between dissolved carbon and oxygen in metal bath with slag FeO, MnO, etc.

Solubility of oxygen in solid steel is negligibly small. Therefore, during solidification of liquid steel, the excess oxygen is rejected by the solidifying metal. This excess oxygen causes defects by reacting with C, Mn, Si, etc. resulting in the formation of blowholes (primarily CO) and oxide inclusions (FeO–MnO, SiO_2, Al_2O_3, etc.). Evolution of CO has a significant influence on the structure and homogeneity of the cast metal as well. Therefore, dissolved oxygen levels in molten steel have to be lowered by the addition of strong oxide formers, such as Mn, Si, Al, Ca (as ferromanganese, ferrosilicon, silico-manganese, aluminium, calcium silicide) in the ladle. This is known as deoxidation.

Chapter18 has elaborated the fundamentals and application of immersion-type oxygen sensors for process control. They are used to determine the concentration of oxygen dissolved in molten steel very quickly. Similar sensors have been employed in the laboratory extensively, and also in secondary steelmaking to assess the extent of deoxidation.

20.3.1 Thermodynamics of Deoxidation of Molten Steel

A deoxidation reaction may be represented as:

$$x[\text{M}] + y[\text{O}] = (\text{M}_x\text{O}_y) \tag{20.3}$$

where M denotes the deoxidiser (Mn, Si, Al, etc.), and M_xO_y is the deoxidation product. The equilibrium constant for reaction (20.3) is given as

$$K_{\text{M}'} = \left\{\frac{(a_{\text{M}_x\text{O}_y})}{[h_\text{M}]^x\,[h_\text{O}]^y}\right\}_{\text{eq.}} \tag{20.4}$$

If the deoxidation product is a pure oxide (SiO_2, Al_2O_3, etc.), then $a_{M_xO_y} = 1$. Since wt. % M and O in steel are generally very low, h_M and h_O may be taken as their wt. percentages respectively (i.e. W_M and W_O). [*Note:* If this assumption is not made, then h_M and h_O are to be related to W_M and W_O through interaction coefficients as per the procedure given in Chapter 4, Section 4.3.4.] Then, Eq. (20.4) may be simplified as:

$$\left\{[W_M]^x [W_O]^y\right\}_{eq.} = \frac{1}{K_{M'}} = K_M \qquad (20.5)$$

where K_M is known as the *Deoxidation Constant*. Variation of K_M with temperature has the form:

$$\log K_M = -\frac{A}{T} + B \qquad (20.6)$$

where A and B are constants, which can be calculated from data available in literature. Table 20.2 presents typical K_M values for some common deoxidisers. The wt. % [O] in equilibrium with 0.1 wt. % M at 1600°C (1873 K) are respectively 0.413, 0.0145, 1.35×10^{-3} and 9.84×10^{-10} for Mn, Si, Al and Ca. According to this, calcium is the strongest and manganese the weakest amongst the deoxidisers. Si is stronger than Mn and Al is stronger than Si. This follows directly from the Ellingham Diagram for oxides (Figure 4.1) showing the relative stabilities of some oxides.

Table 20.2 Values of K_M for some deoxidisers

Deoxidant (M)	Deoxidation product	Concentration range of $M(W_M)$, if any	$\log_{10} K_M$	K_M at 1873K
Al	Al_2O_3	above 10^{-5}	$-\frac{64000}{T} + 20.57$	2.51×10^{-14}
C	CO (g)		$-\frac{1160}{T} - 2.003$	2.39×10^{-3}
Ce	Ce_2O_3		$-\frac{68500}{T} + 19.6$	10^{-17}
Cr	$FeCr_2O_4$	below 3.0	$-\frac{45796}{T} + 18.83$	2.39×10^{-6}
	Cr_2O_3	3.0–8.0	$-\frac{45531}{T} + 20.25$	8.72×10^{-5}
	Cr_3O_4	above 8.0	$-\frac{48850}{T} + 21.45$	2.23×10^{-5}
Mn	FeO–MnO (l) solution	below 0.2	$\log K_{Mn} = -\frac{6440}{T} + 2.93$	0.3102
			$\log K_{Mn\text{-}Fe} = -\frac{6525}{T} + 2.948$	0.29
	FeO–MnO (s) solution	above 0.2	$\log K_{Mn} = -\frac{6990}{T} + 3.01$	0.19

(Contd.)

Table 20.2 Values of K_M for some deoxidisers (Contd.)

Deoxidant (M)	Deoxidation product	Concentration range of $M(W_M)$, if any	$\log_{10} K_M$	K_M at 1873K
			$\log K_{Mn\text{-}Fe} = -\frac{6980}{T} + 2.91$	0.15
Si	SiO_2		$-\frac{30110}{T} + 11.4$	2.11×10^{-5}
Ti	Ti_3O_5	0.0004–0.4	$-\frac{90727}{T} + 29.15$	5.45×10^{-20}
	Ti_2O_3	above 0.4	$-\frac{55751}{T} + 17.90$	2.06×10^{-12}
Ca	CaO		$-\frac{32903}{T} + 7.56$	9.84×10^{-11}
Mg	MgO		$-\frac{32027}{T} + 8.47$	2.35×10^{-9}

When only one deoxidiser is added, it is known as a *Simple Deoxidation*. Mostly, a single oxide is formed as the product, except for mild deoxidisers, such as Cr and Mn, where the product is typically a slag $FeO–Cr_2O_3$ or FeO–MnO. For example, for deoxidation by Mn, the more appropriate equation is:

$$(MnO) + [Fe] = [Mn] + (FeO) \tag{20.7}$$

for which

$$K_{Mn\text{-}Fe} = \frac{[h_{Mn}] \times (a_{FeO})}{(a_{MnO})} = \frac{[W_{Mn}] \times (X_{FeO})}{(X_{MnO})} \tag{20.8}$$

where X is mole fraction, since, both Fe–Mn and FeO–MnO solutions are ideal.

If more than one deoxidiser is added to molten steel simultaneously, it is known as *Complex Deoxidation*. Some important complex deoxidisers are Si + Mn, Si + Mn + Al, Ca + Si, Ca + Si + Al. For this, the deoxidation product is a slag consisting of more than one oxide. Therefore, for thermodynamic analysis, activity vs. composition relationships in oxide solutions (for example, $CaO–SiO_2–Al_2O_3$ system, as shown in Figure 4.3) has to be considered. Generally, this requires the development of elaborate computer programmes with the aid of numerical techniques. Commercial packages (e.g. FACTSAGE) are available. For details, readers may refer to the paper (Choudhary et al. 2005).

EXAMPLE 20.2

Calculate the dissolved oxygen content of liquid steel containing 0.1% Si at equilibrium with solid SiO_2 at 1600°C.

Given: $e_{Si}^{Si} = 0.103$, $e_{Si}^{O} = -0.113$, $e_{O}^{O} = -0.20$, $e_{O}^{Si} = -0.066$

Solution: For the deoxidation reaction: $[Si]_{wt.\ \%} + 2[O]_{wt.\ \%} = SiO_2(s)$, from Table 20.2,

$$K_{Si} = [h_{Si}] \times [h_O]^2 = 2.11 \times 10^{-5} \quad \text{(Ex. 20.1)}$$

i.e.

$$[f_{Si} \cdot W_{Si}] \times [f_O \cdot W_O]^2 = 2.11 \times 10^{-5}$$

or

$$\log f_{Si} + \log W_{Si} + 2(\log f_O + \log W_O) = \log (2.11 \times 10^{-5}) \quad \text{(Ex. 20.2)}$$

$$\log f_{Si} = e_{Si}^{Si} \cdot W_{Si} + e_{Si}^{O} \cdot W_O = 0.103 \times 0.1 - 0.113 \times W_O$$

$$\log f_O = e_O^O \cdot W_O + e_O^{Si} \cdot W_{Si} = -0.20 W_O - 0.066 \times 0.1$$

Combining all these in Eq. (Ex. 20.2), it is possible to get:

$$2 \log W_O - 0.64 W_O = -3.649 \quad \text{(Ex.20.3)}$$

Eq. (Ex. 20.3) requires iterative procedure for solution. By trial and error, $[W_O] = 0.019$ wt. %.

20.3.2 Kinetics of Deoxidation of Molten Steel

Fundamental studies on deoxidation kinetics have been generally conducted in laboratory induction furnaces, and it may be subdivided into the following.

1. *Kinetics of deoxidation*, consisting of dissolution of deoxidisers into molten steel, chemical reaction between dissolved oxygen and the deoxidising element, nucleation and initial growth of the deoxidation product. The process is fast and gets completed in a minute or two.
2. *Kinetics of elimination of deoxidation products from liquid steel*, consisting of further growth of deoxidation products by agglomeration and their elimination from liquid steel; this is a slow process and is thus rate-limiting.

Figure 20.5 shows the change in the oxygen and inclusion content of steel from the tapping to the solidification stage, deoxidisers being added when steel is tapped into the ladle from the primary steelmaking furnace (Plockinger and Wahlster, 1960). The dissolved oxygen content as measured by an immersion oxygen sensor, decreases rapidly indicating the fast reaction kinetics. The *total oxygen content* is determined by collecting samples of molten steel and analysing the sample in a vacuum/inert gas fusion apparatus. It includes the oxygen in the oxides formed as deoxidation products as well. As shown in the Figure, the total oxygen is much higher than the dissolved oxygen, since the elimination of inclusions from liquid steel takes a long time.

The oxide products are lighter than liquid steel and are removed following floatation to the top of the melt. *Stokes' Law of Settling* applicable for *laminar flow*, is often used as a guide. It relates the *terminal velocity* of the particle (v_t) with some physical variables as:

$$v_t = \frac{gd^2(\rho_l - \rho_s)}{18\eta} \quad (20.9)$$

where g is acceleration due to gravity, d is the particle diameter, η is the viscosity of the liquid, ρ_l and ρ_s are densities of liquid steel and solid oxide respectively.

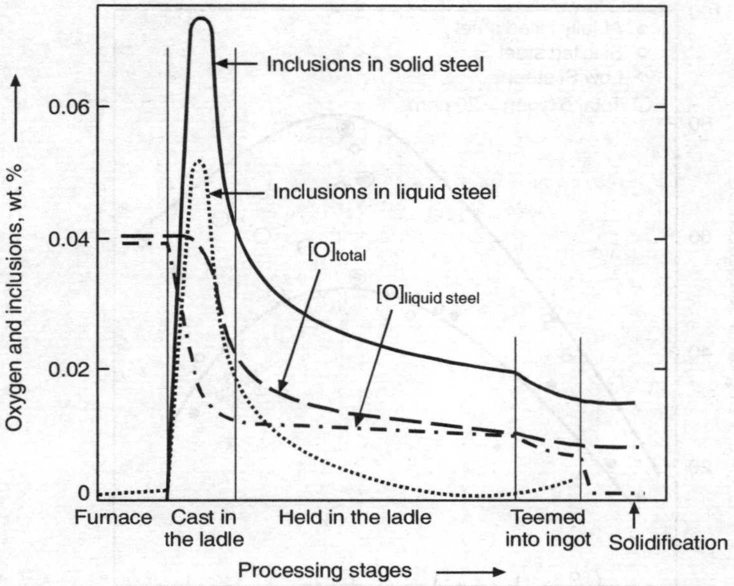

Figure 20.5 Change of oxygen and inclusion content of steel between tapping and solidification.

Since $v_t \propto d^2$, the larger particles float-up much faster than the smaller particles. Deoxidation products grow by collision and agglomeration. Collision of small particles is speeded up by turbulence. Agglomeration is better if the particles are liquid. This is where complex deoxidation has a significant advantage, since the product can be a liquid slag particle.

Turbulence also speeds up flotation of the solid particles. Inert gas purging in the ladle is, therefore, very beneficial as an aid to produce clean steel. This has been well-established through both laboratory and plant-scale experiments. The total oxygen content $[W_O(T)]$ at any time after deoxidiser addition may be approximately related to time by:

$$W_O(T) = [W_O(T)]_{initial} \cdot \exp(-k_O t) \quad (20.10)$$

where k_O is an empirical constant.

It increases with the increase in bottom gas flow rate, i.e. specific stirring power (P) as

$$k_O \propto P^n, \quad \text{where } n < 1 \quad (20.11)$$

However, trials in industrial ladles have established that there is an optimum stirring intensity beyond which, the effectiveness of deoxidation decreases, as shown in Figure 20.6 (Suzuki et al. 1982). This is because the flow in ladles is re-circulatory (see Figure 20.3), and excessive stirring causes re-entrainment of the floated oxides back into the melt. It also causes more oxidation by air. *Actually, from a more rigorous point of view, the final degree of deoxidation achieved is a dynamic balance between the rate of elimination of the oxide particles on one hand, and the rate of atmospheric oxidation on the other.*

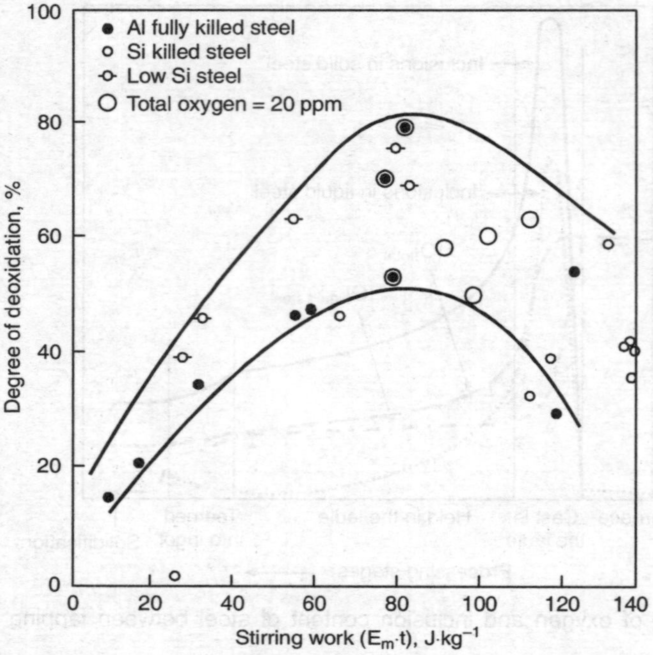

Figure 20.6 Effect of stirring on the degree of deoxidation.

20.3.3 The Ladle Furnace (LF)

Figure 20.7 shows the sketch of a ladle furnace. The ladle with liquid steel is brought to the LF station, where a top cover is placed on the ladle and graphite electrodes are introduced. It is the most commonly used unit in secondary steelmaking. In the LF, deoxidation and composition adjustments are carried out by additions, and the temperature of the melt is adjusted by arc heating. Bath stirring is achieved by means of argon purging from the bottom. The top cover gives significant protection from atmospheric oxidation, but is not completely sealed and some ingress of air is inevitable.

In the LF, besides deoxidiser and alloying additions, the slag is primarily modified by the addition of CaO, and sometimes by CaF_2 as well. The slag is basic, and its typical composition range is 50 to 56% CaO, 7 to 9% MgO (coming from burnt dolomite lining), 6 to 12% SiO_2, 20 to 25% Al_2O_3, 1 to 2% (FeO + MnO), 0.3% TiO_2 and occasionally some amount of CaF_2. The Al_2O_3, and to some extent SiO_2, are products of deoxidation by Al and Si. Percentages of utilisation of ladle additions for low carbon heats are 80 to 95% for Mn, 50 to 70% for Si, and 30–65% for Al. Aluminium is costly, and hence its poor utilisation is a matter of concern. In order to improve it, the modern practice is to go in for aluminium wire feeding instead of addition as ingots or cubes.

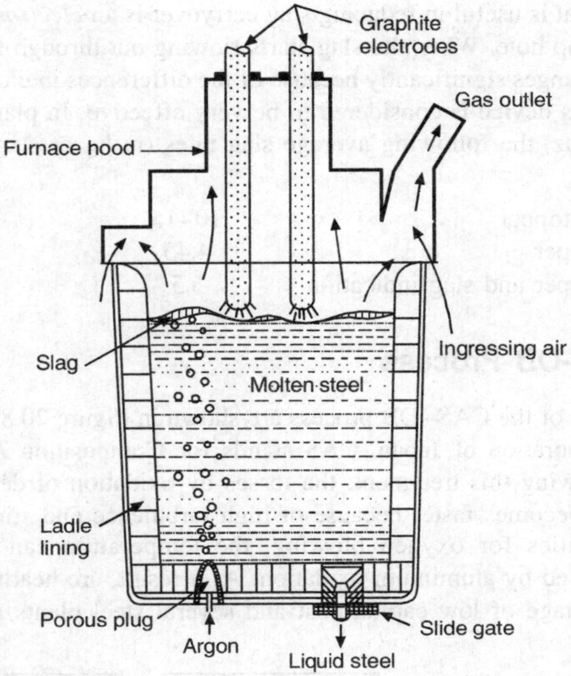

Figure 20.7 Sketch of a ladle furnace.

20.3.4 Problem of Slag Carryover

The primary steelmaking slag has a high percentage of iron oxide (see Section 15.3). A portion of this slag comes into the ladle during tapping because of *slag carryover*. Owing to its high iron oxide content, a significant quantity of deoxidiser is consumed by it. Another serious problem is what is known as *Phosphorus Reversion* in ladles from slag to metal. High concentration of iron oxide in slag is a major factor for the retention of phosphorus in slag. Deoxidation of slag, therefore, tends to transfer phosphorus back from slag into metal. Therefore, modern steel melting shops aim at *slag-free tapping*; however, complete prevention of slag carryover is seldom achieved and minimisation becomes the objective.

Formation of a funnel-shaped gas core during emptying of liquid from a vessel (such as a kitchen sink) is a common experience. During tapping of liquid steel from a BOF or any other furnace, or teeming from the ladle or tundish into the continuous casting mould, such a funnel causes the top slag to flow out along with the metal, towards the end when the liquid metal level is very low. Some fundamental studies have been conducted on this phenomenon in water models (Shankarnarayanan and Guthrie, 1992).

For minimising slag carryover, a plug-shaped refractory piece, known as a *dart*, is dropped into the converter towards the latter stages of tapping. Its density is in between that of slag and metal, which makes it float between the metal and slag layers. When it gets dragged into the funnel owing to vortex formation, it blocks the nozzle and significantly prevents slag carryover. In electric furnaces, eccentric bottom tapping is practiced to minimise slag carry over.

Another device that is useful in reducing slag carryover is an *electromagnetic sensor*, which is placed around the tap hole. When the slag starts flowing out through the tap hole nozzle, the nature of the signal changes significantly because of the differences in electromagnetic induction of slag and metal. This device is considered to be very effective. In plant trials with 130/140 t BOF converters at Linz, the following average slag rates (in kg of slag per tonne steel) were obtained:

- Without slag stopper 10–15
- With slag stopper 4.45
- With slag stopper and slag indication 3.5

20.3.5 The CAS-OB Process

The important features of the CAS–OB process are shown in Figure 20.8. It has been developed by Nippon Steel Corporation of Japan. CAS stands for **C**omposition **A**djustments by **S**ealed argon bubbling. Following this treatment, the losses by oxidation of deoxidisers and alloys is low. The dissolution becomes faster because of high turbulence and stirring at the plume eye. With additional facilities for oxygen blowing, the temperature can be raised because of exothermic heat supplied by aluminium oxidation. As a result, arc heating is not required. The process has the advantage of low capital cost and several steel plants around the world have installed it.

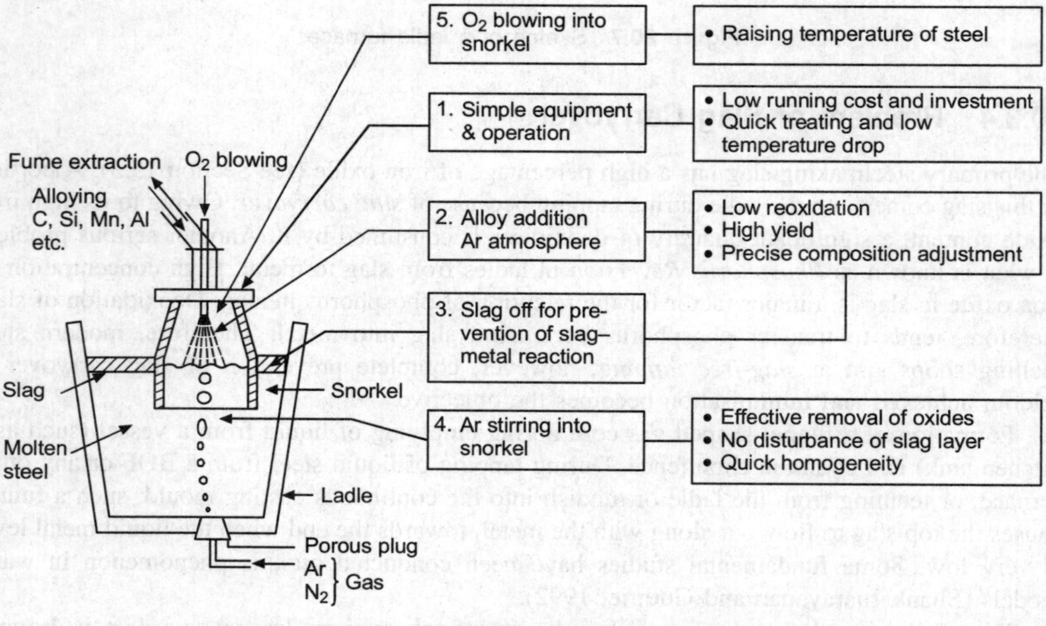

Figure 20.8 Salient features of the CAS–OB process.

20.4 DEGASSING AND DECARBURISATION OF LIQUID STEEL

The gases, i.e. hydrogen, nitrogen and oxygen, dissolve as atomic H, N, O respectively in molten steel. However, their solubilities in solid steel are very low. Section 20.3 has already dealt with oxygen. Removal of oxygen from steel is carried out by adding deoxidisers. When liquid steel solidifies, excess nitrogen forms stable nitrides of Al, Si, Cr, etc. The dissolved nitrogen affects the toughness and ageing characteristics of steel as well as enhancing the tendency towards stress corrosion cracking. Nitrogen is, by and large, considered to be harmful for properties of steel. Its strain hardening effect does not allow extensive cold working without intermittent annealing and hence low nitrogen is essential for deep drawing steels. However, in some applications, nitrogen has a beneficial effect, such as the grain refinement by fine AlN precipitates.

While nitrogen is absorbed by molten steel during steelmaking from nitrogen in air, hydrogen is picked-up from the moisture in solid charges. Hydrides are thermodynamically unstable. Therefore, the excess hydrogen in solid steel tends to form H_2 gas in the pores and also diffuses out to the atmosphere, since H has very high diffusivity even in solid steel because of its low atomic mass. In relatively thin sections, such as those produced by rolling, diffusion is fairly rapid. Hence, excess hydrogen is less, reducing the tendency towards the development of high gas pressure and the formation of pinholes.

However, diffusion is not that efficient in forgings because of their large sizes. So H rejected by the solidifying steel accumulates in blowholes and pinholes, where high gas pressure is developed. During forging, the combination of hot working stresses and high gas pressure in the pinholes near the surface tend to cause fine cracks in the surface region. Efforts to avoid these cracks have led to the commercial development of vacuum degassing processes. Dissolved hydrogen also causes a loss of ductility of steel; hence, low H content is a necessity for superior grades of steel with high strength and impact resistance. These considerations have led to the requirement of low hydrogen in rolled products as well as in several grades of steel.

20.4.1 Thermodynamics of Degassing Reactions

The reactions are:

$$[H] = \frac{1}{2}H_2(g) \tag{20.12}$$

$$[H] = \frac{1}{2}N_2(g) \tag{20.13}$$

$$[C] + [O] = CO(g) \tag{20.14}$$

Table 20.3 presents the equilibrium relations for the above reactions. Degassing is effective under vacuum. Low gas pressure lowers values of *h*. At such low concentrations, *h* may be expressed as concentration in ppm (i.e. parts per million), and in weight per cent at higher concentrations.

Table 20.3 Equilibrium relations of degassing reactions

Sl. No.	Reaction	Equilibrium relation	Unit of *h*	*K* vs. *T* relation	Value at 1600°C and 1 mm Hg
1.	$[H] = \frac{1}{2}H_2(g)$	$[h_H] = K_H \cdot p_{H_2}^{1/2}$	ppm	$\log K_H = -\frac{1905}{T} + 2.409$	0.77
2.	$[N] = \frac{1}{2}N_2(g)$	$[h_N] = K_N \cdot p_{N_2}^{1/2}$	ppm	$\log K_N = \frac{518}{T} + 2.937$	14.1
3.	$[C]+[O] = CO(g)$	$[h_C][h_O] = K_{CO} \cdot p_{CO}$	wt. %	$\log K_{CO} = -\frac{1160}{T} - 2.00$	4.7×10^{-4}
			ppm	$\log K_{CO} = -\frac{1160}{T} + 6.00$	0.47

1 matmosphere = 10^{-3} atm; for [C]–[O] reaction, h_C = 0.05 wt.%, i.e. 500 ppm.

As noted in Table 20.3 (Ghosh Ahindra 2001), a pressure of 1 torr (= 1 mm Hg) in a vacuum chamber is thermodynamically capable of lowering H, N and O to very low levels. This is in contrast to steels not treated under vacuum, where the H and N values can be as high as 5 ppm and 50 ppm respectively. In actual degassing operations, removal of hydrogen is fast and it often attains equilibrium, but nitrogen removal is more difficult because of kinetic reasons. The [C]–[O] reaction is utilised for removal of carbon to very low levels (ultra-low carbon steels) for special applications, such as sheets for automobile bodies. Besides the main reactions during vacuum degassing, there are some minor side reactions such as volatilisation, decomposition of inclusions and melt-refractory interactions, but these are being omitted here for the sake of brevity of this text.

20.4.2 Kinetics of Desorption and Absorption of Nitrogen by Liquid Steel

As mentioned above, the removal of nitrogen during vacuum treatment poses problems on account of slow kinetics. The extent of nitrogen removal is approximately in the range of 20 to 40% Therefore, the salient features of desorption and absorption of nitrogen by molten steel are being presented here. Owing to its importance as well as its complex nature, it has been investigated by many investigators from as early as 1960s in the laboratory along with several theoretical analyses. The findings can be summarised as follows.

1. The rate is controlled by all the kinetic steps, viz. mass transfer in the melt, slow surface chemical reaction, as well as mass transfer in the gas phase.
2. The surface chemical reaction was originally treated as a first order reversible process. The rate of desorption from the melt (r_N) was given by the equation:

$$r_N = Ak_N([W_N] - [W_N]_e) \tag{20.15}$$

   where, A is the gas–metal interfacial area, k_N is the *first-order rate constant*, $[W_N]$ and $[W_N]_e$ are wt. % N in the melt and that at equilibrium with N_2 in the gas phase. However, of late, the surface chemical reaction has been proposed to be a *second-order* reaction.

3. k_N was found to decrease with increasing wt. % of oxygen dissolved in the melt as shown in Figure 20.9 (Pehlke and Elliot, 1963). It was subsequently found that sulphur has a similar effect. It is well-established that O and S are *surface active solutes* in molten iron, copper, etc. Thus they tend to block the surface sites and thus retard the rate.

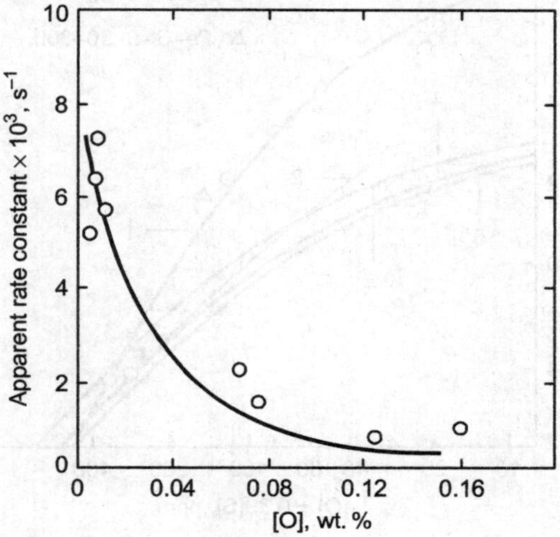

Figure 20.9 Influence of oxygen content on the absorption rate of nitrogen by liquid iron at 1823 K.

Figure 20.10 taken from a comprehensive kinetic study by Harada and Janke (1989), shows the variation of the second-order chemical rate constant (k_c) with oxygen and sulphur contents of the iron melt. Curve 1 and data points correspond to experiments under vacuum. These do not agree with experiments under normal pressure (curves 3, 4, 5). The authors did not provide any satisfactory explanation for the same. The retarding influence of O and S dissolved in molten steel is very well-established for vacuum degassing in steel plants as well. Therefore, the melt should be well-deoxidised and well-desulphurised first for efficient removal of nitrogen from steel.

20.4.3 Vacuum Degassing Processes

For more comprehensive information, besides (Ghosh Ahindra 2001), readers may consult other sources such as (Fruehan 1990). Vacuum degassing processes have been traditionally classified into the following categories:

- Ladle degassing processes (VD, VOD, VAD)
- Stream degassing processes
- Circulation degassing processes (DH and RH).

Currently, stream degassing no longer exists. Ladle degassing processes are widely used. Amongst the circulation degassing processes, DH is virtually non-existent, while the RH (Ruhrstahl Heraus) process and its variants are the most popular.

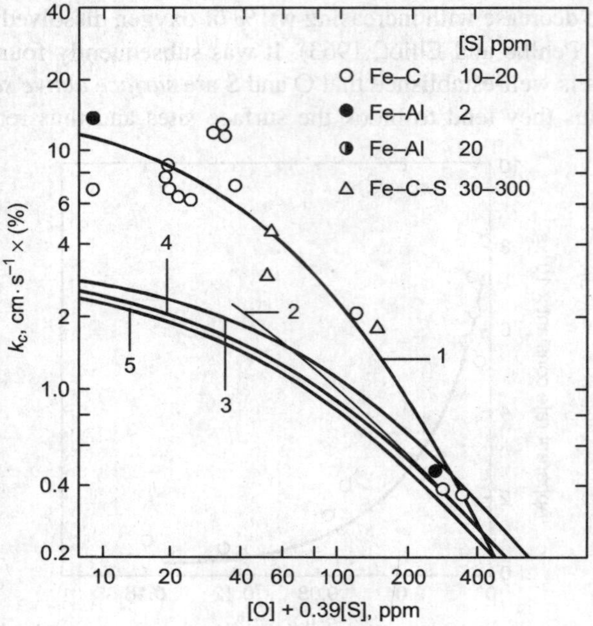

Figure 20.10 Variation of the second order rate constant for nitrogen desorption with dissolved oxygen and sulphur content of molten steel at 1873 K.

Since, an additional temperature drop of 20–40°C occurs during secondary steelmaking and temperature control of the steel melt is important for proper casting, provisions for heating and temperature adjustment have been made in RH, as well as in ladle degassing [*vacuum arc degassing* (VAD)]. *Vacuum-oxygen decarburisation* (VOD) where oxygen lancing is done under vacuum was originally developed for stainless steel refining, but is now used for the production of *ultra-low carbon steels* (ULC) as well. Similarly, RH–OB, where oxygen is blown into the RH chamber, is used for the production of ULC steels.

Besides degassing and decarburisation, modern vacuum degassers are used to carry out various other functions such as desulphurisation, heating, alloying and melt homogenisation. Injection of argon below the melt is a must for good homogenisation, fast processing and inclusion removal. The carry over slag from steelmaking converters has to be modified by the addition of deoxidisers and CaO.

Figure 20.11 shows the RH process schematically. Molten steel is contained in the ladle. The two legs of the vacuum chamber (known as *Snorkels*) are immersed into the melt. Argon is injected into the upleg. Rising and expanding argon bubbles provide pumping action and lift the liquid into the vacuum chamber, where it disintegrates into fine droplets, gets degassed and comes down through the downleg snorkel, causing melt circulation. The entire vacuum chamber is refractory lined. There is provision for argon injection from the bottom, heating, alloy additions, sampling and sighting as well as video display of the interior of the vacuum chamber.

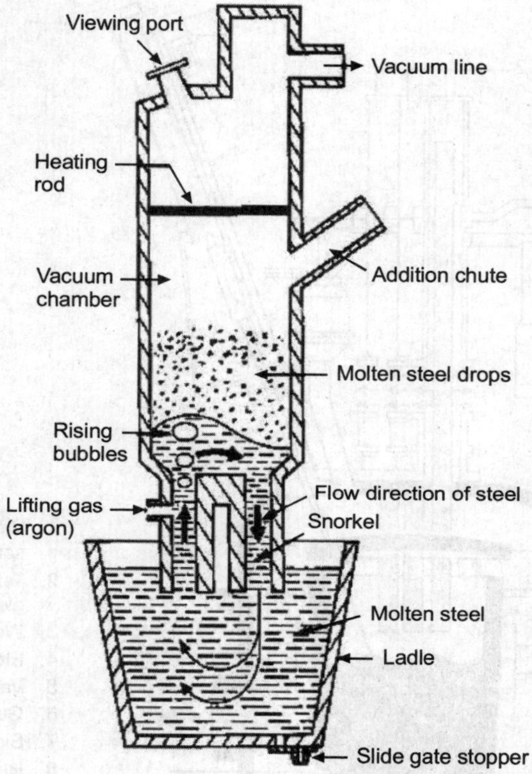

Figure 20.11 Sketch of a RH degasser (Courtesy: Messo Metallurgie).

Figure 20.12 shows the VAD process schematically. Heating is done by the arc with graphite electrodes, as in a ladle furnace. Heating, degassing, slag treatment and alloy adjustment are carried out without interrupting the vacuum.

As far as the vacuum generating system is concerned, mechanical vacuum pumps remove the bulk of air and gas from the chamber. However, they are not capable of lowering the vacuum chamber pressure to very low values of about 1 torr, which is required by the process. This is achieved by the use of steam ejector pumps in conjunction with mechanical pumps. A jet of steam issues through a nozzle at high velocity and drags the surrounding gases along with it (i.e. jet entrainment). Steam also helps in condensing the dust and volatiles coming out from the vacuum chamber. For a modern 200 t VD unit, a pumping capacity higher than 500 kg of air per hour with 1 torr chamber pressure is required.

In industrial vacuum degassing, the treatment time should be short enough to match logistically with converter steelmaking on the one hand and continuous casting on the other. To achieve this, in addition to proper choice and design of the process, the principal variables are as follows:

- Pumping rate of the vacuum equipment (also known as *exhausting rate*)
- Rate of injection of argon below the melt.

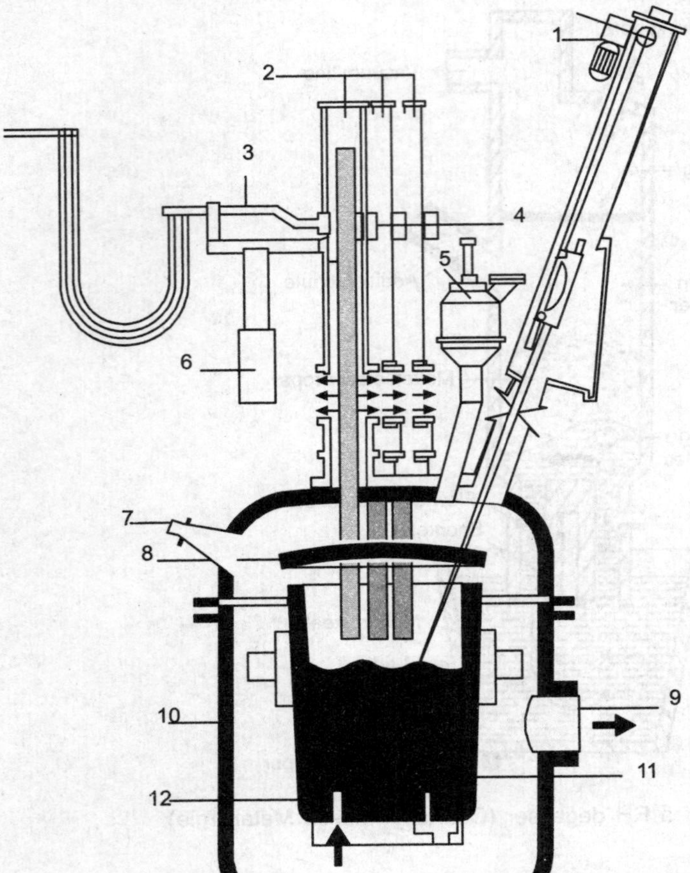

1. Vacuum temperature and sampling lance
2. Telescopic tubes for vacuum-tight electrode sealing
3. Water-cooled high-current system
4. Electrode clamping mechanism
5. Vacuum lock for alloying agents
6. Guide mast for electrode control
7. Sight glass with rotor
8. Heat shield
9. Vacuum connection
10. Vacuum treatment vessel
11. Steel casting ladle
12. Inert gas bubbling brick (porous plug)

Figure 20.12 Sketch of a VAD unit (Courtesy: Messo Metallurgie).

Increasing the argon flow rate increases the rate of degassing and gas evolution. This tends to raise the chamber pressure and requires a higher exhausting rate. Hence, optimisation of the two is required. Figure 20.13 presents some theoretically calculated curves with different values of reaction rate constants (k) for a RH degasser (Soejima et al. 1987). It shows that there is no advantage in increasing the pumping rate if the argon flow rate is not adequate. Also, there is no advantage of having large argon flow rates until there is a certain minimum exhausting rate.

20.4.4 Manufacture of Ultra-Low Carbon (ULC) Steel by RH-OB Process

It has already been mentioned that the use of oxygen blowing under vacuum (VOD process) was started for refining stainless steel. Prior to VOD, the *argon–oxygen decarburisation* (AOD)

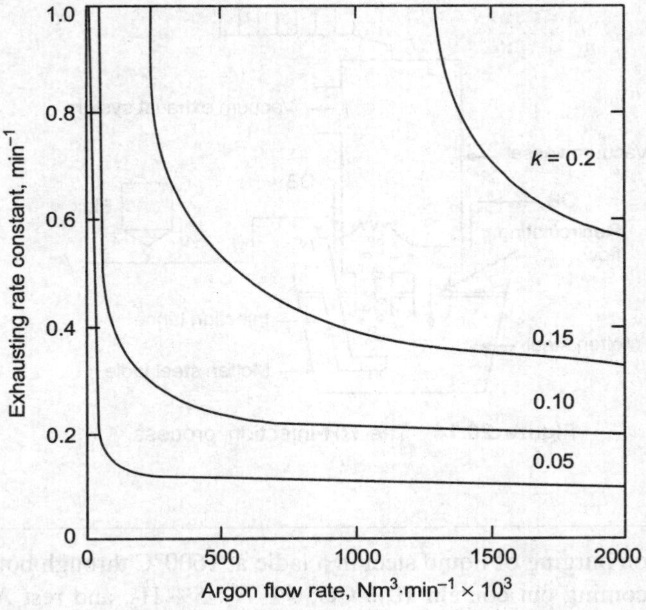

Figure 20.13 Influence of pumping rate and argon flow on decarburisation rate constant in a RH degasser.

process was invented. The thermodynamic basis for these processes had already been known for some time. However, AOD was not commercially viable till the price of argon became reasonably low. These will be taken up further in Chapter 21 dealing with stainless steel manufacture.

To meet the increasing demand for cold-rolled sheets with improved mechanical properties and to cope with the changeover from batch to continuous annealing, the demand for ULC ($C < 20$ ppm) is increasing. As stated in Section 20.4.3 that, in this connection, the RH process was modified by oxygen blowing under vacuum. It is known as RH-OB and was first developed by Nippon Steel Corp. in Japan for producing stainless steel in 1972 and subsequently, employed for the production of ULC steels. The present thrust is to bring down the carbon content of the melt from 300 ppm to 10–20 ppm in 10 minutes. RH-OB was subsequently made more versatile by incorporating provisions for chemical heating by aluminium addition. Oxidation of aluminium generates heat rapidly and counters temperature drop during degassing. Powder injection for desulphurisation, alloy additions, etc. were later incorporated. This versatile and flexible process is known as the *RH-injection process,* and is shown in Figure 20.14.

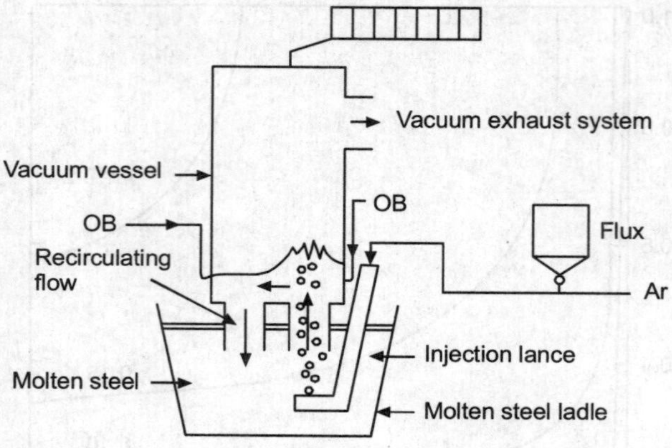

Figure 20.14 The RH-injection process.

EXAMPLE 20.3

(a) Consider argon purging of liquid steel in a ladle at 1600°C through bottom tuyeres. The gas bubbles coming out contain 10% CO, 5% N_2, 5% H_2, and rest Ar. Assuming the gas to be at equilibrium with molten steel at the exit, calculate the hydrogen content of steel. The steel contains 1% C, 2% Mn and 0.5% Si.

Given: $e_H^C = 0.06,\ e_H^{Mn} = -0.002,\ e_H^{Si} = 0.027,\ e_H^H = 0$

(b) Calculate the rate of circulation of molten steel (R) through the vacuum chamber in RH degassing to lower the hydrogen content of steel from 5 to 2 ppm in 15 minutes. Assume that molten steel attains equilibrium with respect to hydrogen gas inside the vacuum chamber.

Given: (i) Composition and temperature of steel same as in (a) above, (ii) pressure in the vacuum chamber is 1 milli-atmosphere, (iii) weight of steel in the ladle (W) is 150 tonnes.

Solution:

(a) The reaction is: $$[H] = \frac{1}{2}H_2(g) \qquad (20.12)$$

From Table 20.3, $[h_H] = K_H \cdot p_{H_2}^{1/2}$; $\log K_H = -\dfrac{1905}{T} + 2.409$, where the unit of h is ppm. T = 1873 K, p_{H_2} = 0.05 atm at the bubble exit at the top of the melt. Solving with the above values, h_H = 5.5 ppm = 5.5×10^{-4} in wt. % scale.

$$\log h_H = \log f_H + \log W_H = e_H^C \cdot W_C + e_H^{Mn} \cdot W_{Mn} + e_H^{Si} \cdot W_{Si} + e_H^H \cdot W_H + \log W_H$$

Putting in values, and solving, the following can be obtained: $W_H = 4.69 \times 10^{-4}$ wt. %
= 4.69 ppm

(b) Hydrogen Balance

$m_1^* $ = Rate of removal of H from steel (g/min)

$m_2^* $ = Rate at which H is transferred to vacuum (g/min) (Ex. 20.4)

$$m_1^* = -W \times 10^6 \times \frac{d[\text{ppm}]\times 10^{-6}}{dt} = -W \times \frac{d[\text{ppm}]}{dt} \quad \text{(Ex. 20.5)}$$

$$m_2^* = R \times 10^6 \times \{[\text{ppm H}] - [\text{ppm H}]_{eq}\} \times 10^{-6} = R\{[\text{ppm H}] - [\text{ppm H}]_{eq}\} \quad \text{(Ex. 20.6)}$$

Equating Eqs. (Ex. 20.5) and (Ex. 20.6),

$$\frac{d[\text{ppm H}]}{[\text{ppm H}] - [\text{ppm H}]_{eq}} = \frac{R}{W} dt \quad \text{(Ex. 20.7)}$$

Integrating Eq. (Ex. 20.7) between the limits: $t = 0$, ppm H = 5, and $t = 15$ min, ppm H = 2,

$$R = \frac{150}{15} \ln \frac{5 - [\text{ppm H}]_{eq}}{2 - [\text{ppm H}]_{eq}}$$

On the basis of part (a), and assuming that the gas in the vacuum chamber is only H_2, calculations give $[\text{ppm H}]_{eq}$ = 0.66 ppm, thus giving R = 11.75 tonnes/min.

20.5 DESULPHURISATION IN SECONDARY STEELMAKING

Except in free-cutting steels, sulphur is considered to be a harmful impurity, since it causes hot shortness. Therefore, it is necessary to limit it to 0.02% for general carbon steels. In special steel plates, the normal specification for sulphur is at present 0.005%, but there is demand for *ultra-low sulphur* (ULS) steels with as low as 10 ppm (0.001%) S in grades such as line-pipe steel, HIC resistant steels and alloyed steel forgings.

Sulphur comes into iron principally through coke ash, and is effectively removed first during ironmaking (see Chapter 5, Section 5.4.3) and further during hot metal pre-treatment in ladles (see Chapter 16). However, levels below 0.01% have to be achieved by further desulphurisation during secondary steelmaking. There are now processes such as the MPE process of Mannesman and the EXOSLAG process of U.S. Steel, where desulphurisation is done, to some extent, by adding a synthetic slag. Desulphurisation by use of synthetic slags is also carried in IGP, ladle furnace and vacuum degasser; but deep desulphurisation can only be achieved by the injection of powders like calcium silicide into the melt.

20.5.1 Thermodynamic Aspects

Chapter 4, Section 4.4.3, has introduced the concept of *Sulphide Capacity* (C_s) as the potential capacity of a slag melt, at a temperature, to hold sulphur as sulphide. Equations (4.50) to (4.52) have given the definition and mathematical expressions related to C_s. Chapter 5, Section 5.4.3 has discussed thermodynamics of sulphur reactions in the blast furnace hearth between slag and metal. The *equilibrium partition coefficient for sulphur* ($L_{S,e}$) is defined as:

$$L_{S,e} = \left\{\frac{(W_S)_{\text{in slag}}}{[W_S]_{\text{in metal}}}\right\}_{eq} = K_{39}\frac{(a_{O^{2-}})}{[W_O]_{eq}} \qquad (5.41)$$

where W_S is wt. % sulphur and K_{39} is the equilibrium constant for the ionic exchange reaction:

$$[S] + (O^{2-}) = (S^{2-}) + [O] \qquad (5.39)$$

It was also mentioned that the reaction can be written in terms of compounds, and that CaO is the most powerful desulphuriser, amongst the basic oxides present in iron and steelmaking slags. Sulphur transfer from metal to slag is better if the value of $L_{S,e}$ is higher. For this, from Eq. (5.41), it follows that the dissolved oxygen in metal, , should be as low as possible. This requires the addition of deoxidising agents into the melt.

Secondary steelmaking slags consist of CaO, Al_2O_3 and SiO_2 as the major constituents. Amongst the common deoxidisers, aluminium is the most powerful (see Section 20.3.1). Low oxygen levels can be achieved by deoxidation (referred to as *killing*, in popular terminology) using Al, and these are known as *aluminium-killed steels*.

On the basis of the above, the overall reaction may be written as:

$$3(CaO) + 3[S] + 2[Al] = 3(CaS) + (Al_2O_3) \qquad (20.16)$$

for which the equilibrium constant is:

$$K_{16} = \frac{(a_{CaS})^3(a_{Al_2O_3})}{(a_{CaO})^3[h_S]^3[h_{Al}]^2} \qquad (20.17)$$

Assuming $h_S = W_S$, $h_{Al} = W_{Al}$, and (W_S) in slag proportional to (a_{CaS}), it is possible to write:

$$L_{S,e} = \left\{\frac{(W_S)}{[W_S]}\right\}_{eq} \propto (a_{CaO})\frac{[W_{Al}]^{2/3}}{(a_{Al_2O_3})^{1/3}} \qquad (20.18)$$

Increasing wt. % of CaO increases a_{CaO} and decreases $a_{Al_2O_3}$, thereby increasing $L_{S,e}$. Figure 20.15 demonstrates this and shows that $L_{S,e}$ increases with increase in wt. % CaO in slag and W_{Al} in molten steel for CaO–Al_2O_3 slags at 1500°C and 1650°C (Turkdogan 1983). K_{16} is a function of temperature, and is given as:

$$\log K_{16} = \frac{48580}{T} - 16.997 \qquad (20.19)$$

where T is the temperature in kelvin. Hence, the lower temperature helps desulphurisation.

Suppose, the initial $[W_S]$ in steel is 0.01% and it is to be brought down to 0.002%. Let the mass of steel be 150 tonne and that of slag be 2 tonnes. It means that the amount of sulphur to be transferred to the slag would be $150 \times (0.01 - 0.002) \times 10^{-2}$ tonnes. Therefore, wt. % S in slag (W_S) would be $\frac{150 \times 0.008 \times 10^{-2}}{2} \times 10^2 = 0.6\%$. So, final $L_S = \frac{0.6}{0.002} = 300$. Since equilibrium may not be attained in the process, $L_{S,e}$ should be larger than 300. Plant trials have shown that it is possible to have effective desulphurisation, if $L_{S,e}$ is 1000 or above. Such a high value is obtained when the slag is almost saturated with CaO.

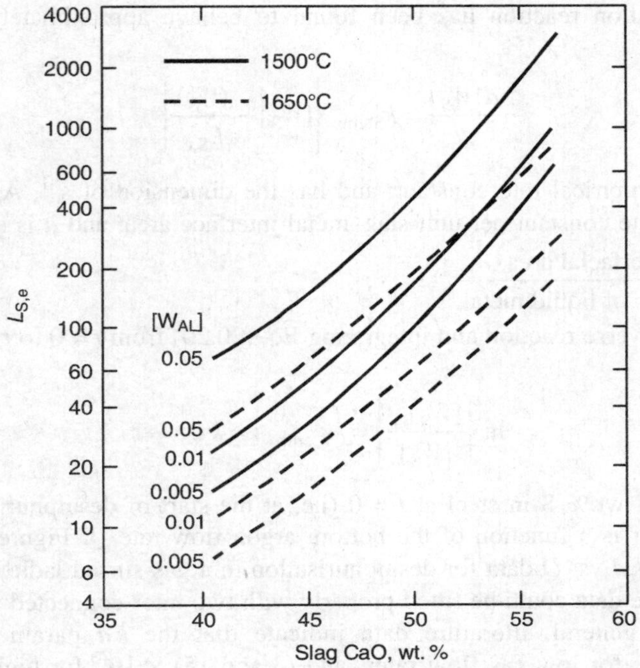

Figure 20.15 Equilibrium sulphur partition ratio between liquid iron with dissolved Al and CaO–Al_2O_3 slags.

20.5.2 Kinetic Aspects

Nowadays it is a standard practice to carry out some desulphurisation of hot metal in the transfer ladle after tapping from the blast furnace and before charging it into the primary steelmaking furnace. This is known as *external desulphurisation* and is a part of *hot metal ladle pre-treatment*. It has been discussed in Chapter 16, and, in this connection, the kinetic aspects of desulphurisation in ladles have been reviewed. Hence, the following brief write-up is concerned only with special kinetic features of desulphurisation in ladles during secondary steelmaking.

The major difference between the two is that normally the hot metal ladles do not have bottom stirring through porous plugs, while in secondary steelmaking, ladles are fitted with bottom porous plugs for argon purging. Therefore, in hot metal desulphurisation, a lance has to be immersed into the melt from the top for gas stirring and injection of desulphurising agents. This comes under the broad area of *Injection Metallurgy* (IM).

As stated in the introductory remarks (Section 20.5), IM is practiced in secondary steelmaking only for deep desulphurisation for the production of ultra-low sulphur (ULS) steels. Otherwise, desulphurisation by treatment with synthetic slag on top of molten steel in the ladle, ladle furnace or during vacuum treatment is sufficient. The principal additions are CaO and Al, though some CaF_2, SiO_2 and Al_2O_3 are also required for slag formation.

The desulphurisation reaction has been found to behave approximately as a first-order reversible process

$$-\frac{d[W_S]}{dt} = k_{S,emp}\left\{[W_S] - \frac{(W_S)}{L_{S,e}}\right\} \tag{20.20}$$

where $k_{S,\,emp}$ is an empirical rate constant, and has the dimension of s^{-1}. Again, $k_{S,emp} = ka$, where k is specific rate constant per unit slag–metal interface area, and a is specific interfacial area, i.e. $a = \dfrac{\text{interfacial area}}{\text{volume of liquid metal}}$.

Neglecting the reverse reaction and integrating Eq. (20.20) from $t = 0$ to $t = t$, the following can be obtained

$$\ln\left\{\frac{[W_S]_O}{[W_S]}\right\} = k_{S,\,emp} \cdot t = kat \tag{20.21}$$

where $[W_S]_O$ is initial wt.% S in steel at $t = 0$ (i.e. at the start of desulphurisation).

The ka parameter is a function of the bottom argon flow rate Q. Figure 20.16 presents a log-log plot of some ka vs. Q data for desulphurisation in a gas-stirred ladle of pilot plant size (Asai et al. 1983). The data could be fitted properly with two inter-connected straight lines with different slopes. In general, literature data indicate that the ka parameter lies between (0.5 and 3) × 10^{-3} s^{-1} for low gas flow rates, and (3 and 15) × 10^{-3} for high gas flow rates.

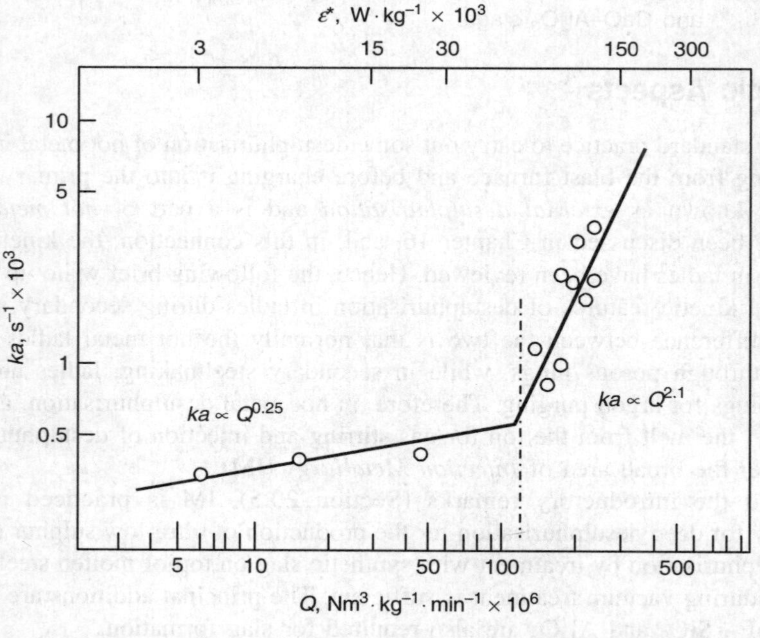

Figure 20.16 Effect of gas flow rate on *ka* parameter for desulphurisation reaction.

Therefore, effective desulphurisation in gas-stirred ladles is possible only above a critical minimum gas flow rate. Porous plugs are not suitable, since only slit plugs are capable of delivering such high flow rates. From experiments in water models, it has been found that at high gas flow rates there is extensive slag–metal emulsion formation, resulting in a large slag–metal interfacial area, which speeds-up sulphur transfer from the metal to slag.

EXAMPLE 20.4

For ladle desulphurisation of liquid steel, calculate the following.

(a) Wt. % sulphur in steel after desulphurisation, assuming slag–metal equilibrium

(b) Initial desulphurisation rate, assuming initial S in slag as 0.1% and $k_{S,emp}$ as 2×10^{-3} s^{-1}

(c) Per cent desulphurisation after 2.5 minutes of slag treatment.

Given: Temperature = 1650°C, Slag is CaO–Al_2O_3 having 55 wt. % CaO, Wt. % Al in metal = 0.05%, Steel weight = 150 tonnes, Slag weight = 2 tonnes, Initial wt. % S in steel = 0.01%.

Solution:

(a) From Figure 20.15, for the conditions mentioned, the equilibrium slag–metal sulphur partition ratio ($L_{S,e}$) is approximately 500. If detailed slag composition is used, a more exact value could be calculated (see Example 4.9, Chapter 4).

Initial amount of sulphur in metal = amount of sulphur in slag + metal at equilibrium (in kg)

i.e. $150 \times 0.01 \times 10^{-2} \times 10^3 = 10^{-2} \times 10^3 \{150[W_S]_f + 2(W_S)_f\}$, in kg

where $[W_S]_f$ and $(W_S)_f$ are final wt. % S in metal and slag respectively.

i.e. $15 = 10\,[W_S]_f\,(150 + 2 \times 500)$ kg

Calculations give $[W_S]_f = 0.0013\%$

(b) From Eq. (20.20), the rate of desulphurisation = $-\dfrac{d[W_S]}{dt} = k_{S,emp}\left[[W_S] - \dfrac{(W_S)}{L_{S,e}}\right]$

Noting that $k_{S,emp} = 2 \times 10^{-3}$, and other data given above,
Rate of desulphurisation initially = $2 \times 10^{-3}\,[0.01 - 0.1/500] = 1.96 \times 10^{-5}$ wt. % S/s.

(c) This will require integration of Eq. (20.20) from $t = 0$ to $t = t$. It is given in Eq. (20.21) ignoring the backward reaction. If the backward reaction is also considered, the sulphur balance in (a) above is to be modified as follows.

$$150 \times \{0.01 - [W_S]\} = 2(W_S);\ \text{i.e. } (W_S) = 0.75 - 75[W_S]$$

Hence, $[W_S] - (W_S)/L_{S,e} = 0.85\,[W_S] - 15 \times 10^{-4}$

Integration of Eq. (20.20), therefore, gives: $\ln\left[\dfrac{0.85\,[W_S]_O - 1.5 \times 10^{-4}}{0.85\,\;[W_S] - 1.5 \times 10^{-4}}\right] = k_{S,emp} \cdot t$

Noting that t = 2.5 minutes = 150 s, and solving, $[W_S]$ = 0.0063 wt. %

20.5.3 Injection Metallurgy (IM)

IM is practised in secondary steelmaking not only for the removal of sulphur from metal, but also for inclusion modification. In Chapter 16, the description of IM processes has already been presented and hence, will not be repeated. The processes may be broadly classified into the following two categories:

1. Continuous injection of solid powdered reagents into molten steel along with a stream of argon, through a lance immersed from the top.
2. Continuous injection (i.e. feeding) of powdered regents, encased in a steel tube immersed inside molten steel. This is known as *Cored Wire Feeding*. Important desulphurising agents for powder injection in secondary steelmaking are indicated in Table 20.4.

Table 20.4 Important desulphurising agents for powder injection in secondary steelmaking

Agent	Composition, wt. %	Injected amount, kg/t steel
Ca–Si alloy	Ca–30, Si–62, Al–8	2–4
$CaO–CaF_2$	CaO–90, CaF_2–10	3–6
$CaO–Al_2O_3–CaF_2$	CaO–70, Al_2O_3–20, CaF_2–10	2–5

The addition of calcium metal into the melt in the form of Ca-Si alloy causes deep deoxidation, deep desulphurisation and modification of inclusions to yield desirable properties. The initiative came after extensive deposits of natural gas were discovered in cold Arctic regions, like Alaska in North America. The line-pipe steel for transporting gas over long distances has to withstand high pressure, corrosion from H_2S in gas, and sub-zero temperatures without any tendency towards brittle fracture. The steel for this purpose required treatment by calcium.

Calcium is a gas at steelmaking temperatures. The vapour pressure vs. temperature relationship for pure calcium is:

$$\log p^0_{Ca}\,(\text{in atm}) = -\frac{8920}{T} - 1.39\log T + 9.569 \tag{20.22}$$

At 1600°C (1873 K), p^0_{Ca} = 1.81 atm. This is quite high and is likely to lead to instantaneous violent vapour formation resulting in a very little Ca reacting with the melt.

In Ca-Si alloy,

$$p_{Ca} = p^0_{Ca} \times [a_{Ca}] \tag{20.23}$$

In the composition of Ca–Si alloy employed, a_{Ca} is approximately 0.1, thus making $p_{Ca} < 1$ atm and eliminating the possibility of vapour formation. Even then, there is considerable loss of Ca as vapour, since the solubility of Ca in steel is very low (0.025 wt. % at 1600°C).

In powder injection processes, therefore, the powders should be injected as deep as possible into the melt. In wire feeding, Ca–Si powder is encased in a hollow steel tube and swaged before the tube plus powder is continuously fed into the melt by a machine. Powder injection gives better desulphurisation owing to the increased surface area. However, wire feeding is particularly suitable for inclusion modification. It is worth mentioning here that wire feeding is practised for other purposes—such as Al wire feeding for deoxidation and alloy powder feeding for precision alloying. Many steel plants, therefore, have provision for both powder injection and cored wire feeding.

20.6 CLEAN STEEL TECHNOLOGY

20.6.1 Introduction

In general, non-metallic inclusions in steel have been found to be harmful for desirable mechanical properties and corrosion resistance of steel. The inclusion particles are mostly oxides and to some extent, sulphides. This is more so in the case of high-strength steels for critical applications. As a result, there is a move to produce what is known as *Clean Steel*, i.e. steel free from inclusions. However, no steel can be made totally free from inclusions and therefore, cleanliness is a relative term. Which steel is clean and which is dirty can be decided only when it is known what the intended application is and what are the consequent property requirements.

The sources of inclusions may be classified into the following.

1. Precipitation due to reaction with molten steel or during freezing because of reaction between dissolved oxygen and the deoxidisers, with consequent formation of oxides (also reaction with dissolved sulphur as well). These are known as *endogenous inclusions*.
2. Mechanical and chemical erosion of the refractory lining
3. Entrapment of slag particles in steel
4. Oxygen pick up from the atmosphere, especially during teeming, and consequent oxide formation.

Inclusions originating from contact with external sources as listed in items 2 to 4 above, are called *exogenous inclusions*. These are formed during the entire process of secondary steelmaking; therefore, it is necessary to make a summary as shown in Figure 20.17. Technological measures for inclusion control are briefly outlined below.

20.6.2 Cleanliness Control during Deoxidation

Section 20.3 has already discussed this subject; however, the important measures for clean steel production are summarised below once again.

1. Carryover slag from the furnace into the ladle should be minimised, since it contains high percentage of FeO + MnO and makes efficient deoxidation fairly difficult.
2. Deoxidation products should be chemically stable. Otherwise, they would tend to decompose and transfer oxygen back into liquid steel. SiO_2 and Al_2O_3 are preferred to MnO. Moreover the products should preferably be liquid for faster growth by coalescence agglomeration and hence faster removal by floatation. Complex deoxidation gives this advantage.

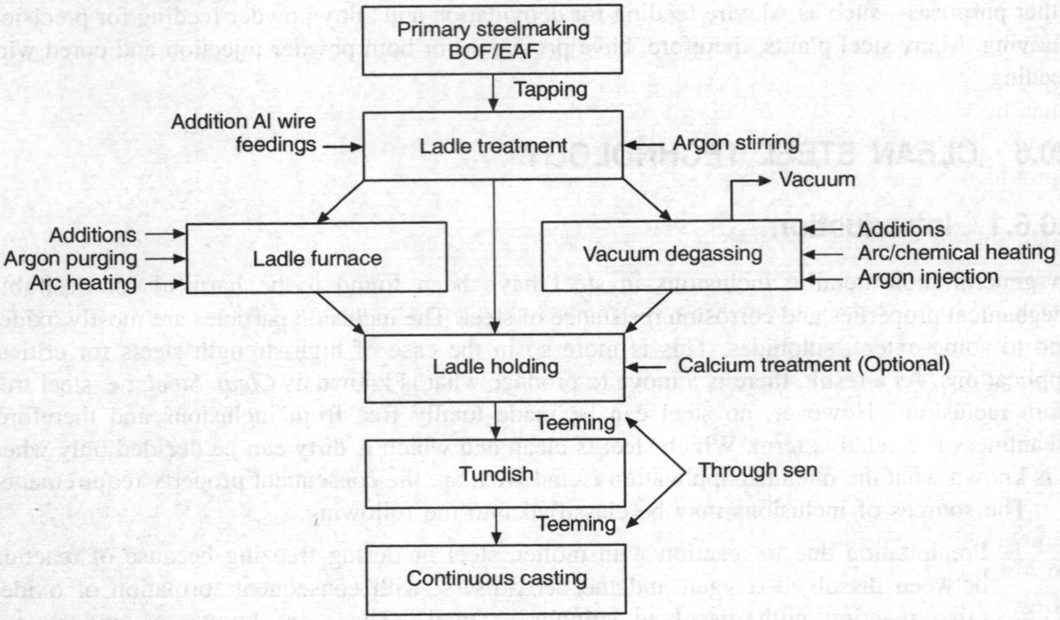

Figure 20.17 Secondary steelmaking route from tapping to continuous casting.

3. Stirring of the melt in the ladle by argan flowing through bottom tuyeres is a must for mixing and homogenisation, faster growth, and floatation of the deoxidation products. However, very high gas flow rates are not desirable from the cleanliness point of view, since it has the following adverse effects:
   - Re-entrainment of slag particles into molten steel.
   - Increased erosion of refractories and consequent generation of exogenous inclusions.
   - More ejection of metal droplets into the atmosphere with consequent oxide formation.

20.6.3 Cleanliness Control during Teeming

Subsequent to processing in LF/CAS-OB/Vacuum degasser and/or injection treatment, the liquid steel is held in the ladle for 20 to 40 minutes before and during teeming. Larger non-metallic particles get plenty of time to float up. The presence of a well-deoxidised top slag does not allow much atmospheric re-oxidation. Refractory erosion is also low, since there is no gas stirring. However, during teeming, if no precautions are taken, the melt will become dirty because of:

1. Oxygen absorption by the teeming stream
2. Slag entrainment consequent to funnel formation
3. Erosion of the nozzle refractory.

The falling stream of liquid steel absorbs oxygen from the surrounding air by the *jet entrainment effect*. The oxygen content of steel has been found to increase by as much as 40 to

400 ppm, depending on the nature of the stream. This leads to the formation of large inclusions, rich in FeO and MnO. Moreover, it increases the dissolved oxygen content and causes further generation of inclusions by reaction during solidification in the mould. Atmospheric oxidation has been eliminated by the use of *Submerged Entry Nozzles* (SEN) in the continuous casting route, where the nozzle tip is submerged into the melt. Additional protection can also be provided by shrouding the stream further with a gentle flow of argon.

Section 20.3.5 has outlined the problem of slag carryover from primary steelmaking furnaces into the ladle during tapping. Formation of a *funnel-shaped cavity* towards the end of tapping causes the slag to flow out along with the metal. This phenomenon also leads to entrainment of slag by metal during teeming from the ladle and tundish. This can be minimised by:

- Not emptying the ladle completely.
- Employing a refractory float on the funnel vortex.
- Using an electromagnetic sensor around the nozzle that gives a signal when entrained slag begins to flow out through the nozzle along with the metal.

For producing clean steels, the refractory used in the teeming nozzles is of considerable importance, since there is a high probability that inclusions and impurities introduced at the stage of teeming will not be eliminated. Here, both erosion and corrosion are severe owing to the high flow velocity of liquid steel through the nozzle. Adequate thermal shock resistance of the lining is also required to prevent its spalling. Nowadays, zirconia (ZrO_2)-based linings are the most preferred—such as ZrO_2–graphite, ZrO_2–CaO–C. Since ZrO_2 is expensive, Al_2O_3-based material (e.g. Al_2O_3–C–SiC) is employed as the back-up layer. One alternative to zirconia is Al_2O_3-based linings.

20.6.4 Tundish Metallurgy for Clean Steel

The tundish is a shallow, refractory-lined vessel that is located in between the ladle and the continuous casting mould. Liquid steel flows from the ladle into the tundish and from the tundish into the mould. A tundish is a must in continuous casting for proper regulation of the rate of flow into the mould.

A detailed description of the tundish and its metallurgical aspects will be taken up in Chapter 23. At this juncture, it will suffice to state that proper design and operational control of the tundish is extremely important for the final cleanliness of steel. It is worth mentioning here that proper metallurgical control is required even in the casting mould (both for continuous as well as for ingot casting) to ensure meticulous fine control of steel cleanliness.

20.7 MISCELLANEOUS TOPICS

20.7.1 Inclusion Modification

Despite all attempts, it is very difficult to make steel with as low an inclusion content as is desired. This gives rise to the second option of inclusion modification, which consists of adding some reagents into molten steel with the specific objective of altering the nature of the inclusions so as to make them relatively harmless as far as the properties of steel are concerned. This is done by injection metallurgy, and again, calcium is the most common reagent. Section 20.5.3 has already discussed this in connection with desulphurisation. These will not be repeated.

One of the defects in continuous casting is formation of *subsurface pinholes* owing to the presence of dissolved gases. Therefore, the oxygen content of the melt should be kept very low by use of aluminiun also as deoxidiser (Al-killed steel). A certain minimum level of dissolved Al is required in the melt. This gives rise to the problem of nozzle clogging in continuous casting owing to sticking of alumina inclusions to the inner wall of the casting nozzle. Calcium treatment at the final stage in a ladle or a tundish has been found to eliminate this, because the deoxidation product is a liquid consisting of CaO and Al_2O_3, occasionally with some amount of SiO_2.

Calcium is a powerful desulphuriser as well, and therefore, reaction (20.16) resulting in the formation of CaS also may occur. However, the liquid sulphide is generally not pure CaS, but a solution of CaS–MnS. The compounds $12CaO.7Al_2O_3$ ($C_{12}A_7$) and $3CaO.Al_2O_3$ (C_3A) have low melting points of 1455°C and 1535°C respectively, and therefore, are preferred.

Figure 20.18 shows thermodynamic predictions for equilibrium inclusion type for calcium-treated steels as a function of its Al and S content at 1550°C (1823 K), assuming CaS to be pure (Fruehan 1985). Although originally Ca-treatment was started to overcome problems of nozzle-clogging, the duplex inclusion of ($C_{12}A_7$) with a ring of CaS–MnS is globular, soft and deformable, and thus relatively harmless to mechanical properties.

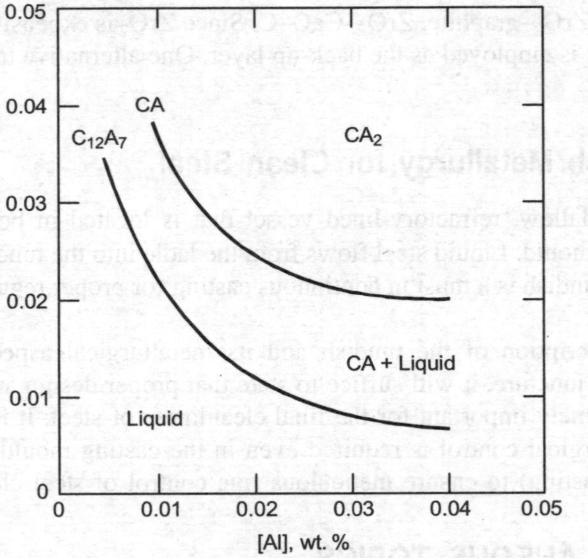

Figure 20.18 Equilibrium inclusions predicted for calcium-treated Al-killed steels, as function of Al and S content at 1823 K.

Rare earths (RE) consist of 14 elements having almost identical chemical properties. Commercially it is available as *Misch metal*, which contains about 50% cerium. REs are both strong deoxidisers and desulphurisers, like calcium. They can modify inclusions as well as act as grain refiners. However, they are not as commonly used as calcium because of difficulties of process control. Tellurium (Te) or Selenium (Se) is also added as a reagent for inclusion modification to improve the machinability of sulphur containing steels. Their basic effect is to make the inclusions globular, thus leading to better deformation characteristics during hot working as well.

20.7.2 Temperature Changes during Secondary Steelmaking

For obtaining the desired cast structure as well as for elimination of some casting defects, the temperature of liquid steel should be controlled within a desired range before it is teemed into the mould. Continuous casting demands more stringent temperature control than ingot casting.

In secondary steelmaking, the temperature may drop by as much as 100°C from the furnace to the mould. Therefore, some secondary steelmaking units, such as LF, VAD and RH have provisions for heating the melt. Pre-heating of the lining of empty ladle is also standard practice so that the interior hot face lining temperature is above 800°C. These measures eliminate the need for tapping at too high a temperature. Moreover, much better and more flexible temperature control of steel is then possible. More alloy additions also can be made. Arc heating is most common, followed by chemical heating, plasma arc or induction heating for reducing the temperature loss during secondary treatment. Chemical heating requires aluminium addition as well as some oxygen lancing, as is the case in RH–OB. Exothermic oxidation of aluminium provides the heat.

The overall temperature change of liquid steel from the furnace to the mould is a sum total of the following:

- Temperature loss from the tapping and teeming stream by radiation and convection
- Temperature loss during holding or purging in the ladle because of conduction to the ladle wall and radiation from the top surface of the melt
- Temperature loss owing to endothermic dissolution of deoxidants and alloying elements added at room temperature
- Temperature gain following exothermic deoxidation reactions (also, atmospheric re-oxidation)
- Temperature gain on account of heating.

Figure 20.19 shows a typical pattern of temperature change from the furnace to the continuous casting mould via the ladle furnace route (Mellinghoff 1991). The estimated decrease in steel temperature during tapping for 1% alloying element addition and assuming 100% recovery (i.e. no reaction) is as follows.

Addition	**Decrease in steel temperature, °C**
Coke	65
High carbon ferrochrome (50% Cr)	41
Low carbon ferrochrome (70% Cr)	24
High carbon ferromanganese	30
Ferrosilicon (50% Si)	0

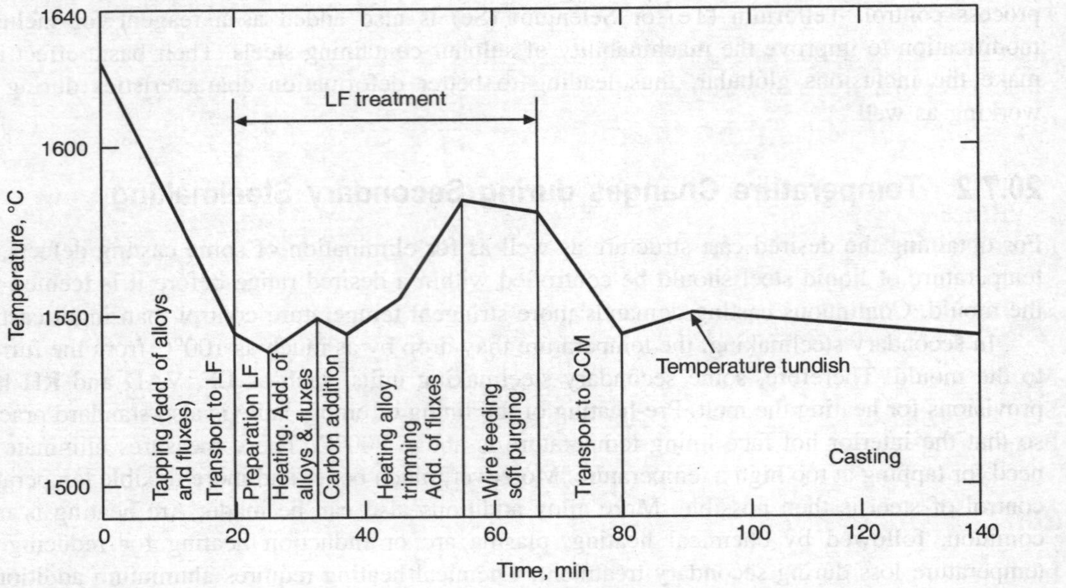

Figure 20.19 Temperature changes in a steel melt from the furnace to the tundish via ladle furnace.

EXAMPLE 20.5

Calculate the change in temperature (ΔT) of 150 tonne of molten steel in a ladle at 1600°C following the addition of 70 kg of ferrosilicon having 50% Si. Assume that half of the silicon reacts with dissolved oxygen of steel, and the rest remains dissolved in steel.

Solution: $70/2 = 35$ kg Si $= (35 \times 10^3)/28 = 1.25 \times 10^5$ gmol of Si

Assuming steel to be pure iron,

$$150 \text{ tonnes of steel} = (150 \times 10^6)/56 = 2.68 \times 10^6 \text{ gmol}$$

From Chapter 15, Table 15.1,

$$[\text{Si}]_{\text{wt. \%}} + \text{O}_2(\text{g}) = \text{SiO}_2(\text{s}); \quad \Delta H_1^0 = -816.2 \text{ kJ/mol}$$

The first column of Table 4.2 of Chapter 4 gives values of ΔH^0 approximately and, from that

$$\text{O}_2(\text{g}) = 2[\text{O}]_{\text{wt. \%}}; \quad \Delta H_2^0 = 2 \times (-117.15) \text{ kJ/mol}$$

From the above reactions,

$$[\text{Si}]_{\text{wt. \%}} + 2[\text{O}]_{\text{wt. \%}}; \quad \Delta H^0 = \Delta H_1^0 - \Delta H_2^0 = -581.9 \text{ kJ/mol} \qquad \text{(Ex. 20.8)}$$

Again, from Table 4.2,

$\bar{H}_{\text{Si}}^m$ owing to dissolution of silicon into the melt $= -131.5$ kJ/mol.

Heat Balance:

Since the above processes are exothermic, they are the sources of heat input. Since, only half of the silicon added reacts with dissolved oxygen,

$$\text{Heat input} = -1.25 \times 10^3 \times \{0.5 \times [-581.9] + [-131.5]\} = 5.28 \times 10^5 \text{ kJ}$$

Assuming the process to be adiabatic,

Heat output = Heat required to raise the steel temperature by ΔT + Sensible heat required to raise the temperature of ferrosilicon from 298 K to 1873 K

Noting that $(H_{1873} - H_{298})$ for Fe and Si are respectively 76.94 and 33.5 kJ per gmol, the sensible heat of Fe-Si addition = $10^3 \times [1.25 \times 33.5 + (0.5 \times 70 \times 76.94)/56] = 0.9 \times 10^5$ kJ

From Table 15.2, ignoring the T^2 term, raising of steel temperature would require heat.

No. of gmol of steel $\times\ 40.9 \times \Delta T = 2.68 \times 10^6 \times 40.9 \times \Delta T \times 10^{-3} = 1.10 \times 10^5 \times \Delta T$ kJ

So, heat output (in kJ) = $1.10 \times 10^5 \times \Delta T + 0.9 \times 10^5$

Equating heat input and output, $\Delta T = 4.0°\text{C}$

20.7.3 Refractories for Secondary Steelmaking

In contrast to primary steelmaking, the slag in secondary steelmaking is deoxidised and contains a high proportion of CaO and Al_2O_3. In primary steelmaking, the choice and design of the refractory lining is governed by the lining life and its impact on the overall steelmaking cost. However, in secondary steelmaking, there are additional concerns about its effect on steel quality, cost of ladle heating, etc. The requirements of the refractory lining for secondary steelmaking ladles are given below.

1. The lining should be stable as well as inert to liquid steel. Otherwise, it will tend to introduce undesirable impurities into the metal.
2. A low thermal conductivity of the ladle lining is desirable to prevent heat loss by conduction through the walls. However, thermal shock resistance should also be satisfactory. Often these are contrary requirements and a balance has to be struck.
3. Steel cleanliness, to some extent, depends on the interaction between liquid steel and the refractory lining. Erosion of the lining increases the number of exogenous nonmetallic particles, whereas corrosion causes a change in the composition of steel, like increasing its oxygen content. This, in turn, tends to generate more deoxidation products during freezing of steel in the mould.

Nowadays, tar or pitch bonded calcined dolomite (CaO.MgO) lining is generally employed as the ladle lining. For clean steel, it should have high purity (total impurity less than 3% or so). Composite linings are normally used. The zone in contact with the top slag has to resist slag attack adequately and calcined dolomite serves the purpose. To reduce the weight, expense and total heat capacity of the refractory system, a fireclay back up lining is provided.

Ladle covers are typically lined with high-alumina refractories (above 85% Al_2O_3). Porous plugs are made of high alumina or magnesia. Slide gate parts undergo high stresses and are generally made from high alumina material. The refractory lining for teeming nozzles has already been discussed in Section 20.6.3.

REFERENCES

Adachi, Y., in *Proc. of the 6th Iron and Steel Cong.*, The Iron and Steel Inst. Japan, Vol. 3, Nagoya (1990), p. 248.

Asai, S. et al., preprints *Scaninject 111*, MEFOS, Lulea, Sweden, Part 1 (1983), Paper 12.

Choudhary, S.K., S. Chandra and A. Ghosh, Metallurgical and Materials Trans. B, Vol. 36B (2005), pp. 59–66.

Fruehan, R.J., *Ladle Metallurgy*, ISS-AIME (1985), Chs. 2 and 7.

Fruehan, R.J., *Vacuum Degassing of Steel*, Iron & steel Soc., USA (1990).

Ghosh, Ahindra, *Secondary Steelmaking—Principles and Applications*, CRC Press, Boca Raton, Florida (2001).

Harada, T. and D. Janke, Steel Research, Vol. 60 (1989), p. 337.

Mazumdar, D. and R.I.L. Guthrie, ISIJ International, Vol. 35 (1995), p. 1.

Mellinghoff, H., in *Int. Symp on Quality Steelmaking*, Ind. Inst. of Metals, Ranchi (1991), p. 144.

Mietz, J. and F. Oeters, Steel Research, Vol. 59 (1988), p. 52.

Pehlke, R.D. and J.F. Elliott, Trans. AIME, Vol. 227 (1963), p. 844.

Plockinger, E. and M. Wahlster, Stahl Eisen, Vol. 80 (1960), p. 659.

Shankanarayanan, R. and R.I.L. Guthrie, *Steelmaking Proc.*, Iron and Steel Soc., USA (1992), p. 655.

Soejima, T. et al., Trans. ISIJ, Vol. 27 (1987), B–146.

Suzuki, K. et al., Ironmaking and Steelmaking (1982), p. 33.

Turkdogan, E.T., Arch. Eisenhuttenwesen, Vol. 54 (1983), p. 4.

21

Stainless Steelmaking

21.1 INTRODUCTION

Amongst high alloy steels, stainless steels (SS) are the most important. The world production of SS is about 20 Mtpa. Therefore, stainless steels production is being dealt with in this separate chapter.

Stainless steels contain 10 to 30% chromium. Varying amounts of nickel, molybdenum, copper, sulphur, titanium, niobium, nitrogen, etc. may be added to obtain the desired properties. SS is used wherever superior resistance to corrosion is desired. Stainless steels are primarily classified as *austenitic*, *ferritic*, *martensitic*, duplex or precipitation hardening grades. Most grades contain 17–18% chromium. Addition of nickel enhances the corrosion resistance further and tends to stabilise the austenitic structure—the most popular SS is the 18% Cr and 8% Ni variety.

In terms of tonnage production, ferritic SS is next. Production of ferritic SS requires the removal of carbon and nitrogen in steel to very low levels. Nickel, which is an integral part of stainless steels is expensive and efforts have been made from the 1950s to replace it, partially or completely, by other elements, such as manganese, which tend to stabilise the austenite phase. However, this can be achieved more easily, if the steel contains high percentages of nitrogen (0.06–0.08%); high nitrogen SS grades are being produced today.

Before 1970, the majority of stainless steels were made in electric arc furnaces. In Chapter 19, the application of EAF steelmaking for producing carbon steel grades has been covered along with the modern developments. Availability of relatively cheap tonnage oxygen led to the practice of oxygen lancing for faster decarburisation and the consequent generation of a foamy slag. This development changed the entire picture.

Owing to rapid growth in SS production from about 1970 onwards, the generation/supply of SS scrap could not meet the demand and other charge materials had to be used. The quantities of various charge materials that are now used are as follows (based on 2001 figures):

Carbon steel scrap	7.0 Mt
Stainless steel scrap	4.5 Mt
Ferrochrome	4.0 Mt
Primary nickel	0.7 Mt

Ferrochrome, which contains about 55 to 70% chromium is the principal source of chromium. This ferroalloy can be classified into various grades, based primarily on their carbon content, such as:

- Low carbon ferrochrome (about 0.1% C).
- Intermediate carbon ferrochrome (about 2% C).
- High carbon ferrochrome (around 7% C).

Amongst these grades, the high carbon variety has the drawback that though it is the least expensive, it raises the carbon content of the melt. This is undesirable, since all SS grades demand carbon contents less than 0.03%. As shown in Figure 4.1, chromium forms stable oxides. Hence, the removal of carbon from the bath by oxidation to CO is associated with the problem of simultaneous oxidation of chromium in molten steel. The higher the temperature, the greater is the tendency for preferential oxidation of carbon rather than chromium. From this point of view, higher bath temperatures are desirable; however, too high a temperature in the bath gives rise to other process problems.

The dilution of oxygen with argon lowers the partial pressure of CO, which helps in preferential removal of CO without oxidising bath chromium. Attempts were made to use this in the EAF, but the efforts did not succeed. Hence, as is the case with the production of plain carbon steels, the EAF is now basically a melting unit for stainless steel production as well. Decarburisation is carried out partially in the EAF, and the rest of the carbon is removed in a separate refining vessel. In this context, the development of the AOD process was a major breakthrough in stainless steelmaking.

AOD is the acronym for *Argon–Oxygen Decarburisation*. The process was patented by the Industrial Gases Division of the Union Carbide Corporation (now known as Praxair Inc.). In an AOD converter, argon is used to dilute the other gaseous species (O_2, CO, etc.). Hence, in some literature, it is designated as *Dilution Refining Process*. After AOD, some other dilution refining processes have been developed. Lowering of the partial pressures, such as the partial pressure of carbon monoxide, is achieved either by argon or by employing vacuum (Choulet and Masson, 1993; also Chapter 20 of this book). Figure 21.1 shows all the processes, including AOD, schematically. In Chapter 20 vacuum degassing and decarburisation processes have been discussed in connection with secondary steelmaking. Figures 20.11, 20.12 and 20.14 have presented some sketches of vacuum degassers.

The combination of EAF and AOD is sufficient for producing ordinary grades of stainless steels and this combination is referred to as a *Duplex Process*. Subsequent minor refining, temperature and composition adjustments, if required, can be undertaken in a ladle furnace. *Triplex refining*, where electric arc furnace melting and converter refining are followed by refining in a vacuum system, is often desirable when the final product requires very low carbon and nitrogen levels. Figure 21.2 depicts the triplex system, which makes the cycle time longer and adds to cost.

About 65–70% of the world's total production of stainless steel is in the austenitic variety, made by the duplex EAF–AOD route. If the use of AOD converters even in the triplex route is included, the share of AOD in world production would become as high as 75–80%.

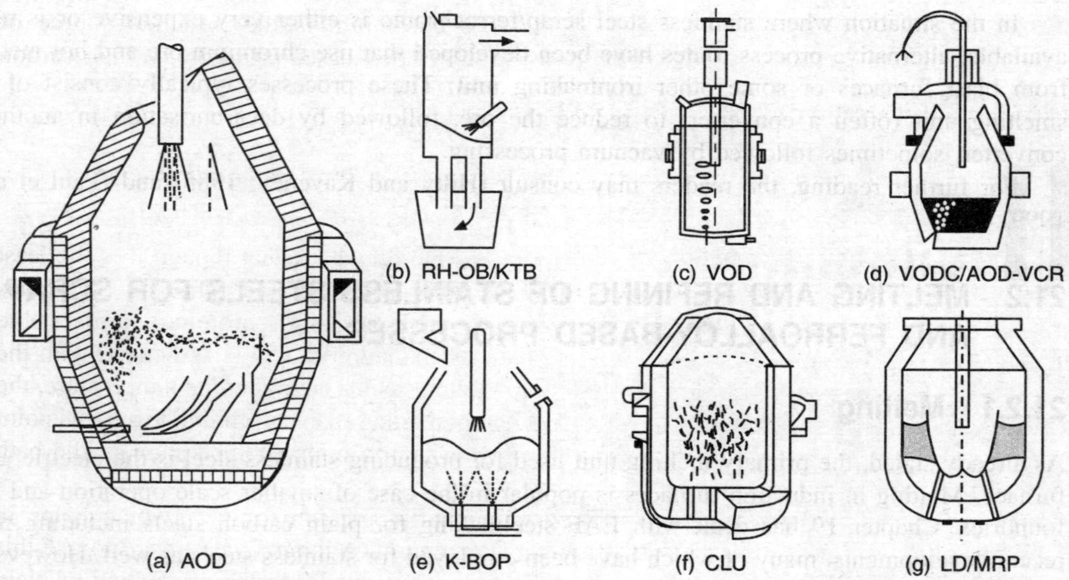

Figure 21.1 Processes for stainless steelmaking.

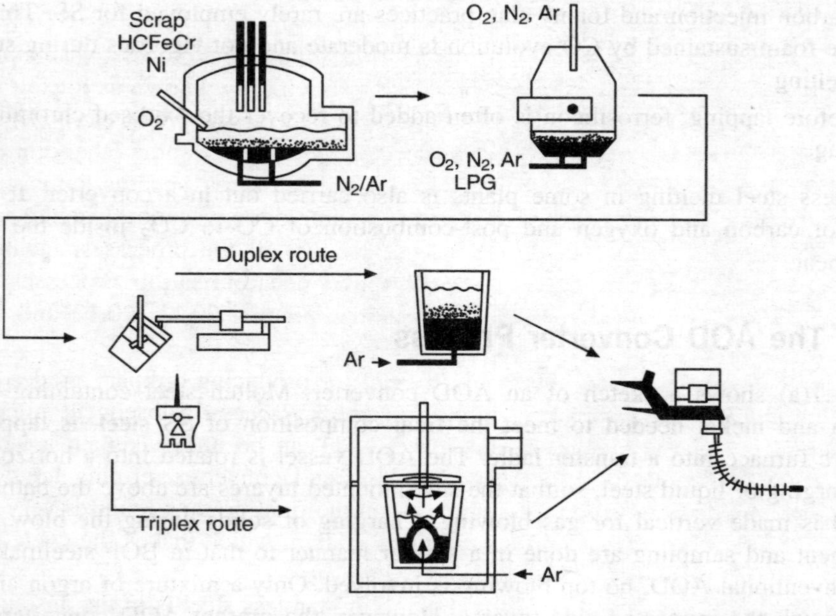

Figure 21.2 Illustration of duplex and triplex methods of stainless steelmaking.

In the situation where stainless steel scrap/ferrochrome is either very expensive or is not available, alternative process routes have been developed that use chromium ore and hot metal from blast furnaces or some other ironmaking unit. These processes typically consist of a smelting unit (often a converter) to reduce the ore, followed by decarburisation in another converter, sometimes followed by vacuum processing.

For further reading, the readers may consult (Hilty and Kaveney, 1985) and (Paul et al. 1999).

21.2 MELTING AND REFINING OF STAINLESS STEELS FOR SCRAP AND FERROALLOY-BASED PROCESSES

21.2.1 Melting

As already stated, the primary melting unit used for producing stainless steel is the electric arc furnace. Melting in induction furnaces is popular in the case of smaller scale operation and in foundries. Chapter 19 has dealt with EAF steelmaking for plain carbon steels including the recent developments, many of which have been employed for stainless steels as well. However, there are some salient differences.

1. Oxidation of chromium and transfer of the oxide to slag is not desirable, as it represents a loss of chromium. This sets a limit to the extent of oxygen blowing.
2. Carbon injection and foamy slag practices are rarely employed for SS. This is because the foam sustained by CO evolution is moderate and not vigorous during stainless steel melting.
3. Before tapping, ferrosilicon is often added to recover the oxidised chromium from the slag.

Stainless steel melting in some plants is also carried out in a converter. It requires the injection of carbon and oxygen and post-combustion of CO to CO_2 inside the converter to generate heat.

21.2.2 The AOD Converter Process

Figure 21.1(a) shows a sketch of an AOD converter. Molten steel containing most of the chromium and nickel needed to meet the final composition of SS steel, is tapped from the electric arc furnace into a transfer ladle. The AOD vessel is rotated into a horizontal position during charging of liquid steel, so that the side-mounted tuyeres are above the bath level. Then, the vessel is made vertical for gas blowing. Charging of solids during the blow, temperature measurement and sampling are done in a similar manner to that in BOF steelmaking.

In conventional AOD, no top blowing is involved. Only a mixture of argon and oxygen is blown through the immersed side tuyeres. However, the present AOD converters are mostly fitted with concurrent facilities for top blowing of either only oxygen, or oxygen plus inert gas mixtures using a supersonic lance as in BOF steelmaking. Initially, when the carbon content of the melt is high, blowing through the top lance is predominant though the gas mixture introduced through the side tuyeres also contains a high percentage of oxygen. However, as decarburisation proceeds, oxygen blowing from the top is reduced in stages and argon blowing increased. As stated earlier, some stainless steel grades contain nitrogen as a part of the specifications, in which case, nitrogen is employed in place of argon in the final stages.

Use of a supersonic top lance as in the case of BOFs allows post-combustion of the evolved CO gas with consequent minimisation of toxic carbon monoxide in the exit gas as well as utilisation of the fuel value of CO to raise the bath temperature. Towards the end of the blow, when the carbon content is very low and is close to the final specification, only argon is blown to effect mixing and promote slag–metal reaction. At this stage, ferrosilicon and other additions are made. Silicon reduces chromium oxide from the slag. If extra-low sulphur is required, the first slag is removed and a fresh reducing slag is made along with argon stirring. The purpose of the other additions is to perform both alloying as well as cooling of the bath, since the bath temperature goes beyond 1700°C following the oxidation reactions.

21.2.3 Thermodynamics of Reactions in the AOD Process

Like iron, chromium exhibits two valencies, viz. Cr^{2+} and Cr^{3+}, when it is oxidised. An issue on which controversies have persisted for long and continues even today is, whether chromium is present in slag as CrO, Cr_2O_3, or some other compound. From investigations carried out over the years, the picture that emerges is as follows. Like iron, chromium is capable of exhibiting a variable Cr^{2+}/Cr^{3+} ratio in slag, depending on the oxygen potential and the basicity. In reducing slags or acid slags, CrO is the dominant oxide, whereas in oxidising or basic slags, Cr_2O_3 is the major species. During the oxidising period in a VOD or AOD, the slag may be assumed to be saturated with chromium oxide in view of the very small quantity of slag per tonne of metal. Based on evidence gathered, this oxide can be considered to be Cr_3O_4.

Hence, the reaction for the process is written as:

$$(Cr_3O_4) + 4\underline{C} = 4CO(g) + 3\underline{Cr} \tag{21.1}$$

Since activity of Cr_3O_4 is 1 (since saturated), the equilibrium constant for the above reaction is:

$$K_1 = \frac{\{p_{CO}\}^4 \times [h_{Cr}]^3}{[h_C]^4} \tag{21.2}$$

Again, Eq. (21.2) may be rewritten as:

$$4 \log h_C = 3 \log h_{Cr} + 4 \log p_{CO} - \log K_1 \tag{21.3}$$

i.e.

$$4 \log W_C + 4 \log f_C = 3 \log W_{Cr} + 3 \log f_{Cr} + 4 \log p_{CO} - \log K_1 \tag{21.4}$$

f_C and f_{Cr} are activity coefficients of carbon and chromium respectively in liquid iron for 1 wt.% standard state. They are functions of temperature and composition, while K_1 is a function of temperature. All these make the resulting equation somewhat cumbersome to use. It was simplified by Hilty and Kaveney (1985) as:

$$\log\left[\frac{W_{Cr}}{W_C}\right] = -\frac{13800}{T} + 8.76 - 0.925 p_{CO} \tag{21.5}$$

Figure 21.3 shows this relationship at one atmosphere pressure of CO (Hilty and Kaveney, 1985). It demonstrates that a very high temperature is required if it is required to obtain less than 0.04% C at above 15% Cr. Lowering of p_{CO} allows the same to be achieved at a much lower temperature. This is shown in Figure 21.4 (Hilty and Kaveney, 1985).

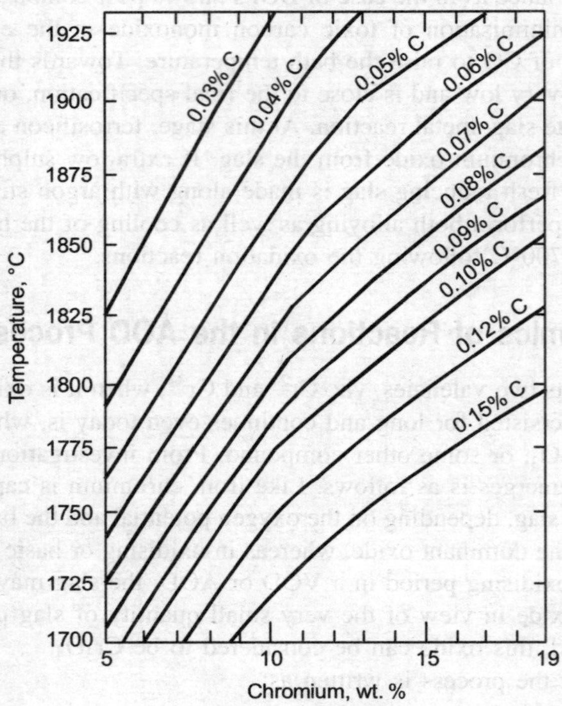

Figure 21.3 Chromium–carbon–temperature relationship in oxygen saturated steel melts.

Since nickel dissolved in liquid iron has a small but significant influence on the thermodynamic activities of carbon and oxygen, Eq. (21.5) was modified as:

$$\log\left[\frac{W_{Cr}}{W_C}\right] = -\frac{13800}{T + 4.21W_{Ni}} + 8.76 - 0.925p_{CO} \tag{21.6}$$

For the reduction of chromium oxide from slag by ferrosilicon during the last stages of VOD/AOD operation, Hilty et al. assumed the following reaction:

$$(Cr_3O_4) + 2\underline{Si} = 3\underline{Cr} + 2(SiO_2) \tag{21.7}$$

$$K_7 = \frac{[h_{Cr}]^3 (a_{SiO_2})^2}{[h_{Si}]^2 (a_{Cr_3O_4})} \tag{21.8}$$

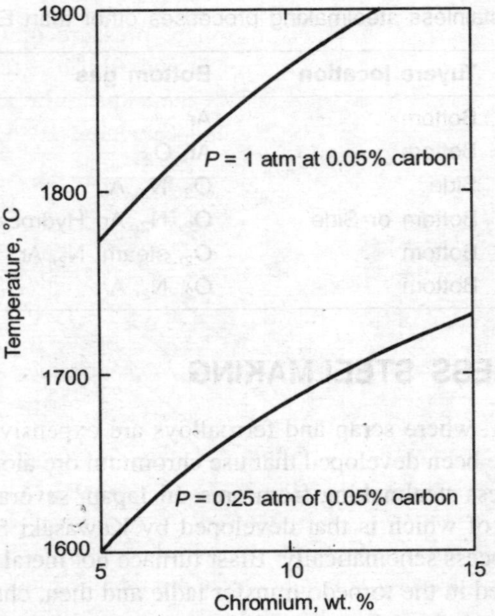

Figure 21.4 Influence of pressure and temperature on the retention of chromium by oxygen-saturated steel melts at 0.05% C.

Noting that a_{SiO_2}, $a_{Cr_3O_4}$ in slag are functions of slag basicity, an equilibrium relation was arrived at from Eq. (21.8). However, for practical purposes, statistically fitted empirical coefficients are recommended, such as:

$$\log (W_{Cr})_{slag} = 1.283 \log [W_{Cr}] - 0.748 \log [W_{Si}] - 1.709 \log V - 0.923 \qquad (21.9)$$

where V = slag basicity = (CaO + MgO)/SiO_2.

21.3 OTHER PROCESSES FOR STAINLESS STEELMAKING

Figures 21.1(b) to (f) schematically show the other types of reactors used; Table 21.1 provides a complete list. The principles and procedures followed in these processes are similar to those in AOD, except for minor details. As noted in Table 21.1, RH-OB/KTB, VOD and VODC/AOD-VCR processes are carried out under vacuum (Paul et al. 1999). Vacuum degassing and decarburisation have already been discussed in Chapter 20; therefore, detailed discussions are being omitted. Only some salient details are included below.

1. K-BOP was developed by Kawasaki Steel Corporation, Japan; K-OBM-S developed by Voest Alpine Industrie-Anlageneinbau (VAI), Austria, is a modified version of K-BOP.
2. CLU is the abbreviation of *Cruesot-Loire-Uddeholm*, jointly developed by Uddeholm, Belgium and Cruesot-Loire, France.
3. MRP is the abbreviation of *Metal Refining Process* developed by Mannesmann Demag, Germany. ASM stands for *Argon Secondary Melting* converter, also developed in Germany.

Table 21.1 List of stainless steelmaking processes other than EAF–AOD/VOD

Process	Tuyere location	Bottom gas	Top gas
RH-OB/KTB (Vacuum)	Bottom	Ar	O_2
VOD (Vacuum)	Bottom	Ar, O_2	O_2
VODC/AOD-VCR (Vacuum)	Side	O_2, N_2, Ar	O_2
K- BOP/K-OBM-S	Bottom or Side	O_2, N_2, Ar, Hydrocarbons	O_2, N_2, Ar
CLU	Bottom	O_2, steam, N_2, Ar	O_2, N_2, Ar
MRP, ASM	Bottom	O_2, N_2, Ar	O_2 (in some)

21.4 DIRECT STAINLESS STEELMAKING

As mentioned in Section 21.1, where scrap and ferroalloys are expensive, or are not available, alternative process routes have been developed that use chromium ore along with hot metal. This is the direct method of stainless steelmaking from ores. In Japan, several such installations are in use, the most well known of which is that developed by Kawasaki Steel Corporation.

Figure 21.5 shows the process schematically. Blast furnace hot metal (or hot metal from any other source) is dephosphorised in the torpedo transfer ladle and then, charged into a concurrent top- and bottom-blown converter. Partially reduced chromite ore and ferroalloys are charged into the converter along with some coke. Reduction smelting of the ore takes place. The process is designated as SR-KCB, i.e. "Smelting Reduction-Kawasaki Combined Blowing".

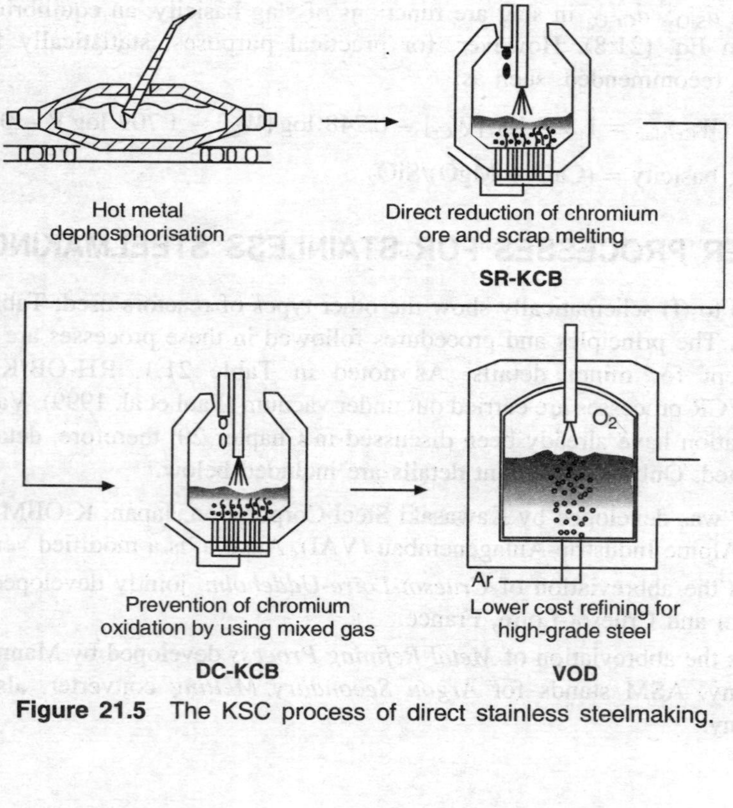

Figure 21.5 The KSC process of direct stainless steelmaking.

The molten steel from the SR-KCB reactor containing chromium and 5–6% C is charged into a K-BOP converter (Kawasaki's version of bottom-blown oxygen converter), where decarburisation is completed followed by final refining in a VOD unit.

REFERENCES

Choulet, R.J. and I.E. Masson, Iron & Steelmaker, Vol. 20, May 1993.

Hilty, D.C. and T.F. Kaveney, in *Electric Furnace Steelmaking*, C.R. Taylor (Ed.), Iron & Steel Soc., USA (1985), Chapter 13.

Paul, B.V., A.H. Chan and R.J. Choulet, in *Making Shaping and Treating of Steel*, Vol. 2, R.J. Fruehan (Ed.), Iron & Steel Soc., USA (1999), Chapter 12.

Part E

Casting of Liquid Steel

- Ingot Casting of Steel
- Continuous Casting of Steel

22

Ingot Casting of Steel

22.1 INTRODUCTION

At present, continuous casting is by far the most predominant method of casting molten steel. Bulk of the liquid steel after continuous casting is shaped by rolling either into flat products, i.e. plates and sheets, or, into long products, such as rods, angles, rails, etc. Ingot casting is still in vogue, in very small volumes, particularly for casting special steel products. For example, for forgings of special shapes, ingot casting is the route. Some very small capacity steel plants still exist in several parts of the world, including India, where ordinary carbon steels, and special or alloy steels in small quantities are ingot cast.

Even though ingot casting of steel is now not extensively practised, this separate chapter is being included in this book for some important reasons. Except for steel cast in foundries, ingot casting was the only method of casting steel for more than 100 years, till the advent of continuous casting. Therefore, extensive investigations and studies have been made on the science and technology of solidification processing, with major emphasis on ingot casting of steel as well as other metals and alloys. This has without doubt contributed significantly towards the present day understanding of the physicochemical phenomena during freezing of liquids, and has laid the foundation for the growth of the continuous casting process. Therefore, some coverage of ingot casting is required, without which knowledge of casting will be incomplete.

Ingot moulds are made of cast iron, having various cross sections such as square, round, polygonal, etc. depending on the end-use of the product. There are various mould designs, such as:

- Narrow-end-up, or wide-end-up
- Open bottom, closed bottom, or plugged bottom
- With, or without hot top.

In most practices, pouring of liquid steel is done from the top. Bottom pouring, i.e. feeding the mould through a bottom opening, is practised only in special cases where ultra pure cast products are required.

Figure 22.1 depicts three common types of ingot moulds, viz. narrow-end-up, wide-end-up, and wide-end-up with hot top. An important issue is the stripping of the solidified ingot from

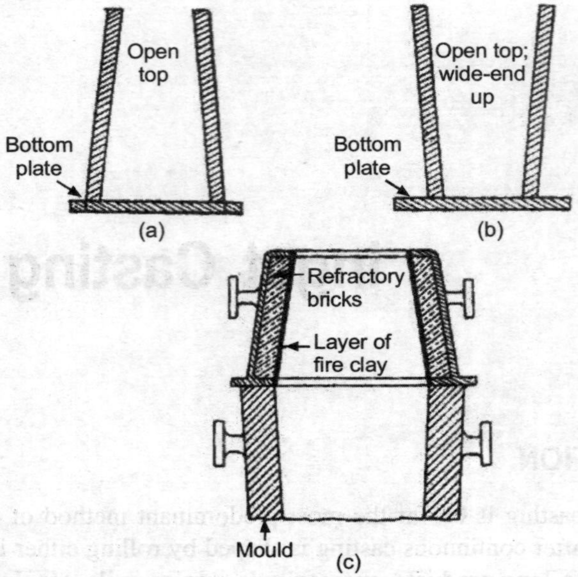

Figure 22.1 Types of ingot moulds: (a) narrow-end-up, (b) wide-end-up, and (c) wide-end-up with hot top.

the mould. Cast iron moulds have an advantage since the coefficient of thermal expansion of cast iron is different from that of steel. Upon cooling, steel contracts more than the cast iron mould, which assists detachment. The conical shape of the moulds facilitates pulling-out of only the mould by a stripping crane, thus separating the mould from the solidified ingot. In this context, the narrow-end-up mould is the most convenient. In addition, the inner walls of the mould are coated with tar, pitch or similar materials at a temperature of about 150–250°C. When the tar or pitch decomposes at high temperature, fine carbon is formed on the mould surface, which prevents sticking of the solidified ingot with the mould. In case the mould is cold, pre-heating is required.

Molten steel from the furnace is tapped into a refractory-lined teeming ladle which has a steel shell. Ladles of the type shown in Figure 22.2 were in use earlier. The teeming nozzle at the bottom of the ladle is eccentric and is closed by a refractory-lined steel stopper rod. During teeming, the rod gets lifted up by a mechanical device after the ladle is centred above the mould set by an overhead crane. Teeming can then start.

Ladles of more modern design are in use now in all large steel plants as well as in mini steel plants. These are fitted with slide gate valves instead of stopper rods, and have provision for argon injection from the bottom. Chapter 20, Figure 20.7 has presented a sketch of a ladle furnace, which shows the ladle design. The top cover with the electrodes, etc. is a part of the ladle furnace station, the ladle with liquid steel moves on a rail track and is brought to the LF station. Once treatment is completed, the ladle is taken to the teeming bay by an overhead crane.

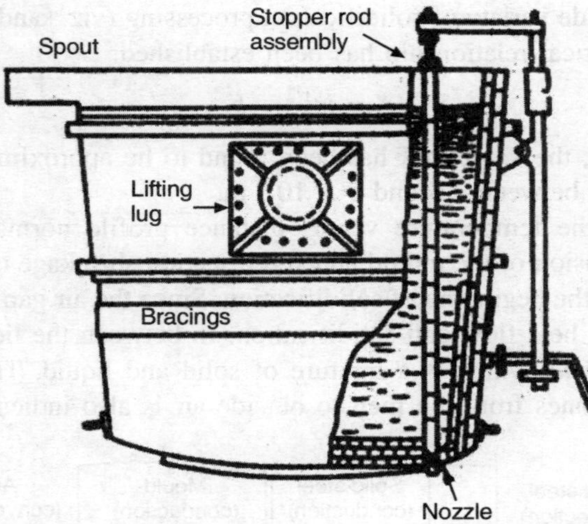

Figure 22.2 Teeming ladle for steel (earlier design with stopper rod).

22.2 FUNDAMENTALS OF SOLIDIFICATION

22.2.1 Heat Transfer and Solidification Rate in Ingot Casting

The rate of solidification of a casting depends directly on the rate at which it loses heat. In the case of an open top ingot, radiation is a minor source of heat loss and most of the heat is lost through the mould walls. The heat balance may be expressed by the equation:

$$Q = qA = \text{mass rate of solidification} \times \text{heat given up per unit mass}$$

$$= A\rho_s\left(\frac{dx}{dt}\right)(\Delta H_f + C \cdot \Delta T_s) \qquad (22.1)$$

where

Q = rate of heat loss, $J \cdot s^{-1}$

A = mould–metal interface area, m^2

q = heat flux through the mould–metal interface, $J \cdot m^{-2} \cdot s^{-1}$

ρ_s = density of solidified metal, $kg \cdot m^{-3}$

X = thickness of solidified metal at time t after beginning of solidification, m

ΔH_f = latent heat of fusion of metal, $J \cdot kg^{-1}$

C = specific heat of metal, $J \cdot kg^{-1} \cdot K^{-1}$

ΔT_s = initial temperature of the melt in excess of liquidus temperature (known as *superheat*), K.

Estimates indicate that for ingot casting of steel, the superheat term ($C \cdot \Delta T_s$) is about 5% of $\Delta H_f \cdot (dx/dt)$, which is the rate of growth of thickness of the solidified metal, is the *linear rate of solidification*, and is typically employed as an index of the rate of solidification. It is a function of time. For a wide variety of solidification processing (viz. sand casting, ingot casting, etc.), the following empirical relationship has been established:

$$X = kt^{1/2} - b \tag{22.2}$$

For ingot casting of steel, the value of k has been found to lie approximately between 2.5 and 3.5×10^{-3} m·s$^{-1/2}$, and b between 2.5 and 5×10^{-3} m.

Figure 22.3 shows the temperature versus distance profile normal to the mould wall. Because of thermal expansion of the mould and solidification shrinkage of the metal, an air gap is formed sometime after the beginning of solidification. Since the air gap is of insulating nature, it slows down the rate of heat flow and solidification. In between the liquid and the solidified steel, there is a *mushy zone*, which is a mixture of solid and liquid. The mechanism of heat transfer for the various zones from the melt to outside air is also indicated in Figure 22.3.

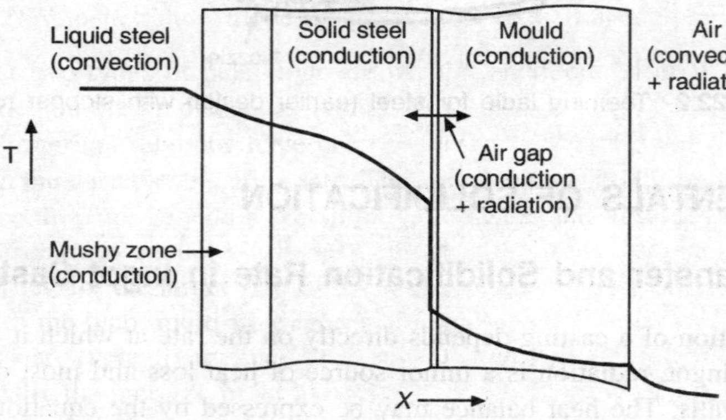

Figure 22.3 Temperature versus distance profile normal to the mould surface during ingot solidification.

22.2.2 Segregation and Crystallisation during Solidification

Segregation fundamentals

During solidification of liquid metals and alloys, crystal formation takes place. The resulting *morphology* has certain characteristics peculiar to cast structures in terms of both *macrostructure* and *microstructure*. Furthermore, *segregation of solutes* also occurs during solidification of alloys. Segregation results in non-uniformity of chemical composition in the cast alloy. The segregation pattern and morphology are inter-related phenomena and hence, for actual castings they cannot be considered in an isolated manner. Therefore, to cover the fundamentals of segregation, the simplest morphology is being assumed, viz.:

- The solidification front is plane
- The solid alloy is single-phase.

The basic cause of segregation is rejection of solutes by the liquid during freezing owing to the lower solubility of the solutes in the solid. In Figure 22.4, at the temperature T, the solute

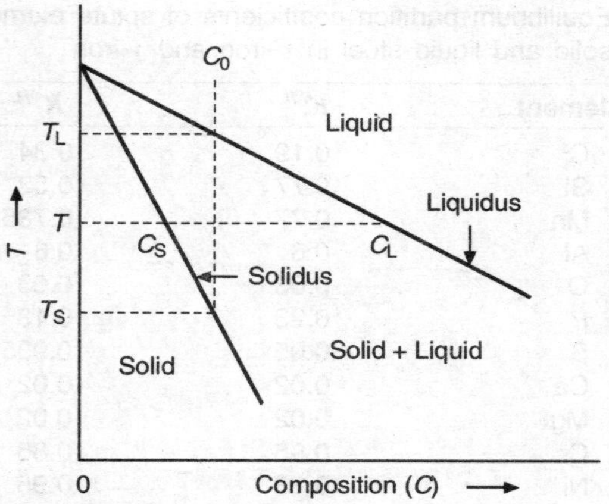

Figure 22.4 Solvent corner of the phase diagram (schematic).

concentrations on the *solidus* and *liquidus* are C_S and C_L respectively. At solid-liquid equilibrium,

$$\frac{C_S}{C_L} = K_e \tag{22.3}$$

where K_e is the *equilibrium partition coefficient*. For freezing of an alloy with an initial solute concentration C_0, according to the *Lever Rule*,

$$C_S f_S + C_L f_L = C_0 \tag{22.4}$$

where f_S and f_L are fractions of solid and liquid respectively, i.e. $f_S + f_L = 1$.

Table 22.1 presents the K_e values for some solutes in iron for solidification into δ-iron and γ-iron (Ueshima et al. 1986, Won et al. 2001, Yamada et al. 1990). It may be noted from the Table that oxygen and sulphur have the maximum tendency for segregation, since the values of K_e are the smallest. Carbon and phosphorus would tend to segregate less. Mn, Ni, V, etc. have very low segregation tendencies.

Equilibrium solidification requires complete mixing and homogenisation of composition in both solid and liquid states, which is not achieved in most cases. A more realistic assumption is:

- Complete mixing in the liquid phase
- No diffusion in the solid.

Such assumptions lead to the equation:

$$C_L = C_0(1 - f_S)^{K_e - 1} \tag{22.5}$$

This equation is called the *Scheil's Equation*, and is regularly used for simple analysis of solidification processes.

Table 22.1 Equilibrium partition coefficients of solute elements between solid and liquid steel in δ-iron and γ-iron

Element	$K^{\delta/L}$	$K^{\gamma/L}$
C	0.19	0.34
Si	0.77	0.52
Mn	0.77	0.785
Al	0.6	0.6
O	0.03	0.03
P	0.23	0.13
S	0.05	0.035
Ca	0.02	0.02
Mg	0.02	0.02
Cr	0.95	0.86
Ni	0.83	0.95
Cu	0.53	0.88
Mo	0.80	0.585
Ti	0.38	0.33
V	0.93	0.63
Nb	0.40	0.22
W	0.85	0.45
N	0.25	0.48

Dendritic solidification and resulting cast structure

In the earlier discussions on segregation, the solid–liquid interface has been assumed to be plane and without any mushy zone. In reality, solidification starts as a plane front, but soon changes into cellular or *dendritic* type (not plane). This is caused by the phenomenon of *constitutional supercooling,* which is illustrated in Figure 22.5. The Figure shows the temperature vs. distance profiles in a liquid alloy during solidification near the solid–liquid interface, which is at $x = 0$. The liquid at $x = 0$ has higher concentration of solutes compared with the bulk liquid because of rejection of solutes by the solid. As a consequence, the liquidus temperature (T_{liquidus}) is lower than in the bulk liquid at $x = 0$. The actual temperature (T_{actual}) also has a gradient owing to heat loss during solidification.

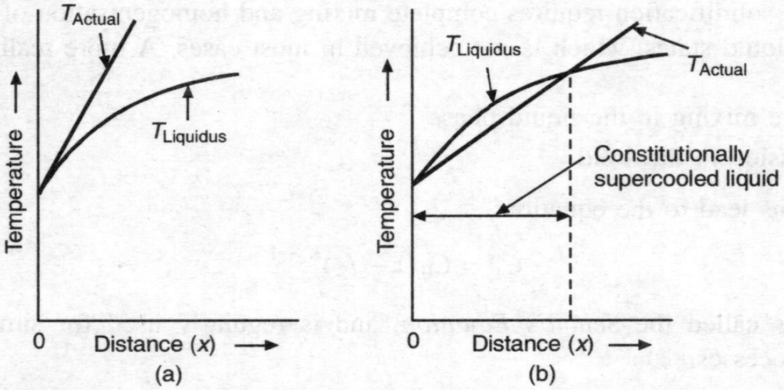

Figure 22.5 Temperature versus distance profile in the liquid ahead of the solidification front: (a) constitutional supercooling not possible, and (b) constitutional supercooling possible.

In Figure 22.5(a), T_{actual} is greater than $T_{liquidus}$. Hence, there is no freezing of the liquid adjacent to the interface and the solidification front is plane. In the situation illustrated in Figure 22.5(b) on the other hand, T_{actual} is less than $T_{liquidus}$ in the region adjacent to the solid–liquid interface. In this case, the liquid is *supercooled.* This supercooling occurs because of segregation, and hence, is called *constitutional supercooling*. This leads to the formation of cells at the interface. At high rates of solidification, rapid growth takes place normal to the interface along some crystallographic directions [such as along <100> in cubic metals]. These are known as *primary dendrites*. After some time, lateral growth of the primary dendrites leads to the formation of *secondary* and *tertiary* dendrites, giving a tree-like appearance. A mixture of solid dendrites and interdendritic liquid constitutes the mushy zone.

Figure 22.6(a) is a sketch of the *macrostructure* of the cross section of an ingot. The chill zone adjacent to the mould wall consists of fine grains arising out of the initial rapid freezing. Growth of dendrites normal to the mould wall after some time gives rise to the columnar zone. The central zone also consists of dendrites, but these are randomly oriented. This is known as the equiaxed zone. Figure 22.6(b) is a schematic presentation of the vertical section of an ingot. It may be noted that the interdendritic liquid is less pure than the bulk liquid owing to rejection of solutes by the growing dendrites. The reason why these are referred to as the structure of *killed steel ingots*, will be explained in the next section.

For further details, the readers may consult Flemings (1974) and Ghosh (1990).

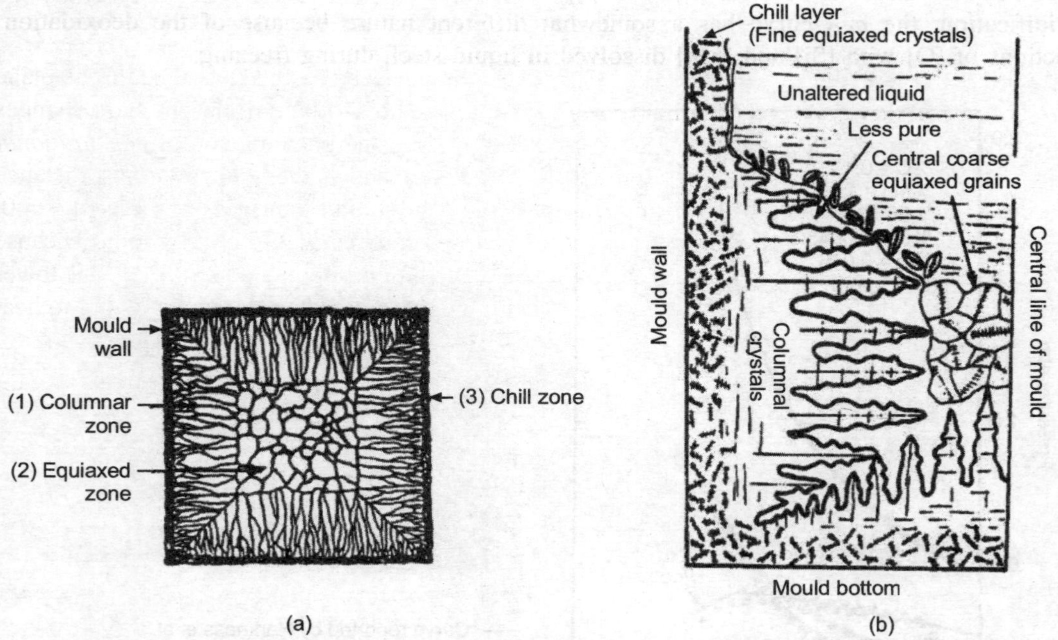

Figure 22.6 Structure of killed steel ingots showing three zones: (a) cross section, and (b) longitudinal section.

22.3 CLASSIFICATION OF STEEL INGOTS

22.3.1 Gas Generation during Freezing

In Chapter 20, Section 20.3 deoxidation of liquid steel was discussed while Section 20.4 covered the gases, i.e. hydrogen, nitrogen and oxygen, dissolved in liquid steel. The amount of dissolved oxygen is lowered by adding deoxidisers. Dissolved hydrogen can be lowered effectively by vacuum degassing. Removal of dissolved N as N_2 is more difficult and requires attention at all the stages of steelmaking. Reactions for the formation of gaseous H_2, N_2 and CO are noted in Eqs. (20.12) to (20.14). Some thermodynamic data have been summarised in Tables 20.2 and 20.3.

In Section 22.2.2, the segregation of solutes during freezing of a liquid solution (alloy, etc.), and consequent increase of solute concentrations in the solidifying liquid have been covered. This phenomenon leads to continuous increase in dissolved C, H, N in the remaining liquid steel. Dissolved oxygen also behaves in a similar fashion when there is no deoxidation reaction during freezing. As a consequence, the partial pressures of CO, N_2 and H_2 *at equilibrium with the dissolved solutes in steel* (*i.e. thermodynamically calculated pressures*) also keep increasing with the extent of solidification.

Figure 22.7 presents results of such calculations for an assumed initial composition of liquid steel (Deo et al. 1985). While p_{N_2} and p_{H_2} increase continuously during the progress of solidification, the p_{CO} curve has a somewhat different nature because of the deoxidation reactions of [O] with [Si] and [Mn] dissolved in liquid steel, during freezing.

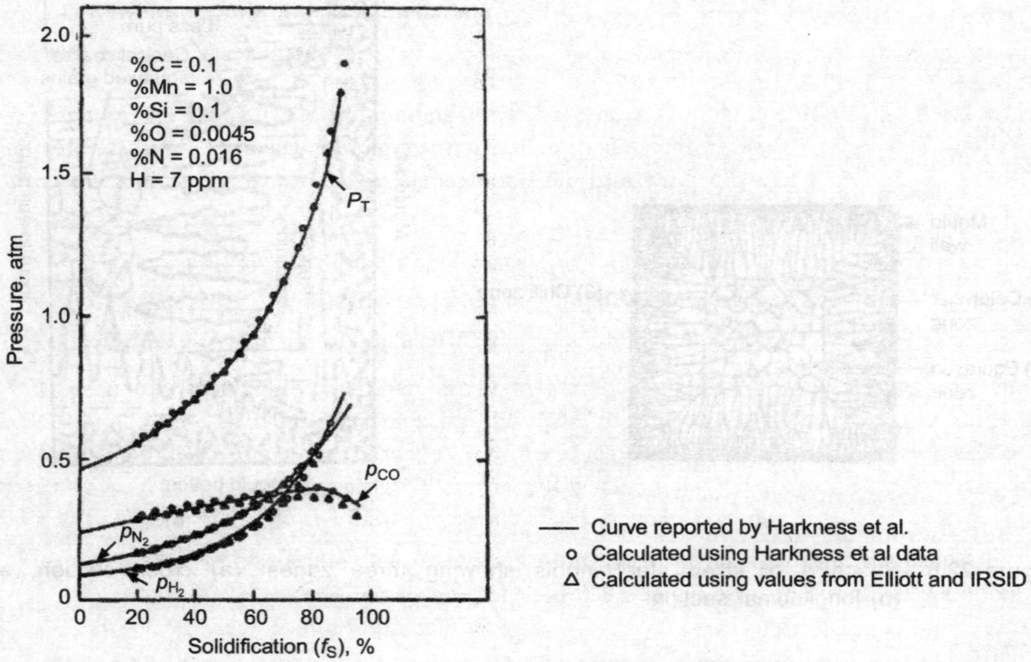

Figure 22.7 Variation of p_{CO}, p_{H_2}, p_{N_2} and P_T with increasing solidification for semi-killed steel ingots.

The total thermodynamic pressure (P_T) is related to equilibrium partial pressures of CO, N_2 and H_2 as:

$$P_T = p_{CO} + p_{N_2} + p_{H_2} \tag{22.6}$$

When

$$P_T > P_a + P_h \tag{22.7}$$

gas bubbles form. P_a is the atmospheric pressure and P_h is the ferrostatic pressure of liquid steel.

22.3.2 Types of Ingots

Detailed classification of steel ingots is possible on the basis of their structures. Ingots can be broadly classified into three categories: *killed*, *semi-killed* and *rimming*, as shown in Figure 22.8. These are explained in greater detail below.

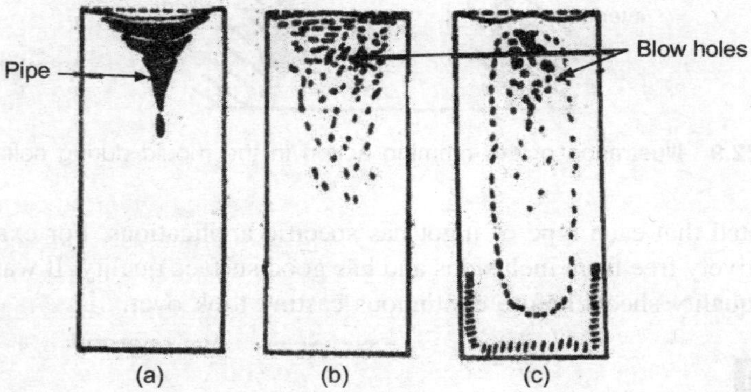

Figure 22.8 Typical macro-structures of steel ingots: (a) killed, (b) semi-killed, and (c) rimming.

(a) In well-deoxidised steels in which strong deoxidiser(s) such as aluminium is added, [O] and hence p_{CO} is very low. Therefore, P_T is always less than ($P_a + P_h$), and gas bubbles do not form. This results in killed steel ingots, whose macrostructure has been shown in Figure 22.6. Because of solidification shrinkage and consequent volume contraction, a hollow cavity (known as *pipe*) is formed at the top of the ingots.

(b) For semi-killed ingots, deoxidation is carried out by Mn and some Si, and hence, the extent of deoxidation is weaker. The [O] content in molten steel after deoxidation and before freezing, typically ranges between 50 and 100 ppm. In this situation, gas bubbles can form only after about 70 to 80% solidification is completed. At this stage, the top of the ingot is already frozen because of the extra heat losses from the top. As a result, the gas bubbles remain entrapped in the solid ingot leading to the formation of gas holes (known as *blow-holes*).

(c) In rimming steels, very little deoxidation is carried out in the ladle. Consequently, the initial oxygen content of the melt is above 200 ppm. As soon as the steel is poured into the mould, on account of the high p_{CO}, copious evolution of gas begins almost immediately. The bubbling action and gas evolution cause ejection of droplets of molten steel into the atmosphere and these droplets get oxidised by atmospheric oxygen. Some, or most of these droplets return to the ingot. This phenomenon, shown in Figure 22.9, leads to continuous absorption of oxygen by the melt, which helps in sustaining the rimming action. The typical pattern of blow-hole distribution in rimming steel ingots is shown in Figure 22.8(c).

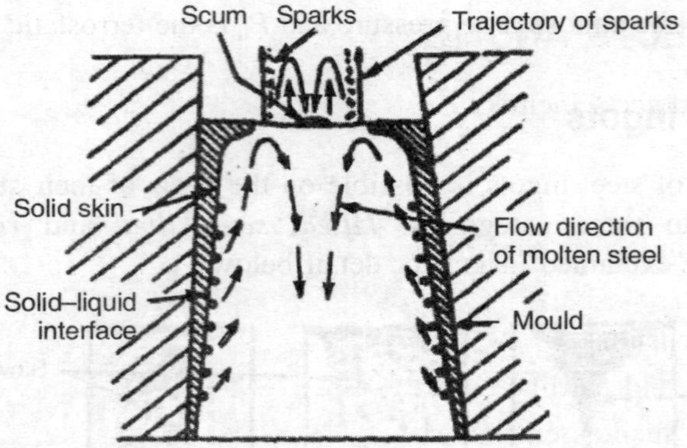

Figure 22.9 Illustration of the rimming action in the mould during solidification.

It may be noted that each type of ingot has specific applications. For example, a rimming steel ingot is relatively free from inclusions and has good surface quality. It was principally used to produce high-quality sheets before continuous casting took over.

EXAMPLE 22.1

Consider solidification of liquid steel isothermally at 1500°C. Calculate the total thermodynamic pressure owing to gases in steel (i.e. P_T) at 50% solidification. Ignore deoxidation reactions. Ignore solute–solute interactions. Take the initial composition of liquid steel as in Figure 22.7.

Solution: Values of equilibrium partition coefficients for solidification of liquid iron into ∂-iron are given in Table 22.1.

Assume equilibrium segregation for carbon, hydrogen and nitrogen, since these are of small atomic sizes and diffusion is fast. Then, combining Eqs. (22.3) and (22.4), i.e. $C_S/C_L = K_e$, and $C_S f_S + C_L C_L = C_0$, and with the relation: $f_S + f_L = 1$, the following equation can be obtained:

$$C_L = \frac{C_0}{1 + f_S(K_e - 1)} \qquad \text{(Ex. 22.1)}$$

Noting that $f_S = 0.5$, and $K_e = 0.25$, 0.32 and 0.19 respectively for N, H, and C, the concentrations after 50% solidification are: $W_N = 0.026\%$, ppm H = 10.6, $W_C = 0.168\%$.

Assume validity of Scheil's equation, i.e. Eq. (22.5) for O,

$$C_L = C_0(1 - f_S)^{K_e - 1} = C_0(0.5)^{K_e - 1} \qquad \text{(Ex. 22.2)}$$

Calculations yield that after 50% solidification, $W_O = 0.00888$ wt. %.

Thermodynamic calculations on the basis of Table 20.3 give the thermodynamic pressures of H_2, N_2 and CO, at equilibrium with H, N, C and O dissolved in liquid steel, at 50 per cent solidification as 0.24, 0.32 and 0.71 atm. respectively.

Hence, $P_T = p_{CO} + p_{N_2} + p_{H_2} = 0.24 + 0.35 + 0.67 = 1.26$ atm.

22.4 INGOT DEFECTS AND THEIR REMEDIES

Various types of ingot defects include:

- Pipe
- Blow-hole
- Columnar structure (also known as ingotism) related defects
- Segregation
- Non-metallic inclusions
- Internal fracture and hairline cracks
- Surface defects, such as cracks, etc.

Each of these will be briefly discussed below.

22.4.1 Pipe

Pipe represents the shrinkage cavity at the top of killed steel ingots, as shown in Figure 22.8(a). Since the pipe is exposed to the atmosphere with consequent formation of oxide scales on its surface, it does not get welded during subsequent hot rolling. Therefore, this portion has to be rejected, leading to loss of yield. The remedy is to use a *hot top*, as shown in Figure 22.1(c). The hot top is an insulated refractory lining inserted at the top of the mould into which some insulating powder or exothermic compounds are added when molten steel is teemed into the mould. Therefore, the metal in the hot top region remains molten till the end, and thus feeds the shrinkage cavity. As a result, only a small fraction of metal which solidifies in the hot top portion is rejected.

22.4.2 Blow-hole

The mechanism of formation of blow-holes has been discussed in the previous section. Blow holes are found in semi-killed and rimming ingots, as shown in Figure 22.8. Blow-holes are structural defects, but they are not necessarily harmful. Blow-holes counter shrinkage and eliminate the shrinkage cavity. Deep-seated interior blow-holes get welded during subsequent hot working. Blow-holes are harmful only if they are present near the surface of the ingot, since they get exposed during hot working and form surface defects. Excessive blow-hole formation causes swelling of the ingot top (referred to as spongy top) and some loss of yield. The remedy is to control the deoxidation practice so as to avoid these harmful effects.

22.4.3 Columnar Structure Effects

The structure has been discussed in Section 22.2.2. The horizontal grains in the columnar zone give rise to the following adverse effects on ingot quality.

(i) They do not allow non-metallic inclusions to float-up properly, making the ingot more dirty.
(ii) They increase the extent of segregation (discussed later).
(iii) They increase the tendency of cracking during rolling.
(iv) Non-isotropy is more in columnar grains.

The volume fraction (i.e. the fraction of the ingot cross-section area) of the columnar zone depends on several variables, such as:

- Ingot size and steel composition
- Extent of gas evolution and blow-hole formation
- The linear rate of solidification (dx/dt), which depends on the rate of heat loss and the initial superheat of the melt (see Eq. (22.1)).

Proper control of pouring temperature and deoxidation practice can partially remedy these effects.

22.4.4 Segregation

The fundamentals of segregation were briefly presented in Section 22.2.2. These fundamental principles are applicable to *micro-segregation*, i.e. segregation in small microscopic regions, such as in interdendritic liquids during dendrite growth. Micro-segregation gets eliminated by homogenisation through solid state diffusion during subsequent hot working and heat treatment.

Movement of the micro-segregated regions over macroscopic distances owing to the motion of the liquid and the free crystals gives rise to *macro-segregation*. The motion of impure interdendritic liquid causes regions of *positive* macro-segregation; whereas, the movement of purer solid crystals yields *negative* macro-segregation. The flow of interdendritic liquid is primarily because of *natural* (*or free*) *convection* arising out of density gradients in the liquid. Such density gradients arise from non-uniform temperature and composition in the solidifying liquid. Some *forced convection* also occurs owing to gas evolution and/or suction by shrinkage cavities.

Macro-segregation constitutes a defect, since it cannot be eliminated during subsequent hot working and heat treatment. Large fractions of columnar zone mean more impure inter-dendritic liquid. As shown schematically in the vertical section of a killed steel ingot, the upward flow of this liquid leads to the formation of a distinct pattern of positive (+) segregation zone. The zone of negative segregation arises out of settling of free crystals, which are purer and denser than the liquid, as shown in Figure 22.10.

Macro-segregation is a complex phenomenon. The patterns of segregation are different in killed, semi-killed and rimming steel ingots and there is no simple prescription for remedial measures. Hence, it is not discussed any further here though it will again be briefly dealt with in connection with continuous casting in Chapter 23.

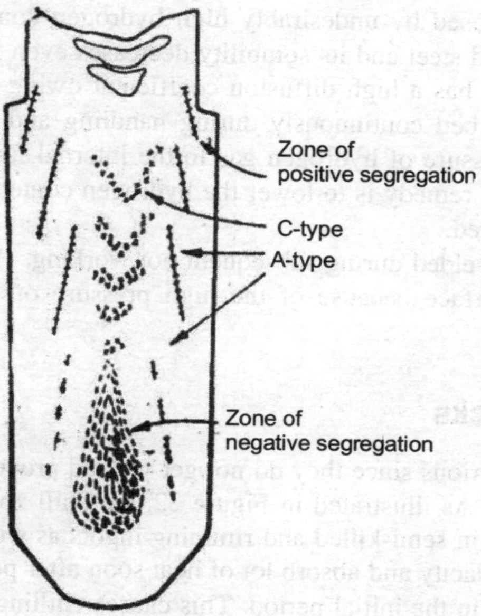

Figure 22.10 Macro-segregation pattern in a vertical section of a killed steel ingot.

22.4.5 Non-metallic Inclusions

This subject has been dealt with in Chapter 20, Section 20.6. Non-metallic inclusions in steel have generally been found to be harmful for the properties of steel. The remedy lies in producing cleaner steels along with some amount of inclusion modification. Extensive efforts are being made in recent times in this area, primarily in connection with continuous casting of steel. Most of these measures were not adopted earlier in ingot casting.

Several investigations have been conducted on the nature and distribution of the inclusions in ingots. Certain broad patterns have been reported, but they are not being included here. Readers may consult Ghosh (1990) for further details. To summarise, these patterns arise out of:

- Complex flow pattern of liquid steel in the mould during solidification
- Entrapment of inclusions by dendrites
- Entrainment of the top scum particles into the mould during solidification of rimming steel.

22.4.6 Internal Fractures and Hairline Cracks

Internal fracture is caused by thermal stresses. If the ingots are cooled fast after the moulds are stripped, or are reheated rapidly before hot rolling/hot forging, a temperature gradient is created from the surface to the centre of the ingots. This causes uneven expansion/contraction across the ingot with consequent development of internal stresses. This leads to internal fractures which can be prevented by slow cooling and heating.

Hairline cracks are caused by undesirably high hydrogen content of steel. Hydrogen has negligible solubility in solid steel and its solubility decreases even further during cooling of the solidified metal. Hydrogen has a high diffusion coefficient owing to its low atomic mass, and hence, keeps getting desorbed continuously during handling and storage of the ingots. Such desorption causes high pressure of hydrogen gas in the internal faults leading to the formation of fine internal cracks. The remedy is to lower the hydrogen content of molten steel by vacuum degassing, wherever required.

Internal fractures get welded during subsequent hot working. However, hairline cracks tend to propagate up to the surface because of the high pressure of hydrogen. This leads to the rejection of ingots.

22.4.7 Surface Cracks

Surface cracks are more serious since they do not get welded properly during hot working, thus leading to surface defects. As illustrated in Figure 22.6, a chill zone exists on the surface of a killed steel ingot. It forms in semi-killed and rimming ingots as well. This happens because the moulds have large heat capacity and absorb lot of heat soon after pouring of the liquid, resulting in rapid extraction of heat in the initial period. This causes chilling of the liquid adjacent to the moulds with the formation of small equiaxed crystals.

Heat absorption and consequent heating of any mould leads to its expansion along with simultaneous contraction of the liquid following solidification. This causes separation of the interior surface of the mould from the ingot skin with the formation of an air gap. The ferrostatic pressure of the liquid core of the ingot then has to be withstood by the ingot skin alone. If the skin is not thick/strong enough to withstand the internal pressure, it gets ruptured giving rise to cracks on the surface. Friction between the mould wall and the ingot skin also can cause surface cracks. Proper design of the mould can lower the incidences of cracking considerably.

REFERENCES

Deo, B., A.K. Bagaria and A. Ghosh, Trans. Ind. Inst. Metals, Vol. 36 (1985), p. 49.

Flemings, M.C., *Solidification Processing*, McGraw-Hill, New York, 1974.

Ghosh, A., *Principles of Secondary Processing and Casting of Liquid Steel*, Oxford & IBH Publishing, New Delhi, 1990.

Trubin, K.G. and G.N. Qiks, *Steelmaking—Open Hearth and Combined Processes*, MIR Publishers, Moscow (1974), Ch. 24.

Ueshima, Y., S. Mizoguchi, T. Matsumiya and H. Kajioka, Metall. Trans B, Vol. 17B (1986), pp. 845–859.

Won, Y.M. and B.G. Thomas, Metall. and Mater. Trans. A, Vol. 32A (2001), pp. 1755–1767.

Yamada, W., T. Matsumiya and A. Ito, Proc. 6th Int. Iron and Steel congress, ISIJ, Nagoya (1990), pp. 618–625.

23

Continuous Casting of Steel

23.1 INTRODUCTION

Chapter 3 has already described the basic process of continuous casting of steel. It is the most dominant method of casting of liquid steel in integrated steel plants as well as in modern mini steel plants.

The advantages of continuous casting (over ingot casting) are:

- It is directly possible to cast blooms, slabs and billets*, thus eliminating blooming, slabbing mills completely, and billet mills to a large extent.
- Better quality of the cast product.
- Higher crude-to-finished steel yield (about 10 to 20% more than ingot casting).
- Higher extent of automation and process control.

Better consistency in the quality of the cast products and higher productivity are other advantages of continuous casting over ingot casting. All these advantages have contributed to substantial savings of capital and operating costs per tonne of steel. The capital cost is lower since less equipment is involved and the cast product is closer to the final product; the operating cost savings arise out of lower manpower and energy as well as higher yield.

Henry Bessemer first propagated the concept of continuous casting of steel in 1846. However, it took more than hundred years to make continuous casting a reality. It was initially successful in casting non-ferrous metals in the 1930s. However, it was more difficult to apply it to steel because of the higher melting temperature and lower thermal conductivity. The first pilot plant for continuous casting of steel was installed in Germany in 1943. By 1970, a large number of machines were in use throughout the world. In 1980, about 30% of world steel was cast by this route, which increased to 65% by 1990, and is at present above 95%. The widespread adoption of continuous casting has been particularly noticeable in major steel producing countries, for example, it accounted for 94% of the total steel production in South Korea, 93% in Japan and 88% in the European Economic Community in 1990.

* Slabs have a flat rectangular cross section, typically 800–1300 mm width and 150–300 mm thickness, billets are typically of square cross section (in some cases, rounds) of a maximum section size of 150 × 150 mm approximately, and blooms are square or rectangular in cross section of larger sizes than billets.

Continuous casting started in India with the commissioning of a billet caster at Mukand Iron and Steel Works and at the Canara Works in 1965. Amongst integrated steel plants of India, Tata Steel, Bhilai Steel Plant as well as the Vizag Steel Plant started continuous casting in the decade of 1980. In 1990, the share of continuous casting in India was about 25% of the total steel production, which is about 90% at present, with machines available in most integrated steel plants and virtually all the modern mini steel plants. Over the last 40 years, extensive research and development efforts have been made throughout the world and huge amount of literature is available.

The commercial processes of continuous casting can be classified into: *slab casting*, *bloom casting* and *billet casting*. The biggest breakthrough in recent years in the area of steel have been the advent of *thin slab casting* and the very recent *strip casting* of molten steel. These developments are generically grouped as *Near-Net Shape Casting*. Since such casters are continuously being installed and the process is still maturing, the discussions in the following sections will be focused mainly on the commercial continuous casting of slabs, blooms and billets. Near-net shape casting will be separately taken up at the end of this chapter.

23.2 HEAT TRANSFER AND SOLIDIFICATION IN CONTINUOUS CASTING

The process of continuous casting consists of teeming liquid metal into a water-cooled copper mould of a relatively short length. The mould is open at both ends, and is kept in the vertical position into which liquid metal is poured continuously from the top, and the partially solidified product is continuously withdrawn from the bottom with the help of withdrawal rolls. At the beginning of casting, the bottom of the mould is kept closed by using a dummy bar, which also gets subsequently withdrawn by the withdrawal rolls.

High rate of flow of cooling water on the mould surface continuously removes heat, which is known as *primary cooling*. The metal is only partially solidified at the mould exit; the remainder of the cooling and solidification occurs below the mould by:

- *Secondary cooling* by water sprays
- *Tertiary cooling* by radiation below the secondary cooling zones.

Figure 23.1 is a schematic representation of the steps involved in continuous casting. The length of the secondary cooling zone is normally 8 to 10 times that of the primary cooling zone. The terminology *Strand* denotes the entire casting machine starting from the mould to the withdrawal rolls. The solidified product has many nomenclatures, but in this book the term 'ingot' will be used. It needs to be pointed out straightaway that at the exit of any CC machine, the ingot is endless and has to be cut into appropriate lengths by a cutter before further processing.

23.2.1 General Considerations

The fundamentals of heat transfer, solidification, segregation and crystallisation during freezing of alloys have been discussed in Chapter 22 along with dendritic solidification and the resulting cast structure during the process of ingot casting of steel. These fundamentals are applicable to continuous casting as well. Therefore, in this chapter, only the unique features of heat flow, etc. as applied to continuous casting will be covered.

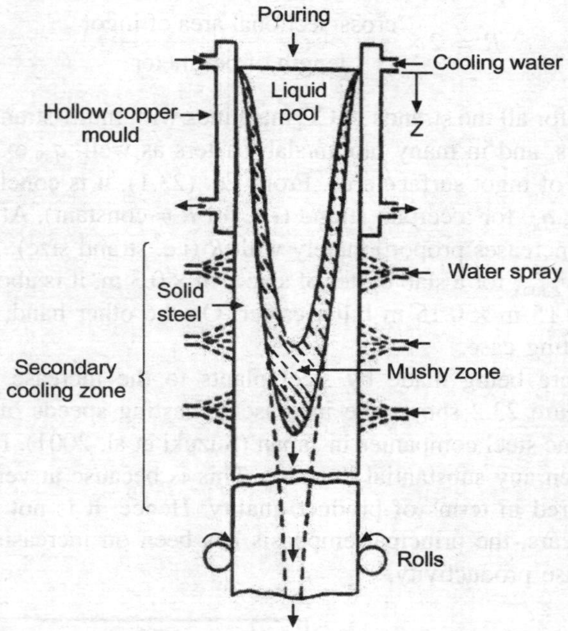

Figure 23.1 Simplified sketch of continuous casting.

With reference to Figure 23.1, the major requirements are as follows:

(a) Solidification must be completed before the withdrawal rolls.

(b) The liquid core should be *bowl-shaped* as shown in the Figure and not pointed at the bottom (as indicated by the dotted lines), since the latter increases the tendency for undesirable centreline (i.e. axial) macro-segregation and porosity (to be discussed later).

(c) The solidified shell of metal should be strong enough at the exit region of the mould so that it does not crack or *breakout* under pressure of the liquid.

All the above requirements can be achieved only if the heat extraction from the metal, both in the mould region and in the secondary cooling zone, is carried out satisfactorily. The higher the casting speed, the lesser is the time available for heat extraction in the mould. By convention, casting speed (v_c) is expressed as the rate of linear movement of the ingot in metres per minute. Therefore, the longer the length of the liquid core as well as the mushy zone, the lesser would be the thickness of the shell when the ingot emerges from the mould. Hence, there is a maximum permissible (i.e. limiting) casting speed ($v_{c,\max}$).

On the basis of the above, it may be shown that

$$v_{c,\max} \propto \frac{q_{av}}{R} \tag{23.1}$$

and

$$P_{\max} \propto q_{av} \cdot R \tag{23.2}$$

where

$P_{\max}$ = maximum rate of production in a strand (say, in tonnes per min)

q_{av} = average heat flux in the primary and secondary cooling zone.

and $$R = 2 \times \frac{\text{cross-sectional area of ingot}}{\text{length of perimeter}}$$

q_{av} is not the same for all the strands in CC machines with multi-strands, which are normally used in all billet casters, and in many bloom/slab casters as well. q_{av} exhibits an overall range of 800 to 2000 kW/m^2 of ingot surface area. From Eq. (23.1), it is concluded that $v_{c,max}$ can be increased by increasing q_{av} for a certain strand (i.e. for R = constant). At the same value of q_{av}, from Eq. (23.2), P_{max} increases proportionately with R (i.e. strand size). For example, a sample calculation shows that $v_{c,max}$ for a slab caster of size 2 m × 0.3 m, it is about 3.5 to 4 times lower than in the case of a 0.15 m × 0.15 m billet caster. On the other hand, P_{max} is 3.5 to 4 times higher for the slab casting case.

Sustained efforts are being made by steel plants to the increase casting speed without sacrificing quality. Figure 23.2 shows the increase in casting speeds of slab casters in recent years in the case of some steel companies in Japan (Suzuki et al. 2001). It will be seen that after 1990, there has not been any substantial increase. This is because at very high casting speeds, problems are encountered in terms of product quality. Hence, it is not possible to increase v_c arbitrarily. In recent years, the principal emphasis has been on increasing the heat flux in the mould region to increase productivity.

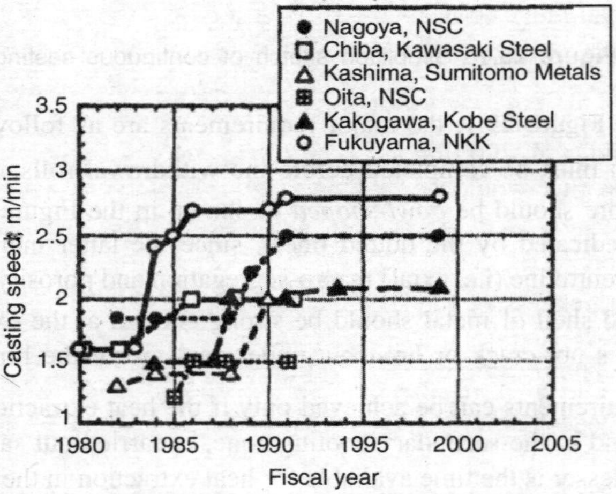

Figure 23.2 Increase in casting speed in recent years in the main slab casters in Japan.

23.2.2 Heat Transfer in the Mould

Figure 23.3 shows the various modes of heat flow from liquid steel to the mould in continuous casting. The phenomenon of formation of the air-gap between the mould and the solidified steel layer arising from solidification shrinkage and thermal expansion of the mould has been mentioned in the case of ingot casting (Figure 22.3). In the continuous casting mould as well, as shown in Figure 23.3, the principal resistance to heat transfer is the air-gap formation following the conduction of heat through the solidified steel shell.

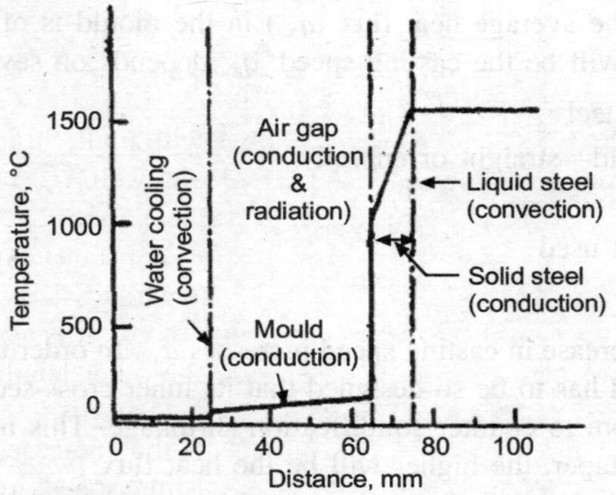

Figure 23.3 Various modes of heat transfer in a continuous casting mould.

The local heat flux (q) in the mould varies from the top meniscus level to the bottom of the mould. Ingot casting is a batch process; therefore, in Eq. (22.2), time (t) means the time from the beginning of solidification till the solidification of the entire ingot. In continuous casting, a horizontal section of metal moves downwards during solidification. Hence, its residence time in the mould increases downwards, from zero at the meniscus, and this becomes the variable t in Eq. (22.2).

Figure 23.4 shows the variation in heat flux with residence time (t) in a slab caster mould at low casting speed (Paul et al. 2000). For high speed casting, the maximum value of t is around 30 seconds and the heat flux would be 3 to 4 times that in Figure 23.4. The reasons for the decrease in q with t are:

- Air-gap formation
- Increase in the thickness of the solid shell.

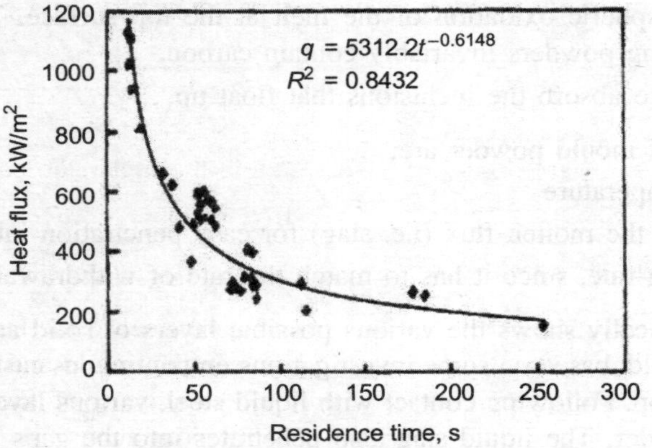

Figure 23.4 Variation of local heat flux with residence time in a slab caster mould.

For practical purposes, the average heat flux (q_{av}) in the mould is of interest. The higher the value of q_{av}, the higher will be the casting speed. q_{av} depends on several variables, such as:

- Composition of steel
- Type of the mould—straight or curved
- Mould taper
- Type of lubricant used
- Casting speed.

As already stated, increase in casting speed increases q_{av}. In order to lower the extent of air-gap formation, the mould has to be so designed that its inner cross-section gradually decreases from the top to the bottom to counter solidification shrinkage. This is known as *mould taper.* Obviously the more the taper, the higher will be the heat flux.

The purpose of lubrication is to decrease the friction between the ingot and the mould, thereby making the withdrawal of the ingot easier. During the early years of continuous casting, only billet casting was practiced. Oil was employed as the lubricant. In some old billet casters, this practice still exists. However, the universal practice for slabs, blooms and in some billets is to employ a mould powder (flux) as the lubricant. The powder penetrates into the air-gap, and increases the effective thermal conductivity thereby enhancing the heat flux. The mould powder flux performs several other functions as well. Considerable research and development has been carried in the development of mould powders—it will now be discussed separately.

23.2.3 Mould Flux

Mould flux (*casting powder*) consists of many oxides. Since it has a low melting point, it melts and forms molten slag when it comes in contact with liquid steel. Besides lubrication and elimination of the air-gap, the casting powder also performs the following useful functions.

1. It reduces heat losses from the top surface of liquid metal leading to better casting performance.
2. It prevents atmospheric oxidation of the melt at the top surface. This is the primary reason why casting powders invariably contain carbon.
3. It acts as a flux to absorb the inclusions that float up.

The desired properties of mould powder are:

- Low liquidus temperature
- Low viscosity of the molten flux (i.e. slag) for easy penetration into the air-gap
- Optimum melting rate, since it has to match the rate of withdrawal.

Figure 23.5 schematically shows the various possible layers of solid and liquid powder in a continuous casting mould, based on some investigations on continuous casting operations. The powder is added at the top. Following contact with liquid steel, various layers are developed in the top layer of the powder. The liquid slag also penetrates into the gaps at the mould–metal interface, where also different layers develop.

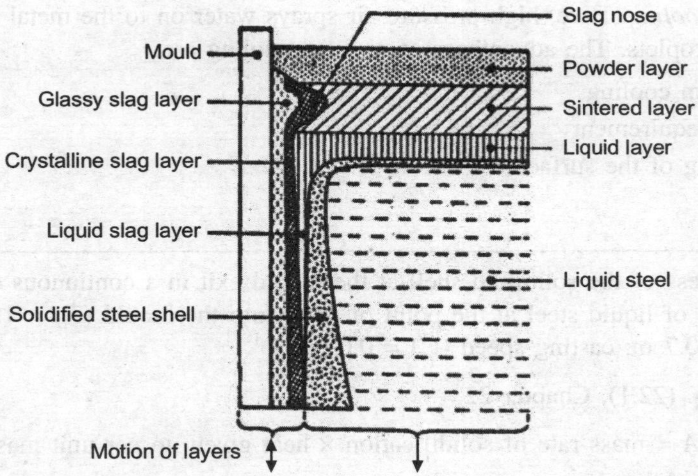

Figure 23.5 Different layers of solid and molten casting powder in the mould (schematic).

Many commercial casting powders have been developed and marketed to suit the overall range of continuous casting requirement. They are essentially mixtures of SiO_2, CaO, Al_2O_3, Na_2O and CaF_2 with minor additions of MgO, MnO, FeO and K_2O. As stated earlier, some carbon powder is always a constituent. An adverse effect of the molten slag formed by casting powder is the possibility of it attacking the refractory lining of the *submerged entry nozzle* (SEN).

23.2.4 Heat Transfer in Secondary Cooling Zone

Figure 23.1 indicates the secondary cooling zone, which is much longer than the mould. The metal solidifies completely in this zone. For steel casting, the outer surface temperature should be above 850°C, so that austenite-ferrite transition does not occur, since it causes volumetric expansion, which can lead to the development of cracks on the surface.

The intensity of heat extraction by water spraying is quantitatively expressed in terms of the heat transfer coefficient (h), where

$$h = \frac{\text{heat flux } (q)}{T_{\text{surface}} - T_{\text{water}}} \tag{23.3}$$

h primarily depends on the flow rate of water ($\dot{W}$). In general, it is possible to write:

$$h \propto \dot{W}^n \tag{23.4}$$

where n ranges between 0.5 and 1.

A major problem is that h is non-uniform over the entire surface—it is high where the water jet impinges, but much less at distances away from the impingement zone. This causes non-uniformity in surface temperature, and consequent generation of stresses on the surface and tendency for surface cracking. A major development has been air-water spray cooling, also known as *air mist cooling*. Here, high pressure air sprays water on to the metal surface in the form of very fine droplets. The advantages of air-mist cooling are:

- More uniform cooling
- Less water requirement
- Less cracking of the surface.

EXAMPLE 23.1

Calculate the thickness of the solidified shell at the mould exit in a continuous casting unit. *Given:* Temperature of liquid steel at the point of entry into the mould (T_l) = 1560°C, length of the mould (L) = 0.7 m, casting speed (v_c) = 0.05 m·s^{-1}.

Solution: From Eq. (22.1), Chapter 22,

$$Q = qA = \text{mass rate of solidification} \times \text{heat given up per unit mass}$$

$$= A\rho_s\left(\frac{dx}{dt}\right)(\Delta H_f + C \cdot \Delta T_s)$$

If z denotes the coordinate along the length of the mould, then $dt = dz/v_c$.

Note that $\rho_s = 7.8 \times 10^3$ kg/m^3, $C_s = 788$ J/kg/K, $\Delta H_f = 15.5$ kJ/mol = 278×10^3 J/kg, $\Delta T = 1560 -$ melting point of iron = 1560 – 1536 = 24°C. Again, q is given by Eq. (23.3) as follows.

$$h = \frac{\text{heat flux } (q)}{T_{\text{surface}} - T_{\text{water}}} \tag{23.3}$$

The average value of q in the mould (q_m) = h_m(1560 – 40), assuming cooling water temperature as 40°C, where h_m = mean value of h in the mould.

From literature sources, $h_m = 1.7 \times 10^3 - 16.2t_m$ (Ex. 23.1)

where, t_m = residence time of steel in mould = L/v_c = 0.7/0.05 = 14 s.

Substitution of all these values in Eq. (22.1) gives $dx/dt = 9.67 \times 10^{-4}$.

$$\frac{dx}{dz} = \frac{dx}{dt} \cdot \frac{dt}{dz} = \frac{dx}{dt} \cdot \frac{1}{v_c} = 0.0193$$

or, x = solidified thickness upon emergence from mould = $0.0193 \int_0^{0.7} dz = 0.0134$ m.

23.3 METALLURGICAL COMPARISON OF CONTINUOUS CASTING WITH INGOT CASTING

In contrast with ingot casting, the mould cross-section in continuous casting, especially for billet casting, is much smaller. In other words, the surface area-to-volume ratio per unit length of continuously cast ingot is larger than that for ingot casting. As a consequence, the linear rate of solidification (dx/dt) in Eq. (22.1) is an order of magnitude higher than that in ingot casting. This is a broad generalisation, which is quite valid for high speed casting of slabs and blooms as well.

There are several consequences of this, as noted below.

1. The dendrite arm spacing in continuously cast products is smaller compared with that in ingot casting. This follows from the general fundamental feature of cast structures, as illustrated in Figure 23.6 (Ghosh, as in Chapter 22).

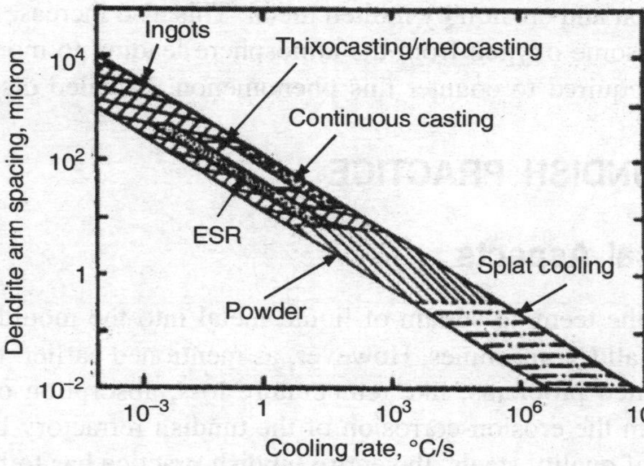

Figure 23.6 Dendrite arm spacing versus cooling rate for different types of solidification.

2. Macro-segregation is less, and is restricted to the centreline zone only.
3. Endogenous inclusions are smaller in size, since they get less time to grow. For the same reason, the blow holes are, on an average, smaller in size.
4. Inclusions get less time to float-up. Therefore, any non-metallic particle coming into the melt at the later stages tends to remain entrapped in the cast product.

In addition to more rapid freezing, continuous casting differs from ingot casting in several ways. These are noted below.

1. Pouring is continuous, and the rate of pouring has to be equal to the rate of withdrawal. This is achieved by pouring via a tundish, where the height of the molten metal pool remains approximately constant throughout the process of emptying a ladle. In addition, instrumentation for monitoring and control of the top level of liquid metal pool is a must.
2. Mathematically speaking, continuously cast ingot is infinitely long. Hence, the heat flow is essentially in the transverse direction, and there is no end-effect as is the case in ingot casting (e.g. bottom cone of negative segregation, pipe at the top, etc.).
3. The depth of the liquid metal pool is several metres long. Hence, the ferrostatic pressure of the liquid is high during the latter stages of solidification, resulting in significant difficulties of blow-hole formation.
4. Since the ingot is withdrawn continuously from the mould, the frozen layer of steel is subjected to stresses. This is aggravated by the stresses arising out of thermal expansion/ contraction and phase transformations. Such stresses are the highest at the surface. Moreover, when the ingot comes out of the mould, the thickness of the frozen steel shell

is not very appreciable. Furthermore, it is at around 1100–1200°C, and is therefore, weak. All these factors tend to cause cracks at the surface of the ingot leading to rejections.

5. Use of a tundish between the ladle and the mould results in extra temperature loss. Therefore, better refractory lining in the ladles, tundish, etc. are required in order to minimise corrosion and erosion by molten metal. This also increases the tendency for the metal to pick-up some oxygen from the atmosphere leading to more inclusions. Several precautions are required to counter this phenomenon. Detailed discussions will follow.

23.4 MODERN TUNDISH PRACTICE

23.4.1 Metallurgical Aspects

To regulate the flow of the teeming stream of liquid metal into the mould, a tundish is always incorporated as a part of all CC machines. However, as mentioned earlier, the use of the tundish has given rise to associated problems, like temperature loss, absorption of atmospheric gases, additional inclusions from the erosion-corrosion of the tundish refractory lining, etc. Therefore, for assuring the casting of quality steels, the entire tundish practice has to be managed properly. Extensive research and development work has been carried out in the last three decades. The tundish is now considered to be a *reactor*, and not simply an inert receptacle of metal.

Figure 23.7(a) is a schematic representation of the longitudinal section of a tundish. The design details vary widely from machine supplier to supplier and from plant to plant. The capacity of modern tundishes ranges from approximately 10 to 80 tonnes of steel. As a continuously operated vessel, one tundish at any time is required to feed molten metal to more than one mould, i.e. more than one strand. For example, the tundish in Figure 23.7 has two exit outlets to feed two moulds/strands. Flow of metal into the mould(s) can be stopped at any time by lowering the tundish stopper rod to close the exit nozzle(s). When one ladle has been completely emptied, it has to be replaced by a new full ladle so that feeding into the moulds continues. During this changeover, the reservoir of liquid metal available in the tundish must be sufficient to keep feeding the mould(s). As long as the tundish does not require shut down for lining repair/any other maintenance, this process continues. It is also not necessary that the grade of steel is the same in all subsequent ladles—it is possible to transit from one grade to another by discarding/downgrading a small portion of the ingot cast in the intermediate time.

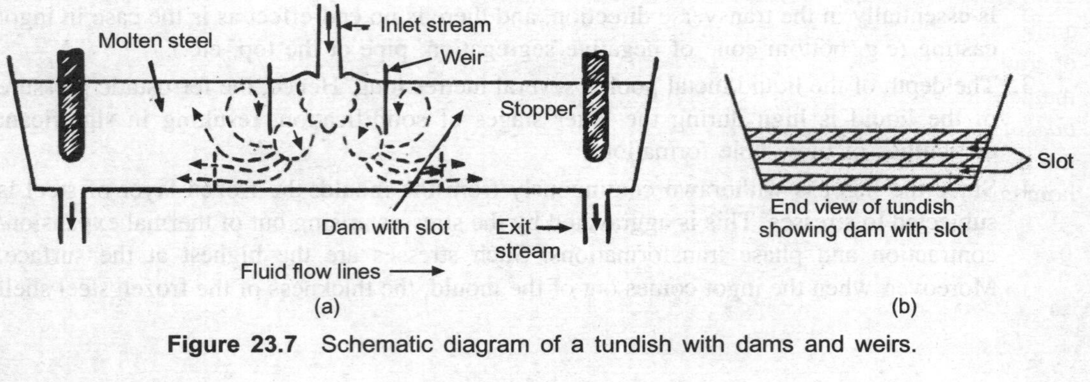

Figure 23.7 Schematic diagram of a tundish with dams and weirs.

For operational convenience, either refractory castables or prefabricated boards are employed to line the tundish. MgO-based working linings have gained in popularity from the point of view of steel quality. For prevention of heat loss, use of a refractory-lined tundish cover has been of considerable help. Furthermore, insulating powders are added on the top surface of molten steel to prevent heat loss—rice husk is commonly used. Typically, a mixture of rice husk (or rice husk ash which is pure silica), fly ash and some synthetic powders are employed to cover the top melt surface.

A steep temperature gradient exists across any layer of the covering powder. At the top, the temperature is only a few hundred degrees Celsius and this layer consists of loose powder. The bottom layer in contact with molten steel becomes molten slag, while sintered and softened powders constitute the intermediate zones. The presence of 5 to 10% carbon in the powder is recommended as it reacts with atmospheric oxygen and helps in lowering the extent of oxygen absorption even further.

The molten slag layer performs the following functions.

1. It acts as a barrier between air and liquid steel for prevention of re-oxidation as well as absorption of nitrogen and hydrogen from the atmosphere.
2. It absorbs the inclusions that float out of molten steel, thus helping in steel cleanliness.

It has been found that, for satisfactory performance, the slag should consist of CaO, SiO_2, Al_2O_3 and MgO, with CaO/SiO_2 ratios above 6.

23.4.2 Tundish Design and Operation for Clean Steel

The type of flow of liquid steel in the tundish plays a significant role in inclusion floatation, interaction with the top slag, and in determining the extent of refractory lining erosion, all of which are important for the manufacture of clean steel. For proper flow regulation, mathematical modelling based on the *Computational Fluid Dynamics* (CFD) as well as water modelling have been extensively employed. Flow regulation is effected by:

- Proper choice of the tundish size and shape.
- Fitting the tundish with flow modulation (FM) devices, such as *dams* and *weirs*, and turbulence dampers (*turbostop*).
- Argon purging at selected locations.

Figure 23.7 shows a tundish fitted with dams and weirs. The flow in the tundish is turbulent and three-dimensional. The optimum design of flow control devices depends on the design and operation of the CC machine in any particular shop, and for this, water model studies and mathematical modelling are resorted to. The fluid flow in the tundish is neither *plug flow* nor *backmix flow* (as in stirred tank reactors), but a mixture of the two. A long residence time allows more time for the inclusions to float-up as well as providing greater opportunity for homogenisation of liquid metal temperature and composition. This can be achieved if:

- The tundish volume is large
- Plug flow is dominant
- The proportion of dead volume is small
- The flow lines are zig-zag so that the path is longer.

The inlet stream of molten steel from the ladle creates turbulence, which enhances refractory erosion and reaction with the atmosphere, and is hence not desirable. Refractory weirs and bottom friction pads assist in confining and dampening turbulence. Dams direct the flow upwards and help in inclusion floatation. Slotted dams have become popular now. Very gentle argon purging from the bottom at selected locations is beneficial, since it assists in inclusion floatation.

Use of ceramic filters in tundishes for absorbing inclusions has not yet been commercially successful for casting of steel, although considerable research and development efforts have been made. Ceramic filters are in use for low melting non-ferrous metals where the filter life is longer owing to lower temperatures than what is encountered with steel.

23.5 CURRENT STATE OF CONTINUOUS CASTING TECHNOLOGY FOR STEEL

23.5.1 General Features

Evolution of continuous casting technology has witnessed several stages of strand design.

(i) Vertical straight mould and strand

(ii) Vertical straight mould and horizontal discharge of the solidified ingot with bending of the ingot after the withdrawal rolls

(iii) Vertical, curved mould and horizontal discharge type (also known as *S-type machine*).

Type (iii) is the latest design and has now been adopted almost universally for continuous casting of most sections, be they billets, blooms or slabs.

Detailed descriptions are available for curved mould billet casters, for example, the one at Tata Steel [Monograph on *Continuous Casting at Tata Steel*, Amit Chatterjee and S. Govindarajan, Jamshedpur (1991)]. Figure 23.8 presents a detailed sketch of the same machine along with the dimensions (Chatterjee and Govindrajan, 1991). The tundish in this machine feeds six billet strands simultaneously. Some other details are as follows.

- Design limits of billet size : 80–160 mm-square
- Casting radius : 6 m
- Metallurgical length (i.e. meniscus to withdrawal rolls) : 16.5 m
- Length of mould : 0.8 m
- Ladle capacity : 130–160 t
- Casting speed : above 3.5 m/min

The general features of curved mould type machines are as shown in Figure 23.8. Individual machines differ in details and dimensions.

23.5.2 The Mould and Its Operation

CC machine moulds are made of copper alloys. High conductivity copper is used. Pure copper has the highest thermal conductivity, but its strength is not adequate; hence, very small amounts

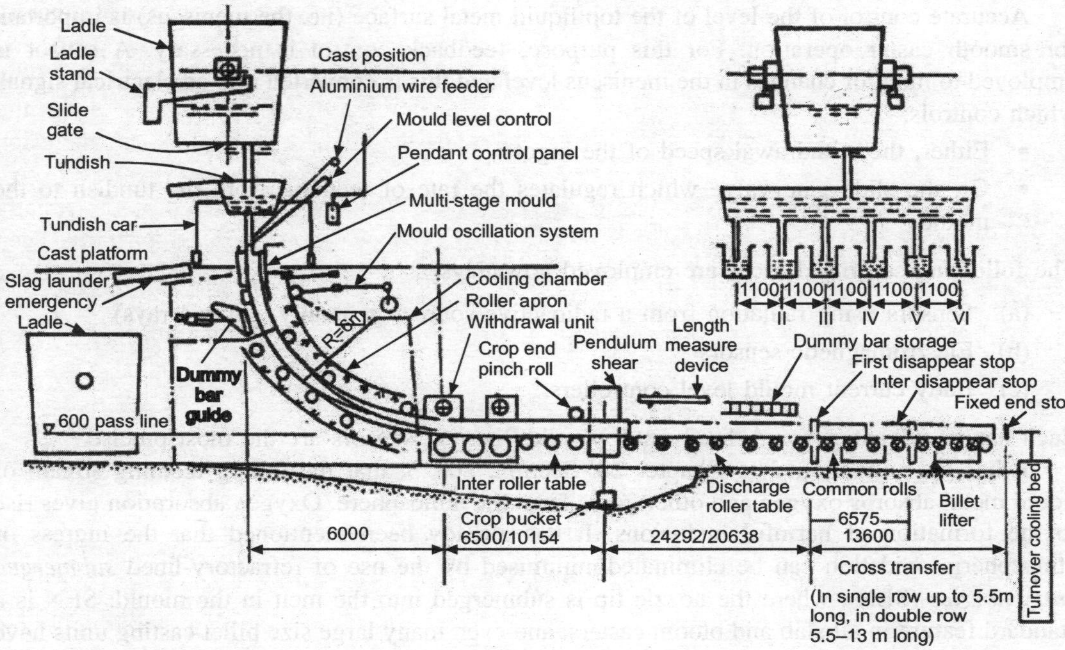

Figure 23.8 Diagram of the curved mould continuous billet caster of Tata Steel.

of alloying elements are added. To protect the inner surface, chromium plating is also practiced. As stated in Section 23.2.2, in order to lower the extent of air-gap formation, the inner cross-section of the mould is tapered, the bottom section being smaller than the top. A typical value of taper is about 1% per metre length. For a section size of 100 mm × 100 mm, the taper is about 1 mm for a 1 m. long mould. The mould is expected to extract about 10% of the total heat content in the metal and its length ranges from 75 to 140 cm, the length being more for larger sections.

For easy withdrawal of the ingot, the mould is oscillated up and down. This is known as *Junghan's principle,* according to the name of the inventor. It is a very important feature of any CC machine strand. If it is not done in a proper manner, surface defects such as oscillation marks will be present in the ingot. The oscillation frequency can be varied, for example, for Tata Steel's slab caster the frequency can be varied between 0 and 250 cycles/min and the stroke length from 0 to12 mm.

The latest development in this field is what is known as the *Resonance Mould*, where the device for executing mould oscillation is not like the earlier devices. It has been installed in several casters around the world. The drive is servo-hydraulic and has several advantages:

- Better guiding accuracy
- Drastic reduction of the oscillating mass
- Much lower frictional force between the ingot and the mould.

It has been established that the incidence of surface defects is much less with resonance moulds compared with conventional moulds.

Accurate control of the level of the top liquid metal surface (i.e. the meniscus) is important for smooth caster operation. For this purpose, feedback control is necessary. A sensor is employed to monitor changes in the meniscus level and this is converted into an electrical signal, which controls:

- Either, the withdrawal speed of the ingot
- Or, the slide gate valve which regulates the rate of teeming from the tundish to the mould.

The following sensing devices are employed nowadays.

(a) Sensors using radiation from a radioactive source (generally, gamma rays)
(b) Electromagnetic sensors
(c) Eddy current mould level controllers.

Each has its advantages and disadvantages; eddy current sensors are the most precise.

It has been mentioned in Chapter 20, Section. 20.6.3, that the falling teeming stream of liquid metal absorbs oxygen and other gases from the atmosphere. Oxygen absorption gives rise to the formation of harmful inclusions. It has already been mentioned that the ingress of atmospheric oxidation can be eliminated/minimised by the use of refractory-lined *submerged entry nozzles* (SEN), where the nozzle tip is submerged into the melt in the mould. SEN is a standard feature in all slab and bloom casters, and even many large size billet casting units have adopted it.

23.5.3 Electromagnetic Stirring

Electromagnetic stirring (EMS) is adopted in order to improve the quality of continuously cast ingots by decreasing the extent of centreline macrosegregation, improving the surface quality and the distribution of inclusions. The essential feature of EMS is to modify the flow patterns of the liquid metal pool in the solidifying strand. Desirable stirring of molten steel in the strand is effected by imposition of an electromagnetic field. There are essentially two types of EMS stirring systems:

(i) Up and down, i.e. axial
(ii) Rotational, i.e. horizontal.

In addition, electromagnetic brakes, which make use of a static electromagnetic field for decreasing the flow velocity in molten metal, as well as for splitting the jets issuing from the submerged entry nozzles are used in modern casters.

Another way of classification of EMS is:

(i) In-mould stirring
(ii) Below-mould stirring.

EMS devices may also be classified into:

(i) AC machines
(ii) DC machines
(iii) Permanent magnet machines.

The AC machines impart the stirring action by electromagnetic induction. This is the most commonly used variety. In DC machines, a current is passed through the strand and this, along with the imposed magnetic field imparts motion in the melt.

The EMS modifies the liquid flow pattern in a complex way. The design and operation also vary considerably. The way they help in improvement of quality will be taken up in the next section. Not all continuous casting machines make use of EMS.

23.6 METALLURGICAL DEFECTS AND THEIR REMEDIES

23.6.1 Centreline Macro-segregation and Porosity

Chapter 22, Section 22.2.2 has briefly discussed segregation and crystallisation phenomena during solidification. Macro-segregation in the cast ingot and the influence of the growth of columnar crystals on the same, have been briefly mentioned in Section 22.4. Macro-segregation is a defect and remedial measures need to be taken.

Segregation defects in continuous casting of steel may be summarised as:

(a) High positive macro-segregation around the centreline of the cast section, often associated with porosities

(b) Random fluctuations in the composition in the longitudinal direction, especially around the centreline.

Figure 23.9 presents an example of carbon segregation in a continuously cast slab, which was common in earlier times. The causes of such segregation are:

(a) *Zone refining action*

(b) *Suction* of impure interdendritic liquid owing to solidification shrinkage, bulging at the withdrawal rolls as well as differential thermal contraction.

The zone refining action follows from the laws of segregation, as briefly discussed in Section 22.2.2. Solidification is much faster in continuous casting than in ingot casting (see Section 23.2). Hence, the extent of segregation is much less than what is predicted by the Scheil's equation (Eq. (22.5)). Inward growth of the columnar crystals pushes the impure liquid towards the centreline, restricting almost all macro-segregation around the centreline. In Figure 23.9 it may be noted that the average carbon concentration is almost uniform throughout the section, and the segregation occurs significantly only when the last liquid freezes around the centreline of the section. Now, with remedial measures, the extent of centreline segregation is much less in modern CC machines.

Figure 23.1 has shown the desirable ideal profile of the liquid pool. However, this is not generally achieved. An extreme case of distortion is what is known as *Mini-ingot* formation. This is shown in Figure 23.10. The solidification front does not advance smoothly; rather it proceeds in jerks. As a consequence, often columnar grains advance up to the centreline and form bridges, thus preventing feeding of the shrinkage cavities below by fresh liquid. This causes suction of impure interdendritic liquid from the surrounding mushy zone into the central region, thereby increasing centreline segregation. Centreline porosity also develops if feeding is not complete.

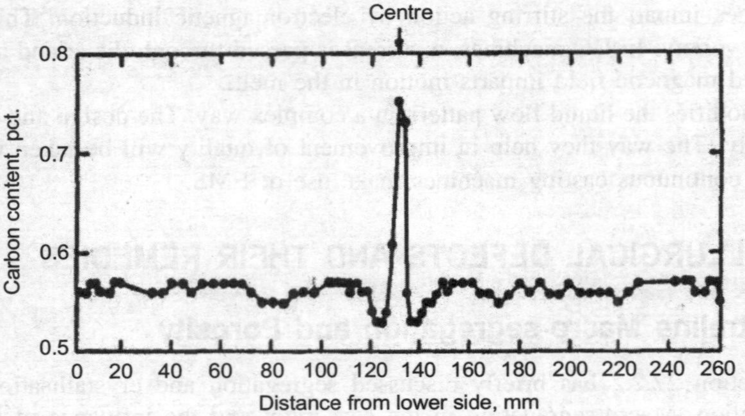

Figure 23.9 A typical concentration profile along the cross section of a continuously cast slab (earlier situation).

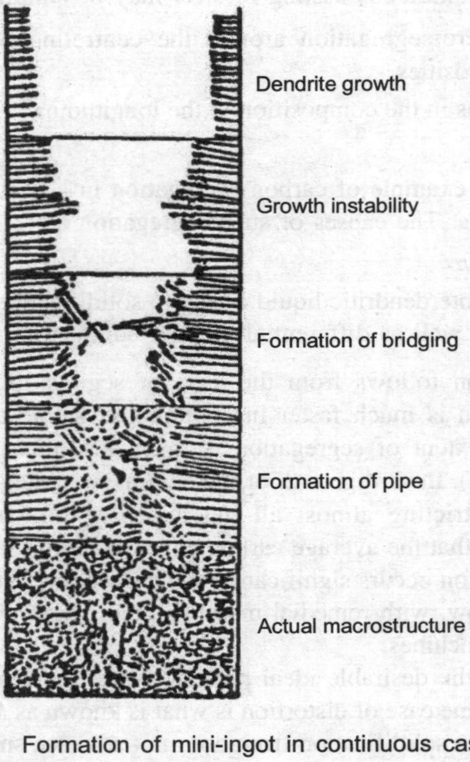

Figure 23.10 Formation of mini-ingot in continuous casting (schematic).

It has been established that bulging of the solid shell owing to pressure at the withdrawal rolls aggravates centreline segregation. Since the shell bulges outwards, a cavity is created in the central liquid region, thus enhancing suction. Heat transfer calculations have revealed that in the lower areas of the secondary cooling zone, the centreline temperature decreases more rapidly than the surface temperature. This causes relatively higher thermal contraction in the central region than at the surface, thus causing more suction.

The principal remedy is early formation of equiaxed crystals and a large equiaxed zone around the centreline. This tends to evenly distribute the micro-segregated regions, and thus makes the zone refining action less predominant. The presence of equiaxed crystals also prevents bridging by the columnar crystals and mini-ingotism. As already stated in Chapter 22, an equiaxed structure is preferred over a columnar structure since it gives other advantages, such as easier mechanical working, prevention of centreline cracks and porosity.

Hence, a major objective in continuous casting of steel is to obtain as large an equiaxed zone as possible, and this is facilitated by:

- Low superheat
- Electromagnetic stirring
- Large section size
- Medium carbon steel.

The accepted mechanism is that the growth of the columnar zone stops when the equiaxed zone starts forming. There are always innumerable tiny crystals (seed crystals) floating in the melt. When the superheat is dissipated, these crystals start growing, thus forming the equiaxed zone. Therefore, the superheat should be low. Electromagnetic stirring speeds-up the dissipation of heat from the liquid, and is thus beneficial. If the section size is large, the temperature gradient in the central region is low, allowing a large equiaxed zone. The equiaxed zone has been found to be the largest in medium carbon steels.

Technology has also been developed for minimisation of suction by bulging by:

- Adjustment of roll gap taper
- Soft reduction in the cross-section of the ingot during final solidification
- Controlled plane reduction.

As a result of all these measures, the incidence of centreline segregation and porosity has been almost eliminated in modern practices.

23.6.2 Cracks

Cracks may be broadly classified as internal cracks and surface cracks. Surface cracks get oxidised following contact with air and do not get welded during subsequent rolling. They have to be removed by *scarfing* (i.e. surface grinding) and are, therefore, a major quality problem. Internal cracks are less harmful since they get welded during subsequent rolling.

Surface cracks get initiated in the mould region of the caster. They subsequently develop in the secondary cooling zone or even later, such as during reheating. Internal cracks get initiated in the secondary cooling zone. Cracks are formed because of:

(i) Mechanical stresses
(ii) Thermal stresses
(iii) Material factors.

Frictional resistance offered by the mould in connection with the withdrawal of the ingot is the principal source of mechanical stress. Improper alignment, jerky withdrawal and other operating snags contribute further towards mechanical stress. Another source of mechanical stress is the ferrostatic pressure of the liquid metal. Thermal stresses on the surface are caused by non-uniform surface temperature. The surface cooling is fast, especially in the secondary cooling zone. Any unevenness in the cooling pattern is expected to lead to a non-uniform temperature distribution.

Some examples of material factors are as follows.

(a) Longitudinal mid-face surface cracking in slabs has been found to be aggravated by $\delta \rightarrow \gamma$ solid state transformation and consequent volume changes.

(b) Higher sulphur content and lower Mn/S ratio increase the tendency for mid-face longitudinal cracks.

(c) Often surface cracks have been found to be associated with the presence of inclusions.

Brimacombe and co-workers carried out extensive investigations on crack formation during continuous casting of steel. Figure 23.11 shows the classification of cracks proposed by them (Brimacombe and Sorimachi, 1977). Since surface cracks are a major quality problem in continuous casting of steel, extensive investigations have been carried out. These include mathematical modelling for computation of stress distributions on the surface and prediction of failure criteria, besides plant data. A variety of remedial measures have already been incorporated in modern practices, as a result of which incidence of cracking has been considerably lowered.

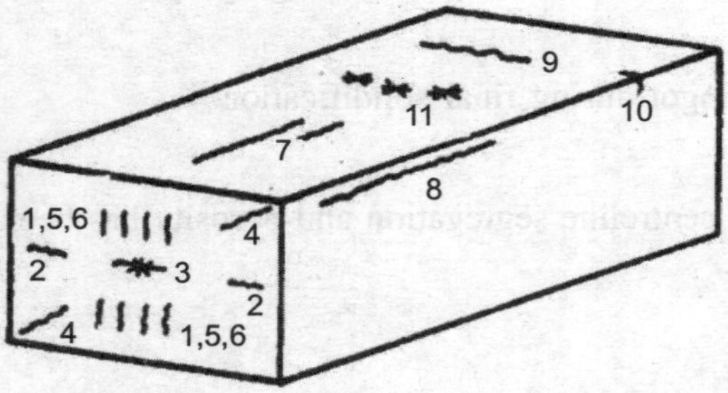

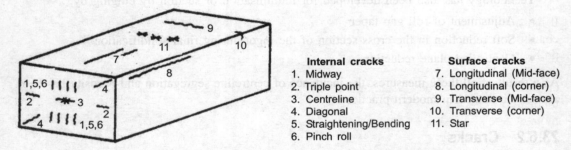

Internal cracks
1. Midway
2. Triple point
3. Centreline
4. Diagonal
5. Straightening/Bending
6. Pinch roll

Surface cracks
7. Longitudinal (Mid-face)
8. Longitudinal (corner)
9. Transverse (Mid-face)
10. Transverse (corner)
11. Star

Figure 23.11 Schematic diagram of a cast section showing different types of cracks.

Qualitatively speaking, mechanical stresses have been reduced by improved mould practices, such as by choosing the appropriate casting powder, controlling the feed rate of the powder, smoother withdrawal by employment of resonance moulds, more accurate strand guidance, automation, etc. Thermal stresses in the secondary cooling zone have been reduced by air-mist cooling by making the heat flux and surface temperature distribution more uniform. Steel cleanliness and desirable distribution of inclusions have received considerable emphasis as well.

23.6.3 Other Defects

Rhomboidity

It is also known as 'off-squareness', and is a common quality problem in casting of billets having a square cross-section. In a square, the lengths of the two diagonals are equal, whereas, in a rhomboid, they are not equal. Hence, the ratio of the lengths of the diagonals is a measure of rhomboidity. This defect is basically related to the asymmetry in the cooling characteristics in the mould and gets aggravated in the secondary cooling zone. It cannot be completely eliminated, but has been made less severe by proper mould design.

Oscillation marks

As already stated in Section 23.5.2, the mould is oscillated at a certain frequency for easy withdrawal of the ingot. This causes surface unevenness in the ingot in the form of horizontal ridges and troughs at intervals. These are known as oscillation marks and constitute a quality problem. Oscillation marks cannot be totally eliminated. If the depths of these are abnormally high, scarfing of the surface is required to remove them before reheating and rolling. Therefore, the strategy is to render the marks shallow and relatively harmless so that scarfing is not required. This has been achieved by improvements in technology by adopting the same measures which have helped in decreasing mechanical stresses on the surface for the prevention of cracks.

Inclusions

It has already been mentioned in Section 23.3, that the inclusions get less time to float up in continuous casting moulds, and therefore, pose a more serious problem than in ingot casting. The problem tends to become more acute because of the necessity of employing a tundish for flow control, and consequently a higher temperature in the ladle. Hotter steel causes more lining erosion. The molten metal stream has to flow through nozzles twice (ladle-to-tundish and tundish-to-mould) and also has to flow over an open tundish. Hence, atmospheric oxidation is more severe compared with ingot casting.

To overcome these problems, better cleanliness of steel in terms of less number of inclusions is the first remedial step. Chapter 20 has presented discussions on clean steel technology during secondary steelmaking. The use of submerged entry nozzles has eliminated the problem of atmospheric oxidation during teeming. Section 23.4 has elaborated the modern tundish practice whereby inclusion control has received considerable emphasis. As far as the mould practice in continuous casting is concerned, a brief discussion is presented below.

Inclusions in the mould arise from the following sources:

- Formation of inclusions by reactions in the mould during freezing
- Inclusions coming with incoming molten steel
- Entrapment of mould powder below the surface, which causes several kinds of internal and surface defects in steel products, e.g. slivers and scabs on steel sheets.

Causes for the formation of inclusions during freezing have been mentioned earlier. To prevent the formation of oxide inclusions, the strategy is to keep the dissolved oxygen content in steel very low, by employing aluminium and, if required, calcium-based deoxidisers. *Like the tundish, here also, the level of residual inclusions in the cast product is governed by the dynamic balance between the rates of inclusion formation and inclusion removal.* The casting powder melts when added to the mould, and then floats on the top of the steel melt. The resulting slag prevents oxygen pick-up from the atmosphere. Furthermore, it absorbs inclusions that float-up. Therefore, the choice of the casting powder requires considerable attention in terms of its efficacy in mould lubrication and its chemical stability.

During freezing in the mould, the solidified metal entraps some inclusions, which impedes the free floating-up of other inclusions. The fluid flow pattern in liquid steel in the mould also has a marked influence on inclusion distribution in the cast product. In continuous casting, upward flow in the liquid pool in the mould is primarily a result of the impingement of the teeming stream. Appropriate design of the SEN outlets has a governing influence; SEN design is therefore important. The flow should have an upward component for facilitating inclusion floatation. At the same time, any horizontal outward flow component is undesirable, since that will tend to push the inclusions towards the surface. In some designs, provision is made for slow injection of argon into the melt so that the rising bubbles help the inclusions to move up. Equiaxed grains allow better floatation than horizontal columnar grains. Electromagnetic stirring, if properly tuned, can have beneficial effects. Entrapment of the mould powder can also only be reduced by proper fluid flow management in the mould region.

Pinholes

Continuously cast products are either killed or semi-killed steels. Grades which are fully killed, either by aluminium alone, or aluminium and calcium, have very low oxygen contents and therefore, there is no possibility of the formation of blow-holes. For semi-killed steels, sometimes, tiny blow-holes, known as pinholes, form just below the surface.

The tendency for blow-hole formation becomes more pronounced as solidification proceeds, as has been briefly discussed already in connection with ingot casting, where blow-holes in semi-killed ingots are deep seated. However, in continuous casting, the last portion of the liquid freezes in the secondary cooling zone, where the ferrostatic pressure is of the order of a few atmospheres. Therefore, deep-seated blow-holes do not form. Sub-surface blow-holes are likely to form only if the dissolved hydrogen, nitrogen and oxygen contents are undesirably high. The only remedy for this is to control the amount of dissolved gases in liquid steel.

23.7 SOME SPECIAL TOPICS

23.7.1 Round Caster and Combination Caster

Rounds of small diameters are required for the production of seamless tubes. The conventional route for casting of rounds has been ingot casting. However, technology is now available for casting round blooms/billets by the continuous casting route. It gives dual benefits of higher productivity and better quality. Since for manufacturing seamless tubes, centreline segregation and porosity in the feedstock are very undesirable, in-mould electromagnetic stirring is a must when continuously cast blooms/billets are made. The rotary stirring action of EMS enlarges the central equiaxed zone, thereby reducing the centreline defects considerably. The other precautions normally taken for billet/bloom casting, of course, have to be followed as well.

However, in many steel plants, it is uneconomical to install a CC machine solely for producing rounds, because of the limited volume. This has given rise to the development of combination casters, which are designed to produce both blooms (round sections) as well as slabs (square or rectangular cross-section) in the same machine. Of course, changeover from one to another requires changing of moulds, roller apron, cooling sprays, withdrawal rolls, etc. There are quite a few combi-casters producing slabs-cum-blooms in plants throughout the world.

23.7.2 High Speed Casting

The basic advantage of high speed casting is to increase the productivity of a CC machine, thus cutting down both capital as well as operating cost per tonne of steel. For the production of flats, slab casting is followed by reheating and then rolling in a hot strip mill. These mills have high capacities, and the rates of production in conventional slab casters are often not adequate to meet the demand. Therefore, typically more than one caster is required for matching the production rates of the caster(s) and the hot strip mill. This is where high speed slab casting (at speeds up to 3 m/min) can find application in terms of additional cost advantages. Figure 23.2 contains data on the increase in casting speeds in some slab casters in Japan. It shows that after 1990, it has not been possible to increase the casting speed significantly, and the optimum speed has reached between 2 and 2.8 m/min. All the latest improvements in technology and operation of CC machine have contributed towards this increases in casting speed.

As mentioned already, the principal constraint is not the inability to attain higher heat extraction rates, but various quality problems that arise at higher casting speeds. As a matter of fact, as mentioned in Section 23.2, the rate of heat transfer in the mould increases with increasing casting speed. Figure 23.12 presents a compilation of data from various sources, which shows that higher casting speeds increase mould heat transfer, irrespective of differences in caster design and operating conditions (Chow 2002).

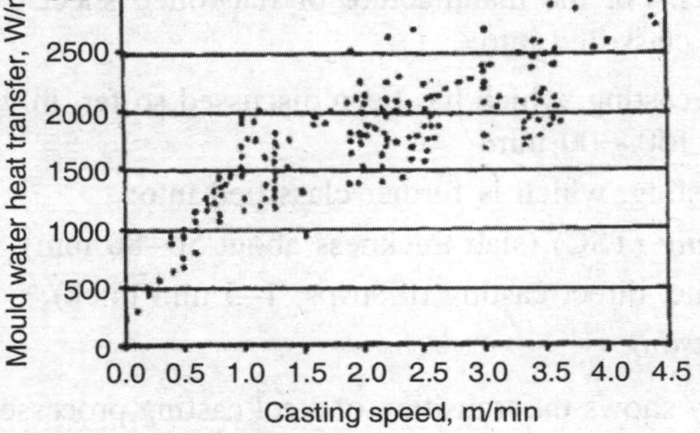

Figure 23.12 Mould heat flux versus casting speed for several casters.

In a recent review, Suzuki et al. (2001) have presented a comprehensive analysis of problems in high speed slab casting. These are given below.

(a) *Heat transfer and lubrication in the mould*

As already discussed, infiltration of the molten casting powder into the mould–metal interface is important, both for better lubrication and for more uniform heat flux. Failure to provide this results in more surface defects and break-outs. However, the lubrication between the solid steel shell and the mould begins to become worse with increasing casting speed, thus leading to problems.

(b) *Break-outs*

The phenomenon of rupture of the solidified steel shell and break-out after emergence from the mould is a serious operation-cum-quality issue in continuous casting. Section 23.6.2 has elucidated the formation of surface cracks and its causes. Break-out is an extreme situation of the same. For its prevention, the fracture strength of the solidified shell at the exit of the mould should be higher than the stress between the ingot surface and the mould, arising out of frictional forces. Theoretical calculations and experimental investigations have predicted that if the heat flux is uniform, then, it is theoretically possible to attain a casting speed of more than 4 m/min in slab casters.

(c) *Mould powder entrapment*

With increasing casting speeds there are more chances of mould powder entrapment with consequent quality problems as mentioned in Section 23.6.3. Again, extensive studies, especially on fluid flow in the mould, have been carried out to minimise this risk.

23.8 NEAR-NET SHAPE CASTING

This is one of the latest and perhaps the biggest breakthrough development in the area of continuous casting of steel. For the manufacture of flat-rolled sheet products, the continuous casting processes may be classified into:

(i) Conventional slab casting, which has been discussed so far, in which the slab thickness is in the range of 150–300 mm.

(ii) Near-net shape casting, which is further classified into:

- *Thin slab casting* (TSC) (slab thickness about 50–80 mm)
- *Strip casting* (i.e. direct casting of strips, 1–5 mm thick)
- *Beam blank casting*.

Figure 23.13 schematically shows the transition of steel casting processes from ingot making to strip casting over the last few decades.

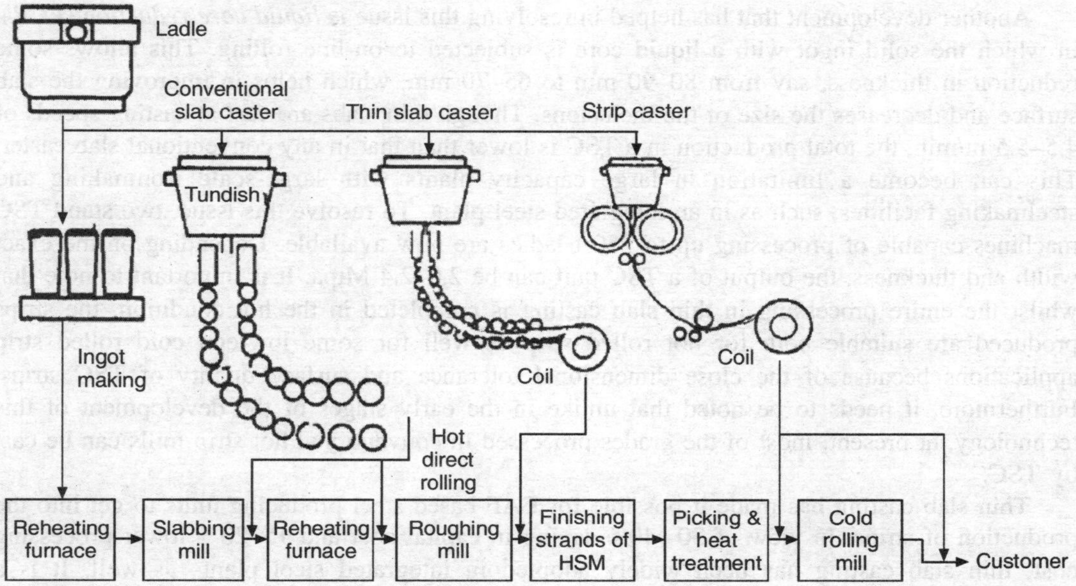

Figure 23.13 Different types of steel casting processes (schematic).

23.8.1 Thin Slab Casting

Thin slab casting (TSC) was commercially introduced around the year 1990. It grew rapidly to about 40 Mtpa processing capacity by 1998, which has increased further to over 75 Mtpa today. Today, the technology is well established. In India, the Ispat Group has installed TSC in their Raigarh Plant, Maharashtra. The main manufacturers of TSC machines are:

- SMS (Schloemann Siemag, Germany)—Compact strip processing (CSP)
- MDH (Mannesmann Demag, Germany)—In-line strip processing (ISP)
- VAI (Voest-Alpino Industrieanlagenbau, Austria)—CONROLL process
- Danieli, Italy—Flexible thin slab casting (FTSC).

As shown in Figure 23.13, TSC bypasses the roughing mill completely. The thin slabs cast in thicknesses from 50 to 80 mm straight away enter the continuous reheating furnace (of the roller hearth or walking beam type) and after reheating enter the finishing strands of the hot strip mill (HSM), thus saving both capital cost and operating cost in terms of lower energy consumption.

Since the cross-sectional area of any thin slab caster mould is smaller than that in a conventional slab caster, the turbulence induced in the mould by the teeming stream increases markedly. This can cause mould flux entrapment on the surface and give rise to surface defects. Use of a funnel-shaped mould with enlarged cross-section near the meniscus is one remedy. For parallel moulds, *electromagnetic brakes* are very effective in damping turbulence. Of course, SEN design is even more critical in TSC than it is in conventional slab casting.

Another development that has helped in resolving this issue is *liquid core reduction* (LCR), in which the solid ingot with a liquid core is subjected to on-line rolling. This allows some reduction in thickness, say from 80–90 mm to 65–70 mm, which helps in improving the slab surface and decreases the size of the inclusions. Though thin slabs are cast at casting speeds of 4.5–5.5 m/min, the total production in a TSC is lower than that in any conventional slab caster. This can become a limitation in large capacity plants with large-scale ironmaking and steelmaking facilities, such as in an integrated steel plant. To resolve this issue, two stand TSC machines capable of processing up to 250 t ladles are now available. Depending on the exact width and thickness, the output of a TSC unit can be 2.0–2.4 Mtpa. It is important to note that whilst the entire processing in thin slab casting is completed in the hot condition, the strips produced are suitable both for hot rolled strip as well for some low-end cold rolled strip applications because of the close dimensional tolerance and surface quality of TSC strips. Furthermore, it needs to be noted that unlike in the early stages of the development of this technology, at present, most of the grades processed in conventional hot strip mills can be cast by TSC.

Thin slab casting has made it possible for EAF-based steel producing units to get into the production of strips. In view of 30–40% saving in capital cost and 15–20 $ lower processing cost, thin slab casting has been widely adopted in integrated steel plants as well. It is a technology that will become even more widespread in the years ahead, since high-quality strips with lesser segregation, finer grain size and higher strength can be produced.

23.8.2 Strip Casting

As shown in Figure 23.13, the set-up for strip casting is totally different from that used in thin slab casting insofar as there is no mould at all. The most popular method is to use a *twin-roll* caster, which employs two water-cooled rotating rolls. The liquid metal is directly fed into the gap and the solidified rolled strip emerges from the caster, which can be directly marketed or cold-rolled into the final shape.

Strip casting has not yet been widely adopted for carbon steel production, but the technology has been applied for producing stainless steel strips in plants in Japan/the USA; and some plants are processing both carbon steels and stainless steels in a strip caster. The as-cast strip undergoes even more rapid solidification in this case than what it does in thin slab casting (in the latter itself, the solidification rate is much faster than in conventional casting giving rise to the advantages enumerated above). Accordingly, as cast thin strip has many unique features, such as very small equiaxed grains, much less segregation and distinctly finer inclusions. These characteristics result in superior mechanical properties and higher corrosion resistance. The total issue of economics of thin strip casting has not yet been finally resolved, particularly for relatively less expensive grades like carbon steels.

23.8.3 Beam Blank Casting

It was first developed by SMS, Germany and belongs to the category of near-net shape casting since beam blanks (and even dog-bone shapes) can be directly cast from liquid steel. Because of the obvious advantages, many steel plants in the world have installed this facility to produce beams used for building heavy structures in the construction and infrastructure sectors. In the conventional method, extensive hot rolling of slabs has to be carried out to reduce the section thickness required for producing beams. This calls for several steps of processing including intermediate heating. Beam blank casters now cast thicknesses, which are close to the final section size and, hence, much less hot rolling is required. The advantages and problems are akin to those for thin slab casting.

REFERENCES

Brimacombe, J.K. and K. Soramachi, Met. Trans. B, Vol. 8B (1977), p. 489.

Chatterjee, A. and S. Govindarajan, *Continuous Casting at Tata Steel*, Jamshedpur (1991), p. 9.

Chow, C. et al., Ironmaking and Steelmaking, Vol. 29 (2002), p. 65.

Paul, A. et al., Scand. J. Met., Vol. 29 (2000), p. 143.

Suzuki, M. et al., ISIJ International, Vol. 41 (2001), p. 672.

Part F

Miscellaneous

- Ironmaking and Steelmaking in India
- Appendix I—List of Major Iron and Steel Plants in India
- Appendix II—Supersonic Jet(s): Relevance to BOF Steelmaking

24

Ironmaking and Steelmaking in India

24.1 INTRODUCTION

Steel is amongst the most widely used engineering materials. What is perhaps the most significant in today's ecology conscious world is that, steel can be recycled over and over again, almost *ad infinitum*. In fact, every new steel product contains some amount of previously discarded steel products that find their way back into steelmaking furnaces in the form of scrap.

India's association with iron and steel dates back more than three millennia, as briefly mentioned in Chapter 1. Steel has a glorious heritage in India, one of the best examples of which is the Delhi Iron Pillar (Figure 24.1)—about 1500 years old and still with no trace of rust.

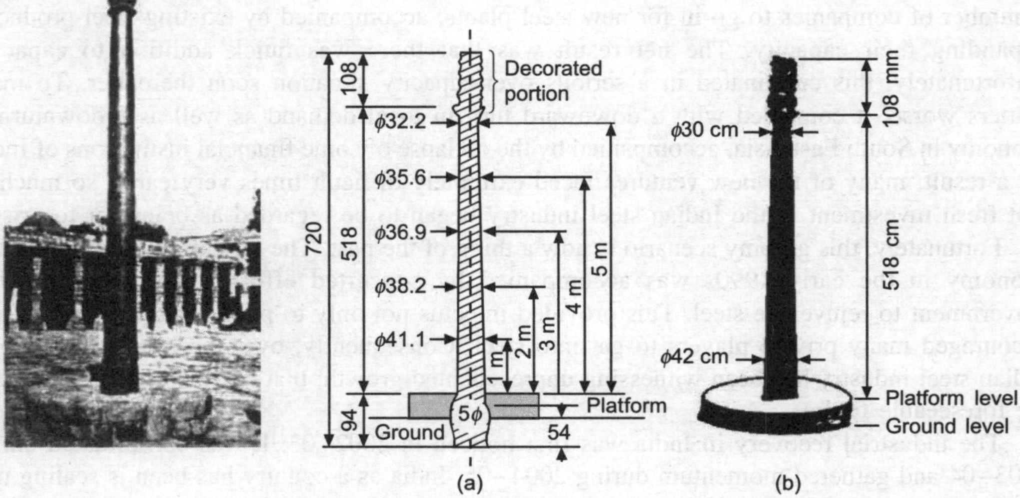

Figure 24.1 The famous Delhi Iron Pillar.

24.2 EVOLUTION OF GLOBAL/INDIAN STEEL

Table 24.1 shows the evolution in world steel consumption since the late nineteenth century. Though the increase in consumption was gradual in the early stages, it is evident that remarkable increase in consumption has taken place in the last two decades, and particularly so in the last three years. This period was preceded by a decade of relative stagnation, clearly bringing out the cyclical nature of the steel industry in terms of demand.

Table 24.1 Evolution in world steel consumption

Year	Change
1873–1948	+100 Mt in 75 years
1948–1973	+400 Mt in 25 years
1973–1983	+/– 0 in 10 years
1983–1993	+115 Mt in 10 years
1993–2003	+230 Mt in 10 years
2003–2009	+265 Mt in last 5 years

The Indian steel industry had a modest beginning when The Bengal Iron and Steel Co. was set up at Barakar in 1875. The real fillip to this industry was given when Jamsetji Nusserwanji Tata began The Tata Iron and Steel Company (now Tata Steel Limited) at Jamshedpur in 1907. Very early, Tata Steel made steel rails to British specifications. In World War II, British tanks were called Tatanagars, since the steel was made in Tatanagar (then the name for Jamshedpur). The steel for the famous Howrah bridge was provided by Tata Steel in the early 1940s. Chapter 1, Section 1.5 has presented a brief outline of the subsequent developments of the Indian steel industry.

The decade of the 1980s (and even early 1990s) saw the Indian steel industry at crossroads. In the early 1980s, spurt in domestic demand coupled with the South East Asian boom prompted a number of companies to go in for new steel plants, accompanied by existing steel producers expanding their capacity. The net result was that there was quick addition to capacity. Unfortunately, this culminated in a serious over-capacity situation soon thereafter. To make matters worse, it coincided with a downward turn in local demand as well as a downturn in economy in South East Asia, accompanied by the collapse of some financial institutions of India. As a result, many of the new ventures faced extremely difficult times very early; so much so that fresh investment in the Indian steel industry began to be regarded as being far too risky.

Fortunately, this gloomy scenario is now a thing of the past. The liberalisation of the Indian economy in the early 1990s was accompanied by concerted efforts made by the Indian Government to rejuvenate steel. This provided impetus not only to public investment, but also encouraged many private players to get into steel. Consequently, over the last few years, the Indian steel industry has been witnessing unprecedented growth, that is expected to continue in the foreseeable future.

The industrial recovery in India was first noticed in 2002–03. It was consolidated during 2003–04 and gathered momentum during 2004–05. India as a country has been is scaling new heights since then. The significant decline in interest rates and turnaround in public investment through the infrastructure development programmes have been two crucial drivers. The low interest rates have fuelled the housing, automobile and consumer durable booms, which have augured well for steel. While just four years back, steel companies across the globe, including those in India were in trouble, over the last few years, the situation has been totally transformed. The steel industry (particularly in Asia) is upbeat about the present and buoyant about the future. This dramatic turn around has largely been driven by the sharp rise in Chinese demand.

Appendix I contains a list of the major integrated steel plants and mini steel plants in India along with their crude steel production capacities. Steel plants under the Steel Authority of India Ltd. (i.e. SAIL) and the Rashtriya Ispat Nigam Ltd. (RINL) are in the public sector, and the rest in the private sector.

24.3 INDIA'S POTENTIAL IN STEEL

At present, India's per capita steel consumption is very low—only 45–50 kg crude steel compared with the world average of 210–220 kg (Figure 24.2). This is primarily because India's rural population (around 70% of the total population of India) remains, even today, almost totally unexposed to the multifaceted uses of steel. As a result, the consumption of steel in rural India is as low as 2 kg per capita. In order to change this state of affairs, the Government of India has, over the last couple of years, enunciated rural oriented policies. The earning capacity of those in rural India has also been increasing. These factors are expected to double steel consumption in villages, which would have a major influence on the growth of steel consumption in India, over and above the need for additional infrastructure in urban areas.

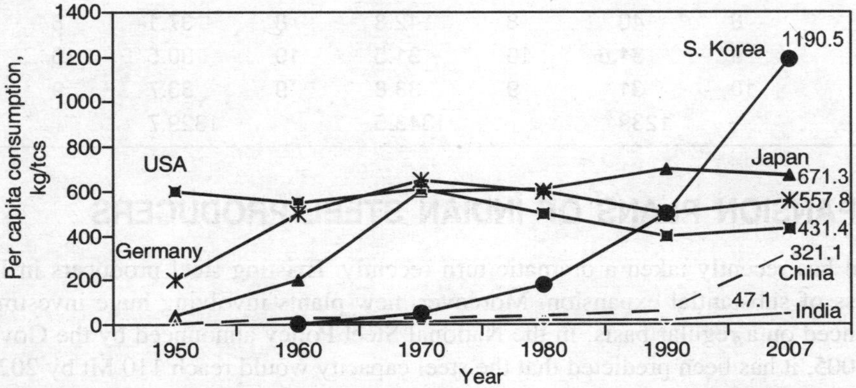

Figure 24.2 Per capita consumption of crude steel in some selected countries.

On this basis, it is generally agreed that the future of the Indian steel industry is promising. This appears logical since India is amongst the few countries in the world that has the dual advantage of fast growing domestic demand coupled with access to raw materials. Further, the axis of global steel production/consumption is shifting towards Asia—a trend that is already clearly discernible. With their large populations, China and India already account for 45% of the total world steel production—more than double that of Europe. Asia is expected to outpace the other regions of the world to an even greater extent in the coming years.

24.4 GROWTH OF THE GLOBAL STEEL INDUSTRY

Figure 1.5 in Chapter 1, has already dealt with the growth in world steel production between 1900 and 2000. 2004 was a landmark year in global steel production, since the 1000 Mt mark in any one year, was crossed for the first time. The leading steel producing countries in the years 2006 to 2009 are listed in Table 24.2 (IISI—Worksteel Association). In 2007, India produced 53.1 Mt, and occupied the fifth position in the world steel league. In 2008, India produced 55.1 Mt and in 2009, the production was 56.6 Mt (fifth position). There is no doubt that the growth in Indian steel production has been extremely slow—quite the reverse of India's Asian neighbour China. In fact, in the late 1940s, China and India both produced similar quantities of steel. In the intervening years, China has 'leap-frogged' very far ahead to become the global *numero uno.*

Table 24.2 Major steel producing countries between 2006 and 2009

Country	2006		2007		2008		2009	
	Rank	Mtpa	Rank	Mtpa	Rank	Mtpa	Rank	Mtpa
China	1	420	1	489.2	1	502.0	1	567.8
Japan	2	116	2	120.2	2	118.7	2	87.5
USA	3	98	3	98.2	3	91.5	4	58.1
Russia	4	71	4	72.4	4	68.5	3	59.9
South Korea	5	48.4	6	51.5	6	53.5	6	48.5
Germany	6	47.3	7	48.6	7	45.8	7	32.6
India	7	44	5	53.1	5	55.1	5	56.6
Ukraine	8	40	8	42.8	8	37.1	8	29.7
Italy	9	31.6	10	31.5	10	30.5	10	19.7
Brazil	10	31	9	33.8	9	33.7	9	1219.7
World		1239		1343.5		1329.7		

24.5 EXPANSION PLANS OF INDIAN STEEL PRODUCERS

The situation has recently taken a dramatic turn recently. Existing steel producers in India are in the process of substantial expansion. Moreover, new plants involving huge investments are being announced on a regular basis. In the National Steel Policy announced by the Government of India in 2005, it has been predicted that the steel capacity would reach 110 Mt by 2020. More recent forecasts indicate figures of even 200 Mt by 2020. At least 60 million tonnes of annual capacity is expected to be added by 2010. Besides traditional players like SAIL and Tata Steel, many relatively new players (Essar, Jindals, Bhushan Steel and RINL) as well as fresh entrants (like POSCO, Mittal Steel) have also announced plans for Greenfield plants, most of which would be integrated steel plants. The secondary sector is also planning at least 10 Mt of additional annual capacity. When all these projects are completed, India is expected to be at a much higher position in the world steel league. Of course, for these plans to fructify, major concurrent investments have to made on infrastructure development (ports, rail-roads, roads, etc.), and other areas like reliable sources of water and electricity. An active programme of skilled manpower development, oriented towards iron and steel, is also required.

24.6 RAW MATERIALS SCENARIO IN INDIA

24.6.1 Coal for Ironmaking

The total proven coal reserves of the world exceed one trillion tonnes, out of which 50% is hard coking coal that is required for producing high-quality blast furnace coke (Chapter 8). The largest reserves are in the USA (23%), the former Soviet Union (23%) and China (11%). Today, China is the world's leading coal producer followed by the USA. India's total coal reserve is only 7.6% of the world's reserves. Coking coal constitutes only 15% of the Indian coal reserves (Table 8.1, Chapter 8). This meagre quantity also exhibits some inherent problems—high ash content (up to 30%) and low rank (MMR 0.8–1.1). Coal is without doubt the biggest cause for concern for increasing steel production in India, at least using the conventional BF–BOF route.

Over the last few years, Indian demand for coal (~400 Mt and 8% growth) has consistently outstripped supply (~375 Mt and 2% growth). In 2006–07, the demand is projected to reach around 475 Mt, against a supply of 430 Mt. In the case of coking coal, over and above the limited availability, high ash and low rank are additional constraints. Therefore, for the last ten years or so, Indian integrated steel producers have had no other option, but to use imported high-grade, low ash coking coal from Australia amounting to 30–50% of their total requirements. Once ports capable of handling Cape-size (large cargo ship with capacity greater than 150,000 tonnes) vessels are built, coking coal from other countries like the USA, Canada and Poland, and non-coking coal from South Africa and Indonesia, will find increasing use in the Indian steel industry. Consequently, many of the new steel plants in India are being located around the coast (quite different from the situation that prevailed earlier), so that they are competitive.

24.6.2 Iron Ore Scenario

The current Indian commercial mining capacity of iron ore is around 175 Mtpa. In 2006–07, 150 Mt was mined of which 80 Mt was exported. Much more iron ore mining capacity will be needed in future and restrictions on easy, long-term export of iron ore, particularly high-grade ore, is an issue that is already under close scrutiny. When domestic steel production grows to 180 Mtpa by 2020, the iron ore requirement would be 330 Mtpa compared with 60–70 Mtpa at present. It may not be very difficult to meet such iron ore requirements for the next fifty years or so, provided appropriate policies on export are put in place.

24.7 ALTERNATIVE IRONMAKING IN INDIA

While India has a major advantage over many other countries (including China) in terms of rich iron ore that is sufficient for the next fifty years or so, this advantage is negated by the limited availability, as well as poor quality, of coking coal. The lack of adequate coking coal (both in terms of quantity and quality) to match the iron ore reserves makes India a textbook case for the exploitation of the alternative ironmaking technologies, based either on non-coking coal or natural gas (Chapters 13 and 14).

24.7.1 Direct Reduction

Because of the availability of high-quality iron ore, widespread reserves of non-coking coal and the finding of off-shore natural gas, India has already emerged as a prime location for the exploitation of the alternative methods of producing iron units, without using coke. Direct reduction and smelting reduction (Chapters 13 and 14) have already been extensively adopted. This has helped to disperse the Indian steel production centres away from eastern India, where most of the integrated plants were originally located, primarily because both coking coal and iron ore were found in close proximity.

Direct reduction, which entered the scene in India in 1981, has grown at a fast pace in the last twenty-five years. At least 180 DR units have already been installed, and many more are in various stages of planning, construction and commissioning. Consequently, over the last few years the production of DRI (sponge iron) in India has been the highest in the world, overtaking even traditional gas-rich countries like Venezuela (Table 24.3). In countries like Mexico and Venezuela, DRI is exclusively produced in gas-based processes like Midrex and HYL. However, in India, both non-coking coal and natural gas are used as reductants in rotary kilns and shaft furnaces respectively.

Table 24.3 Production of sponge iron (Mt) in selected countries

Country	2001	2002	2003	2004	2005	2006	2007	2008	2009
India	5.7	5.7	7.1	9.1	12.1	15.0	18.1	20.2	22.03
Venezuela	5.5	6.8	6.6	7.8	8.9	8.4	7.8	7.1	5.6
Mexico	3.7	4.7	5.5	6.3	6.1	6.2	6.3	5.9	4.15
Iran	5.0	5.3	5.0	6.4	6.9	6.9	7.5	7.4	8.2
Trinidad and Tobago	2.0	2.3	2.2	2.2	2.1	2.1	2.1	1.6	1.99
South Africa	1.6	1.7	1.5	1.6	1.8	1.8	1.7	1.2	1.39
Canada	0.0	0.2	0.5	1.1	0.6	0.4	0.9	0.7	0.34
Saudi Arabia	2.9	3.3	3.3	3.4	3.6	3.6	4.1	4.5	5.03
Russia	2.5	2.9	2.9	3.1	3.3	3.3	3.4	0.0	4.67
Total world	37.8	43.2	45.9	53.4	56.7	59.5	64.7	56.8	64.5

There are three large gas-based units, namely Essar Steel, Ispat Industries and Vikram Ispat with capacities of 3.60, 1.60, and 0.9 Mtpa respectively, in western India, close to natural gas from Bombay High. A large number of coal-based plants with capacities ranging from 30–400 ktpa (in the later case, using multiple units) are operating, predominantly in the states of Orissa, Chattisgarh, Jharkhand and West Bengal, where high-grade lump ore (mandatory for DRI production) is available along with non-coking coal. India is expected to consolidate its position further as the world leader in sponge iron in the next five years, as indicated in Table 24.4 (Muthuraman and Chatterjee, 2006).

In India, sponge iron is used primarily by the secondary sector in mini steel plants. It has also been intermittently used by integrated plants, particularly at times whenever ironmaking capacity became a bottleneck. The use of DRI in electric induction furnaces (IFs), particularly DRI fines below 3 mm without any agglomeration, has been a major innovation that was made in India. The use of fines below 3 mm directly in EAFs is normally not possible, because it tends to get lost as dust. Following the success of the innovation made in the secondary sector, IFs

Table 24.4 Projection of installed capacity and production of sponge iron in india

Year	Installed capacity, Mt			Production, Mt		
	Gas-based	Coal-based	Total	Gas-based	Coal-based	Total
2004–05	6.1	6.0	12.1	4.6	5.5	10.1
2005–06	6.1	8.5	14.6	5.7	6.5	12.2
2006–07	7.1	11.0	18.1	7.0	8.5	15.5
2007–08	7.1	13.0	20.1	7.0	10.0	17.0
2008–09	7.1	15.0	22.1	7.0	11.0	18.0
2009–10	7.1	18.0	25.1	7.0	14.0	21.0

have proliferated all over India. In fact, today India is the only country in the world where IFs are used extensively for steel production in limited quantities. In this connection, it needs to be noted that unlike in most other countries, EAFs in India are not very suitable for using large quantities of even-sized DRI, because they are of relatively old design, are of smaller capacity (5–25 t) and have low transformer power ratings (10–30 MW). These furnaces are also not equipped with facilities for continuous charging of DRI through the roof. For all these reasons, EAFs in India have found it difficult to use DRI, even at times of scrap shortage. The fact that they also depend on purchased power from the state electricity boards, makes EAF steel quite expensive. Consequently, many mini-mills in India have been forced to shutdown their EAFs, and have since installed IFs of 2 to 10 t capacity, at relatively low investment. Though these IFs also use expensive electricity, their power demand is not very high, and they are able to use more readily-available feedstock. All these factors have resulted in the proliferation of IFs in preference to EAFs in the secondary sector—currently, 970 IFs are operating in India compared with 350 EAFs.

Since the secondary producers are located in all parts of India and are able to cater to specialised demands of regional markets, their share in India's total steel production has been rising, reaching almost 80% in 2008–2009 (Table 24.5). In this context, it needs to be emphasised that though the secondary sector is not basically economic in terms of the process route employed, scale of operation, efficiency, etc., the fact that they are in a position to make steel to order for small volume regional markets outweighs the drawbacks.

Table 24.5 Crude steel production (Mt) in India

Producers	2001–02	2002–03	2003–04	2004–05	2005–06	2006–07	2007–08
Integrated steel plants	17.6	18.8	19.8	19.8	21.7	20.8	21.2
Electric arc furnaces	5.9	6.7	8.2	10.2	11.3	19.1	20.7
Induction furnaces	4.3	4.8	6.0	8.2	8.2	8.5	10.1
Total crude steel (taking all other producers not included above)	28.0	30.4	34.3	38.5	41.6	49.5	53.1
Share of secondary producers,%	36.5	37.6	41.6	48.0	47.9	55.9	58.2

24.7.2 Smelting Reduction

Paucity of coking coal of the appropriate quality and in sufficient quantity, has fuelled interest in smelting reduction in India. The world's largest Corex plant consisting of two C-2000 (2000 tpd) Corex units was installed by Jindal Vijayanagar Steel Ltd. (now Jindal South West) at Toranagallu, near Bangalore in 1999. The production has risen steadily to 1.63 Mt (against a capacity of 1.6 Mtpa) in 2003–04, along with a decrease in coal consumption from an initial 1163 to 995 kg/thm. The net result has been that the two modules rated at 100 tph are both operating at 10–20% above their rated capacity. Hot metal at high temperature (1480–1510°C) containing low sulphur, low nitrogen and very little impurities, has been consistently produced. However, the cost of Corex hot metal at Toranagallu is high on account of 10–15% coke usage and relatively high fuel rate. Two Corex-2000 have also been installed recently by Essar.

24.7.3 Mini Blast Furnaces (MBFs)

In India, extensive use is also made of MBFs to produce hot metal both for steelmaking as well as for foundries. The hot metal produced is either of basic grade (over 2% silicon) or with less than 0.8% silicon for steelmaking, along with sulphur less than 0.025% and phosphorus less than 0.080%. Though the cost of MBF hot metal is always higher than that from blast furnaces, MBFs have carved a niche for themselves—small-scale operation and the ability to produce foundry grade iron are their strength. It is likely that MBFs will continue to supplement smelting reduction processes to produce hot metal in India in the years ahead.

24.8 STRUCTURE OF THE INDIAN STEEL INDUSTRY

As stated earlier, India uses BOFs, EAFs and IFs for steelmaking. The BOFs in integrated steel plants (six in number) are located primarily in eastern India, on account of the availability of iron ore and coking coal in close proximity. The rated capacity of BOF steelmaking amounts to around 50% of India's total steelmaking capability. On the other hand, both EAFs and IFs have been used by a large number of small-scale producers spread throughout the country. While the integrated producers have captive sinter plants, coke ovens and blast furnaces, the secondary sector depends on purchased sponge iron, scrap, and in most cases, purchased power. In many of these units, MBF hot metal is also used in the charge.

The concurrent usage of BOF steelmaking and EAF/IF steelmaking has helped in dispersing the Indian steel industry to all regions, even after accounting for the fact that the cost of steel production is sometimes higher in the smaller units (EAF/IF). While the integrated producers predominantly make flat products, long products are made via the EAF/IF route. The long-term sustainability of these secondary producers would depend, to a large extent, on the use of captive power from MBFs, DRI rotary kiln off-gases, as well as power generated from solid wastes like coal char. At present, the secondary producers are often not in a position to operate when the market conditions become difficult, for example, in 2005 they produced only 45% of India's total steel and many secondary units remained shutdown.

24.8.1 The Future

In India steel production plans to reach at least 180 Mt if not over 200 Mt by 2020 (how much of these plans will become reality is a matter of conjecture given the present difficulties in obtaining mining rights land allocation, etc.), the integrated producers using the BF–BOF route are expected to contribute 130–150 Mt. The secondary sector using electric furnaces fed by 50% sponge iron, 10% return scrap and 40% hot metal are expected to produce the remaining 40–50 Mt. For this to happen India's DRI production has to reach 60–70 Mtpa and that of BF hot metal 180 Mtpa. The secondary sector's share in the total production capacity (which is often much higher than actual production on account of poor capacity utilisation in this sector), is expected to come down slightly to 40–45%, which would still be higher than in traditional steel producing countries.

As stated earlier, the axis of global steel production/consumption is shifting towards Asia. In the years to come, Asia is expected to outpace the other regions even further. Several macro trends would favour this change. First, Asia is now experiencing what the developed nations faced in the previous century—a strong industrial demand led by infrastructural and construction needs. Second, rules on industrial pollution control have become so stringent in the US and Europe that the capital cost required to meet the ecological demands often makes new capacity addition, in an already industrialised area, prohibitive. This is not the case in developing regions like India, where conforming to the same environmental standards becomes easier on account of less overall industrialisation, e.g. less SO_x, NO_x, etc. Third, for long-term sustenance of the industry, access to raw materials is a must, and Asia as a whole has some of the best and largest deposits of iron ore and coal.

24.8.2 Concluding Comments

At the same time, it needs to be remembered that there are some possible constraints to the growth of the steel industry in India. Steel is a highly cyclical industry and concern has been expressed about India's ability to cope with such downturns. To become more resistant to price fluctuations, the steel industry is going through a process of consolidation and the two largest producers, SAIL and Tata Steel, are in the process of acquiring global status, through expansion, establishment of new units, and in the case of Tata Steel through acquisitions (Nat Steel, Millennium Steel and Corus). Others like Essar and Ispat have also begun acquisitions overseas. Steel producers like Jindal South West, Jindal Steel and Power, as well as Essar Steel, POSCO, Mittal Steel, etc. are planning major green field projects in Orissa, Jharkhand, Chattisgarh, etc. Mittal Steel has become the world's largest steel producer following the acquisition of Arcelor.

REFERENCES

Chatterjee, Amit, Millennium Steel, 2006.

Muthuraman, B. and Amit Chatterjee, The Hindu Survey of Annual Industry 2006, March 2006.

Steel Statistical Yearbook 2008.

Appendix I

LIST OF MAJOR IRON AND STEEL PLANTS IN INDIA

Sl. No.	Name of the plant	Capacity, Mtpa	Process route	Location	Product mix
1.	Bhilai Steel Plant (SAIL)	5.0	BF–BOF	Bhilai, Chhattisgarh	Rails, heavy structurals, heavy plates, wire rods
2.	Durgapur Steel Plant (SAIL)	1.8	BF–BOF	Durgapur, West Bengal	Forging blooms, billets, merchant products, skelp, wheels, axles, sleepers, fishplates, etc.
3.	Rourkela Steel Plant (SAIL)	1.9	BF–BOF	Rourkela, Orissa	Plates, hot-rolled strips, cold-rolled strips, galvanised plain and corrugated sheets, tin plate, electrical steel sheets, ERW pipes, spiral welded pipes
4.	Bokaro Steel Ltd. (SAIL)	4.5	BF–BOF	Bokaro, Jharkhand	Hot-rolled strips, cold-rolled strips, galvanised plain and corrugated sheets
5.	IISCO (SAIL)	1.0	BF–OH	Burnpur, West Bengal	Billets, rails, structurals, merchant products, bars, hot-rolled sheets, galvanised sheets
6.	Alloy Steels Plant (SAIL)	0.25 (incl. 0.09 SS)	EAF	Durgapur, West Bengal	Bar products, sheet products, forged products.
7.	Salem Steel Plant (SAIL)	0.22	—	Salem, Tamil Nadu	Cold-rolled stainless steel sheets
8.	Visvesvaraya Iron and Steel Limited (SAIL)	0.077	BF–BOF	Bhadravati, Karnataka	Forged items, bars
9.	Rastriya Ispat Nigam Ltd.	3.5	BF–BOF	Visakhapatanam, Andhra Pradesh	Light/medium merchant products, wire rods, universal beam mill products, billets
10.	Tata Steel Limited	5.0	BF–BOF	Jamshedpur, Jharkhand	Rods, plates, hot and cold strips, galvanised sheets, bearings, ferro-alloys, agricultural equipment, etc.
11.	Essar Steel Ltd.	3.6	DRI/HBI–EAF	Hazira, Gujarat	Iron ore pellets, HBI, cold- and hot-rolled products, galvanised sheets

(Contd.)

LIST OF MAJOR IRON AND STEEL PLANTS IN INDIA

Sl. No.	Name of the plant	Capacity, Mtpa	Process route	Location	Product mix
12.	Jindal South West Steel Ltd.	1.6	Corex–BOF	Toranagallu, Karnataka	Hot- and cold-rolled sheets, galvanised sheets
13.	Jindal Stainless Steel Ltd.	0.05	EAF	Hissar, Haryana; Daburi, Orissa	Cold-rolled stainless steel sheets, ferro-chrome
14.	Jindal Steel and Power Ltd.	2.9	DRI/MBF–EAF	Raigarh, Chattisgarh	Blooms, billets, rods, 120 m rails, medium- and large-size parallel flange beams
15.	Ispat Industries Ltd.	3.0	BF/DRI–EAF–CSP	Dolvi, Maharashtra	DRI, hot- and cold-rolled sheets, galvanised- and colour-coated sheets
16.	Saw Pipes Ltd.	0.95	MBF–Sub. arc welding	Kosi Kalan, UP; Mundra, Gujrat	Ductile iron pipes, large diameter size (16–48 inches) arc welded pipes
17.	Mahindra Ugine Steel Company Ltd.	0.11	EAF	Taj Maval, Pune, Ambad Nasik	Blooms, rods
18.	Mukand Ltd.	0.44	MBF–EAF	Kalwe, Maharashtra; Hospet, Karnataka	Blooms, billets, rods, wire rods
19.	Tata Metalliks Ltd.	0.7	MBF	Redi, Maharashtra; Kharagpur, West Bengal	Pig iron for foundries
20.	Uttam Steels Ltd.	0.6	CRM	Khopoli, Maharashtra	Cold-rolled and galvanised sheets
21.	Kalyani Steel Ltd.	0.3	MBF–EOF	Hospet, Karnataka	Blooms, billets, engine and vehicle chassis components, forged items
22.	Electro Steel Castings Ltd.	0.3	MBF	Khardah, West Bengal	Ductile iron pipes
23.	Sesa Goa Ltd.	0.22	BF	Goa	Pig iron
24.	Lloyds Steel Industries Ltd.	0.72	Scrap/DRI–EAF	Wardha, Maharashtra	HR and CR coil, galvanised sheet
25.	Usha Martin Ltd.	0.36	MBF–EAF	Jamshedpur, Jharkhand	Steel wire, steel wire rope, optic fibre cable and jelly-filled telecommunication cable.

Note: SAIL is abbreviation for Steel Authority of India Ltd.

Appendix II

SUPERSONIC JET(S)—RELEVANCE TO BOF STEELMAKING

In order to increase the productivity of BOFs, more oxygen, at velocities close to Mach 2–2.5 is being used. The Mach Number denotes the velocity of oxygen as a proportion of the velocity of sound. A basic understanding of the behaviour of supersonic jets (Mach Number greater than 1.0) is, therefore, essential for understanding BOF steelmaking.

The feature of primary interest is the interaction between the jet and the bath. Appreciation of this interaction requires knowledge of nozzle design, velocity distribution within the jet, entrainment of the converter atmosphere by the jet, etc. In the subsequent sections, each of these factors will be dealt with in detail.

Characteristics of Supersonic Jets

Free gas jets may either be supersonic or subsonic, depending on whether the velocity of the gas *at the nozzle exit* is greater or less than the speed of sound in that medium. In the case of oxygen at 300 K, the critical or sonic velocity is about 320 m/s. This velocity increases in proportion to the square root of the temperature and since the oxygen jet (s) in BOFs discharge into the hot converter atmoshphere, this factor should not be lost sight of.

The nozzle used for blowing oxygen converts the pressure energy in the gas into kinetic energy. Initially, as the pressure energy changes into kinetic energy, the gas velocity increases faster than the volume, because of the reduction in pressure. However, once the gas velocity attains the speed of sound, sound waves are propagated and consequently, the rate of increase of volume is greater than the rate of increase of velocity. This is why nozzles used for supersonic jets must have convergent-divergent sections. In principle, any convergent-divergent nozzle is correctly designed for only one particular driving pressure (corresponding to one velocity), at which the velocity of the gas at the throat of the nozzle is sonic, and the pressure of the gas at the exit of the nozzle is equal to that of the ambient medium. In the case of incorrectly designed or incorrectly operated nozzles, in which the pressure at the exit is either greater or less than that of the surroundings because the jet has either expanded too much or has not expanded enough in the divergent portion of the nozzle, a pressure equalising mechanism is automatically set up.

This results in a large proportion of the kinetic energy of the jet getting dissipated close to the nozzle exit. This pressure equalising mechanism gives rise to disturbances within the jet, which are generally referred to as *shock waves*.

Therefore, strictly speaking, any supersonic nozzle is correctly designed only for one particular flow rate. However, in practice, it is possible to operate the nozzle under slightly off-design conditions, without producing detectable changes in the jet characteristics. At appreciable off-design conditions, however (greater than 20% from the design conditions), the changes become noticeable. This can lead to major disturbances. For example, if the flow rate of oxygen through the nozzle is too high, the pressure at the nozzle exit will also be high, and uncontrolled expansion followed by compression would then occur outside the nozzle. These *normal shock waves* will continue downstream until the velocity of the jet becomes subsonic. A jet of this type is referred to as an *under expanded jet*. When the flow rate through a nozzle is substantially lower than the theoretical design rating, the jet will be *over expanded,* and *oblique shock waves* will be produced at the nozzle exit.

Characteristics of Subsonic Jets

A subsonic jet emanating from a nozzle can be subdivided into three flow regions as shown in Figure AII.1. At the nozzle exit, the jet has uniform velocity; but thereafter, tangential shear forces between the moving jet and the stagnant surrounding medium gradually begin to slowdown the jet around its periphery. For a distance of up to about 3 to 7 nozzle throat diameters, the axial velocity remains unaffected. This conically-shaped region is known as the *potential core*. The apex of the cone denotes the furthest point from the nozzle, at which the velocity on the jet axis is equal to the exit velocity. The potential core subsequently makes way for the region of *fully developed flow*, which starts at a distance of about 8 to 10 diameters from the nozzle exit and extends downstream. The comparatively short intermediate zone is one of *transition*.

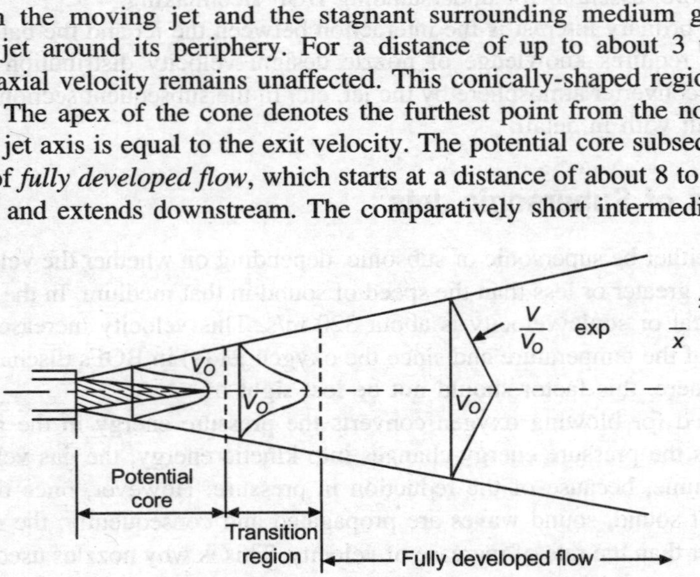

Figure AII.1 Schematic representation of a subsonic jet showing the relative positions of the component areas.

Structure of Supersonic Jets

Supersonic jets are characterised by a *supersonic core* as shown in Figure AII.2. Once again, in the region nearest to the nozzle exit, the axial velocity of the jet remains constant. This region is denoted as the potential core of a supersonic jet. It is analogous to the potential core of a

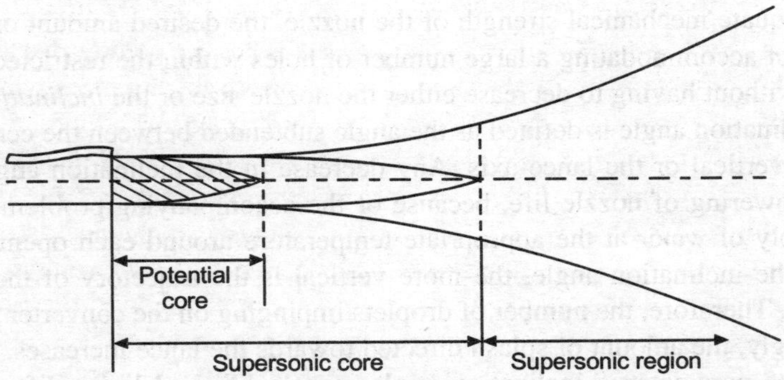

Figure AII.2 Shock-free supersonic jet showing the relative positions of the supersonic and subsonic regions.

subsonic jet, where the velocity, of course, is less than the speed of sound. In the region beyond the potential core, the axial velocity of the jet gradually decreases but, until a certain position downstream is reached, the axial velocity remains above the velocity of sound. The entire region over which the centreline velocity of the jet remains higher than the speed of sound, is referred to as the *supersonic core region,* which includes the potential core. Beyond the supersonic core, the subsonic portion of the jet begins which is similar to the region of fully developed flow in subsonic jets.

The length of the potential core in supersonic jets (and therefore also the supersonic core), increases almost proportionally with an increase in the Mach Number of the jet. The Mach Number affects the ratio of the density of the gas in the jet as a proportion of the density of the ambient medium. At a given Mach Number, this density ratio can also increase, if the gas jet is exhausted into a hotter medium. This is exactly what happens in BOFs when oxygen at room temperature comes in contact with the hot gases present in the converter atmosphere.

The entrainment close to the nozzle in a shock-free supersonic jet is much lower than in a subsonic jet. For example, in the supersonic portion of a Mach 1.8 jet, the entrainment rate is around 0.46 m^3/m length of the jet, and the spreading angle is 10°; while in the subsonic portion of the same jet, the corresponding figures are 1.2 m^3/m and 23° respectively.

Multi-hole Lances

Large capacity BOFs requires huge amounts of oxygen. To supply such large volumes of oxygen within the restricted blowing period (the blowing period in BOFs is virtually independent of vessel capacity), lances equipped with multi-hole nozzles at the tip are employed. The main advantage of increasing the number of outlets on the lance tip is to allow the total oxygen throughput to be increased, without simultaneously increasing the pressure exerted by the jets impinging on the bath surface. It is important to remember that it is this pressure (to be more exact jet momentum), which determines the depth of the depression(s) formed in the bath and, consequently, the amount of liquid splashed from the bath surface. By increasing the number of nozzle openings and thereby distributing the total energy of the jet over a larger surface area of the bath, it is possible to increase the rate of oxygen supply without simultaneously decreasing the metal yield (owing to spitting), or increasing the risk of burning the converter bottom because of too deep a penetration. The limitation in increasing in the number of openings often lies in guaranteeing adequate mechanical strength of the nozzle, the desired amount of cooling as well as the difficulty of accommodating a large number of holes within the restricted space available at the lance tip, without having to decrease either the nozzle size or the *inclination angle* of each opening. The inclination angle is defined as the angle subtended between the central axis of each opening and the vertical or the lance axis. Any decrease in the inclination angle automatically leads to severe lowering of nozzle life, because of the accompanying problems of maintaining an adequate supply of water at the appropriate temperature around each opening. At the same time, the lesser the inclination angle, the more vertical is the trajectory of the metal and slag droplets splashed. Therefore, the number of droplets impinging on the converter lining decreases, and correspondingly, the amount of splash directed towards the lance increases. The relationship among these three parameters—inclination angle, nozzle life and lining life—shows that the lance life decreases when the inclination angle is decreased, while the lining life increases. The actual values of the lining life and lance life vary widely from plant to plant.

Depth and Diameter of Bath Penetration

The two most significant parameters characterising the interaction of supersonic jets of oxygen and the molten iron bath in BOFs are the depth to which the jets penetrate and the diameter of the depressions formed. For any given bath conditions, the first parameter is influenced mainly by the axial velocity of the jets, while the second parameter depends primarily on the diameter of the jets at the bath surface.

It has been found that the depth to which an oxygen jet penetrates into a metallic bath is given by:

$$n_O = \frac{1.5\ P_4\ d_t}{V^h} \times 4.5 \qquad \text{(AII.1)}$$

where, n_O is the depth of depression along the jet axis, d_t is the diameter of the nozzle at the throat, and h is the lance height (both in inches) and P_4 is the pressure in lb/in^2. By substituting typical operating data, using a nozzle with throat diameter of 3.5 inches, the depth of depression would vary from 20 to 50 inches (500–1250 mm). Calculations, also reveal that for a Mach 2 oxygen jet discharging into an atmosphere of 85% CO, 10% CO_2 and 5% N_2, the computed variations in the depth of depression formed at an ambient atmosphere temperature of 1000°C are a function of the lance height and the nozzle throat diameter. For any given lance height and nozzle throat diameter, the temperature of the ambient atmosphere has considerable influence of the diameter and depth of the depression (s) formed. As a result, the depth of depression varies considerably during the blow, even when the blowing conditions are kept constant. This is one possible reason for the variation in the rate of decarburisation even under constant blowing conditions (oxygen flow rate and lance height).

Other Issues

Another consideration that is often not given due weightage is the extent of coalescence of jets from multi-hole nozzles (i.e. the extent of interaction between the individual jets by the time they reach the bath surface). Substantial loss in velocity, totally different peripheral flow characteristics, inadequate flow at the nozzle tip axis, etc. are some important areas that need to be taken note of when using multi-hole nozzles in LD converters.

Bibliography

Ironmaking

Biswas, A.K., *Principles of Blast Furnace Ironmaking*, 1st Indian ed., SBA Publications, Kolkata, 1984.

Chatterjee, Amit, R. Singh and B. Pandey, *Metallics for Steelmaking—Production and Use*, Allied Publishers Ltd., New Delhi, 2001.

Gupta, S.S. and Amit Chatterjee (Eds.), *Blast Furnace Ironmaking*, Tata Steel, Jamshedpur, 1993.

Chatterjee, Amit, *Beyond the Blast Furnace*, CRC Press, Boca Raton, Florida, USA, 1992.

Peacy, J.G., and W.G. Davenport, *The Iron Blast Furnace—Theory and Practice*, Pergamon Press, Oxford, 1979.

Tupkary, R.H. and V.R. Tupkary, *An Introduction to Modern Iron Making*, 3rd ed., Khanna Publishers, Delhi, 1998.

Wakelin, D.H. (Ed.), Ironmaking Volume, *The Making, Shaping and Treating of Steel*, 11th ed., AISE Steel Foundation, USA, 1998.

Walker, R.D., *Modern Ironmaking Methods*, The Institute of Metals, London, 1986.

Steelmaking and Steel Casting

Deo, B. and R. Boom, *Fundamentals of Steelmaking Metallurgy*, Prentice Hall Inc., New York, 1993.

Brimacombe, J.K., I.V. Samarasekera and J.E. Lait (Eds.), *Continuous Casting*, Vol. 2, The Iron and Steel Soc., Warrendale, USA, 1984.

Chatterjee, Amit and S. Govindarajan (Eds.), *Monograph on Continuous Casting at Tata Steel*, Tata Steel, Jamshedpur, 1991.

Fruehan, R.J. (Ed.), Steelmaking Volume, *The Making, Shaping and Treating of Steel*, 11th ed., AISE Steel Foundation, USA, 1999.

Ghosh, A., *Secondary Steelmaking—Principles and Applications*, CRC Press, Boca Raton, Florida, USA, 2001.

Ghosh, A., *Principles of Secondary Processing and Casting of Liquid Steel*, Oxford & IBH Publishing Co., New Delhi, 1990.

Tupkary, R.H. and V.R. Tupkary, *An Introduction to Modern Steel Making*, 6th ed., Khanna Publishers, Delhi, 1998.

Turkdogan, E.T., *Fundamentals of Steelmaking*, The Institute of Materials, London, 1996.

Others

Ward, R.G., *An Introduction to The Physical Chemistry of Iron & Steel Making*, Edward Arnold Publishers, London, 1962.

Index